CMP

3RD WORLD CONFERENCE ON ENGINEERING EDUCATION

ORGANISING COMMITTEE

Conference Chairman:
Eur Ing Professor T.V. Duggan
University of Portsmouth, UK

Academic Conveners:
Dr B.E. Mulhall
University of Surrey, UK
G.P. White
University of Portsmouth, UK

Secretary and Treasurer:
Dr M.R.I. Purvis
University of Portsmouth, UK

Co-Chairman (SEFI):
Professor B.L. Button
Nottingham Polytechnic, UK

Co-Chairman (University of Surrey):
Professor A. Walker
University of Surrey, UK

Conference Executive and Secretariat:
Mrs Christine Asher (Conference Secretariat)
University of Portsmouth, UK
Mrs Drusilla Moody
Conference Executive, Portsmouth, UK
Miss Denise Olway (Conference Secretariat)
University of Portsmouth, UK

Members of the Local Organising Committee:
Eur Ing Dr J.M. Bement
University of Portsmouth, UK
Professor J.T. Boardman
University of Portsmouth, UK
C. Douthwaite
University of Surrey, UK
D. Dring (Exhibition Director)
University of Leeds, UK
J.G.W. Huffell
Consultant, Portsmouth, UK
Dr D.E.P. Jenkins
Past President, SEFI, UK
Professor P.B. Morice
University of Southampton, UK
Professor B.S. Plumb
University of Plymouth, UK
Dr Z.J. Pudlowski (Secretary ILG-EE)
University of Sydney, Australia
Professor R.A. Smith
University of Sheffield, UK

L. Sucharov
Computational Mechanics Publications, Southampton, UK

International Liaison Group for Engineering Education and International Advisory Committee:
Professor M.S. Agarwal
Indian Institute of Technology, Bombay, India
Professor Ludmila Amani
New York Institute of Technology, USA
Professor G. Augusti
Universita di Roma, Italy
Mr H. Bedalian
Balfour Beatty Construction Ltd, UK
Professor J.T. Boardman
University of Portsmouth, UK
Professor B.L. Button (Co-Chairman SEFI)
Nottingham Polytechnic, UK
Professor Benzhu Chen
Shenyang Institute of Aeronautical Engineering, PR China
Dr S.R. Cheshier
Southern College of Technology, Georgia, USA
Professor T. Cole
University of Sydney, Australia
Dr B.J. Cory
Imperial College of Science and Technology, UK
Professor P. Darvall
Monash University, Melbourne, Australia
K. Davies
IBM Europe, Belgium
Professor Dr Ing K. Detert
Universitat Gesamthochschule Siegen, Germany
Professor A. Dewedar
Suez Canal University, Ismailia, Egypt
C. Douthwaite
University of Surrey, UK
D. Dring (Exhibition Director)
University of Leeds, UK
Eur Ing Professor T.V. Duggan (Chairman)
University of Portsmouth, UK
Dr H. Falk
Royal Institute of Technology, Stockholm, Sweden
Professor G. Frade
Ecole des Mines de Paris, France
Professor Marcus Giorgetti
Escola de Engenharia de Sao Carlos, Brazil
Dr S. Goodland
Imperial College of Science and Technology, UK

Members of Organising Committee

Back row L-R: Cliff Douthwaite, Derek Dring, Peter Morice, Mike Purvis, Lance Sucharov, Mike Bement
Front row L-R: Denise Olway, Brian Mulhall, Graham White, Terry Duggan, Bryan Button, Drusilla Moody, Christine Asher

3rd World Conference on Engineering Education

Vol 3: Industrial Links, Computers and Design

Proceedings of the 3rd World Conference on Engineering Education, held in Portsmouth, UK, during 20-25 September 1992

Editor: T.V. Duggan

Computational Mechanics Publications
Southampton Boston

T.V. Duggan
Faculty of Engineering
University of Portsmouth
Anglesea Building
Anglesea Road
Portsmouth PO1 3DJ
UK

British Library Cataloguing in Publication Data

A Catalogue record for this book is available
from the British Library

ISBN 1-85312-192-4 Computational Mechanics Publications, Southampton
ISBN 1-56252-120-9 Computational Mechanics Publications, Boston, USA

Set
ISBN 1-85312-189-4 Computational Mechanics Publications, Southampton
ISBN 1-56252-117-9 Computational Mechanics Publications, Boston, USA

Library of Congress Catalog Card Number 92-81591

Printed and bound by Bell & Bain Ltd, Scotland

PREFACE

This major World Conference on Engineering Education, held in Portsmouth, UK (20-25 September, 1992), is the third in the series. It follows the World Conference on Education in Applied Engineering and Engineering Technology held in Cologne, in the Federal Republic of Germany, in April 1984, and the World Conference on Engineering Education for Advancing Technology, held in Sydney, Australia, in February 1989. It was organised by the University of Portsmouth in partnership with the University of Surrey, on behalf of the International Liaison Group for Engineering Education, combined with the Annual Conference of the Société Européenne pour la Formation des Ingenieurs (SEFI).

These volumes represent the edited versions of most of the papers presented at the conference. They have been collected into theme areas covering a very wide spectrum of interests in engineering education. These include international issues, quality aspects, courses and teaching issues, widening access and provision, academic-industrial links, and subject specific topics such as environmental engineering, computers in teaching, projects, design and manufacture.

The main theme of the conference was that of Engineering Education for the 21st Century, and the enthusiasm with which this theme has been grasped is very encouraging. The response to the call for papers was overwhelming, and it is evident from the papers published in these volumes that the subject of Engineering Education is now well established as a subject area in its own right.

There are many who have assisted with the preparation of the conference and the publication of these papers. Whilst it might be invidious to mention individuals, I would like to thank especially all those members of the Organising Committee who have contributed in any way, but in particular the Conference Secretariat and Executive who have handled most of the administration so effectively; the Academic Conveners who largely put the programme together; and the Publisher, Computational Mechanics, for their care and attention in ensuring the highest quality of these books. I should also like to express my appreciation to the International Liaison Group for recommending that this Conference take place in Portsmouth in 1992. Finally, I wish to express my personal appreciation, as well as that of the Organising Committee, to the University of Portsmouth for its support and encouragement throughout the planning and delivery of this event, and also to all those who have given support or assisted in any way in sponsoring the conference. The quality of papers presented, the innovation and experiences shared will, I hope, make the Conference and these proceedings a milestone in the history of Engineering Education.

Terry Duggan
Conference Chairman

CONTENTS

SECTION 2: PROJECTS, DESIGN AND MANUFACTURE

SECTION 1: COMPUTERS IN TEACHING

Integrating the Computer into the Learning Process

I.D. Benest

Department of Computer Science, University of York

Abstract

This paper proposes a way of exploiting information technology in order to provide an integrated approach to computer-based learning that embraces all aspects of teaching. Implicit in that integration is the exploitation of a single high-level user-interface, the book metaphor, which is proposed because of its simplicity of operation and the world knowledge that it evokes.

Keywords: Information Technology, Computer-Based Learning, Hypertext, Hypermedia, Computer Conferencing.

1. Introduction

If the predictions that were made in the mid-sixties (Sugarman, 1978) had been right, by now the traditional talk-and-chalk method of teaching would have been replaced by computer controlled lesson programmes. The early work in programmed learning demonstrated an efficient and effective means of teaching, and when provided on a computer, new questions could be repeatedly posed and marked without human intervention. Furthermore, real world artefacts (such as an electronic circuit) could be modelled and simulated and the results graphically displayed (Katzenelson, 1966). All this functionality provided the optimism for predicting this revolution in teaching. But engineering is still largely taught using a modern form of talk-and- chalk (using overhead projector and view-foils produced with desk-top publishing software). Computer-based learning facilities if used at all are often mere adjuncts to the lecture. Commercial simulators provide training in the use of such systems instead of an education in the general behaviour of real-world objects. Thus, neither are integrated in the teaching process.

By the 21st century, desk-top computers with high addressability raster-based screens, substantial raw processing power, access to a large volume backing store, and hypermedia forms of communication (pictures, speech, sound, diagrams, and video) will be available at a price that tertiary education establishments can afford for timetabled student activity, and possibly be available for renting by the student. Prior to the advent of this equipment, only the calligraphic-based display could provide the quite precise control over the temporal and spatial presentation necessary for it to be employed as the platform upon which to base a teaching aid for engineering. Even when these were employed as an intelligent terminal connected to a general purpose time-shared system, such displays were too expensive for large scale student provision. So we are poised to embark on the revolution, about ten to fifteen years later than predicted.

The key elements to this revolution are: 1. full integration of information technology into the teaching process; 2. courseware authoring made straightforward and shared between institutions; 3. powerful computers for each student; 4. a consistent and straightforward user-interface mechanism which ensures that the courseware is delivered to the student without undue interference from the mechanism itself. Furthermore, the authoring of the courseware must not be the time consuming exercise that it has been in the past.

This paper is concerned with both the exploitation of information technology within the whole of the teaching/learning process, and the consistent user-interface mechanism through which the material is presented.

2. On-Line Lecturing

It is arguable that traditional lecturing (if performed well) is an efficient means of conveying information from teacher to student (the arguments for and against are discussed by Beard and Hartley, 1984). The pace, the illustrations, and the demonstrations are powerful manipulators of enthusiasm that encourage students to read further in order to absorb and understand more fully the material. This initial motivating introduction is quite absent from a text book or from a dry computer-based learning package. Furthermore, the lecturer can be interrupted and precise questioning (though perhaps imprecisely worded) can identify to the lecturer, key misconceptions that would otherwise hinder the further absorption of information not only by the questioner, but also by others in the class less inclined to ask. Thus the lecture should remain the central element of a taught course.

It is proposed that the overhead projector/blackboard is replaced by a large screen projector that displays the information contained on the same type of computer screen that is used by the students. The information on the computer screen would consist of an electronic book full of 'overhead equivalents' for that lecture. The emphasis here is that the bound overheads would be viewed through software that had a similar 'look-and-feel' to a real book, with all the advantages of spatial cues and world knowledge that goes with a real book. Where necessary, animation designed to reinforce temporal or procedural information would be included so that the 'on-line lecture' did provide an improvement on simple transparencies. The 'covering-up' method of gradual revelation of material would be available if required. Other forms of identifying progress such as making bold the current key point, or moving the current key point horizontally to another place on the screen and gradually revealing sub-points, would also be available to the courseware author.

At least two lecturing threads would exist. First, a 'single-step' thread in which the lecturer would use a hand-held control like that of a slide projector (perhaps a mouse held remote from its pad), in order to move on to the next point or see some illustrative animation. Second, a 'continuous play' thread would exist that unless signalled to stop, would cause the lecture to play continuously until it finally terminated at the end. The latter would be used in conjunction with a scripted narrative synchronised with the progress of the lecture. If the lecturer were ill, the lecture could still be given by another member of staff who would start it in 'continuous play' mode, possibly stopping it where it was thought that a point needed amplification or clarification, or where a student had signalled a need to ask a question.

The same material as that shown in the lecture, and the same software medium as that used in the lecture would be available for students on their computer screens for private study. The scripted narrative would be available through head-phones. Thus the student could view the courseware like a video, or single-step through it as in the live lecture. But there could also be a few isolated 'hot-spots' that provided further animation and simulation for students to explore during their private study. Of course the 'continuous play' mode would not have the frustrating rewind/fast-forward/play type interface that makes finding material so difficult on video or audio tapes. Instead there would be 'hot-spots' visually located in the material marking the continuation restart at particular points in the exposition. This would constitute the ultimate in lecture notes, particularly if they could be personally annotated such as with a highlighter or with underlining.

3. The Case for Linearity

A faithful book metaphor is proposed because of the inherently linear manner in which engineering information is gradually presented. This linear structure and the 'continuous play' mode would clearly identify the courseware author's preferred order of presentation. However, provided students can navigate this electronic text with the same ease as with a real book, the preferred order can be ignored by the students. Furthermore, if the spatial location is cued as with a real book, then with true browsing the student can quickly find the key point that was not totally understood during the lecture, and revise that material.

4. Support For Teacher-Directed Problem-Solving

If the one-hour lecture equivalent is played to the audience in 'continuous mode', then it would probably span about half the time that the 'live' lecture would take (Beard et al, 1978). This would enable the teacher and students to take part in a more participative period during the lecture slot. For example this time could be usefully employed by the teacher to direct a problem-solving activity. It is one thing to understand the facts and the design procedures available, but it is quite another for the novice engineer to be able to apply that knowledge to solving real problems. Thus it would be beneficial to the students if the lecturer could exploit this 'extra' time to demonstrate how theory is applied.

A possible scenario might, for example, involve the complete design of a digital circuit. The basic outline of the problem would have already been created by the teacher and kept somewhere in a 'blackboard book', leaving the full solution to develop in response to student direction and teacher leadership. The tables (state-transition tables, Karnaugh maps) could be selected from a library book and brought into the 'blackboard book'. The tables would be filled in through active participation, and the circuit diagram specified and drawn. If the 'blackboard book' were connected (i.e. was the user-interface) to an appropriate application, the diagram could be translated into a specific nodal description and passed on to a simulator. The simulator's output would then be translated into a form suitable for display in the 'blackboard book'. Thus a book of solved problems could be established for the class, and it would be made available for students to study and revise in private.

5. Support For Problem Classes

The next stage in learning is the problem class or laboratory session designed to consolidate concepts by means of encouraging the student to think for themselves, but still providing both 'over-the-shoulder' guidance, and help when completely unable to apply the theory. On- line problem classes could be located within the lecture book close to where the theory was covered; though during the 'continuous' lecture this would be skipped over.

The simplest approach is to test using multi-choice questions. If the student selected a correct answer, then the book would respond with a statement that identified the reasons why the other choices were not correct. If an incorrect choice were selected then the reason why it was incorrect would be conveyed. The student may select another choice just to see why that answer is not correct; it might seem equally plausible. It is for this reason that the book would not be turned automatically to where the concept was originally conveyed in order to give remedial teaching.

The second approach is to make students take part in guided practice as in, for example, learning to prove mathematical propositions or to turn mathematical equations into different forms. This might take the form of providing all the steps, but in an arbitrary order, and the student would then be required to put them in the correct order. Since that order would only be a spatial ordering, it would be relatively straightforward for the computer to check for correctness and respond appropriately. A similar idea has been demonstrated in PLATO for practising the assembly of distillation apparatus (Sugarman, 1978). Notice that here too, the linear progression commensurate with increasing difficulty may be simply cued within the book metaphor.

6. Support For Peer Teaching

Students are often very commendable teachers when it comes to helping colleagues understand difficult concepts. They themselves have struggled with the problem and therefore appreciate the source of the difficulty. Information technology can provide problem-guided conferencing. For example, several students could join an on-line conference presented through the book metaphor. On every two pages, a question relevant to the course would be posed and there would be space below for each student to write (type) their answer. Each student could see the responses of the others. On a daily basis, the spaces would be checked by a monitoring program for the students' responses and if all four students had made an attempt then a model answer would be revealed to those students. It should be emphasised however that the keyboard is a poor medium for discussing a difficult concept.

7. The Book Emulator

The foregoing has suggested that a consistent user-interface be used for all learning support methods described and that the book metaphor is the most appropriate user-interface for the information delivery system. Indeed such a user-interface exists as the Book Emulator, which has been well documented (Benest, 1990 and Benest, 1991).

Its presentation is that of an open book with two pages in view. The previous and subsequent pages are shown as splayed pages, indicating to students their approximate position within the information space. This cue also provides a very powerful identification as to how much material is in the lecture and how much there is still to learn. The student can turn a page either forwards or backwards using mouse keys, and the page turn is animated across the screen. Continuous pressure on the mouse keys enables the user to 'flick' through the book, and the splayed pages grow and shrink accordingly. This enables the user truly to browse through the information and the animation provides a 'real' cue as to the direction of travel. Browsing enables interesting information to provoke attention; it can also enable a student to have sight of future lecture material that can help the student accept the need to study the current material.

In principle, any illustrative technique used in real books can be exploited in the Book Emulator. It supports animation such as that required for gradual revelation of material or for cycling through graphs to show the effect of parameter changes. These animation facilities are displayed as if on an overlay foil and are removed automatically when the page is turned.

The author can specify links from one page to any other within the same book (similar to hypertext links). Since the location in the book is always cued, it is unlikely that the student will ever feel lost as is commonly felt in pure hypertext networks (Conklin, 1987).

Pre-recorded speech can be specified in 'sound/concept-bites' (one or two sentences), a number of which can be pre-read prior to playing through a sequence of such sound-bites. Speech can direct attention to specific positions within the book (an eye-mover), provide introductory comments that invite further attention (arousal stimulator), and most importantly provide an additional information channel. Care must be taken to avoid the parallel presentation of animation and speech since the student cannot attend to simultaneous changes in both channels (Fitts and Posner, 1967) if what is being said and illustrated are equally important, but convey different aspects of the concept.

The Book Emulator allows personal annotations to be made such as with a highlighter or free hand pen sketching using the mouse. The keyboard may also be used, and book-marks can be inserted. It also provides for schematic data capture, with sufficient semantic information for the resulting drawings to be capable of being analysed. All annotations and the schematic entry are normally private to an individual, but they can be shared so that with appropriate page layout, on-line conferences can be supported (Benest and Dukic, 1992). The Book Emulator can operate as a user-interface to an application or can invoke a sequence of computation processes.

8. Summary

The Book Emulator is an information delivery (and capture) system with a basic look-and-feel similar to that of a real book. It can operate as a user-interface to applications such as a simulator (with additional translation software). Thus the Book Emulator can provide an information technology based vehicle through which all aspects of engineering teaching can take place.

References

Beard, R.M., Bligh, D.A., and Harding, A.G. (1978) Research into Teaching Methods in Higher Education, Fourth Edition, Society for Research into Higher Education.

Beard, R.M. and Hartley, J. (1984) Teaching and Learning in Higher Education, Fourth Edition, Harper and Row.

Benest, I.D. (1990) Computer-Assisted Learning using Dynamic Electronic Books, in: Computer Assisted Learning, (ed. M. Kibby,), Pergamon Press, 195-203.

Benest, I.D. (1991) An Alternative Approach to Hypertext, Educational and Training Technology International, 28(4), 341-346.

Benest, I.D. and Dukic, D. (1992) Computer Supported Team-work, to appear in: CSCW in Practice: An Introduction and Case Studies, (ed. D. Diaper and C. Sanger), Springer-Verlag.

Conklin, E.R. (1987) Hypertext: An Introduction and Survey, IEEE Computer, 20(9), 17-41.

Fitts, P.M. and Posner, M.I. (1967) Human Performance, Wadsworth.

Katzenelson, J. (1966) AEDNET: A Simulator for Nonlinear Networks, Proceedings of the IEEE, 54(11), 1536-1552.

Sugarman, R. (1978) A Second Chance for Computer-Aided Instruction, IEEE Spectrum, 16(8), 29-37.

Teaching and Assessment of Control Engineering with a Computer Aided Design Package (CODAS-II)

J.W. Golten, A.A. Verwer

Department of Mechanical Engineering, Design and Manufacture, Faculty of Science and Engineering, Manchester Polytechnic

Abstract
The use of computer aided control system design (CACSD) packages allows remote, student centered learning and removes the necessity for tedious and repetitive calculations. However, problems arise in monitoring student progress, making sure that fundamental manipulative skills are not lost. These packages also raise questions on the methods employed for student assessment. This paper examines the use of CODAS-II in a learning situation, a design assessment and in a laboratory experiment. The paper discusses the manner in which CACSD is integrated into the course and how it affects assessment procedures.
Keywords: Computer Aided Design, CODAS, Control System Design, Assessment, Learning, Teaching

1 Introduction

CODAS-II is a control systems design and simulation package which has been used in control engineering courses at Manchester Polytechnic for several years. Its introduction has had a fundamental impact on the way control engineering is taught and assessed. The methods adopted in teaching control engineering as a result of introducing the package are described more fully in "Control system design and simulation", Golten (1991).

The introduction of CACSD has had a liberalising effect on students as it takes away the drudgery of calculating frequency responses and drawing root loci accurately. There is no need for students to become highly skilled in sketching Nyquist diagrams or in calculating break points in the s-plane. However in replacing these old fashioned skills by a simple key press, there is a certain danger of assuming that the student has gained insight at the expense of performing lengthy and routine calculations, when in fact he has merely become skilled at pressing keys! There is a fundamental difference between "Computer Aided Design" (CAD) and "Computer Aided Control System Design" (CACSD). CAD in the sense of component design, plant layout, NC pathtracing, scheduling and even finite element analysis is a concrete technique which is directly understandable by the average engineer without requiring any profound mathematical and abstract insights. Control system design on the other hand is an abstract process of which only the final outcome of the time response can be interpreted in a physical sense, and even that requires a degree of abstraction.

CACSD packages make many demands on students (and lecturers) which did not occur formerly. With hand methods there was actually no time to verify designs even if one stuck simply to meeting frequency domain specifications. It was simply not possible to confirm the time domain performance without the time consuming and highly skilled activity of setting up an analogue computer. There are many design examples in respected text books that are completely wrong, because there was insufficient time to simulate each system and verify the design. Now with the availability of good quality CACSD software, it is possible to set realistic time domain targets which are easy to verify, but not always easy to achieve. The complex interrelationship between the frequency domain, the s-plane and the time domain are exposed and it is not always easy to explain why the system behaves in the way it does.

Student progress can be very rapid but there is a danger that this progress is superficial and when faced with different or unseen situations the student cannot cope. Another danger is that the student will become too dependent on the computer and cannot solve simple problems in a conventional examination situation. Students may also adopt an uncritical and unrealistic attitude to the computer solution. For the majority of problems, CODAS-II provides the correct solutions and so students tend to accept the results uncritically. But it is always possible to produce inaccurate or even wrong solutions. For example we all know that a first order system is unconditionally stable, yet a CODAS-II simulation can show an unstable closed-loop response by choosing a very high value of gain and a time scale which is far greater than the time constant of the system. This behaviour is unavoidable when using numerical techniques adopted in the package to predict closed-loop time responses. When this happens students loose confidence or tend to put it down to a "bug". It is important to instil an understanding of the limitations of numerical techniques and to make sure that they are able to make rough predictions and perform simple calculations to check the computer output.

Thus here are a number of conflicting outcomes of using a CACSD packages. The rest of the paper examines how CODAS-II is used in three areas of study.

2 Student centred learning: Time domain/s-plane correlations

A worksheet is provided which starts by reinforcing the correlations of the s-plane pole positions of a standard underdamped second order system with its open-loop step response. The student verifies the formulae for the peak overshoot and settling time.

An additional real pole is introduced and its effect on the time domain performance criteria are investigated. The student draws conclusions for himself on pole dominance and how a remote real pole affects the open-loop step response.

An area which is often left untreated in standard courses and text books is the effect of zeros on the response of the system. Yet this is probably more important in the way it affects the shape of the response than the presence of well attenuated poles.

A very useful feature in CODAS-II is the use of parameters. It is simple to introduce a term of the type "(1+[1/a]s)" into the numerator of the open-loop transfer function. This term does not affect the steady state gain, but by changing the parameter "a", the position of the zero can be changed without having to type in the transfer function again and again. The student examines how the zero affects the step response and is asked to draw conclusions on the effect of the zero on the time domain behaviour.

The student is then shown how to produce root-loci plots using the package with a simple system. This topic will have been covered in class using the same example. The student predicts the closed-loop step response of the system based on the closed-loop pole positions and builds up confidence on his ability to predict time-domain behaviour.

Finally a more complex system is considered, and the gain is adjusted to give the dominant poles a certain damping ratio. The student predicts and verifies the nature of the closed-loop transient response.

Of course all this takes time and normally 3 hours of class time is given up to this exercise and the student is expected to augment it with a further 3 hours of his own time. Many students have their own student edition of the software and PCs of their own so that they can work at home. With well motivated students this approach is very successful and rewarding, but inevitably other "distractions" prevent students from devoting the time required and a carrot or a stick is perhaps useful to administer to help increase motivation (see next section).

3 Assessment: Compensator design

Assessment of students is more difficult when using a CACSD package. The traditional 3 hour end of year exam does not lend itself easily to applications orientated questions involving the use of computer packages. It is our view that the role of the end of year examination is to test basic principles and that more open ended design is best done through assignment/laboratory work. The beauty of the end of year exam is that it is a guaranteed way of assessing the individual without any clouding issues of external help, collaboration or cheating. It, however, is very limited in its scope as it precludes the use of CACSD software. The assignment/laboratory work is excellent for showing the practical application of the techniques (see next section) but there is an ambivalence in the role of the tutor. Is he a teacher or a tester? How much help do you give the individual? Here there is serious conflict between using the assignment to promote the student's understanding and to encourage him to explore the subject with helpful advice and suggestions and the aspect of assessment. There is also the problem of collaboration whether or not it is a group or individual assignment.

There is however a median solution to the assessment problem and that is the use of the *phase test*. The phase test has a number of advantages. It can be of quite short duration, its scope can be quite specific, allow the use of software and it can be open-book. The advantage for the student is that he needs only to understand a limited topic area does not need to commit formulae etc to memory.

This approach is used to assess the area of compensator design. Initially a tutorial is provided on compensator design (lead and lag) which is done at the computer terminal. A frequency domain technique ("D" contour) has been developed which allows compensators to be designed quickly and accurately, Golten (1991), Verwer (1992). The approach is semi-automated where the compensator is designed interactively with the package. In this phase the tutor is totally unfettered in his relationship with the student and can give as much help as is required. The student is well motivated (usually) as he/she knows that there will be a test on this topic.

Subsequently the students are given a one hour test in which they design compensators for a different system with a new design specification and report on the performance of the compensated systems. The test is done individually at the computer. The student is usually given a steady-state requirement which involves calculating a gain constant. He then reports on the dynamic performance of the uncompensated system in a table that is provided.

The student is then required to design a lag and a lead compensator to satisfy the new design criterion. They report the transfer functions of the compensators used and complete the table of performance figures for the two compensated systems.

The advantages of this approach are very great. Without the CACSD software it would be impossible to cover all the aspects of the test. The student has to exercise judgement on selecting frequency ranges, time scales etc. He requires some basic understanding of error constants even to make a start. The time constraint ensures that only the student who has applied himself earlier will have sufficient skills and knowledge of short-cuts to complete the exercise. There are no problems about cheating or collaboration and it does not take long to mark the test which is a factor not to be dismissed to lightly.

One further aspect of this type of phase test is worth reporting. Although it is a test, the tutor can help students without compunction on operational aspects of the package. The structured and progressive approach to the test is designed to help weaker students make a start and gain confidence. However on some occasions a student gets completely stuck and cannot progress. If this is observed the tutor can advise the student that help may be given to solve the immediate problem and simply not award marks for that component of the test. This technique is one that has evolved over a number of years and is one that is reassuring to students who can get nervous and stressed in a test situation such as the one described.

The marks for the test form part of the continuous assessment (CA) for the subject. Typically the CA component for the subject is 20%.

There are usually two phase tests, a group design assignment and two practical laboratory exercises.

4 Laboratory: open-loop unstable systems

Laboratory work and assessment, in our opinion, have conflicting objectives. We regard the laboratory as a teaching/learning environment and certainly at final year degree level any assessment must be minimal.

Root locus is very suited for analysis but on the whole frequency domain techniques are preferred for design. However, for servo-systems with well defined dynamics root-locus is a powerful tool for design and in particular for designing controllers for open-loop unstable systems where the open-loop frequency response is not easily obtained.

A rig has been developed which uses a servo to drive a carriage to which an inverted pendulum is attached, see figure 1. This apparatus is now available commercially (Bytronic, Coleshill Road, Sutton Coldfield)

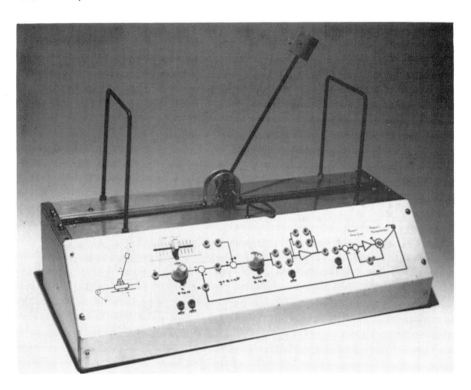

Figure 1. Inverted Pendulum Apparatus

The student is given a simple dynamic model of the system and fits parameters to it by experimenting with the rig. Having done this he designs a compensator on a computer located in the laboratory. The compensator is implemented and its performance examined. It is very rewarding for the student to see this system under control. To reinforce the difficulty of controlling this system, the pendulum is unscrewed and students are invited to try and balance it themselves on their hand. This provides some amusement and confirms to them that it is really quite a difficult system to stabilise.

The response of the real system exhibits a limit cycle. Students are asked why this is so and with some prompting attribute it to stiction in the servo drive. The degree of hysteresis is measured and the computer model is modified to incorporate the nonlinearity. The resulting simulated time response now shows a limit cycle. The frequency and amplitude of the observed limit cycle are compared with that simulated on the computer.

Students who have covered describing function techniques can draw a describing function contour and compare the frequency domain results with those found from the time-domain simulation. However this aspect can be done at any time and does not require access to the experimental rig.

5 Conclusions

The introduction of CACSD in the undergraduate curriculum brings a number of benefits. However care must be exercised in monitoring student understanding of principles and methods of assessment need to be considered carefully. Phase tests are a useful means of assessment. The theoretical aspects and use of the computer must be reinforced with some vivid and interesting practical work.

6 References

1) Golten, J. W. and Verwer, A. A. (1991) Control system design and simulation, McGraw Hill, 1991

2) Verwer, A. A. and Golten, J. W. (1992) Automated compensator design in CODAS, IEE Colloquium on "Computer aided control system design algorithms, packages and environments", Digest 1992/004

Computer Aided Learning of Numerical Methods for Electrical Engineers

D.C.Ioan, I. Munteanu, B. Ionescu, M.Popescu, R.Popa

Department of Electrical Engineering, Polytechnic Institute of Bucharest

Abstract

In this paper is presented the numerical methods course and computer lessons, as studied by the students of the Dept. of Electrical Engineering, Polytechnic Institute of Bucharest. This introductory course combines elements of numerical analysis, programming techniques and methods for computer analysis of electrical circuits and electromagnetic fields. The structure of the numerical methods computer lessons and the main parts of the software package for computer-aided learning of numerical methods are described. The applications of these methods in Electrical Engineering are emphasized.

Keywords: Numerical methods, Computer Aided Learning, Electrical engineering education, Electrical circuit, Electromagnetic field.

1 Introduction

Computer aided solving of electrical engineering problems, implies the use of specialized CAD/CAE software packages. Modern software packages of this sort contain a user-friendly interface, which tries to hide the analysis methods and techniques that are being used, in order to ensure a maximum efficiency. Utilization of these programs in the early stages of engineers' education might create a misleading image upon efficient computer systems using. In order to obtain a well balanced engineering culture, it is necessary to study and correctly understand the techniques and methods used in the CAD/CAE software packages.

The course "Numerical Methods in Electrical Engineering" deals with algorithms, data structures and numerical analysis of electrical circuits and electromagnetic fields. It has the following objectives:

- emphasizing ways of solving the main mathematical problems, computer aided;
- presenting the main electrical engineering problems which need computer-programs for their solving;
- developing the algorithmic thinking of the students;
- understanding the difficulties that arise while computer-solving an electrical engineering problem.

2   The structure of a computer lesson

Students are performing the laboratory works according to a laboratory guide-book, which has the following structure for each lesson:
- a short theoretical part, in which the method's principle is exposed
- the algorithm, written in pseudo-code;
- the theoretical analysis of the computing time and errors;
- experimental procedure;
- questions and exercises.

The laboratory class is carried out by the student in front of the computer. A software package called **NUMEE** (NUmerical Methods for Electrical Engineering) has been implemented. This package has been developed in the Turbo C environment and runs on IBM-PC or compatible computers.

The first step of a laboratory work consists in the execution of an illustrative program whose input data (e.g.: equations system's matrix, polynomial coefficients) are entered by the student. The program steps over the algorithm pointing out the effect of each step upon the initial data.

The second part allows a computing effort and accuracy analysis for the algorithm, by using a standard set of input data. The theoretical results are compared against those experimentally obtained.

During the third step the student must translate to PASCAL, the pseudo-code algorithm from the laboratory guide and type a short test program for the procedure, which solves a precisely defined simple problem. The procedure and the test program should be simple in order to give the student a clear idea on the algorithm.

The last phase in the laboratory work consists of an automatic knowledge testing.

3   Description of the software package NUMEE

The first lesson (**Numerical Algorithms and Mathematical Data Structures**), introduces the student to the implementation of the fundamental mathematical structures (vectors, complex numbers, matrix and polynomials) and to the main operations which can be performed upon them (addition, multiplication, division, evaluation). The goal is to achieve the ability of using a pseudo-code and translating it into a programming language, opening the perspective towards the implementation of abstract data types and object-oriented programming.

The second lesson is dedicated to **numerical algorithms analysis**. The concept of "algorithm complexity" is introduced. An experimental evaluation of computing time versus the problem's dimension is performed for some typical algorithms (the norm of a vector, multiplication of two vectors, multiplication of two matrix). The numerical stability is analysed by pointing out round-off, truncation errors and their propagation in the arithmetical operations. Typical (Taylor, Fourier, Bessel) series partial sum are computed and the truncation error variation is plotted.

The greatest part of the lessons are dedicated to **algebraic linear systems**, because most of the engineering problems can be finally reduced to such a problem. The demonstration programs for the **Gauss methods** display the coefficients matrix and the right-side vector for each elimination stage, and the solution's evolution durng the back-substitution stage. The computing time and various error norms, are   displayed while solving systems with user defined dimension and random coefficients.

While studying **pivoting strategies** the student analyzes the influence of different pivoting methods (partial, total or diagonal) on computing errors.

Linear systems having a common matrix can be solved by using the LU decomposition method, by inverting the system's matrix or by using the simultaneous systems' method. A comparison between computing time and errors of the above mentioned techniques, for different system dimensions is performed.

The lesson dedicated to **sparse matrix techniques** visually demonstrates the effects of the various pivoting strategies (pseudo-optimal, static, dynamic) upon a sparse matrix' fill-in. The variation of computing time and required memory versus the matrix' dimension and sparseness are analysed.

The demonstrative program for **iterative methods**, displays the numerical solution at each iteration, when solving a linear system using the Jacobi and Gauss-Seidel methods.

The program   which   deals with **successive overrelaxation** displays the dependence of convergence rate versus the relaxation factor.

Two lessons are dedicated to **linear electrical DC and AC circuits analysis**. For DC circuits, each branch is described as follows: initial node number, final node number, resistance and source voltage. The program analyzes the circuit, displays the current and voltage for each branch and checks the power balance.

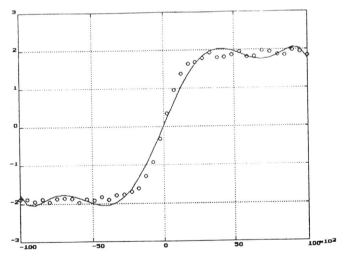

Fig. 1. Approximation of magnetisation characteristic using the least-squares method

In addition, for AC circuits, the type and value of the passive element (R, L, C), the magnitude and   phase for the source voltage are entered for each branch. The program analyzes the circuit for a defined frequency using the phasorial representation of the circuit and the nodal technique. The current magnitude and phase for each branch are displayed. The active and reactive power balance is checked.

The **interpolation polynomials** are plotted for equally spaced or distributed points according to the Tchebishev polynomials roots, for different functions: sin, exp, log, th. The analysis program allows a comparison of interpolation errors and computing time between three algorithms (classical, Lagrange, Newton).

The lesson referring to the **piece-wise polynomial interpolation** comprises a program which plots the piece-wise linear, Bessel, Akima, natural cubic spline interpolations for various functions.

The **approximation of functions using the least-squares method** is illustrated by the approximation of "experimental data" sets, affected by random errors, through polynomials or piece-wise linear functions (Fig. 1).

The demo program for the **functions derivation** lesson computes the value of the derivative for some elementary functions (sin, log, exp) using divided differences of different orders, backward, forward or centered, allowing a comparison between the numerical result and the exact value.

The **numerical integration** lesson consists in computing defined integrals of elementary functions (polynomials, sin, exp, log), using methods of different orders (piece-wise linear approximation, Simpson), with constant or data-adapted step.

The lesson referring to **nonlinear equations solving** demonstrates the convergence of the simple iteration, parallel tangents, Newton (Fig. 2) and secants algorithms applied to algebraic nonlinear and transcendent equations.

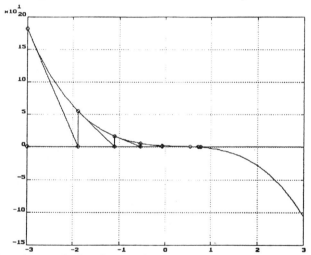

Fig. 2. Iteration evolution for nonlinear equation solving using Newton's algorithm.

The **nonlinear system solving** lesson analyses electrical circuits composed of linear resistors, DC voltage sources and nonlinear elements (semiconductor diodes). They are solved by means of the linearized equivalent circuit (Newton), which is analyzed by the nodal technique. For each iteration the program computes the errors and finally, displays the branch currents and checks the power balance. The computing time depending on the circuit's complexity (no. of nodes) and refinement degree of the nonlinear characteristic is measured.

Euler's method is exposed by computing the numerical solution of the differential equation $dy/dt = a.y + b$, with initial condition $y(0) = c$, using both implicit and explicit Euler methods. The error analysis is performed on a simple test equation: $dy/dt = -y$, with $y(0) = 1$.

An ordinary differential linear equations system with constant coefficients and non-zero initial conditions is solved using **Runge-Kutta's method**.

The **transient linear electrical circuits analysis** is illustrated by a program which simulates dynamic circuits containing R, L, C elements, step time varying voltage and current sources. The analysis method is the incremental equivalent circuit generated by the implicit Euler formulae. The program displays the numerical values and plots the currents or voltages selected by the student.

Using the **finite difference method - FDM**, the Laplace equation for a square domain, with constant Dirichlet boundary condition on each side is solved. For corner points the conditions are distinctly prescribed.

The Laplace equation is solved by means of the **finite element method - FEM**, for a circular domain with Dirichlet boundary conditions, constant on all quadrants.

The **boundary element method - BEM** is used to compute the electrostatic field in the whole space, produced by two plain electrodes (fig. 3).

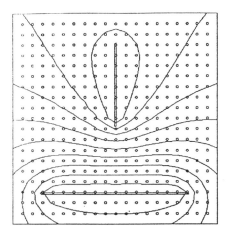

Fig. 3. Plot of the electrostatic field produced by two
plain electrodes in the whole space.

For each case the system's matrix is generated and is solved using iterative techniques. The student is invited to explore by means of a cursor the equipotential plots. The field's direction and magnitude are continuously displayed. The analysis stage evaluates accuracy and computing time for both direct and iterative methods.

4   Conclusions

Although the scientific level of the lessons that compose the **NUMEE** CAL package may seem low with respect to CAD/CAE packages, they represent an absolutely necessary educational phase for each future engineer. It ensures the achievement of a scientific background which distinguishes him from a simple technician.

Contrasting to the study of a textbook, the students interest in such a learning approach is much higher. They have the satisfaction of direct computer aided experimenting the possibilities and limits of algorithms. The algorithm implemented by the student must be simple, in order to give him the confidence that, he would be able to develop himself an engineering computer task. This step should not be regarded as "reinventing the wheel" but rather as "rethinking the circle", which stimulates the inclination towards creativity. In order to help the student perceive the whole complexity of the professional approach of numerical algorithms and techniques, he is encouraged to study and use standard mathematical   libraries   routines.

The number of students who are eager to develop further their own algorithms in a professional manner is relatively small(about 5%). However, the gain obtained by using the NUMEE CAL package consists of the fact that all the students acquire a solid and coherent basic knowledge, which allows them to comprehend and use in an efficient way, professional CAD/CAE packages.

The authors intend to develop the **NUMEE** package as follows:
- enhancing the tutorial part, in order to transform it into a computer-aided learning tool in hypertext style;
- ameliorate the knowledge test part, which should adapt to the student's level;
- adding new lessons which are of interest from the mathematic, algorithmic or electrical engineering point of view.

The "Numerical Methods Laboratory" team , which developed this package, is highly interested in cooperation with other similar groups, in view of experience exchanges or joint development of CAL tools.

References

Press, W.H., Flannery, B.P., Teukolsky, S.A., Vetterling, W.T. (1987)
    Numerical   Recipes, Cambridge University Press, Cambridge
Rice, J.R. (1983)**Numerical Methods, Software and Analysis. IMSL**
    Reference   Edition, McGraw Hill Book Co., N.Y.
Dorn, W.S., Cracken, D.D. (1972) **Numerical Methods with FORTRAN IV**
    Case Studies, John Wiley & Sons Inc., N.Y.
Carnahan, B., Luther, H.A., Wilkes, J. (1969) **Applied Numerical Methods,**
    John Wiley, N.Y.
Huelesman, L.P. (1986) **Engineering and Scientific Computations in PASCAL,**
    Harper & Row, New York
Chua, L.O., Lin, P.M. (1975) **Computer Aided Analysis of Electronic**
    Circuits, Prentice-Hall.
Ioan, C.D., Munteanu, I., (1991) **Numerical Methods for Electrical Engineers**
    Education, Proceedings of CAEE, Prague.

A Computer Network for Interactive Computer-Assisted Education in Electrical Engineering

X. Li, Z.J. Pudlowski

Electrical Engineering Education Research Group, Department of Electrical Engineering, The University of Sydney

Abstract

This paper discusses an interactive, computer-based training system currently being developed in the Department of Electrical Engineering, The University of Sydney. The principal objective of this research is to implement a computer network which will allow the computer-based training environment to supplement first and second year electrical engineering teaching. A special strength of the system is its ability to facilitate collaborative teaching and learning. The development of a suite of integrated software aids, giving high-level support to authoring/learning in an environment of networked workstations and servers, is of practical significance for engineering education.

1 Introduction

The new information technologies have opened up a number of opportunities for substantially increasing the efficiency of computer-based training and for supplementing the traditional teaching process. Up to now, in the classroom, computer-assisted education has allowed students to work alone in a direct and exclusive interaction between individual students and the software. However, to use computers only in this way is to under-use their potential. Instead, a flexible, complex, effective learning system can be created by combining instructional design, courseware delivery, and networking technology. This can enable more efficient learning and teaching to take place.

This presentation places particular emphasis on the integration of modern technology with classical teaching strategies through computer-based training for the engineering disciplines. It discusses the design and development of an interactive computer-based training system (ICBTS), suitable for fundamental subjects in electrical engineering at tertiary level. The use of the system will help first and second year engineering students master basic concepts and broaden their knowledge, while assisting the lecturer by providing individual, self-paced instruction. Furthermore, it will be easily adapted to other subjects.

2 Background

One of the main problems preventing the acceptance of computer-based learning is the lack of quality tools for courseware developers and for learners. Although there are a number of authoring systems on the market (Coyle 1990), most only support the instructional design and courseware development process. We have been unable to indentify any software designed specifically and appropriately for electrical engineering. The ICBTS seeks to better meet these needs.

The study of learning networks involves three aspects (Areitio 1990): namely, the hardware and system software needed to create the network; the communication patterns planned by the courseware developer; and, finally, the environment of each learner.

The Network The systems, in which a large number of separate computers are inter-connected, are referred to as computer networks. On a learning network, the computer-assisted instruction (CAI) courseware is downloaded from the file server via the communication medium into the training stations, where the student works through lessons. If any results have to be returned to the file server, the opposite route is followed. The network can also support collaborative learning.

The Authoring The authoring program consists of a series of templates, which gives non-programming teachers the framework to write their own courseware using that structure. An authoring program must provide at least a text editor and a graphic editor (Dobrinsti 1989).

The Instruction The instructional program leads students through the lessons at their own pace. Being an interactive teaching program, it combines strategies for teaching with a method of progressively testing the student's knowledge.

3   The ICBTS System

The ICBTS system (Li 1991) can perform two important functions. Firstly, when acting as an authoring program, it allows a teacher who has no knowledge of programming to interactively develop: lessons, lectures, tutorials, laboratory experimental procedures, questions/answers, and to add HELP/HINTs for each question. In electrical engineering education, it can be clearer for students if they are presented with computer graphics such as electrical drawings, figures, plots, and diagrams. Therefore, the authoring program will enable the teacher to develop and deliver lessons and instructions which combine text and graphics.

Secondly, when a student attempts to log on to this system, she or he will be prompted for an authorised user name as well as a valid password. It is intended that this service could be used each time she or he wishes to access computer-based training (CBT) files or a printer. Once a student has logged into a lesson, some of the options that will be presented are:–

- Choosing one of the accessible subjects.
- Choosing one of the accessible sections of a subject.
- Choosing one of the accessible activities.

Students can approach the lessons in an interactive way. For example, during a test, they can call up commands such as: VIEW, which shows them general information about the test, but not the contents of test questions; TEST, where the on-line marking facility is implemented simultaneously; HELP; or EXIT. Upon exiting, the result is saved in a student record file. The system is then able to collate individual students' results, calculated on the time taken, the number of problems attempted, and correctness. Overall class results can be obtained to give feedback to the teachers.

An additional advantage of ICBTS is that it will allow the teacher to communicate with students via the teacher's own workstation and it will provide the teacher with the facilities for tutoring and inspecting the work students are doing. The main possibilities offered by such a system are:-

- To send a screen image to a particular training station to help one student or to broadcast it all around the network.
- To inspect data from a training station to resolve or correct any problems.
- To control another terminal or all terminals so that students can see at their own station how to deal with any problems they may have.

The infrastructure of the system consists of three major components as shown in Fig. 1. The first one is the authoring program for authors to handle the database (including courseware database and student record database) and store the database that is ready for distribution to students. The second one is an instructional program for making knowledge accessible to the student, for evaluating student's work, and for collecting and analysing statistics on student performance. The last one is a computer network for distributing this courseware, and for supporting collaborative learning.

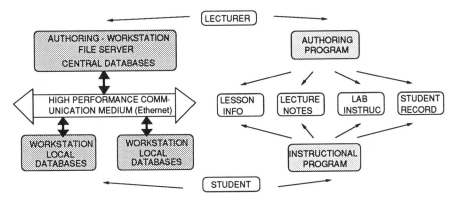

Figure 1: System configuration of hardware and software.

4 System Development

Some of the research work done in constructing the system, particularly the instruction part, is shown as follows;

Presentation and Instruction The aim of this section is to allow the student to interactively review a lesson step-by-step. Being the interface of the system, it should be user-friendly, and motivational to the student.

Management of Databases The lesson information database stores the information on a particular lesson, including problem type, answers, answer type, marks for each question, so that the system is provided with detailed information about the current lesson. It enables on-line marking to take place. The record database deals with record keeping, by accommodating students' records on all lessons, providing analyses and statistics of students' performance.

Student Modelling An essential component of the system is student modelling, which plays an important role in improving the quality of learning. As the system interacts with a student, it infers a model of the student's current understanding of the subject matter and uses this individualised model to adapt the instruction to the student's needs (Polson 1988). The detailed record of work of a student will also enable the teacher to see how many correct and incorrect answers there are and how much time the student has put into a lesson, thus finding out which problems are specifically difficult for the individual, or for the class at a later time. The teacher can then adopt effective teaching strategies to adapt and individualise the courseware.

Question and Answer The complexity of the teaching and learning process requires a comprehensive question/answer facility, thereby intensifying the level of interaction. However, the implementation of this facility is not particularly easy because of the limitation of human/machine interaction and the complexity of the algorithmic type of problem-solving and learning activities. The question/answer teaching strategy employed in the system, suitable for an engineering discipline, is being designed to offer the following types of question (Pudlowski 1990):–

- Multiple choice;
- True/false;
- Numerical;
- Tables;
- Graphs;
- Phasors;
- Keywords.

Students will be able to use the system in basic laboratory work: they will do calculations; input numerical observations which record the entered data of particular events; verify engineering theorems; plot and analyse characteristics with the aid of graphs and phasors; and, subsequently, read values and quantities directly from the computer screen so that they can experience typical engineering problem-solving strategies. They will also be able to do work - at their own pace, possibly at home - with their PCs connected to the network, instead of doing it in the tutorial room as they do now.

Object-Oriented Programming Object-oriented programming (Wiener 1988) is quite different from conventional procedural programming. Programs are no longer organised in terms of procedures and program statements but in terms of *objects* and *messages*. The class definition describes the behaviour of a model that encompasses a type and an associated set of operations, which are called *methods*, by defining the interface to all operations that can be performanced on the type. An *object* is defined in terms of classes. Objects communicate with each other by *sending messages*. The methods describe whether and how an incoming message can be reacted. The reaction can be to update the value of a variable, to send new messages to other objects, to return a value to the sender, etc. It is important to note that the objects decide themselves how to react to an incoming message. This is what is called *encapsulation* - the foundation upon which object-oriented problem-solving and programming are built.

Some use of object-oriented programming in developing the instructional program for ICBTS is briefly examined below (Fig. 2). At the highest level, two objects are identified. The first one is the student object. It describes a detailed record of a student's work, including: the number of correct answers, the time taken for doing the lesson, general performance assessment (GPA), final result, etc. The second one is the lesson information object, which represents thorough information on a lesson, containing: problem type, answer type, the intended answers, marks, etc. For example, when the student selects Lesson One, the on-line marking function will ask the lesson object for information about Lesson One, evaluate the student's work, and save his or her result in the student object. The student object can then use this information to enable record-keeping, analysis and statistical computation.

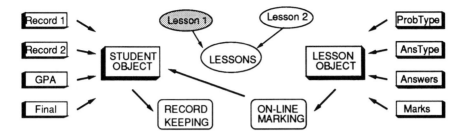

Figure 2: Simplified structure of the instructional program.

Network Collaborative Learning The issue of collaborative learning is a complex one. There is much research to indicate that individual problem-solving can be aided by peer interaction (Chan 1988). A learning network can aid this process. Two important uses for networking are (Nobar 1991):–

- To make all databases and resources available to anyone on the network, without regard to the physical locations of the resource and the user.
- To establish a powerful communication medium among widely-separated people.

This indicates the great potential of real-time classroom activities with network technology. The ICBTS presently employs a dedicated file server using Ethernet networking hardware running Novell Netware ELS 286 Level II (1991). However, Novell Netware does not provide facilities to support the real-time classroom activities described above. Although there are several commercial software packages on the market such as Close-Up/LAN (1989), LAN-Assist (1987), they only work for transmitting text screen, the inability to send graphics in most current systems makes them of little value to engineering courses (Crecraft 1991). Research work in this area is still under way.

5   Discussion & Summary

The ICBTS system offers the student individual, self-paced lessons. It can be seen as a work-horse, taking over much of the low-level, repetitious work from teaching staff in areas where the material is technically stable, and the number of students is high. Simple applications are cost-effective and practical. Not only will the system help students consolidate their fundamental engineering knowledge, and supplement lecturer's teaching, but also it has great potential to be adapted to many other subjects.

This paper describes an initiative which integrates computers, software, and teaching and learning material, into one flexible system for undergraduate engineering training. It discusses three essential aspects of a learning network - the network, the authoring, and the instruction. The ICBTS system is then described in some detail. Special emphasis is put on the system's development in general, and the instructional part of the system in particular. It includes presentation and instruction; management of databases; student modelling; question and answer; the use of object-oriented programming; and network collaborative learning.

Work on the development of the software has been under way for more than one year, and a stable base has been produced. We are currently developing the instructional program which will support the user interface described in this paper. The authors expect to complete the development and integration of a base tool set, to produce a desired-feature prototype of the system early next year.

6   References

Areitio, J. & Areitio, C. (1990) Low cost microcomputer network, an important help to evolved CAT system, in **Proceedings of the International Conference on Computer-Aided Training in Science and Technology**, (ed. E. Onate *et al*), Jorge Girona Salgado 31, Barcelona, Spain, 541-547.

Chan, Tak-Wai & Baskin, A. (1988) Learning companion system, in **Proceedings of the International Conference on Intelligent Tutoring Systems**, (ed. C. Frasson & G. Gauthier), Ablex, Norwood, New Jersey, 6-33.

Close-Up/LAN, Produced by Norton-Lambert Corp. (1989).

Coyle, K. & Schaper, J. (1990) NESTOR - A proposed system solution for courseware authoring and learning, in **Proceedings of the International Conference on Computer-Aided Training in Science and Technology**, (ed. E. Onate *et al*), Jorge Girona Salgado 31, Barcelona, Spain, 224-250.

Crecraft, D. I. (1991) SEFI and computer-aided engineering education in Europe, in **Proceedings of the International Conference on Computer-Aided Engineering**, (ed. J. Michel & Z. Pitra), Czech Technical U., K237, Technicka 4, 16607 Prague 6, Czecho-Slovakia, 8-13.

Dobrinsti, J. & Ottmann, T. (1989) How can educational software survive current hardware, **Computer Assisted Learning: 2nd International Conference, ICCAL'89**, Springer-Verlag, N.Y., 65-76.

LAN Assist Plus, Produced by Clay Jones (1987).

Li, X. & Pudlowski, Z. J. (1991) Designing a computer-based training system for electrical engineering education, in **Proceedings of the 3rd AAEE Annual Convention and Conference**, (ed. J.B. Agnew & C. Cresswell), AAEE, Engineering Faculty, Adelaide U., South Australia, 169-174.

Nobar P. M. (1991) A multilayer view of computer-based learning and training software (from machine code to hypertext), in **Proceedings of the East-West Congress on Engineering Education**, (ed. Z. Pudlowski), AAEE, School of Electrical Engineering, Sydney U., Australia, 387-391.

Novell Inc. (1983 - 1991) **NetWare Manuals Ver 2.2**, Novell Inc., Utah.

Polson, C. M. & Richardson, J. (1988) **Foundations of Intelligent Tutoring Systems**, L. Erlbaum, Hillsdale, New Jersey.

Pudlowski, Z. J. (1990) Developing computer programs for engineering education - important issues, in **Proceedings of the International Conference on Computer-Aided Training in Science and Technology**, (ed. E. Onate *et al*), Jorge Girona Salgado 31, Barcelona, Spain, 34-44.

Wiener, R. (1988) **Introduction to Object-Oriented Programming and C**, Addison-Wesley, Mass.

Graphical Computer Aids to the Teaching of Materials Science and Engineering

P.J. Goodhew

Department of Materials Science and Engineering, University of Liverpool

Abstract

This paper discusses the use of graphical computer software in a field, materials science and engineering, which has small student numbers. The ways in which software can be used are considered, as is a strategy for encouraging its writing and use. The software already available in the field is reviewed and suggestions are made for topics which are appropriate for treatment in the future.

Keywords: PC, Computer Graphics, Materials Science, Demonstration

1. Introduction

Computers are in widespread use in all engineering disciplines. Much work is done with relatively standard software packages which enable students to perform tasks similar to those they will meet in employment. Such use of computers does not significantly contribute to teaching other aspects of the curriculum. In this paper the potential for illuminating "standard" areas of the curriculum is explored. The discussion is set firmly in the context of a small subject area: This contributes many special constraints to the availability of materials. Materials Science & Engineering (embracing at least metallurgy, polymer science and ceramics) is a small discipline: the total undergraduate body in the UK is less than 1000 at any one time, and the world population is probably below 10000. The special problem which this size brings is that commercial software packages aimed at this market could expect very small sales and there is therefore little commercial incentive for software development. To compound the problem there is no single type of specialist software package which is very widely used by materials scientists or engineers in employment. These facts have a profound influence on the development of software for use within education in this field.

Since there are so many styles of software available it is worth defining closely what is meant in this paper by "graphical" software. Packages described by this phrase will include text and colour diagrams, and will usually involve the user in entering or selecting parameters which will alter the display. They may include animations, simulations of processes or mechanisms, microscope images and even graphs. They are not, however, graph plotting packages.

2. Software currently in use

Most software which is in use regularly is locally written by enthusiastic lecturers and very little of it is used outside its department of origin. Examination of the CTI catalogue for Engineering, Software for Engineering (1991) reveals that about

23 packages with specific materials science content are available in the UK. Of these 18 are published in a series by the Institute of Materials and exploit colour graphics to the EGA standard on standard IBM PCs. Of the other five none runs on standard PC hardware without either additional hardware or specific software. They are thus unlikely to be used outside their home department. Several of the Institute of Materials packages were described in the Sheffield conference by Goodhew (1991). The series is far from comprehensive, but the packages have in common that they are menu driven, use animated colour graphics and are designed to have a common "feel". Examples of the subject matter covered are crystallography (Crennell & Glasser, 1987), phase diagrams and microstructure (Dahl & van Tyne, 1988; Pilling, 1992), and electron microscopy (Humphreys, 1987; Goodhew, 1988; Goodhew et al, 1991).

2.1 Styles of use

Software aimed at assisting with teaching can be deployed in several ways. Many lecturers would find it useful to break up the formal nature of lectures by making use of computer-based demonstrations in the lecture room - effectively animated overhead projections. The problem here is the availability of both computers and display devices in the appropriate place. Very few lecture rooms in UK tertiary education establishments cater for the display of microcomputer output. It is difficult to maintain enthusiasm for this style of teaching when you have to carry your own computer to the classroom and then struggle with (at best) a low-contrast, low-resolution, weak-colour overhead projection screen.

Use in tutorial groups is simpler and more widespread, since five or six people can cluster around a single micro.

Laboratory classes could often benefit from the availability of a dynamic simulation or description of the (real) experiment under investigation. This is perhaps the simplest form of use since small numbers of fixed micros suffice. Graphical experiment "handouts" based on the Guide hypertext system and Autodesk Animator are being tested in Chemistry laboratories at Liverpool (Walker, 1992).

Student self-help, remedial work and assignments are ideal cases for the use of graphical programs. The two issues here are availability of hardware and ensuring that useful learning takes place in the absence of direct academic guidance. Hardware is considered in the next section. The important lesson which arises from several years experience in using computer-based material at the Universities of Surrey and Liverpool is that it is most effective when the student has to produce a written response to each piece of work. There are many ways in which this can be achieved but in essence the lecturer must set a task which results in a report from the student. This can be qualitative or quantitative - the important point is that it requires more of the student than simple reading from the screen.

2.2 Hardware issues

The main consideration must be the access to hardware by the intended users, that is primarily the students. A secondary, but essential, requirement is access to the hardware by the author(s). For software to be useful it therefore has to run on the platform available to students in the HEI. Since this article is concerned with graphics- based software text-only mainframe terminals are useless. The installed base, in 1992, is likely to be MS-DOS PC, Mac or UNIX workstation. There are even computer rooms equipped with BBC microcomputers still in use in many institutions. No common graphics standard is available across all these systems, so the only current way to make software available universally is to translate each package. This has rarely been considered economic in large subject areas such as mechanical or electrical engineering and is certainly not appropriate in materials engineering.

Analysis of the CTI listing (Software for Engineering Education, 1991) reveals that more than 75% of the available packages run on only a single platform, and the commonest single platform is MS-DOS, which will run 85% of the software. This probably reflects the majority installed base in 1992. However the software for use in 1993-2000 is being written now and it is far from obvious what hardware or graphics system to use. This remains a problem which will deter potential authors who (wisely) seek wide exposure for their efforts. This problem is considered in the next section.

3. How to extend the software base

If we start from the premise, advanced in section 1, that there is unlikely to be a commercial motive for producing teaching software in the materials area, then three particular problems emerge:

How will academics be persuaded to write appropriate software?
How can they be persuaded to produce it in a distributable form?
How can they use it?

In the UK, the pressures of academic audit, unit costs and appraisal all suggest that there must be measurable output from the efforts of an individual academic. The best evidence of innovative effort put into teaching will be published output. In the past this has tended to be limited to textbooks written by a minority of teachers. If credit is to be gained for software writing, then the software must be published. If there is negligible commercial gain then it must be published in the same way as research, in the equivalent of a technical journal. A start has been made by the Institute of Materials with its Materials Engineering Software Series. If software is published and, most importantly, refereed then there will be academic credit for the activity and standards of user-friendliness and documentation can be set and maintained. The final problem, of using the software, can only be solved by the spread of hardware and the encouragement of academics. At the current rate of cost reduction it will be reasonable to expect every student to have access to appropriate hardware within a few years. However it will take longer, and will involve the right guesses now, to prepare the software.

4. Areas where software would be useful

Because the writing of publishable software is so time-consuming it is vital that duplication of effort is minimised. This was the primary motive of the Institute of Materials in setting up its software publishing activity. Eighteen titles have so far been published in the series, but without any co-ordination: All offers of topics have been encouraged but the number of willing authors is small and "commissioning" has not been feasible. However very recently the Institute has conducted a survey of first-year materials science and engineering syllabi in the UK, with a view to encouraging or even commissioning software in appropriate under- developed areas. Examination of the subjects taught in the first year by many University materials departments reveals considerable diversity but the common areas contain many promising topics for graphical software treatment. It would be useful to review these, for the benefit of teachers who are considering directing some of their effort in this direction.

Four major areas emerge, large elements of which are treated by all Materials departments in the UK during the first year of their undergraduate courses (or first and second year for four year courses). These are crystallography, phase diagrams and microstructure, thermodynamics and kinetics and materials processing.

Several suites of programs which deal with aspects of crystallography are already available (eg Crennell & Glasser, 1987). However there are many gaps and plenty of scope for a unified treatment. Among the topics not yet covered by PC-based programs at undergraduate level are the stereographic projection, symmetry or the reciprocal lattice. These are all concepts which most students find difficult at first and which would be suitable for graphical treatment.

A second large area is concerned with the relationship between the phase diagram and microstructure in metals and ceramics. Again there is some provision in this area (Dahl & van Tyne, 1987; Pilling, 1992) but comprehensive coverage has not been achieved and there are some notable gaps. Most microstructural observations by undergraduates are carried out by light microscopy, yet there is no package available on this most central of topics. This is an area in which we should see major advances because it is now becoming feasible to incorporate "real" images in PC-based programs. The teaching of metallography (better described as hyleography, Goodhew (1992)) could be revolutionised if good quality images were available via PC packages.

A huge set of topics which are difficult to teach conventionally without terminal student boredom is related to the processing of materials. These subjects usually contain a significant theoretical background, together with a description of the mechanical process. This combination of large-scale action plus mathematical description is ideal for computer treatment. It is often difficult to show the full-scale process to students (at least at the appropriate time) and considerable depth of understanding is required to deal with the underlying theory. Examples of this type abound in materials syllabi: Casting, forging, rolling, drawing, welding and injection moulding are all carried out on a large scale on a variety of types of material; all are underpinned by substantial theory and mathematical description and all are nowadays modelled on computers in industrial and academic laboratories. However there is a serious lack of teaching material at the appropriate level.

The last subject area to be dealt with is thermodynamics and kinetics.

Materials scientists use a specific set of thermodynamic concepts and kinetic equations, often applying them to the solid state. Thus although the theory is in principle identical to that taught to chemists, physicists and chemical or mechanical engineers, the applications (from which examples must be drawn) are rather different. As a general rule materials students perceive this as a very difficult area, especially as it is almost entirely conceptual and mathematical. The writing of graphical software in this subject is thus both very important and very difficult. However the dividends in stimulating student interest would also be high.

5. Conclusions

In this paper the usefulness of graphical software for teaching has been emphasized and some criteria for its development in a small subject area such as materials science have been identified. Specific topics which are suitable for treatment but where appropriate software does not yet exist have been identified. The is a great deal of scope but the activity needs encouragement from senior academics, co-ordination at national or international level, and widespread agreement on the appropriate platform. What is missing is not ideas but time to write computer-based material at the appropriate level.

6. References

Crennell K M and L S Dent Glasser (1987) Atomic Packing and Crystal Structure, **Institute of Materials Engineering Materials Software Series**

Dahl K S & Van Tyne C J (1988) Use of Phase Diagrams, **Institute of Materials Engineering Materials Software Series**

Goodhew P J (1991) Computers in the teaching of materials science & engineering in **Innovative Teaching in Engineering** Ed R A Smith, Ellis Horwood 128-133

Goodhew P J (1988) The Transmission Electron Microscope, **Institute of Materials Engineering Materials Software Series**

Goodhew P J, G Cliff and F J Humphreys (1991) Analysis in the Electron Microscope, **Institute of Materials Engineering Materials Software Series**

Goodhew P J (1992) Microstructural Metrology in **Materials Metrology and Standards for Engineering Design** Elsevier, in press

Humphreys F J (1987) The Scanning Electron Microscope, **Institute of Materials Engineering Materials Software Series**

Pilling J (1992) PHAUST: Relationships Between Phase Diagrams and Microstructure,**Institute of Materials Engineering Materials Software Series** Software for Engineering Education (1991) CTI Centre for Engineering, ISSN 0960 -295X

Walker S M (1992) private communication

Power Electric Apparatus Courses in Poland

T. Lipski

Chair of Electrical Apparatus, Technical University of Gdańsk

Abstract

This paper gives a description of M.Sc. courses on Power Electric Apparatus offered by four Polish Technical Universities of: Gdańsk, Łódź, Poznań and Warszawa. Although there are some differences among the programs of those courses but the set of the core disciplines and subject syllabi are nearly the same. That's why given informations about the course run by the Technical University of Gdańsk represents the situation in this respect in Poland. At the beginning the paper deals with the basic knowledge the students are getting at the first 3.5 years of study and then specialist subjects and their syllabi over the last period of study which leads finally to M.Sc.degree. The paper ends by a number of suggestions how to save mentioned courses before their eventual cancellation due to expected reformation of the Polish engineering education system.

Keywords: Power Electric Apparatus, M.Sc. Course, Subject Syllabi, M.Sc. Projects.

1. Introduction

Already in the second half of the 3rd decade of this century the Germans at first introduced lecturing in the Power Electric Apparatus (PEA) on tertiary education level. In Poland the same was done just after World War II firstly in the Gdańsk Technical University. Some years later on one existing discipline then was split into several narrower ones such as: Power Switching Theory, Design of PEA and others. For the time being a special course is offered for those who are doing M.Sc. degree in PEA. But because the engineering education principles in Poland now are strongly criticised and the expected changes aimed to transformation them into a system which would resemble rather the British one, the PEA courses can

abruptly finish. That's why the first purpose of the paper
is to chronicle the most important points of those courses
run up to now by 4 Polish Technical Universities in:
Gdańsk, Łódź, Poznań and Warszawa. The second purpose, may
be a more important, is to indicate how to save those
courses for the future engineering education in Poland. The
problem is important not only for Poland but also for the
all post-communist countries. The information below
concentrates on courses in Gdańsk Technical University. But
the majority is true or similar to what is happening
with PEA courses run by Łódź, Poznań and Warszawa Technical
Universities.

2. General Informations

Power Electric Engineering Faculty, called in Polish in
fact Faculty of Electrotechnics, usually separated is from
the Electronic Faculty. The idea of such an independence,
introduced in the mid of 50-th, was to give, beside more
broader basic profesional discipline, a deeper preparation
also in some particular specialities, e.g.: electrical
appparatus and machines, power electric utilization a.s.o.
On the other hand., nowadays it is hard to imagine Power
Electric without Electronics.
Specific terms in the paper used are:
i   study direction, - Electrotechnic;
ii   study speciality, - part of Electrotechnic, in which
     students can get narrower formation;
iii diploma direction, - means an optional part of
     speciality to get a preparation in given (M.Sc.)
     Thesis.
For the time being the Faculty in Gdańsk offers the
following specialities:
i   Automation and Electrical Metrology;
ii   Electricity Generation and Delivery;
iii Utilization of Electrical Energy;
iiii PEA and Machines.
   The education program consists from 3 groups of the
subjects:
A - basic and basic profesional, which are obligatory for
    whole flow of the students irrespectively of the
    speciality, - usually covers a period of the first
    3-3.5 years of study;
B - additional basic profesional, but in 2 different
    versions: one for Automation and Electrical Metrology
    students, and second for remaining specialities, -
    usually these subjects are on fourth year of study;

C - subjects of specialities and diploma directions, -
   usually the 1.5 year of study; in here lies PEA course.
   At least the following subjects are believedas the basic
professional ones; Principles of Electrotechnic, Electrical
Machines, Electrical Arrangements, Bases of
Elektroenergetics and Thermokinetics, Electronics, Power
Electronics, Automation and Control, Principles of
Mechanical Constructions.
   The PEA courses the paper speaks about are included in the
subjects group C. An exemplary sequence of the basic and
basic professional subjects is demonstrated in the Table 1,
whereas the Table 2 shows the PEA subjects.
   Total number of the student contact hours over the 5
year study period is about 4300. In it about 62 % are basic
and basic professional subjects A, about 12 % - subjects B
and about 26 % - subjects C.About 50 % of the subjects C are
optional but in correlation with the M.Sc. Thesis.
   It is assumed that A and B subject blocks give a good
general preparation to start with further study in PEA. In
addition to that every M.Sc. student in PEA has to choose
few extra subjects which are in an avenue leading to the
Thesis, of which list of those subjects in principle is
every academic year subject of renovation. For instance, if
an M.Sc. candidate did a choice in High Voltage Technics and
has to investigate a problem with PE cables, he is advised

Table 1. Subjects A and B

Subjects	Contact hours
General basic subjects such as: philosophy, social science, foreign language	825
Mathematics,	345
Physics	180
Mechanical construction	180
Principles of electrotechnic	315
Computers and programming	90
Electrical metrology	150
Electronics	90
Electrical machines	165
Electrical materials	45
Automation and control	165
Power electronics	60
High voltage technics	60
Mathematical modelling	45
Basis of elektroenergetics and thermokinetics	180
Electrical hazard	30
Electrical arrangements	45
Power switching technology	38
Electric drive I	60
Scientific information and patents	8

Table 2. Subjects C

Subjects	Contact hours
Selected topics of mechanics	45
High voltage insulation	60
Selected topics of electrical arrangements	60
Electric drive II	30
Processing of constructional materials	45
Principles of manufacturing of electrical equipment	60
Electrical machines	105
Investigation of PEA I	60
Electrical apparatus	60
Electrical traction	45

to select at least 3 extra subjects, e.g.: Power Electric
Cables, High Voltage Cables, Coordination of Insulation.

3. Examples of Subject Syllabi of PEA Courses

Amongst subjects shown in Table 2 for a closer look two
examplary subject syllabi are selected only.
E l e c t r i c a l   A p p a r a t u s
Electrodynamic   forces,   mechanical resonance   including.
Electric arc, physics, calculation. Recovery voltage and
its   calculation. Switching phenomena in high-voltage
systems: interruption of unloaded long lines, unloaded
transformers, short-line fault, influence of long lines on
recovery voltage by short-circuit interruption. Switching
arc in open space, in plate-deion chambers and narrow slot
chambers, calculations.
I n v e s t i g a t i o n   o f P E A   I
Short-circuit tests. AC and DC short-circuit test stations.
Generator short-circuit stations. Network stations. Test
technics. Direct tests. Synthetic tests. Short-circuit
endurance tests. Measurements in electrical apparatus.
Oscillographic and digitalized records. Investigations of
fuses, contactors, circuit-breakers. Statistical treatment
of results.
Besides, below are given syllabi of two optional subjects.
H i g h - V o l t a g e   A p p a r a t u s
SF_6, vacuum, pneumatic, small oil, electromagnetic technics
of arc-quenching. Contact movement influence on breaking
capacity. High-voltage fuses, disconnectors, circuit-
breakers.Mechanical drives of apparatus. Short-circuiting
and earthing switches. Short-circuit protection chokes.
Swithchboards. Trends in high-voltage appartus development.
L o w - V o l t a g e   A p p a r a t u s
Load switches, switching conditions. Contactors, switching

contitions. Electromechanical, semiconductor and hybrid
contactors. Circuit-breakers, switching conditions.
Classical, selective, high-speed circuit- breakers.
Thyristorized circuit-breakers. Fuses. Semiconductor fuses.
Apparatus assemblies. Switchboards. New trends.
E x a m p l e s   o f   M. Sc.   T h e s i s
Investigations of recovery strength of SF_6 fuses.
Investigations of cylindrical SF_6 arc-quenching chamber of
a load-switch. Investigation of a system to compensate of
electrodynamical forces in contacts. Low-voltage power
permanent fuse on mercury base, design and preliminary
investigations. Design and investigation of special fuses
working as indicators of recovery voltage of short-circuit
test station.

4. Chances of Future Existence of PEA Courses

The whole philosophy of the existence of highly specialized
M.Sc. courses described in PEA were a requirement for   good
M.Sc. graduated engineers able to take over immediately
responsible positions in the post-World War II destroyed
industry of Poland. Afterwards during the long post-War 4.5
decades PEA courses found out a good support in the
laboratory infrastructure.

In each of the four Polish Univerities running PEA
courses there are modest direct (generator or network) low
and medium voltage short-circuit stations, large current
and high-voltage test facilities, specialized diagnostic
equipment and digitalized transient recorders included into
a computer system. But now due to expected reconstruction
of Polish engineering education system the cancellation of
highly specialized M.Sc. courses like PEA courses is to be
threatened. So arises a dramatical question,what to do with
such courses.

The problem, it **seems**, could be solved in many ways.
Some of them are indicated below.

Similarly to freshly called into being the International
Faculty of Engineering as a joint-project of the Sydney
University and the Technical University of Łódź Poland,
initiated by Dr.Z.J.Pudłowski (1992) one can extend the
idea onto M.Sc. courses in PEA.Another possibility is on the
base of existing academic staff and laboratory background
to arrange European Master Degree Courses in PEA. Still
another option is to organize the M.Sc. courses in PEA for
graduate students from third world countries, using
eventually additionally UNIDO scheme.

From many visits to various university labs on PEA in
Western Europe the author carrried out a lesson that the

laboratory and teaching infrastructure in PEA of all four
Polish Technical Universities running those courses are well
prepared to even develop above given activity instead to
finish abruptly.

5. References

Pudłowski Z.J. (1992) An undergraduate engineering degree
    program in electromechanics, EEE Research and
    Development, Issue No.1 (Australia), 1-19.

Tools for Computer Science Education in Engineering Using the Hypertext Approach

E.I. Giannotti, F. Ricci

Department of Communications, Computer and System Sciences (DIST), University of Genoa

Abstract

Computer science education at University Schools of Engineering is currently undergoing a revision process aimed at better suiting it to the discipline evolution, and at making it more efficient and stimulating for students. The paper presents the instructional strategies that have been followed to satisfy these requirements. Moreover, it describes the design of tools (based on hypertext technology) that can be used to integrate lab activities with lectures. In particular, a tool for learning abstract data types, i.e. HyperADT-Tour, is proposed. Finally, the first reactions of students to this approach, which represents a new way of studying and working, are discussed.

Keywords: Computer Science Education, Hypertext, Hypermedia, CAI, Algorithm Animation, Data Structures.

1 Introduction

The considerable, dynamic evolution of the methods, tools and applications associated with computer science strongly influences also the education in this field. Computer education curricula may follow different guidelines at the University level. For instance, for an introductory course, at least five different approaches can be selected: 1) providing an overview of the discipline, 2) presenting concepts in a formal and theoretical way, 3) introducing software engineering principles, 4) concentrating on program analysis (reading), and 5) emphasizing algorithmic problem solving.

The authors are engaged in developing suitable didactic tools for the first two courses in computer science (equivalent to an introductory course and to a second course in algorithms, data structures and programming) at the Engineering School of the University of Genoa. They have chosen to deal with topics related to these courses in a way suitable for this kind of School, using a combination of approaches 3,4,5.

This choice stems from the following considerations. Engineering Schools have to face the issue of an ever-increasing number of students, with different educational backgrounds and different practical and theoretical skills. Universities should allow all these students to acquire design capabilities, which can be attained by using operational tools and instructional strategies well-suited to developing problem-solving and synthesis abilities. One primary goal to be reached lies in making the processes of instruction (considered as a combination of teaching and learning activities) and of conveying concepts very efficient. By "efficient" we mean economical (fast, easy, cost-effective, etc.); moreover, we want to avoid misconceptions, usually associated with the teaching of concepts.

In order to improve traditional instruction, it is necessary to produce a new generation of learning and training systems, which should be more economical and more suitable for the different learning skills of students. For these reasons, new tools and new technological supports should be devised, and exploratory programming environments and rapid-prototyping tools should be provided to allow evolutionary design and implementation of educational software. To this end, hypertext technology (see Jonassen and Mandl 1990) appears the most appropriate solution. Some interactive visual tools have already been developed (see Giannotti and Ricci 1991), using different hypertext systems, to support the instructional activities involved in the two computer-science courses. Such tools have been designed to teach both fundamental concepts of informatics and programming based on software engineering principles, in a more effective and more formative way. In the following sections, the guidelines followed in the development of these tools and in their integration into the instructional contexts of the above courses will be described. In particular, the organization of the tool HyperADT-Tour will be presented.

2   Instructional Strategies in Computer Science Education

The main objective has been to offer students a new learning framework based on an environment where to explore the various topics, and where concepts, algorithms, and data structures are represented in a visual and dynamic way. Since 1983, we have developed algorithm animation tools which were experimented successfully (see Giannotti 1987). At present, graphic simulation is widely used in computer science education, and recognized as a powerful aid in teaching this discipline. Then, we have pursued the integration of textual descriptions and visualization tools into powerful navigation tools to provide students with a more effective learning environment.

In order to employ systems compatible with two different platforms, we have chosen two widely used systems, namely, HyperCard for Macintosh, and Plus for PC-DOS. We have designed various tools with such systems; in particular, we shall describe the application of Hypercard and Plus to abstract data types (ADTs), called HyperADT-Tour. This tool uses graphic metaphors, where possible, to make explicit concepts, examples, and program behaviour.

The introduction of these tools has changed the organization of the first and second courses in computer science. Figure 1 presents the organization of the didactic activities for such courses.

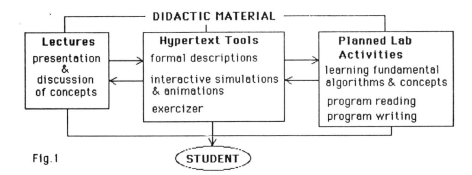

Fig. 1

We have planned a model for computer science education that utilizes the engineering design laboratory. This model couples lectures, home-work and programming projects with the laboratory component to form a unified course framework. The laboratory component must be organized in such a way as to constitute the basic place where students can be both active and creative partners in the learning process.

The laboratory activities are organized into different phases. For example, if a lecture presents the concept of an abstract data type (ADT) and the Modula-2 mechanism to realize it, the students are invit-ed to explore freely the HyperADT-Tour, where they can browse the theo-retical and formal contents, visualize the effect of each operation on an example of the ADT considered, and, in addition, manipulate the ADT directly through a specific data-structure editor. The editor repre-sents an efficient mean to teach students the use and the effects of the main operations. This activity allows students to acquire a deep understanding of concepts, and to experiment with them. Moreover, the students must write a personal version of an ADT in the classroom, develop it on the computer, evaluate the performance of the implementa-tion, and discuss it with the teacher. Subsequently, they are assigned a problem to solve which they can use previous work, made by themselves or available as course material.

An interesting result of this organization has been observed: stu-dents improve the quality of their programming projects. The creation or the availability of routines, of libraries of ADTs, and of algo-rithms favours the development of good software design, highlights the importance of modularization as a problem-solving strategy, and encour-ages students to use such tools later on for more exacting programming projects. The aforesaid result was obtained with difficulty, when the first lab assignment was to develop the computer solution of a problem, therefore, it was easier for students to create a monolithic

program. The strategy that encourages students to try a problem solution by choosing from among different software components previously
implemented and tested make it possible to assign students more realistic problems. Moreover, it prepares them for software projects to be
developed outside the classroom, i.e., in a place where they need to
work on portions of new projects, or to modify existing ones.

3   The Hypertext Tool HyperADT-Tour

This section describes the organization of HyperADT-Tour and explains
how to browse it. This hypertext tool presents, as a first card, the
ADT index, where each different ADT is listed by name and by a graphical representation. Each ADT is organized into a stack, where the majority of cards have the same background. The user can select an ADT
and navigate through the related set of cards, from which it is always
possible to return to the ADT index. If the user clicks the ADT Queue,
the first card of this stack (Fig.2) is presented, which contains the
data structure definition, and a summary of applications, and uses.
The user can browse this stack according to a linear path, following
the arrows; otherwise, he can follow other paths, using the iconic buttons at the bottom of each card. To help the navigation, a button to
see the map is provided on the upper left portion of each card. The
ADT map (Fig.3) illustrates the arrow navigation (continuous lines) and
the button navigation (dotted lines) through the main cards associated
with the corresponding navigation button, which the user may click. To
know the operations possible for the ADT, there is a card "Queue
Operation Index" which lists constructor, selector, and iterator operations, each of which has a button to go to the corresponding card
"Formal Description: Operation name". Each operation is described according to the specification language adopted by C. Lins. The user may
better understand the single details of each operation by observing
the animation of the logical representation of a queue obtained clicking the button "Logic Animation", or he may analyze the code listing
related to the two different implementations chosen for the ADT queue,
i.e., bounded and unbounded. Even in the case of the unbounded queue
implementation for each of the main operations it is possible to go to
a specific card, by clicking the button "Physic Animation", and to
see the operation animation on the physical representation (usually,
the unbounded one) of the ADT queue.
The user may read the listing of the definition module. By clicking
the button "Implement. Index", he may analyze the different implementations chosen for the ADT. For this ADT, there are only two different
implementation modules.
   We have decided to introduce two different editors: one for the logical data structure and the other for the physical data structure.
These two kinds of representation are focused during the animation of
each operation: the user can understand the effect of each operation on
the logical data structure, and appreciate the details related to implementation of the physical data structure.

By using iconic buttons containing the logical and physical(bounded and unbounded) data structure representations, it is possible to activate the corresponding editor in the first card of each ADT. The editor is presented in a card. Students can select an operation through a menu (obtained by clicking the button "Show Primitives"). They can insert the input data in the input field of the card, and obtain output values for the data structure in the output field, and messages for the possible exceptions in the exception field. The central space is devoted to the animation of the data structure. Fig.4 represents the animation of the operation "Assign" in the physical editor for the bounded representation of the queue..

4   Remarks

Learning methods are undergoing a notable evolutionary process, therefore it is important to devote efforts to exploring the capabilities of any new learning-related technology. In particular, hypertext technology, which can be tailored to specific applications as described in the previous sections, is very promising and stimulates us to explore new learning modalities, even though the development of hypertext and hypermedia for learning is still in a very early stage. Hypertext tools offer simulation facilities, and exploratory environments that allow the learner to browse at will, and that encourage the application of content-oriented information-seeking strategies. Moreover, browsing the tools, even when no specific learning goals are to be attained, may result in the acquisition of a considerable amount of implicit learning.

In an early application of a new technology, special attention must be given to collecting baseline data that are extensive and varied. There exist no proven methods for assessing the process of learning. However, one important advantage that the medium itself offers is the potential of capturing many of the interactions between the learner and the tool itself. We are developing a computer-monitored data-collection method to evaluate these interactions and to verify the student's learning level and the validity of the hypertext-tool design.

5   References

Giannotti, E. (1987) Algorithm Animator: a tool for programming learning, ACM SIGCSE Bullettin, 19, 308-314.

Giannotti, E., and Ricci, F. (1991) A hypertext application to a learning environment, in Proceedings of 6th Int. PEG Conference, (eds. Bottino, Forcheri, Molfino) Rapallo, Italy, 587-594.

Jonassen, D.H., and Mandl, H. (eds) (1990) Designing hypermedia for learning, NATO ASI Series, Series F, 67.

Lins, C. (1989) The Modula-2 software component library, Vol.1,2,3, Springer-Verlag.

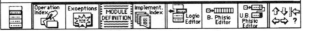

Fig. 2

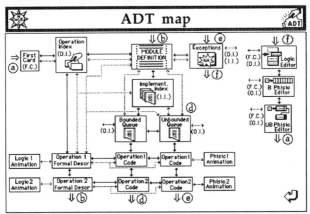

Fig. 3

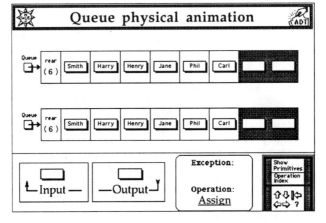

Fig. 4

COMPI16 - An Interactive Tool for Elementary Computer Education

H. Pangratz

Institut für Datenverarbeitung, Technical University of Vienna

Abstract
An educational computer model is presented, which illustrates on the one hand the functions of a basic "Von Neumann" architecture, on the other hand the operation of assembler and linker programs. The model runs on an IBM-compatible PC. The underlying computer is a simple accumulator machine with 32 instructions, indirect addressing and a 512 x 16 bit memory. When running a program all information transfers are illustrated either by arrows indicating the data path or by moving the information on the screen from one location to another. For the students the model combines hands-on experience on a computer console with the demonstrational power of a film.
Keywords: Education, Computer, Abstract Machines, Model, Assembly Language.

1. Aims and Motivation

First it should be pointed out that the educational goals of COMPI16 are restricted to elementary computer architecture and program development in assembly language. These subjects are of interest mainly in the field of computer science and electrical engineering. In other fields programming courses are mostly confined to high level languages, which are not included in the scope of COMPI16.

Also, COMPI16 is designed just to give a first introduction to the subject. The motivation in developing of COMPI16 was to create a simple interactive computer model to get across the basic concepts. In later courses more complex systems, typically commercial systems, will have to be used. To start off with an artificial model instead of using a real life system right from the start may seem to many teachers an unnecessary waste of time. However, the complexity of commercial systems is rather high for beginners; in working with such systems, many students have difficulties to extract the basic concepts and severe misunderstandings may result, especially by mixing up machine functions with software functions. These problems can be avoided by employing a purely educational model like COMPI16 to establish a correct model in the brain of students first, before moving on to more complex and realistic systems.

2. Overall Design of COMPI16

Working with COMPI16 covers a complete program development cycle for
programming in assembly language: the system consists of an Editor,
Assembler, Linker and the computer COMPI16 itself. An assembler program is written with the help of an editor, translated into machine
code with the assembler and linked with other pretranslated modules
using the link program. Finally, the whole program is loaded for execution and testing.

The benefits of the model stem not only from the simple architecture but also from the way processing is visualized. To give an example: An assembler program normally works in black-box fashion. It
takes source code as an input and outputs machine code and an error
list. What happens in between remains hidden. In contrast, COMPI16
makes the assembly process transparent: in running the assembler
students can watch the whole process on the screen, which displays not
only the source code but also an intermediate label table and the
machine code eventually produced (Fig. 1).

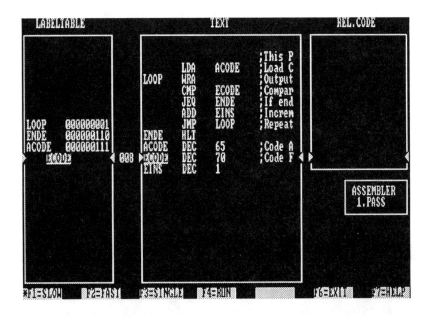

Fig. 1. Screen of COMPI16 assembler

To enhance the understanding of the ongoing process information is
moved on the screen. Thus, if a new label is encountered in the source
code, the label is shifted on screen to the label table (in Fig. 1 the
label ECODE). The linker works in the same way.

The COMPI16 computer itself is not built in actual hardware but simulated on a PC. All necessary information, registers, a window of the memory and input/output are displayed on screen. Although it is obvious for the students that they do not work with a real piece of hardware, COMPI16 will give them - in contrast to normal simulation or debug programs - the overall feeling of working on a computer console instead of interacting with software only. The main educational goal here is to understand the execution of the program as a sequence of basic machine cycles, comprising instruction fetch, instruction address register update and execution of the operation itself.

When working with normal simulation or debug programs students must know beforehand what happens inside the computer. For instance, it is difficult to realize that one register is copied onto another if one doesn't know that this is going to happen. With COMPI16 it is different. Before any information transfer is actually performed, the data path is highlighted by an arrow moving from source to destination. So if students start off with a poor knowledge they have a chance to learn by working with the model.

3. Description of the Model

3.1 Architecture of COMPI16

First it should be noted, that details of the architecture like instruction set and word length are not vital points and could be changed to meet other needs. The main point is simplicity. All instructions have a word length of 16 bits and are coded in one format:

15	14	13	12	11	10	9	8	7	6	5	4	3	2	1	0
T	O	O	O	O	O	I	A	A	A	A	A	A	A	A	A

Operation is encoded in bits 10 - 14, permitting 32 machine instructions including 8 branch instructions. Bit 9 denotes indirect addressing, in fact the only address modification the model offers. The operand address is encoded in bits 0 - 8. The tag bit 15 is used to distinguish operations from data. Such a tag bit is not provided in normal processors. In the model it serves two purposes: on the one hand it allows to display instructions and data in a different format on screen: instructions in a mnemonic format and data as decimal numbers. On the other hand it permits detecting specific run time errors - data loaded in the instruction register or instructions loaded in the accumulator. This run time error detection can be switched off in order to demonstrate the consequence of such errors or to run program tasks with self-modifying code.

The arithmetic/logic section is designed with one accumulator and two additional registers for temporarily storing a second operand and the result of an operation.

Characters are input on the keyboard and output on a miniature screen. In addition, process input and output and a single interrupt are provided. Thus it is possible - with the appropriate hardware connected - to use the model for simple control tasks, which is especially motivating for the students.

In the normal course of program development, an assembler program must be written, translated and linked before simulation (except when entering the program directly in memory which is a tedious chore). Since the simulator is closely related to the architecture of the model it is described next.

3.2 COMPI16 Simulator

The screen display of the simulator is shown in Fig. 2. Due to the simplicity of the model, screen layout requires no manipulation of windows. In the figure the first instruction of a short program is fetched from memory and copied to the instruction register (IR).

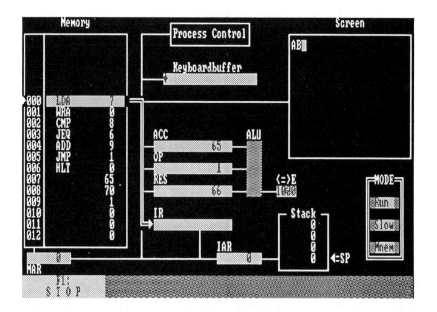

Fig. 2. Screen of COMPI16

The program can be run in slow mode, where all information transfers are visualized, or in fast mode, where only the contents of instruction address register and accumulator (IAR and ACC) are updated and the program runs at full speed. Singlestepping is provided. The transparency of the model makes testing very easy; a breakpoint register is included to further enhance debugging capabilities.

3.3 COMPI16 Editor
The editor is used to create and modify assembler programs. Of course any editor familiar to the students can do this job. If no other editor is preferred, the system provides a simple editor with preset tabs for entering the source code.

3.4 COMPI16 Assembler
The assembler program translates the assembler source code in a re-locatable machine program. Relocatable means that the location of the program in the memory remains free and can be assigned by the linke program later on. In this way it is possible to link a program with pretranslated routines. The assembler works in two passes. The first pass creates the label table, while the second pass does the trans-lation itself. The whole process is visualized on screen. Assembling can be done in slow mode or fast mode (without visualization). Single-stepping is possible as well.

3.5 COMPI16 Linker
The linker can link several modules into one object program with a fixed memory address. It works in three passes. The first pass assigns a memory start address to all modules based on their length. The second pass sets up a table of external and entry addresses and re-solves them into real addresses. The third pass forms the object pro-gram. All three passes are visualized as usual on screen. Linking can again be done in slow or fast mode (without visualization). Single-stepping is possible again.

4. Practical Use of COMPI16

Before students work with COMPI16, some theoretical introduction is necessary. One way to give this introduction is to present the model and the principles of assembly language in a lecture before laboratory work. Another way is to use written material, which has to be studied in advance. Practical work can be done by students individually or by a team of two or three students. One laboratory set-up must include a PC and a printing facility. Process control tasks require an appropri-ate process model (e.g. railway, robot arm, assembly line).

Before students start off with their programming task, some "war-ming-up" is desirable. This is best done by using the simulator for entering a short prepared program directly into memory and running it. In this way students get familiar with the controls of COMPI16 and rehearse the principal functions of the computer. After that, the actual program task is given. Also, a library of subroutines, espe-cially for input and output, is offered for solving the problem. Some subroutines may be deliberately removed from the library, so that stu-dents have to develop equivalent routines themselves. To encourage a top-down approach, students have to design an overall program struc-ture before proceeding to assembly coding. Desired program length is about 50 to 100 lines of assembler code: this is sufficient to repre-sent some complexity. Longer programs would be cumbersome and produce no benefit at this level. Also, owing to the use of library subroutines, this program length is perfectly sufficient to solve motivating tasks, even in control applications.

The program must be edited, assembled, linked and tested. The final version has to be approved by the teacher and a listing with adequate comments has to be handed in as documentation. Generous time allowance, preferably a full day, should be available for the job. If students feel free of time pressure, they will be more willing to make experiments and to run the model more often in the slow mode, thus gaining more insights and benefit. If laboratory time is restricted, the time required can be cut down considerably by announcing the programming task in advance. In this way the program can be prepared beforehand and laboratory work is concentrated on debugging. However, this approach bears the risk, that students may rely on outside help or try to use programs developed by groups before them.

In the author's experience the model can indeed help students get a clear and concise understanding of basic machine functions, which is a significant benefit. As a tradeoff, more time has to be spent in the complete curriculum, when starting off with an educational model instead of a real-life system. The method of visualization employed in COMPI16 could be used to similar benefit on other educational problems.

References

Nievergelt, J., et al. (1978) XS-0: A Self-Explanatory School Computer, ACM SIGCSE Bull., 10/4, 66-99.
Pangratz, H. (1981) COMPI - An Instructive Model for Elementary Computer Education, ACM SIGCSE Bull., 13/2, 12-15.
Decker, W. (1985) A Modern Approach to Teaching Computer Organization and Assembly Language Programming, ACM SIGCSE Bull., 17/4, 38-45.
Koneva, L., Denev, J. (1990) EASY/VI - A New Instructional Computer, ACM SIGCSE Bull., 22/2, 55-58.

Matlab Toolbox for Teaching Circuit Theory - Formulation of Circuit Equations

S. Osowski

Institute of Theory of Electrical Engineering and Electrical Measurements, Technical University , Warsaw

Abstract
    The paper presents the application of MATLAB programming in teaching circuit theory. The new CIRCUIT toolbox of MATLAB is introduced and developed. Its implementations in education of circuit theory and computer aided circuit analysis are discussed. The important feature of the proposition is that it provides the students with easy and flexible tools of understanding of the methods of circuit equation formulation and solution.
Keywords: Circuit Theory Teaching, Formulation of Circuit Equations, Computer Aided Circuit Analysis.

1. Introduction

    Recent development in microcomputer technology as well as expansion of the software available on these computers have caused revolution in electrical engineering education, i.e. Huelsman (1989). The introduction of PCs into the university as well as their increasing use at home by students, enable us to think of them as the basic instruments in cognition of the phenomena of electrical engineering, especially on the basic level. Many specialized computer programs, like SPICE, NAP, i.e. Prigozy (1989), Rubner-Petersen (1978) etc, have been released for PC and are now available for the general use for students. They are extremely easy in everyday applications even for students not familiar with electrical engineering. With such powerful instruments at hand many students do not see reasons for thorough study of the bases of electrical engineering. As a result, the understanding of the basic techniques of circuit theory as well as the knowledge of circuit laws are not satisfactory from the engineering practice point of view.
    It seems that the gap between the higher level computer programs like SPICE or NAP and the knowledge of the basic laws of circuit theory should be filled out with some intermediate level of programming, where student can build his own programs, using and practicing all circuit rules forming the foundation of electrical engineering. The programming language should be enough user friendly to encourage students to build their own programs and to practice them.
    In my opinion all these requirements are fulfilled by the program

MATLAB, the product of MathWorks, Inc. The name MATLAB stands for matrix laboratory. It is an interactive system whose basic data element is a matrix that does not require any dimensioning. Entering matrices into program as well as the format of solution produced by MATLAB are almost exactly as they are written mathematically.

The extremely rich matrix operations (many different kinds of factorizations, decompositions, inverses, eigenvalues, eigenvectors, singular values, basic matrix functions etc) as well as very good 2-D and 3-D graphic capabilities make this program very interesting from the circuit theorist point of view. Additionally the practice of so called M-files enable to develop the program into specialized toolboxes oriented on solving sofisticated engineering problems, like control, identification, ordinary differential equations, signal processing, optimization, i.e. MATLAB manual (1989).

In this paper the new application toolbox of MATLAB directed to circuit equation formulation will be proposed. The hybrid, nodal, state space description of electric circuits are step by step introduced. These basic subprograms in conjunction with some more sofisticated techniques like sensitivity, symbolic analysis etc, form the specialized toolbox of circuit theory.

On the basis of them student can easily build his own M-files for solving particular problems of electrical engineering or simply practice circuit laws and rules by applying functions and operations offered by the general program or by calling the existing, already written specialized M-files.

2. The goals of the proposed MATLAB program

Developing MATLAB files into specialized CIRCUIT toolbox has at least two major goals. The first of these is to show the easy way of studying circuit laws. With all powerful matrix operations available in the program the student can describe the circuit, starting from the basic equations and get the results in a small fraction of time it would take to write a program in a language like FORTRAN or C. This will encourage the student to practice circuit laws at the basic level instead of coding circuit problems into highly specialized languages without any comprehension of the electrical rules.

The second goal is strictly connected with software development and is very important at higher level of education directed at the computer aided approach to the electrical engineering. Following step by step the student can understand and build the elements of his own "SPICE" program. At proper organisation of the projects within the student's group the new user friendly complete program may be easily developed at the end of the course. Because of the modularity of such program the student can trace the succeding stages of the solution of the problem beginning with circuit equation formulation through the solution up to the graphical presentation of the results. At the final stage of the project student can use the program to study and graphically visualize different phenomena of electrical circuits. Even at this stage MATLAB application is more universal - the results may be given in different forms: circuit equations, partial numeric solution, 2-D or 3-D curves depicting the relationships among the variables in the circuit.

3. Algorithmic formulation of the circuit equations

In this section we describe the algorithmic approach to the formulation of the basic circuit equations and their implementation in MATLAB. They start with the topological functions (tree, cotree, incidence, loop and cutset matrices), and on the basis of this the admittance and hybrid descriptions are developed. The hybrid matrix is applied in the formulation of nonlinear resistive circuit equations as well as canonical state space description of the linear circuit. In conjunction with the adjoint network theory it forms also the basis of sensitivity calculation of the network. All these M-files create the new CIRCUIT tolbox of MATLAB which may cooperate with other M-files existing in the program, providing easy way for the analysis of the general circuits.

The input parameters describing the circuit are given in the form of 6-column matrix S. The succesive columns of S have following meaning:

column 1   - the succesive number of the element in the circuit
column 2, 3 - the node numbers of element
column 4 : - type of the element; the elements are coded as follows
             resistance R - 1, inductance L - 2, capacitance C - 3
             ideal voltage source E - 4, ideal current source J - 5
             controlled sources: CCVS - 6, VCVS - 7, CCCS - 8, VCCS - 9
column 5   - value of the parameter of the element (R, L, C etc)
column 6   - the numeration of the controlling element (only for
             controlled sources).

For example in the case of circuit presented in Fig. 1

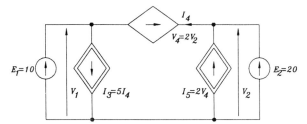

Fig. 1 The circuit of the example

the matrix S has the following form

$$S = \begin{bmatrix} 1 & 1 & 3 & 4 & 10 & 0 \\ 2 & 2 & 3 & 4 & 20 & 0 \\ 3 & 1 & 3 & 8 & 5 & 4 \\ 4 & 2 & 1 & 7 & 2 & 2 \\ 5 & 3 & 2 & 9 & 2 & 4 \end{bmatrix}$$

On the basis of input matrix S topological quantities such as tree, cotree as well as incidence matrix A, loop matrix B and cutset matrix D are generated in an algorithmic way by applying series of elementary row operations on the matrix A, reducing it to the echelon form. The first task that is done by the program is choosing a tree with the preference as to the order of the different types of network elements included in the tree. Student can state his own preference by changing only one vector inside the M-file. The usual, built in preference for the purpose of state equations formulation is as follows: independent voltage sources, controlled voltage sources, capacitors, resistors, inductors, controlled current sources and independent current sources. The M-file generating the topological matrices is named TOPOL.M . Calling it in the way

$$[A, B, D, L, T] = TOPOL(S)$$

results in the generation of matrices A, B and D, the link vector L and tree vector T, indicating the numbers of branches forming tree (vector T) and cotree (vector L).

The topological M-file is directly applied in the admittance matrix description of RLC circuit, $Y_n V_n = J_n$, where V_n is the vector of node-to-datum voltages (node numbers are defined by the student in S matrix), Y_n - nodal admittance matrix, J_n - equivalent nodal current source vector. The M-file NODAL.M generates all these complex matrices and vectors at the defined frequency ω and is called as follows

$$[Y_n, J_n] = NODAL(S, \omega)$$

The other description of the circuit, the hybrid one, is defined here only for the resistive circuits and can be called to generate different kinds of descriptions. We denote by a and b the vectors containing the indexes of branches corresponding to independent voltage and current excitations, respectively. Calling the hybrid file CONSTR.M as follows

$$[C, a, b] = CONSTR(S)$$

results in generation of the constraint matrix C and vectors a and b corresponding to the general implicit hybrid description

$$[C] \begin{bmatrix} V_a \\ I_b \\ V_b \\ I_a \end{bmatrix} = 0 \qquad (1)$$

For the matrix S given above the results will be

$$C = \begin{bmatrix} 0 & 0 & -1 & -1 \\ -1/4 & 1 & 2 & -2 \end{bmatrix} \quad a = [1, 2] \quad b = [] \qquad (2)$$

where the symbol [] stands for empty matrix (matrix of zero dimension). Calling the other hybrid function HYBRID.M as follows

$$[H, HS] = HYBRID(S, a, b)$$

one gets matrices H and HS of specified hybrid description (vectors a and b are now specified by the user)

$$\begin{bmatrix} I_a \\ V_b \end{bmatrix} = [H] \begin{bmatrix} V_a \\ I_b \end{bmatrix} + HS \qquad (3)$$

The vector HS corresponds now to the independent excitations inside the circuit. Calling it in our example as [H, HS] = HYBRID(S, [1], [2]) results in

$$H = \begin{bmatrix} 16 & 4 \\ -1 & 0 \end{bmatrix} \quad HS = \begin{bmatrix} 0 \\ 0 \end{bmatrix}$$

The third hybrid M-file HYBRIDN.M called in the form

$$[HN, a, b] = HYBRIDN(S)$$

generates the sequence of all existing hybrid descriptions of the form

$$\begin{bmatrix} I_a \\ V_b \end{bmatrix} = [HN] \begin{bmatrix} V_a \\ I_b \end{bmatrix} \qquad (4)$$

by assuming that all independent excitations form the external ports.

These forms of hybrid description have found practical application in formulation of the state equations of the circuits. Extracting all reactive elements to form N-port with a associated with the capacitors and b with the inductors, allows us to create the hybrid description of the resulting N-port, described by the relation (3). Once this equation has been obtained we eliminate all capacitor currents I_a and inductor voltages V_b by the use of $I_a = C \, dV_a/dt$ and $V_b = L \, dI_b/dt$, and in this way the so called "initial state equation", i.e. Chua and Lin (1975) has been generated. The next step is to uncover dependent variables among capac-itor voltages and inductor currents and to eliminate them. The whole program of formulation of minimal state description for lin-ear circuit is called STATE.M . At its present form it assumes that at most 6 depe-ndent variables may be automatically eliminated. The state space descr-iption of the circuit assumed in the program is of the form

$$dx/dt = ax + Bu + B_1 du/dt + B_2 d^2u/dt^2 + \ldots + B_6 d^6u/dt^6 \qquad (5)$$

where x is the minimal state vector, u – the external excitation vector while A, B, $B_1, \ldots,$ B_6 are corresponding state matrices. To get the minimal state space description we have to call the STATE.M file as follows

$$[A, \ B, \ B_1, \ B_2, \ B_3, \ B_4, \ B_5, \ B_6, \ x] = STATE(S)$$

where x contains the indexes of reactive elements forming the minimal state vector. The proces of elimination of dependent variables is recursive one and the partial results of it may be traced by student.

Another application of hybrid description of the circuit is the computer formulation of the hybrid equations for resistive nonlinear network. By extracting all voltage controlled resistors (ports a) and current controlled resistors (ports b) we can create a linear N-port for which the hybrid description of the form (3) is generated by calling the M-file HYBRID.M .

The existing M-files of MATLAB do not contain the nonlinear analysis packages directly applicable to the solution of nonlinear equations. They can be built by students on the basis of Newton-Raphson algorithm. An example of such file is NLNOD.M used to solve the nonlinear nodal equations formulated for nonlinear circuit. Calling it in the way

$$[V, \ n] = NLNOD('Circuit\_file', \ 'Function\_file', \ V0)$$

with Circuit_file and Function_file - the names of M-files containing description of the circuit and functions of nonlinear elements, respectively, results in generation of the description of the nonlinear circuit and iterative solution of these equations with application of Newton-Raphson method at the initial guess solution contained in V0 and the final solution V obtained after n iterations.

It should be pointed out here that the basic M-files described above form some kind of foundation for further development and investigation. On the basis of them student can buld in an easy way more advanced programs illustrating further concepts of circuit theory. A good example of this is the sensitivity function of any network response R (either voltage or current) to the changes of the parameter x of the circuit dR/dx. It is known from the adjoint network theory that such derivatives may be calculated as the product of two signals: one of the original circuit and the other of the adjoint one, i.e. Chua and Lin (1975). By applying the hybrid description concept twice: once for original circuit and the second one for the adjoint one, the sensitivity function can be easily obtained. The M-file applying this concept for resistive linear circuit is named SENS.M and is called as follows

$$[B] = SENS(S, R, x)$$

where S is the input matrix describing circuit structure and B the sensitivity (derivatives) vector of the response R to the   parameters x_i contained in the vector **x**.

In the same way students can make their own extensions of the existing M-files to perform similar or more complicated tasks, for example formulation of objective function, gradient vector, etc.

The task given to student can be formulated either in an universal way to buid the general program for performing some circuit analyses or in a simplified way to perform the analysis of pecular circuit without any demand for generality. In the last case MATLAB may be treated as the calculator performing matrix operations. The results are obtained in an interactive way without tedious manipulations on the numbers, to the great satisfaction of the student.

4. CONCLUSIONS

The important feature of the CIRCUIT toolbox is, that it provides students with easy and flexible tools of understanding of the methods of circuit equations formulation and solution. Programs written in MATLAB are easy to trace. Students may immediately write their our extensions of the existing M-files. In contrast to the other simulation languages like SPICE or NAP, MATLAB files are placed very nearly to the basic rules of electrical engineering. Their main task is to free students from tedious numerical work not loosing their direct contact with the laws of circuit theory.

Therefore this package should find practical application in teaching circuit theory as well as computer aided circuit analysis subjects at Technical Universities and Polytechnics.

REFERENCES

Huelsman L. (1989) Circuit theory and personal computer, IEEE Trans. on Education, 32, 266-269

Prigozy S. (1989) Novel application of SPICE in Engineering Education, IEEE Trans. on Education, 32, 35-38

Chua L. O., Lin P. M. (1975) Computer Aided Analysis of Electronic Circuits, Prentice Hall Inc., Englewood Cliffs, N. Jersey

MATLAB, user manual (1989) MathWorks Inc., Natick, USA

Rubner Petersen T. (1978) Nonlinear Analysis Program (NAP) for electronic circuits, user manual, Technical University, Copenhagen

Teaching Electronic Design Automation at Portsmouth Polytechnic

R.D.M. Hunter, A.P. Miller

School of Systems Engineering, Portsmouth Polytechnic

Abstract

The paper describes the response of the former Department of Electrical and Electronic Engineering to a requirement that Computer Aided Engineering (CAE) be introduced into the curriculum of its Degree programme. In particular the paper discusses what this has meant for the teaching of electronic engineering analysis and design. The paper reveals how early experience with Electronic Computer Aided Design (ECAD) software led to the adoption of a systems approach to the application of software tools and to the purchase of a complete systems toolkit from a major software house. The dilemma of relating education and training in ECAD exercises is discussed and the development of a coherent ECAD strategy covering all years of the degree programme is outlined.

The strategy for the future of adopting VHDL as a major electronic systems design platform is introduced and its probable impact on the teaching of electronic systems design and electronic design automation is discussed.

Keywords: Electronics, Education, ECAD, VLSI, VHDL.

1 Introduction

A major consequence of a Degree validation exercise carried out in 1985 was the requirement to introduce ECAD into the curriculum of the degree course in electrical and electronic engineering [1]. This resulted in the purchase of eleven networked Apollo workstations. These were mainly of the DN330 type and the system was enlarged by the acquisition of twelve DN4000 machines in 1988. More recently (1990) the School has acquired 12 Model 400T machines and is currently actively pursuing additions and upgrades to the presently installed system.

The Government's ECAD initiative enabled the Department, during the early period, to install a number of design software packages such as Silvar-Lisco's SL2000 electronic design suite, Meta-Software's analogue circuit analysis package HSpice, and PAFEC Systems graphics design suite, among others. These packages were introduced into the undergraduate laboratory programme during the 1986/87 session. This process involved a steep learning curve for the staff concerned but it was augmented by training courses organised under the auspices of the ECAD initiative.

One of the early decisions it was felt necessary to take with regard to undergraduate teaching was whether or not to include all three main forms of Application Specific Integrated Circuit (ASIC) design in the digital laboratory programme. Since Gate-Array appeared to be the easiest with which to 'get started' it had considerable appeal, not least because it was felt that this could also be the path that Original Equipment Manufacturers (OEMs) might choose in order to 'get into' ASICs. However, it was felt that this simplistic approach would, in the long run, be disadvantageous both educationally and practically, even if looked at simply from the point of view of die costs for student projects, since gate array is expensive in its use of silicon area. Also, if 100% autorouting is employed, this design method implies that the interest of the student in the final product stops at circuit capture and simulation and that problems associated with layout, such as back propagation of loading capacitances etc., are the domain of the Silicon Foundry.

It was felt that students should have some awareness of 'silicon level' problems and, therefore, gate array was discarded in favour of semi-custom design. Semi-custom was chosen, rather than full-custom, because it was considered that full-custom could not be justified in terms of the length of training that would be required in the use of the necessary software (layout tools).

Finally, it was recognised that, at the workstation level at least, the exercises involved in electronic analysis and design must include aspects of training (the acquisition of technical skills in the use of the software) as well as education in the design philosophies of the new technologies, and that questions needed to be answered regarding the relativities between training and education. For example, how far should one go in recognising the fact that, for many graduates, the need for acquaintance with such tools may never progress beyond the casual? The degree to which tool driving skills acquisition should intrude into the mainstream purpose of teaching electronic analysis and design is a problem yet to be satisfactorily resolved but it is one which is continuously being addressed within the School.

2 Development of the teaching programme

Although the ASIC design suite of programmes proved satisfactory in the beginning it soon became apparent that the product was becoming inadequate to the needs of the School. Because of the deteriorating situation it was resolved to seek a new supplier and investigations led to the conclusion that Mentor Graphics ECAD tools most nearly fitted the School's requirements.

Mentor Graphics is an Electronic Design Automation (EDA) Software House and, as such, had the potential of supplying all of the School's requirements for the foreseeable future. As the EDA work of the School has expanded this has indeed proved to be the case. At the time of writing this article the School uses, or intends to use in the very near future, virtually all of the tools supplied by Mentor Graphics in its undergraduate courses. This means that some 400 hundred students are exposed to the tools on an annual basis and the applications range from simple Printed Wiring Board (PWB) layout through analogue circuit analysis and Programmable Logic Device (PLD) synthesis to the most sophisticated Very Large Scale Integration (VLSI).

Such tools need close monitoring and support from the supplying company and this has been most generously forthcoming from Mentor Graphics with whom we have established very close links. Without such contact it would be impossible to sustain the pace of change necessary to keep in touch with advancing technology. It should also be said that it would have been impossible to purchase the tools from Mentor Graphics at commercial prices, a problem which four years ago had barely impacted the collective conciousness of the Company. In order that our needs should be satisfied the contract between us would have amounted to some £2.5M. It is much to the Company's credit that the School of Systems Engineering did not have to pay anything like that amount in order to have educational access to their software.

The first two academic sessions in which the teaching of electronic analysis and design was augmented using ECAD tools highlighted some areas of potential concern. For example, the speed of assimilation of the skills required appears to be extremely variable among students. This anomaly may be due to simple aptitude differences or to lack of exposure to the use of microcomputers. Whatever the reason large disparities were in evidence such that, during laboratory sessions designed to last nine hours, some students would finish an exercise in less than half the time allocated whilst others were barely able to proceed beyond the first stage.

Now, it is recognised that aptitude may be defined as 'the amount of time required by the learner to attain mastery of a learning task. Implicit in this formulation is the assumption that, given enough time, all students can conceivably attain mastery of a learning task' [3]. Therefore, beyond allowing more time to slow learners, or providing them with one-to-one support, it is difficult to see what to do about this divergence of abilities. One method used by the authors is to use the system's copying facilities to enable slow students to keep pace with the timetable set for the session. This procedure, of course, requires that the teacher must prepare a step-by-step version of the exercise and make it available on the network. A perceived difficulty with this approach is that the 'lazy' student will not be discouraged from his indolence unless access to the model solution is restricted by a 'key', which is available only at the dispensation of the lecturer.

3 The 'education versus training' dilemma

There is a conceptual conflict to be resolved between the notions of education and training. It is clear that, with the emergence of increasingly sophisticated CAE tools, there will be a very steep learning curve for students (and Staff) to climb and continuous exposure to the tools is necessary if one is not to forget what has already been learnt (this is known locally as 'the casual user syndrome', but it may be less of a problem to 'young' students than to 'aged' lecturers). Also, whilst Software House manuals are invariably comprehensive they are not invariably comprehensible and it can take some time simply to interpret the 'in-house' jargon which the system designer or manual writer leaves in his operating system. For example, some of the so-called HELP statements in manuals are triumphs of obscurantism and others are no help at all.

It is all too easy, in developing a ECAD student exercise, to allow the procedures and processes of tool manipulation to dominate the laboratory session at the expense of the intended exercise of practice in electronic analysis and design. This may happen simply by default if steps are not taken to 'hide' tool manipulation 'behind' the educational exercise. What this means for the deviser of the exercise is that the operational steps of, say, circuit capture and simulation, must be meticulous and unambiguous. Nevertheless, having said that, confidence in the tools must always be maintained and this is only possible if the instructor is thoroughly familiar with their operation and is able, expertly and quickly, to retrieve any errors in manipulation made by the student.

4 Changing the Teaching Pattern

Traditional teaching methods, even within the rapidly changing scene in electronic engineering, have laid much stress on a programme of theoretical studies supported by directed practical experimentation. Resource limitations have usually dictated that the desirable sequence of exposure to theory reinforced by analysis and confirmed by experimentation cannot normally be followed. Recognition must also be given to the fact that electronic engineering has been regarded, hitherto, as an experimentally based course and that students choose to read for a degree in their subject on the premise that they will be engaged in the translation of ideas, developed through theoretical investigation, into artefacts. It is this aspect which is uppermost as a source of attraction to them as prospective engineers. Fortunately, most engineering students are very happy to become 'computer-literate' and therefore readily accept the new concept of designing in the abstract with the aid of a computer programme provided that the practical realisation of the design is an element of the total exercise. In furtherance of this aim a learning exercise, using a coherent set of CADCAM tools, is being introduced which will be linked and progressive throughout the three years of the course. Each element of the exercise will stand alone in support of the work of a particular year but will also be connected from year to year as enhanced tasks, coming together as a final assignment for award assessment. This process has already started in the ECAD element of the B.Eng. in Electrical and Electronic Engineering in so far as the work done in the first year forms a basis for the exercise in circuit capture and simulation in the second year which, in turn, is the starting point for a task in Design for Testability in the final year. Experience with this approach leads the School to believe that it should be extended into other strands of the course and expanded within the exercise in which it is at present implemented.

The other main component of the desired educational sequence was introduced over two years ago. As mentioned above, this concerns the ability of the student to relate the abstraction of computer simulation of a design to its hardware realisation. Therefore, in the second year of the exercise referred to above, the students build a hardware version of the design in discrete (LSI and MSI) components and are, as a consequence, able to compare actual with predicted performance. A final element of this part of the task is a software version of the circuit, into which system variables can be entered. This has been written in order that students may observe, by means of a histogram, the function of the circuit being analysed.

Finally, if the project proves educationally successful for the courses in Electrical and Electronic Engineering(and the School has every confidence that it will) the techniques will be imported into the full range of courses offered by the School.

5 The Future

The speed at which electronic integrated circuit design has developed into VLSI (up to 10^6 devices on a single chip), since it was first proposed as an electronic systems design technology in the late '50s, has been phenomenal. For example, from a position where Silicon Vendors alone had the capacity to design and to innovate integrated circuits to the present time, where even a single person enterprise (with access to the appropriate software) can design the largest, fastest and the most complex of circuits, has taken less than 15 years.

In this short period computer-aided electronic circuit design philosophy has described a full circle. Early, esoteric, attempts into vendor-independent software (or programmatical) approaches were soon replaced by easier to use schematic capture methods bringing about a surge of interest in the design of single chip ASICs. These new methods had limitations, however, which were not present in the original programme techniques and recently there has been a move back towards the more sophisticated approaches of Behavioural Language Models (BLMs) and to Hardware Description Languages (HDLs).

The engine for the drive towards HDLs was the successful attempt by the USA's Department of Defense to develop a vendor independent procedure for the documentation of the design of electronic systems supplied to it [2] (a similar process in the UK led to the adoption of the Electronic Logic LAnguage product ELLA for Ministry of Defence contracts). The result is the Very High Speed Integrated Circuit Hardware Description Language V(HSIC)HDL or VHDL (IEEE1076).

The pace of progress, generated mainly in the USA and Japan, has been so swift that Europe, by the mid-eighties, found itself in danger of being left behind strategically, commercially, militarily and educationally. Fortunately the educational problem was recognised and addressed by the European Commission through, among others, the ESPRIT initiative. This led to the setting up of the EUROCHIP training programme in VLSI design, the first two years of which was completed in September 1991.

The continuation of the EUROCHIP project for a further three years was marked by the first Workshop on VLSI Design Training in Grenoble in October 1991. In recognition of the fact that Europe has a shortage of Analogue integrated circuit designers and that there is a strong move towards VHDL in digital design the Workshop devised a European-wide competition for Higher Education Institutions (HEIs) to participate in a competition to design two circuits to given specifications. This competition is a very real challenge to HEIs in Britain and the rest of Europe since many institutions may only just be starting along the path of developing undergraduate teaching programmes in analogue IC design and VHDL design. Part of the challenge is, of course, the necessary, but very expensive, exercise of upgrading hardware and software tools. As an exponent of the teaching of the latest available VLSI design technologies the School of Systems Engineering has decided to grasp this particular nettle and is investing in the necessary hardware and software upgrades.

6 The outcome for Students and courses

Recent experiences with design projects [4,5,6] have convinced the authors that the traditional engineering method of design, that of a structured, schematic, or graphical, approach (although admirably supported by today's schematic capture tools) is actually proving to be a limitation to creativity. Notwithstanding the fact that the concept of top-down design is as old as design itself, it has, hitherto, been very much an ad-hoc process and usually locked into the working practices of companies or company divisions.

VHDL and, in the very near future, an Analogue Hardware Description Language (AHDL) will offer the designer formal methods recognised world-wide for the description of their designs and, at the same time, greater freedom to specify and analyse designs at an abstract, or behavioural, level before attempting realisation at the lower, structural, level.

It is recognised that these processes will probably be firmly in place by the mid-nineteen nineties [6] and the authors are, therefore, taking the necessary steps to introduce them into curricula over the next few years. This has led to the complete overhaul of electronic and related syllabuses to take account of developments in electronic systems design and to the introduction of a new, major, option in VLSI Design for the BEng/MEng undergraduate course as well as the development of an MSc in Electronic Systems Design and Electronic Design Automation.

The authors are also well aware of the potential dangers that 'Designing at your Desk' infer, for example - that necessary practical skills, say, for the 'feel' of the realities of hardware could be lost. Nevertheless, they are confident that the building into the new tools of the distillation of decades of human experience will ensure that such fears will prove to be unjustified.

Once again Mentor Graphics has been pivotal in enabling the School to take a lead in this burgeoning area of electronics education by generously supplying it with the necessary software and documentation support. This has meant the earliest possible introduction of up-to-date techniques in the design and manufacture of electronic systems and the opportunity to evaluate new tools as soon as they become available.

7 Conclusion

As can be deduced from the thrust of this paper the teaching of electronic engineering design in the modern age is subject to rapid change and any institution offering such a course needs to run very fast indeed just to stand still. The School of Systems Engineering intends to be among the fastest of the runners and is prepared to make the necessary investment in material resources and intellectual effort in order to remain so.

References:

[1]   Report of the Validation Committee on the submission of a proposed degree programme for the degree of BSc in Electrical and Electronic Engineering, June 1985.

[2]   The VHDL Reference Manual (IEEE 1076)

[3]   Handbook on Formative and Summative Evaluation of Student Learning, Benjamin S Bloom et al., McGraw-Hill 1971.

[4]   'Conception d'un CMOS IC pour le traitement du signal d'un Accelerometre Capacitif'; Dahan J, Hermel R, Hunter R D M, Stiles G C, Internal communication Groupe ESIEE - Paris, June 1990

[5]   'A Digital Phase-locked loop ASIC'; Fosten A, Hunter R D M, Internal communication, Philips Components, July 1989

[6]   'A 32-bit floating point matrix co-processor'; Hunter R D M, Miller A P, Pirat V, EUROCHIP Workshop, Grenoble, Sept. 1991. See Appendix

Appendix

The photograph shown below is of the manufactured chip. The device contains 29447 stages and about 135000 gates. The die size is 8.65 mm by 11.37 mm and has 138 pads whose pins are arranged in pin grid array format. The chip was designed using European Silicon Structures MODEL Hardware DescriptionLanguage. The system block diagram is shown alongside.

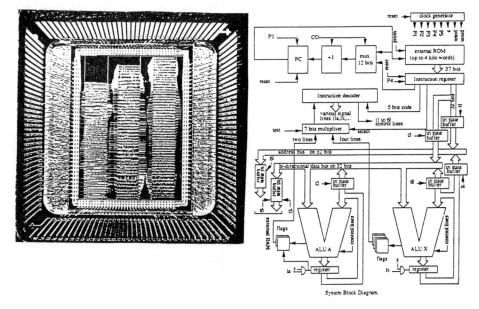

System Block Diagram.

Student Centred Learning in Mechanics

G. Roberts, D.J. Grieve

School of Manufacturing, Materials and Mechanical Engineering, University of Plymouth

Abstract

This paper describes the changes that have been made in the past 8 years in teaching Mechanics in the School of Manufacturing, Materials and Mechanical Engineering. These changes have been made with two objectives: To improve students performance and to introduce an appropriate amount of Computer Aided Engineering (CAE). The changes made to meet these objectives have meant a significant move towards student centred learning in all three academic years of the course.

Keywords: Assignments, Student Centred Learning.

1 Introduction

The past 25 years have seen major advances in the range of problems that engineers have been able to solve. This has been brought about by the rapid development of the digital computer from research tool to low cost accessory affordable by almost any professional engineer. In parallel with this there has been a rapid increase in the availability of sophisticated CAE software for engineering applications.

Demographic and other changes have meant that students coming foreward to study Engineering have less interest in analytical subjects than was the case in the past. This has generated an urgent need to make courses more interesting to students while at the same time ensuring that they still learn the important principles of Engineering.

When student teaching and assessment are being considered, it is necessary to analyse how professional engineers will carry out much of their work. Although Mechanical Engineers can perform a very wide range of job functions, the following tasks are typical of those engineers whose jobs involve significant engineering as opposed to those who work essentially in management:

Design - outline and detail.

Performing calculations to obtain numerical results, perhaps by spreadsheet or FEA etc.

Directing and supervising junior engineers and technicians.

Searching for, reading and evaluating information - involving catalogues and specifications.

Writing "reader friendly" ("accountant friendly"?) reports.

For all of the above tasks the engineer will normally have access to textbooks and references where similar situations will be explained. Only the small portion of engineers who work in largely research or highly specialised industries will not have a significant body of reference material for guidance and will have to carry out significant analytical work alone. Now however there are mathematics software packages and advanced calculators that carry out symbolic analytic work, including integration.

Once these requirements have been understood, it is possible to develop appropriate teaching and assessment strategies

2 Underpinning Student Performance

An important part of ensuring students perform to the best of their abilities is to provide good quality teaching material. This has involved the staff teaching Mechanics in providing specially written notes for all the 3 academic years of the course. While these notes are designed for use in "guided learning", they include sufficient detail and explanation to be used in a "self learning" situation. It is expected that the notes for the first year will be available in text book form in the near future. Sheets of graded tutorial questions have also been developed to provide students with appropriate practice in solving "exam type" questions.

Although it is at first year where the greatest difficulties occur and the failure rate and dropout rates are highest, there are often high failure rates at the end of the second year. The motivation amonst final year students is generally better, possibly because most of them have had a years industrial placement which has given them a broader perspective. Also Mechanics in our final year is an option, which means those students who really dislike the subject can avoid it. A portion of the failures at the end of the first year is doubtlessly due to the change from the aproach used at schools or colleges where courses are studied in a strongly directed manner to the more "open" approach traditionally favoured by Polytechnics and Universities. Bearing in mind these factors, it makes sense to provide a high level of support to students in their first year and to reduce this for the second and final years. The details of the developments in the teaching of Mechanics and how support has been provided for students are described below.

3 The First Year

The main thrust of the effort at first year level has been an intensive tutorial approach. For Mechanics the class has been split into groups of between 15 and 20 students. The students have been provided with the "guided learning" notes (which they have had to pay for) and sheets of tutorial problems. The class time is split between the lecturer providing additional explanation of points in the notes and assisting students with tutorial problems. To provide further encouragement for students to complete tutorial questions, the lecturers collected them in and marked them, providing feedback for the students and also a small portion of the final assessment in the subject - at the expense of considerable time on the part of the lecturers concerned.

The other part of the subject which has always provided student interest and helped with motivation is the Engineering Assignment Case Study (EA). This is essentially a student centred activity where students spend time investigating, preferably by both analysis and experiment, some system (usually of their own choice) and write a report of their findings. Students work in groups of two or three on these assignments, which experience indicates is a good group size for optimum learning and progress at this stage. The final component of the course consists of some laboratory experiments, again the students work in groups of two or three. Sixty percent of the assessment is provided by the examination mark and forty percent by the EAs and laboratory marks.

4 The Second Year

The approach used for the second year was similar to that described above for the first year, but with the following changes: Apart from a one year trial, the tutorial solutions were not marked unless a specific student requested this, and there is no credit given in the overall course mark for completing tutorial problems. Students are introduced to finite element analysis (FEA) in the context of framework problems. Derivation of simple elements is described and very simple problems are solved by hand and with PC packages. The final exam provides 70% of the assessment and the other activities provide 30%.

5 Response of Students to First and Second Year Mechanics Courses

In general students responded favourably to the system and close rapport was established between tutor and student group. A relatively small number of students opted to work mainly in private and their attendance at class was spasmodic, in the main these were probably students who would have been poor attenders in a conventional lecture course. The students complained about the amount of work thay were expected to do, but the majority solved most of the tutorial problems.

Questionaires that could be filled in anonymously were prepared and circulated to students, these substantiated the above obsevations and were helpful in improving notes and tutorial sheets.

6 The Final Year

The changes instituted for the final year were much greater than those for the other two years and involved a marked shift to student centred activity. These changes required a fortuitously timed course review for them to be implemented. The new approach was needed because the lecturers concerned wanted to introduce a significant amount of FEA into the course, while covering some of the topics traditionally taught in final year Mechanics courses. Because of our previous favourable experience with EA work in Mechanics, it was decided to base the final year course on a series of Case Studies. A Case Study here means an investigation into a system which can be carried out by at least two of the following three techniques: An analytical solution, solution by FEA and experimental measurements. Because assessing understanding of FEA by examination is not satisfactory, this lead immediately to a decision to assess the course by means of the reports on the Case Studies that the students submit.

The students work in pairs for virtually all the Case Studies, and carry out six during the year. These include problems in both Stress Analysis and Vibration and the selection of problems is altered every year. In vibration, the assignments are designed to include the use of the latest instrumentation, the dual channel analyser. Assignments include investigations into beam bending, stress concentrations, modelling an offshore structure, torsion of thin wall sections, modal analysis of simple structures and the response of a frame to sinusoidal excitation, Roberts and Grieve (1991).

7 Response of Final Year Students

The response of final year students has been very positive. They have been pleased that they are having the opportunity to use up to the minute techniques. The difficulties of obtaining good agreement between FEA, experiment and theory, even for quite simple configurations is providing clear indication of the need to use sophisticated techniques with considerable care.

8 Discussion of Results

There are several problems in comparing results from different cohorts of students: The class size (40 to 60) is not large enough to provide accurate statistics and there is quite a bit of evidence to show that the average ability of student cohorts can vary significantly from year to year. The other problem concerns assessment, in this academics are divided, the traditionalists believe that the only satisfactory way of assessing a student's capability in a subject is by means of a conventional exam. However many lecturers believe that the assessment chosen should be appropriate for the subject matter and the way it was taught. As an example of this, it is not really feasible to assess a students capability in FEA by means of a conventional exam, whereas this can readily be assessed by coursework.

On the basis of comparison of examination results, the changes made have not made a significant difference. This taken on its own is somewhat disappointing for students and staff. However the better motivated students tend to score higher percentages in student centred activity - the EA coursework assignments. The increased weight put on student based EA activity has meant that more students have passed than would be the case previously when the exam mark counted for a higher percentage of the assessment. This leads to a number of questions which are discussed below.

8.1 How Important is a Fundamental Knowledge of Mechanics to a Graduate Mechanical Engineer?

A common reaction to this question is that it is the basis of all engineering analysis. Universities have tended to teach principles whereas at one time Polytechnics tended to teach topics. More recently the Polytechnics have moved to teaching a combination of principles and their applications. This approach can be satisfying to enthusiastic lecturers and able students, but often leaves less able students floundering.

8.2 Does the Problem of High Failure Rates Stem From a Lack of Fundamental Ability in Our Students?

This is a more emotive issue than the previous one. Whenever the question of entry standards being lower is discussed, the "powers that be" respond with "where is the evidence". Unfortunately quantitative evidence either way does not seem to exist, but virtually all staff engaged on actually teaching undergraduates maintain that the standard of student capability has fallen in the past 7 years.

8.3 Has Student Motivation Decreased?

Over the past 10 years the emphasis on project type work in the area of EA, introduced in the wake of the Finniston Report, has resulted in a significant improvement in the motivation of engineering students.

    There however remains a problem in motivating students towards an appreciation of analytic methods and skills such as required in the area of Mechanics. Subjective evidence is that students spend less and less of their own time pursuing these areas, when challenged on this matter the popular response is to quote the much lighter workload of students taking other courses. A matter beyond our control.

8.4 Does the Fault Lie in Lack of Staff Committment, Out of Date Teaching Methods and Lack of Motivation?

It is believed by the authors that there is a very high level of committment to teaching by most members of staff within the School. This is substantiated by comments from external examiners, H. M. Inspectors and by students transferring to the course from other colleges. Certainly in the context of the developments described here the committment has been 100 %. There has been much debate within the Polytechnic but most of this has been concerned with 'economies of scale' whereas the experiment described here has tended in the opposite direction. There is a case for more time and management effort to be invested in this area.

8.5 Is it the Examination System That is at Fault?

Discussions with students on their poor results almost invariably leads to criticism of the standard of the examination paper.

The setting of assessments is certainly critical if true evaluation of the students ability is to be made.

For some years we have provided data sheets in mechanics exams to minimise the need to memorise or to carry out lengthy derivations of formulae. The next stage, an open book examination, has not yet been used.

Our final year course in advanced mechanics is designed to subject students to the sort of tasks they may meet in their careers and with the facilities to tackle them in the same sort of manner. We have found that the sophisticated CAE type facilities described above, have reduced simple errors, and most mistakes arise because the student has not interpreted the problem correctly, the appropriate boundary conditions have not been fully understood, or inappropriate approximations have been made. It is in this area that our teaching and assessment of mechanics should be concentrating, and less emphasis can be placed on the traditional analytical skills, as these are increasingly done automatically by computer. Some of these competences could be assessed by essay type exam questions, however a much better way of assessing the students capability in this area is by means of investigative case studies where student centred activity is a key feature. As this approach is being used sucessfully in our final year, it is logical to refine this approach, already implemented to some extent, in the first and second years. This may involve increasing the weighting on the case study work in the second year to 50 %.

9 Conclusion

We believe that by shifting towards a student based activity, provided the correct support is available, we are producing a better graduate engineer. Conventional examinations do not adequately reflect the demands on graduate engineers.

References

Roberts, G. and Grieve, D. J. (1991) A Case Study Approach to Teaching Mechanics to Final Year Students, in Proceedings of International Conference on Innovative Teaching in Engineering (ed. R. A. Smith), Ellis Horwood.

The Use of CAI in Engineering Education

M.A. Hessami, T.Burrows

Department of Mechanical Engineering, Monash University

Abstract

Abundance of computers in educational institutions has greatly assisted in research on Computer Aided Instruction (CAI) and its inclusion in the syllabi of various engineering subjects. Students now receive computer-related instructions not only to write simple computer programs to solve close-ended questions but also to model realistic engineering problems. Such simulations provide the students with skills which they can readily use when they are faced with real-life situations in the work environment.

This paper reports on a computer simulation program which was prepared to assist the students to learn the relevant theories behind a laboratory experiment in heat transfer. The computer program is based on the Socratic dialogue in which students learn about the subject by answering a series of properly worded questions; they can receive guidance from the computer when they fail to answer the questions correctly. The major benefit of a CAI code is the availability of assistance through the computer on one-to-one basis at students' pace as well as the optimisation of the usage of laboratory and staff resources.

Keywords: Computer Aided Instruction (CAI), Computer Aided Learning (CAL), Engineering Education, Heat Transfer Experiment, Socratic Dialogue, PLATO.

1   Introduction

Computer Aided Instruction (CAI) and its various synonyms (such as Computer Aided Learning and Computer Based Instruction) are penetrating engineering classrooms and laboratories at a rapid rate. The prominence which CAI is currently enjoying can be mostly attributed to today's relative abundance of personal computers (PCs) in learning institutions; PCs which were previously accessible by senior academics and researchers only are now regarded as a tool that everyone should be able to use. Although there is theoretically no limit to the applicability of CAI in any particular field, in this paper the use of CAI in conjunction with a simple heat transfer laboratory experiment is illustrated.

The program which has been specifically prepared for this purpose is based on the Socratic method in which "a novice seeker after truth" converses with an expert philosopher (Samuel and Lewis, 1988). During the exchange, the expert, through careful questioning and supposition, shows that the learner's knowledge of the subject is inadequate, simultaneously guiding the learner towards the truth.

The program is set up such that the students can, at their own pace, learn about the theories relevant to the experiment through the use of a computer. Using available experimental data, they can simulate the experiment and perform the required calculations before actually going into the laboratory. The expectation is that the students will then be able to perform the actual experiment more effectively during the designated time thereby maximising the usage of the available laboratory facilities and tutors' time. Also, the students can learn from, and appreciate the value of the real experience in the laboratory as opposed to the computer simulation.

2   Background Information on CAI

Computer Aided Instruction (CAI) has been in existence since well before the invention of what we now call the computer. The earliest use of a computer in teaching was in the scoring of multiple choice papers by a simple mechanical machine which used a method similar to that of a punched card reader.

Since this early version of CAI, the minicomputer and subsequently the microcomputer have undergone unusually rapid technological advances. In fact, it has been said that if the motor industry had developed at the same rate as the computer industry, we would now "be able to buy a Rolls-Royce for $2.75, it would do three million miles to the gallon, and it would deliver enough power to drive the Queen Elizabeth II!" (Braun, 1981).

Over the years, various formats of CAI have evolved. The initial concept of the early "drill and practice" programs was that of a general purpose educator. In reality, this type of CAI is generally more suited to those situations in which rote learning through repetition is the main objective. Although some criticism has been aimed at drills over the years, Alessi and Trollip (1985) have made the point that any criticism should really be directed solely towards the multitude of badly written drill programs rather than the overall idea behind the program.

Drill programs have been gradually complemented with more technique orientated "tutorial" programs. This more advanced format presents information to the students and teaches them the rules and principles of problem solving in a manner which is more conducive to learning.

More recently, computer education has seen the introduction of "simulation" programs which link the model with reality, thereby providing the students with greater motivation. This is an important aspect of CAI design which is said to have been frequently overlooked in the past (Chambers and Sprecher, 1983).

The imagination of programmers has produced a plethora of programs of varying educational quality. However, it is the constraint of economics which seems to be holding back the development and implementation of better programs. For example, although the powerful computer hardware and software necessary for basic artificial intelligence exist, the high cost has put it out of reach of all but the richest institutions, especially for undergraduate use. To circumvent this economic difficulty, several powerful programs such as PLATO (McDaniel, 1985) have been used effectively on time sharing basis. As computers become even more cost effective we may eventually see these powerful CAI programs available for private use. Nevertheless, simple, cheap and well-written programs will always be required. So, it has become desirable to provide our existing less technologically advanced machines with theoretically accomplished programs and concepts.

3   Learning Theories

In many ways, the valuable educational tool used by Plato in around 400 BC and its subsequent use in the development of the so-called Socratic dialogue (Samuel and Lewis, 1988) has been lost to modern education as it requires a small class (preferably one to one) and much thought and preparation by the teacher. However, this difficulty can be alleviated by using computers which can be programmed in such a way that the necessary thought and preparation can be input by an expert just once, for the use of many students on one-to-one basis at their own pace and convenience.

Chambers and Sprecher (1983) have provided a concise historical record on research in educational psychology which began with the field of behaviourism in about 1913. They have noted that Watson, one of the leaders in this field, pioneered studies in the area of stimulation-response psychology; later, Thorndike stressed the importance of reinforcement of the response upon learning; in the 1930's, Skinner decided to ignore the stimulus, instead concentrated on response and reinforcement which has led to the successful drill and practice programs.

Although behaviourism has proved to be very useful for low level learning*, it seems inadequate in the teaching of higher level processes of problem solving. For this type of learning, the field of cognitive science which studies the mental processes that are involved in learning has emerged. Cognitive science combines experimental psychology, linguistics and computer science in the modelling (or simulation) of the learning processes. Cognitive theory suggests that the effect of long and short memory operations, stimuli effect on receptors, decoding and encoding of information and retrieval of information affects the learning process. This is supported by Bandura's (1977) social learning theory which states that simulations are useful educational tools as they provide a link with reality, and take into account motivation of the learner.

Research results indicate that a combination of the learning theories mentioned above would provide the best tools to facilitate learning. In general, it seems that students require contiguity (stimulus-response) followed by reinforcement and repetition (Chambers and Sprecher, 1983), which are features that can be readily included in a computer simulation program.

4   Experiment Description

The experiment on which the program is based is currently run by the Department of Mechanical Engineering (Monash University, Melbourne, Australia) as a compulsory laboratory exercise in the third year "Energy Conversion and Heat Transfer (MEC3401)" subject. The objective of the experiment is to study the performance of a tube heat exchanger shown in Figure 1 under various laboratory conditions. During the experiment, students measure the temperature of the cold water at the inlet and outlet of, and the mass flowrate through the tube in addition to the hot water temperature. Then, they calculate the energy absorbed by the cold water and compare it with the predicted value using the convective heat transfer theory.

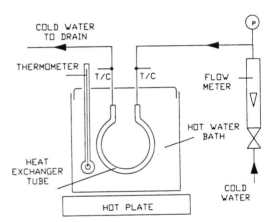

Fig. 1: Schematic Diagram of the Experiment

In the absence of the computer simulation program reported herein, students need to study certain sections of the prescribed textbook in order to "brush up" on the relevant theories. Then, armed with this knowledge, students attend the laboratory session and receive the relevant laboratory instruction sheets which contain the aim, theory, method and a list of variables which should be recorded, along with others to be calculated. After a brief explanation by the tutors, the students perform the experiment and fill in the corresponding values of the variables in the blank spaces on the sheets.

---

*   Learning according to Chambers and Sprecher (1983) can be defined as any experience that produces a change in behaviour.

The problem with this procedure is that students are expected to learn the relevant theories from the textbook prior to the laboratory session. Although textbooks may never become redundant as they are a cheap and efficient source of information, it is often difficult for a novice to learn from them primarily because students cannot ask questions when a difficulty is encountered. This problem can be solved with a well-written CAI program as was done in the present project described below.

5   CAI Program Description

The philosophy of the CAI program prepared for this project was that
(1)   students simulate the laboratory experiment on a PC before performing the actual experiment to learn about the relevant theories, and
(2)   they then perform the real laboratory experiment to reinforce what they have learned previously, and to appreciate the value of such an experience.

In general, a good CAI program should have some specific features (see Alessi and Trollip, 1985 for details) which according to cognitive theorists can be expanded to create perhaps the most realistic flowchart of learning processes as listed below in a chronological order (Chambers and Sprecher, 1983):
(1)   Gain attention and give motivation.
(2)   Give lesson's objective.
(3)   Recall prior learning.
(4)   Show distinctive stimuli.
(5)   Guide learning.
(6)   Elicit performance.
(7)   Provide feedback.
(8)   Assess performance.

Tutorials seem to be the best method of teaching the first five items, while drill and practice programs are suitable for the sixth and seventh parts; a test can be used for the final assessment (Alessi and Trollip, 1985). For example, to teach students their multiplication tables, a drill and practice type of program would probably be most suitable since these are generally regarded as useful in the acquisition of low level learning (Chambers and Sprecher, 1983). As problems become more difficult and complex, the drill and practice format will become less effective in teaching, especially when the problem requires several steps for solution. In these cases, the tutorial mode followed by a drill is most effective; it is this form of CAI (without the drill) which is discussed in detail in the following paragraphs.

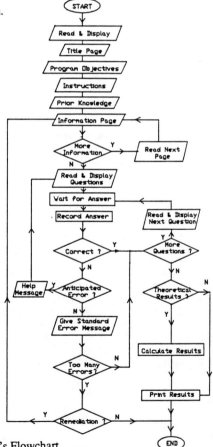

Fig. 2: CAI Program's Flowchart

As shown in the flowchart of Figure 2, the CAI code of the present study is based on the above list of criteria.

5.1 Program Introduction: The program begins with a Title Page which gives the name and subject of the program. This page is designed to motivate the students by making them think *this looks interesting.* Note that the motivation that the students receive should obviously be relevant to the type of person they are likely to be. For example, a program prepared for primary school students would probably achieve best results if the introduction includes information on the incentive of a game sequence as a reward for achieving the stated objective; however, such an incentive may not motivate a college student who might have different expectations.

After reading the Title Page, the lesson's objectives are stated. Alessi and Trollip (1985) suggest that behavioural objectives such as *You will be able to calculate the effectiveness of a heat exchanger* are not as desirable as non-behavioural objectives such as *You will understand the reasoning behind heat transfer calculations* because students tend to ignore any other information that is presented if the former approach is adopted. Thus, the objectives are kept as non-behavioural as possible. This is followed by a summary of program usage which is kept relatively brief since the program is quite short by CAI standards.

The simulation begins with some recall information on heat transfer, eg, Newton's law of cooling, to get their brains *into gear.* As Alessi and Trollip (1985) note "students will learn more if they can relate new information to what they already know".

5.2 Presentation of Information: Useful information relevant to the experiment is shown on a schematic diagram indicating the various possible heat exchanges which can take place in the experiment. Despite the apparent limited applicability of computer animation techniques in this particular situation (ie, heat transfer is a dynamic process involving an invisible property in transit), the information pages utilise graphic images highlighted by text captions explaining the various heat exchange processes.

5.3 Questions: In order to force practice, assess understanding and keep the attention of students, questions follow each short information sequence. In accordance with the Socratic dialogue, much attention was paid to the wording of the questions so that they are open-ended such as *What type of thermodynamic characteristic is useful?* rather than *What is the value of the fluid specific heat?* which is close-ended (Samuel and Lewis, 1988). During such a session, in terms of CAI, clearly the expert is the pre-programmed computer, while the "novice seeker after truth" is the student.

The student may request help at any stage of the simulation. Rather than penalising the students for taking this action, or limiting their requests for help as many programs do, we feel that excessive use of help command is probably indicative of poor information presentation or the wording of the questions. Therefore, it would seem more useful to record students' responses for later analysis, ie, these records will assist in altering the questions and the corresponding information that show excessive use of the help function.

5.4 Judging of Responses and Feedback: From a programmer's point of view, Socratic questions are necessarily vague which can therefore attract responses ranging from spot on to wildly incorrect. In order to be able to deal with such a diversity, it would seem that the best program would utilise a form of artificial intelligence which "understands" what the students say and "decides" upon the most appropriate action. In lieu of this incredibly complex but desirable approach, a simpler (if slightly less effective) alternative (Alessi and Trollip, 1985) is available in which
(a)   responses are limited by carefully worded questions so that the answers are short and concise;
(b)   probable responses to each question are anticipated; and
(c)   unanticipated incorrect answers are catered for.

An example of this situation may be seen if one imagines some responses to *What is the most important parameter to determine when the cold water flows through the tube which is immersed in the hot water bath?* The correct answer here is *HEAT TRANSFER RATE*, but one might expect *MASS FLOWRATE* as an answer. This could be dealt with quite easily by explaining that the mass flowrate is an important variable but it is not sufficient to determine the stated objective, ie, heat transfer rate. Alternatively, a wildly off-the-track answer such as *AIR TEMPERATURE* may be given. This type of an answer cannot really be anticipated, and it is therefore important to keep a record of such responses so that specialised assistance can be provided in order to point the students in the right direction.

Of course, if the student makes too many errors, and is using the help facility continuously, it makes no sense for them to continue with the program. In this case, the program halts, and advises them to consult relevant pages of a textbook or see the lecturer/tutor. Alternatively, the option is given for review of different sections of the tutorial in the hope that the student can understand more clearly.

With a CAI program, students should continue using them until they can score a 90% correct mark 90% of the time (Gagne and Briggs, 1979). This concept, known as mastery, is a very good measure of satisfactory progress of a student. However, this approach cannot readily be used in the classrooms as obviously it is easier to progress all students at the end of a semester than to progress each student as they master a concept. This constraint is not evident in a CAI program and can therefore be used for better effectiveness.

6   Conclusions

Computer Aided Instruction (CAI) has come a long way since the days of "drill and practice" routines which were mainly used for applications where rote learning was considered appropriate. With the availability of more advanced personal computers (PCs) in educational institutions, and the advancement of research in CAI as well as learning behaviours of students, it is now possible to combine computer programming and educational psychology to model (or simulate) complicated engineering problems which in the past could only be studied by performing real laboratory experiments. Since such experiments are costly from both manpower and laboratory facilities point of view, computer simulation has become more common in engineering education.

In this paper, the use of CAI as an educational tool in relation to the teaching of a simple heat transfer experiment was described. The program which is based on the Socratic dialogue was prepared so that students can perform the experiment on a computer before the designated time when the real laboratory experiment should be performed. The expectation is that the students can become familiar with the experiment and learn the basic theories prior to going to the laboratory thereby optimising the usage of laboratory facilities and the tutors' time.

References

Alessi, S., and Trollip, S. (1985) **Computer Based Instruction: methods and development**, Prentice-Hall, NJ.

Bandura, A. (1977) **Social Learning Theory,** Prentice-Hall, Englewood Cliffs, NJ.

Braun, L. (1981) **Computer-Aided Learning and the Microcomputer Revolution,** PLET, 18(4), 223-229.

Chambers, J., and Sprecher, J. (1983) **Computer Assisted Instruction: its use in the classroom,** Prentice-Hall, NJ.

Gagne, R.M., and Briggs, L.J. (1979) **Principles of Instructional Design, 2nd ed.,** Holt, Rinehart and Winston, NY.

McDaniel, E. (1985) **Realities of Computer-Based Engineering Education: Developing a PLATO Statics Course,** Eng Educ, 285-287.

Samuel, A. E. and Lewis, W. P. (1988) **Teaching Less and Learning More - A Socratic Approach to Engineering Design Education,** Int J App Eng Educ, 4, 211-216.

Bibliographical Information:

Dr. M. Akbar Hessami received his BSc in Mechanical Engineering in 1976 from Kabul University which was followed by MSc from the University of Hawaii in 1979 and PhD from the University of Calgary in 1983 before arriving in Australia to work at the University of New South Wales as a Professional Officer, and then at BHP Australia as a Research Officer. He started his teaching career in 1987 at the Victoria University of Technology where his interests in engineering education were nourished. He is currently working in the Department of Mechanical Engineering of Monash University as a Senior Lecturer in the Energy Research Group. His research specialty in the mainstream engineering field is in heat transfer and thermodynamics with emphasis on energy technology, production, utilisation and conservation.

Mr. Tim Burrows is a graduate Mechanical Engineer from Monash University (1991). He wrote his final year thesis on CAI which laid the foundation for the present paper. He is interested in using his engineering and computer simulation knowledge to solve more applied engineering problems in manufacturing. He is a keen volleyball and drum player, and is interested in travelling; he has managed a good deal of travelling despite his busy schedule during the past four years at the university.

Short Computer Aided Modules for Engineering Students

D.K. Harrison, T.T. Al-Shemmeri
School of Engineering, Staffordshire Polytechnic

Abstract
This paper describes the benefits gained from four modules which have been employed in the Schools BEng (Hons) in Computer Aided Engineering course over the past five years. The modules covered the areas of CAD, CAM, Microprocessors and General Mechanics. Following completion of the course the students were invited to complete a questionaire to enable effectiveness of the course to be monitored. An analysis of the responses is given together with refinements made during the life of the course. The paper concludes with a review of the value of such an approach and how it has influenced the School policy for developing new courses.
Keywords: Monitoring, Modular Courses, Development Policy, Course Effectiveness.

1   Introduction

The School of Engineering at Staffordshire Polytechnic is one of few Institutions teaching computer aided engineering up to degree level. The Department offers, among other courses, two degree courses namely a BEng degree in Mechanical Engineering and a BEng in Computer Aided Engineering. Both consist of four years divided between the Polytechnic, industry and vacation. Computing, as a subject, is taught in the first and second years and at the end of the second year in the former scheme, just before the students leave for the second industrial period, a modular "Hands-On" course was conducted, comprising four units.

The subject areas taught in this course were Computer Aided Design (CAD), Computer Aided Manufacture (CAM), Microprocessors (MP) and Solid and Thermofluid Mechanics (GM).

The details of each were left to the lecturers involved, but generally the use of a standard package for CAD was assumed, whereas in thermofluid mechanics a computer simulation was used to study the effect of each component in a typical gas turbine plant. Each subject was allocated 1.5 days so that a maximum benefit for the students was achieved from available resources and staff involved. The class was divided into small groups in order to ensure each student had a terminal and hence 'Hands-On' experience.

For each subject several lecturers were involved to provide instructions, supervision and organisation of the course. The students were instructed for the course in general terms on the first day and subsequently they were given some written hand-outs and/or oral instructions, then they were allowed to carry out a given assignment with supervisors available for help when needed.

2   Course evaluation

Naturally for any course under development, monitoring and continuous modifications are essential. A questionnaire (Figure 1) was designed, for this course, and given to the students for that purpose at the end of the session to complete anonymously so that a free opinion could be expressed and constructive conclusions may be drawn. The formulation of the questionnaire was based on the following:-

(a)   Resources:- It was felt that one needs to critically examine the suitability, availability and effectiveness of the resources involved. This aspect of the course is very important. Since the course was short, it meant that it was resource intensive and consequently some form of reflection was necessary in order to assess the degree of utilization of these resources and their effectiveness.

(b)   Supervision:- The majority of lecturers involved in the day-to-day teaching of subjects on the Degree courses were taking part in this short course, some to a lesser extent than others. This supervision took the form of an introductory lecture, provision of notes and manuals, instructions, and the support during the execution of the programmes of work. Therefore, it was essential to gauge the opinion of the students in regards to the degree and quality of supervision provided.

(c)   Overall Benefit of the Course:- This was the most important aspect of the questionnaire. This was the only transparent indication to whether or not the course had been successful!

(d)   Accuracy and Straightforwardness:- The students, having completed the course, were not likely to be easily persuaded to stay for an extra hour in order to fill in a form. Therefore, it was logical to design the questionnaire such that only essential questions were asked. This encourages more students to complete the questionnaire.

The questionnaire consists of '13' entries comprising all the aspects described above. The final entry '13' was designed to invite additional opinions to cover matters not dealt with in the main body of the questionnaire.

3   Questionnaire analysis

As mentioned earlier, the questionnaire was designed to generate an effective response from which we hoped to get an indication of the efficiency of running the course and to improve subsequently any aspect of this feedback as deemed necessary. Careful study of individual questionnaires is important. Tables 1, 2, 3 and 4 show a collective average of responses based on total number of students of 30,36,31,36 and 22 corresponding to the academic years 86,87,88 ,89 and 90 respectively.

The present analysis considers the following aspects as derived from the questionnaire:

(a)   Computing Experience:- The overall benefit in computing experience is (Q2-Q1). Table 1 shows the computing benefit for each subject for the academic years 1985-90. It is clearly evident that there is a steady improvement in the students computing experience of all subjects covered.

(b)   Improvement in Theories Involved:- The gain in theory achieved during this course is (Q5-Q4). Table 2 shows that the student's theoretical experience has increased steadily as a consequence of this course.

(c)   Course Support:- This includes computers, manuals, supervision and notes. Table 3 shows the arithmetic average for all four subjects which appear to enjoy a good degree of success over the years.

(d)   Execution of Assigned Work:- This category is represented by questions 11, 12 and 13 corresponding to the stage of completion, worthwhileness and enjoyment of activities involved. The analysis to this section is shown in Table 4 where all subjects are seen to be improving each year.

4   The move to modularisation

When reviewing the School's undergraduate provision, the Course Committee considered many criteria including the effectiveness of the "Hands on" course and in order to provide greater flexibility decided that the courses should be set in a modular framework (Figure 2). The chosen framework is driven by the course rather than the modular structure, accordingly the basic module corresponds to a subject in the previous scheme.

The standard size of a module is 120 hours of student learning time and students are expected to devote a minimum of 1080 hours to study over a 30 week academic year. The term "student learning time" implies that all the study activities; lecture, tutorial, seminar, laboratory, directed reading, private-study and assignments are included in the 120 hour time allocation. This is a departure from previous schemes and seeks to reduce class contact time without compromising standards and to give students greater responsibility for the management of their own learning. On average there is direct staff support for 50% of the allocated time but this varies from module to module, depending on the nature of the learning experience.

Staff subject groups have been encouraged to subdivide each module into nominal 20 hour (or multiple of 20 hour) units. This enables material to be delivered in a series of generic packages comprising approximately 10 hours of staff centred learning and 10 hours of student centred learning.

The scheme is rated in accordance with the CNAA Credit Accumulation and Transfer Scheme (CATS) to provide a formal mechanism for transfer within and outside the scheme.

Subsequently, it will enable the Course Committee to take advantage of the European Credit Transfer Scheme (ECTS) developments if and when they gain wider acceptance. With the implementation of the Single European Act it is expected that this facility will assume greater importance, as students from the continent travel to the UK to study.

Table 1. The net percentage increase in computing benefit

COHORT	CAD	CAM	MP	GM	Average
1985/86	10	12	13	10	11
1986/87	10	16	16	11	13
1987/88	23	26	30	20	25
1988/89	22	27	36	22	27
1989/90	18	20	24	21	20

Table 2. The net percentage increase in theoretical gain

COHORT	CAD	CAM	MP	GM	Average
1985/86	12	16	11	13	13
1986/87	13	12	18	10	13
1987/88	16	13	22	12	16
1988/89	17	17	24	22	20
1989/90	14	17	15	19	16

Table 3. The percentage mark for course support

COHORT	CAD	CAM	MP	GM	Average
1985/86	66	59	72	59	64
1986/87	71	65	70	59	66
1987/88	69	64	67	67	67
1988/89	75	69	71	76	73
1989/90	58	54	63	63	60

Table 4. The percentage execution of assigned work

COHORT	CAD	CAM	MP	GM	Average
1985/86	72	69	70	56	67
1986/87	77	76	72	59	71
1987/88	85	79	79	75	79
1988/89	85	80	72	83	80
1989/90	76	72	58	73	70

Please give your rating (0-10) to the following questions:-

QUESTION	CAD	CAM	MP	GM
1. Your experience in the use of computers PRIOR to this course.				
2. Your experience in the use of computers AFTER this course.				
3. The level of computing taught so far, including Hands-On course.				
4. Your knowledge of the theory, involved PRIOR to this course.				
5. Your knowledge of the theory involved AFTER this course.				
6. Access to computers.				
7. Access to manuals.				
8. Availability to supervisors.				
9. Provision of notes.				
10. What stage did you reach in the activity.				
11. Did you find the activity worthwhile.				
12. Did you find the activity enjoyable.				
13. Any other aspect do you wish to report in connection to this course.				

Fig. 1. The questionnaire used to evaluate the 'Hands-On' course

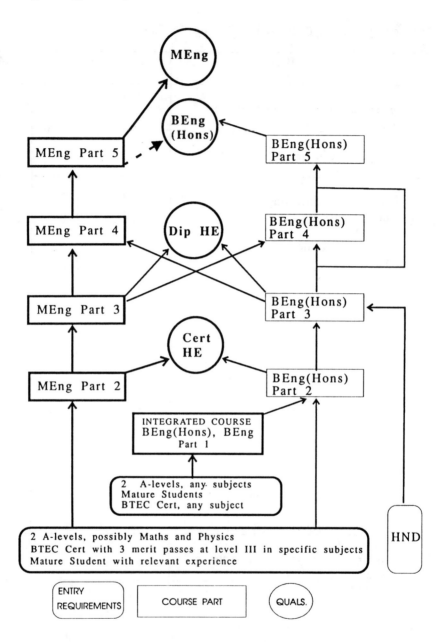

Fig. 2.   The course routes

Educational Experiences in Operating Simulation Software in Aircraft Propulsion

W.A. Woods, P. Nobar

Department of Mechanical Engineering, Queen Mary and Westfield College, University of London

Abstract

The simulation software for design point studies of a turbo-jet engine, which was presented at the 1989 World Conference on Engineering Education in Sydney, is briefly reviewed. The educational experiences gained by students in using this software during an undergraduate course on aircraft propulsion are discussed. This has revealed major advantages and some minor shortcomings of the facility.

<u>Keywords</u> Aircraft Propulsion, Simulation Software, Educational Experiences.

1 Introduction

Computer simulation software is being used increasingly in engineering courses. It can be used at different levels of understanding, ranging from performing routine calculations to investigating innovative endeavours and resolving design uncertainties. The objectives of the present paper are to report on the operational experiences of using a software simulation for design point studies of a turbo-jet engine in a final year undergraduate course on aircraft propulsion.

In what follows, the simulation software is reviewed and the educational objectives of it are mentioned. The aircraft propulsion course and the simulation exercise used in it are discussed. The operational experiences reveal that the students rapidly become familiar with the software and are able to use it very effectively. However, they may become too concerned with small changes and may not think broadly enough when stress problems in a cylinder are introduced. Normally the pressure outside the cylinder is the sea level atmospheric value whereas, here, it is much lower. New developments highlight the importance of the turbo-fan engine.

2 Review of the turbo-jet simulation

The turbo-jet simulation software was discussed briefly at the World Conference on Engineering Education in Sydney, and a more detailed account was given in an educational journal, Woods and Nazha (1989). This simulation uses the data given in the appendix to calculate the specific fuel consumption, SFC and the specific net thrust, SNT. The SFC gives a measure of the fuel flow rate required to give a unit of thrust. It, therefore, gives a measure of how effectively the fuel flow is being used. On the other hand, the SNT gives a measure of the net thrust produced for a unit air flow rate. It therefore indicates how effectively the air flow is being used. A turbo jet with reheat has a high SFC and high SNT and is used on a high performance military fighter aircraft. High by-pass turbo fan engines have a low SFC and a low SNT. They are used on large, long-haul civil transport aircraft where the engines can be made large enough to provide sufficient thrust but maintain good fuel economy. Thus, these two parameters give an overall assessment of the performance of the power plant under investigation. A further aspect of the simulation which should be stressed is that it is a design point simulation and that different points on the SFC~SNT map apply to different pressure ratios, turbine inlet temperatures etc., and this implies different compressors and turbines built into different designs. This approach should be contrasted with an off-design performance in which a given design is operated over a range of flight and engine conditions.

Full details of the simulation are given by Woods and Nazha (1989) but more specific information about the simulation is given in the appendix. Before doing this, it is appropriate to consider the educational aspects of the simulation in the context of an engineering course.

3 Educational Objectives

Extending the ideas of Sparks (1989), the educational objectives of the simulation software are to provide help in three stages and at two levels. They are:-
   (i)   knowing and learning; here, the students have to be made aware of the existence of certain knowledge through lectures, directed reading and by using the simulation. Next, there is the task of committing it to memory; this can be done by the student using the simulation with one or more of the recognised techniques.
   (ii)   Understanding; here the students can use the simulation to resolve specific uncertainties, and to check-up on preliminary ideas.
   (iii)   Using; here it is vital that the simulation has been developed to be user-friendly and, clearly, this is a pre-requisite to achieving the other objectives.

The two levels concern surface learning and deep learning. At the first level, the students begin to know what the engine is and how to use the simulation package in a routine way to produce numerical values of the performance at a prescribed operating point. The second level provides an opportunity for the student to use the simulation in a non-routine way, perhaps to resolve a design problem or to answer an operational uncertainty. Particular examples of these are given in the appendix.

4 The Aircraft Propulsion Course and the Jet Engine Exercise

In this section, comments are given on the Aircraft Propulsion course and on an assignment called the Jet Engine Performance exercise. This has been used in recent years with students at Queen Mary and Westfield College who were taking the course on Aircraft Propulsion. The students are drawn mainly, but not exclusively, from the Departments of Mechanical and Aeronautical Engineering. The course has been undergoing continuous development and, in the last five years, the number of students taking it have increased by a factor of almost three.

The course normally runs for twelve weeks, with three one hour lectures per week plus course work and tutorial or problem classes. The Computer-aided teaching unit (CATU) exercise has been used during the last third of the twelve week period. However, with increasing numbers, it has necessitated starting the exercise earlier in the course. As the Jet package is most user-friendly, this has not caused intellectual difficulties with the students.

The students are given a printed sheet to explain what they are expected to do and an extract from this is given in the appendix.

5 Operating experiences

Generally, the students learn how to use the software very quickly. This gives them interest and confidence to proceed. The following comments apply to the numbered items given in the appendix, set out under the 'Tasks to be carried out'.

(i)   This is a routine exercise and does not normally cause difficulty.

(ii)   This is carried out in the students' own time and it is equivalent to doing a homework problem in which the student has a computer generated output which enables him to check each stage of the calculation, but some degrees of understanding must have been gained during the lectures to allow the student to do each stage of the calculation.

(iii)   The students generally produce graphs which show about 15% increase in SFC and a 30% decrease in SNT by increasing the Mach. No. from 0.4 to 1.4. They also find almost zero change and exactly zero change in the strato-sphere, in both SFC and SNT, as they increase the altitude from 8000 m to 14000 m. The students very often show their results to very large scales using the whole page to show practically no variation.

(iv)   This is generally carried out satisfactorily by the students. It was reported by Woods and Nazha (1989) that better results came from improved efficiencies.

(v)   This question really tests the students' understanding of stress analysis under unusual circumstances. It also reveals a pitfall one author has detected when acting as an external examiner. Questions of stresses in cylinders are often posed by giving unqualified values of internal pressures. The stresses depend upon pressure differences between the inside and the outside of the cylinders. The unqualified values of internal pressures are intended to be interpreted as gauge pressures and the outside pressure is, almost always, 101.3 kPa. In the present case, the turbo-jet may be operating at high altitude and the outside pressure for the compressor and the jet pipe will, in general, be much lower e.g. at 22.6 kPa for an altitude of 11 km.

6 New developments

Since the turbo-jet was introduced half a century ago, developments have taken place in two directions, according to the mean temperature of the exhaust jet stream. Higher temperatures, in which the compressor became less and less important, gave rise to the turbo-jet with reheat and, ultimately, to the ram jet for operation at high Mach numbers. On the other hand, reducing the mean exhaust gas temperatures, in which the compressor plays an increasingly important role, gave rise to the by-pass engine, then the turbo-fan and, perhaps the ultimate development, the unducted fan. These developments produced dramatically improved economy as shown by the specific fuel consumption. This explains why the turbo-fan dominates the power plants used for long-haul civil aircraft. Because of these, a new software package is under development as a student final year project.

The above account of engine types and the exhaust jet temperature has been illustrated diagrammatically by Woods et al. (1991). The diagram shown in Fig. 1 is taken from the same publication. This clearly shows the reduction in specific fuel consumption for the turbo-fan engine.

7 Conclusions

1.   A software simulation for turbo-jet engine design point studies has been reviewed.
2.   The educational objectives of the simulation have been set out in terms of knowing, understanding and using.
3.   An outline of the course on which the software is used and the details of the exercise included have been presented.
4.   The operating experience has shown that the students readily become familiar with the simulation, can rapidly use it in a routine way and are soon able to use it in an innovative way.
5.   The operating experience has shown that some students may highlight very small changes in a dependent variable, when the main effect to be observed is the almost unchanging nature of it.
6.   A test which overlaps with stress analysis has highlighted a pitfall which occurs in some stress analysis courses. This concerns the recognition that stresses in cylinders depend on the pressure differences.
7.   The importance of the turbo-fan is outlined and preliminary results from a new simulation given.

8 References

Sparkes, J J (1989) "Quality in engineering education". An occasional paper produced by the Engineering Professors' Conf.

Woods, W A and Nazha, M A A (1989) "A turbo jet engine simulation for design point studies in aircraft propulsion. Int. J. Appl. Engng. Ed. Vol. 5, No. 2, pp. 193-198.

Woods, W A , Chew, Y T, Chan, W K and Thevathasan, R V (1990) "Engineering education for the aerospace industry in Singapore". Conf. on new challenges in aircraft maintenance and engineering organised by Assoc. of Singapore Licensed Aircraft Engineers and Pete Marketing Services, Singapore, pp. 1-22.

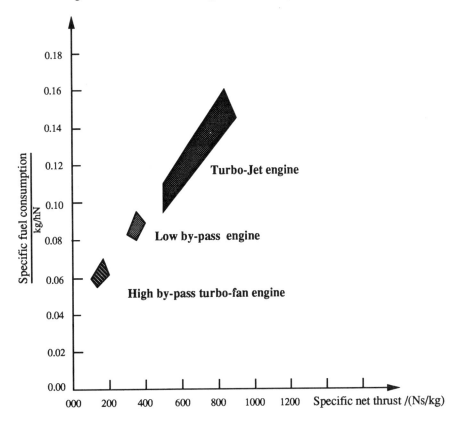

Fig. 1 Comparative study of engine performance at 11000 m Mach number 0.8

APPENDIX
JET ENGINE PERFORMANCE EXERCISE

The CATU program accepts the aeroplane Mach number and altitude with other information given below to calculate the specific fuel consumption and the specific net thrust. The former is the fuel flow rate divided by the net thrust, and the latter is the net thrust divided by the air-flow rate.

Use the following data:

      The altitude in metres, 11,000

      The aircraft Mach number - this is non-dimensional, 0.8

      The intake efficiency - non-dimensional, expressed as a fraction, 1.0

      The range of compressor pressure ratios - 2 values should be supplied, 5 & 25

      Compressor isentropic efficiency non-dimensional- shown as a fraction, 0.85

      Turbine isentropic efficiency - non-dimensional, expressed as a fraction, 0.9

      Pressure loss due to combustion - shown as a percentage, 3

      Air mass flow rate at intake - this is in kg/s but it has been included for further development of the program and a figure of 1 should be inserted.

Either (a)   The range for the turbine inlet temperature (this is T_3) insert 2 figures in K. 1000 to 1800.

or   (b)   Two values of the equivalence ratio are selected.

The output from the program is both graphical and in the form of a table.

  The table shows a set of figures for the first temperature and covers values of pressure ratio divided equally between the two values supplied.

Tasks to be carried out

(i)   You are required to produce a set of printed results and a graphical output for the altitude and Mach prescribed for the engine conditions.

(ii)   Carry out a hand calculation to check one of the conditions included on the computer output sheet.

(iii)   Using the graphical display on the VDU, investigate how the SFC and SNT changes with altitude and aircraft Mach No.

      For a given turbine inlet temperature and given compressor pressure ratio, determine the partial derivatives of the SFC and SNT with respect to both Mach number M and altitude h.

(iv)   Compare the sensitivity of SFC and SNT to changes in turbine isentropic efficiency η_t and compressor isentropic efficiency η_c.

(v)   From stress considerations first, on the compressor casing and, secondly, on the jet pipe, what condition is the most severe:

      a)   running on a sea level test bed, or

      b)   operating at 9000 m at Mach 1.5

      What influence will the aircraft intake have on this result?

Independent Learning Through the Development by the Student of Independent-Learning Software

C.M. Archer

School of Civil Engineering, University of Portsmouth

Abstract
This paper describes a final-year project in which the student, operating in an independent-learning mode, developed independent - learning software in a topic new to him. An attempt is made to locate the project within the framework of student-centred experiential learning. It is postulated that the student, through his software, will become a peer tutor to students who follow him. It is argued that the project is of significance in that it exemplifies the required change in approach to engineering education, if professional engineers able to exercise judgement and responsibility in solving real engineering problems, are to be developed.
Keywords: Independent Learning, Autonomous Learning, Experiential-Learning, Student-Centred Learning, Peer Tutoring, Student Project, Software, Student-Prepared Material, Computer-Assisted Learning.

1 INTRODUCTION

Final-year projects enable students to undertake an in-depth study of a particular topic in engineering and provide a good opportunity for them to develop a wide range of skills important to their subsequent careers. This paper describes a project in which the student was given the task of developing independent-learning software in a topic new to him. The idea was that a student, who has undertaken a project of this type, may produce material forming the basis of independent-learning material of benefit to future students.

The type of learning experience described here requires the student to develop an understanding of the subject matter, to develop expertise in computer applications and also to develop an understanding of, and experience in the philosophy and practice of independent learning.

The paper attempts to locate the project within the framework of student-centred experiential learning. It is suggested that the work undertaken could also be described as an unusual form of peer tutoring.

Activities, in which students are required to develop independent-learning material, whether software, text, video or some other form, are not rare, particularly outside engineering. Within the field of engineering, the CTI Centre for Engineering at Queen Mary Westfield College, for example, has produced many software packages, some written under commercial arrangements, but others by project students. The interesting feature of the project taken as a case study is that it combined several features found in projects elsewhere. In some projects the students have been familiar with the subject matter forming the basis of the activity; in other cases the first task has been to master the subject matter, usually through the medium of formal instruction. Here, the student was required to master the subject matter and develop software in an independent-learning mode.

It is vital that engineering students are encouraged to exercise autonomy and to assume responsibility for their learning. This involves providing opportunities for them to exercise independence of thought and proactive behaviour so that they can mature into dynamic professional engineers who are able to solve real-life problems. This was an important aim of the project.

2 CASE STUDY

2.1 Introduction
In the academic year 1990/91 the author supervised a final year degree project student who was interested in computer applications. The School of Civil Engineering at Portsmouth had recently purchased a comprehensive software package, WATNET 3, developed by WRc (Swindon, UK) for the analysis and simulation of water supply pipe networks. The software, which was new to the student, was intended to be used by future students in pursuance of integrated design projects. These students would have less time available for familiarisation with the package than is desirable.

2.2 Objectives of the Project
The objectives agreed with the student were:
(1)   To become familiar, in an independent-learning mode, with the use of WATNET 3. The student had access to the software manual and to the supplier's telephone 'help-line'.
(2)   To develop user-friendly independent-learning software which would quickly lead a new user to familiarity with the application of WATNET 3 to both analysis and simulation.

2.3 Facilities Available
A suite of 30 286 PC's would be available to the future student users of the software, who would operate at any one time in groups of less than 15. The student decided that each user would have access to two adjacent PC's; on one the user would run WATNET 3 and on the other the user would have access to the educational software. The latter would be entitled WATNET HELP.

2.4 Terms of Reference
The brief given to the project student was:
(1)   The conjoint use of WATNET 3 and WATNET HELP must be straight-forward.
(2)   The future users were assumed to be reasonably familiar with the use of commercial software in general, but to have no prior experience of WATNET 3, and to be as knowledgeable about the bases of pipe network analysis as was initially the project student himself.

2.5 The Independent-Learning Software

The software, written by the project student in TURBO BASIC, consisted
of thirty-two Pages, twenty-seven of which are text files similar to
that in Figure 1.

```
| Among the main uses of WATNET are:                                |
| design of systems and reinforcement of existing networks          |
| - assessment of network capacity                                  |
| - provision of information for investigation of water quality,    |
|   consumer demand, pipe deterioration, etc.                       |
| The WATNET program has the following main functions:              |
| (a) to create/inspect/amend a network schematic diagram,          |
| (b) to enter/inspect/amend associated network model data,         |
| (c) to create/inspect/amend a description of the network          |
|     operation,                                                    |
| (d) to enter/inspect/amend field data for calibration purposes,   |
| (e) to perform a network analysis or simulation,                  |
| (f) to inspect the results of a network simulation by             |
|     appropriate graphical or tabular means,                       |
| (g) to compare simulation results with field data,                |
| (h) to store and retrieve network schemes, associated data and    |
|     simulation results.                                           |
|                        Page 4                                     |
```

Fig. 1. WATNET HELP - typical screen display

The remaining five Pages are diagrams produced using minor
subroutines, Slide 0 to Slide Four. The Page Up and Page Down keys
are used to move between Pages.

Pages 1-5 instruct the user how to operate together the two sets of
software, introduces WATNET 3 and explains the screen layout. Pages
6, 7 and 8 offer guidance on drawing a network using WATNET 3. There
then follow on Pages 9-16, instructions on inputting network data.
Simulation data instructions are found on Pages 17-26 and Pages 27-30
explain how to undertake the simulation and produce copies of the
results. A welcome Page and a farewell Page complete the list. The
sample network and water demand data used were derived from a water
supply network in the South of England.

2.6 Development, Validation and Appraisal by the Student

The project student enlisted fellow students to test successive draft
versions. The final version was tested by two students and the author
(the latter had used WATNET 3 in industry). In total, seven new-
comers to WATNET 3 were involved in the development and validation of
WATNET HELP. The student expressed himself satisfied with the
reaction of the learners who used the software. He recommended that
an improved version would avoid providing the user with sample problem
data step-by-step, and would offer the facility of direct entry to any
desired page.

3   DISCUSSION

This project is presented, not as an exemplar but because it is an example of an attempt to encourage the student to take responsibility for his/her own learning in addressing a particular real-life problem. The development of the approach to projects outlined here has considerable potential in developing in the student the skills required in industry. Since in addition there are implications for the role of the supervisor, some of which relate to resources, wider applications of this type of project are worth exploring.

3.1   Novelty

At the start of the project, the student, an Ordinary Degree student, was familiar with the application of continuity and energy principles to the iterative, manual analysis of small pipe networks. He had no prior knowledge of the simulation of the time-dependent operation of water-supply networks and had not met WATNET 3. Similarly, he was a stranger to the philosophy and practice of independent learning.

3.2   Independent Learning

It was deemed to be necessary for the student to be able to empathise with a future WATNET 3 first-time user. To this end he was offered no assistance with the technicalities of WATNET 3, but his progress was monitored. Fortunately, at no stage was intervention necessary; the student even initiated the procedure for stage-testing by other students (and the author!). Initially, it was hoped that the student would investigate independent learning in general, but time did not permit this.

Burden (1990) suggests that 'Independent Learning' involves both learning independently and learning to be independent. During the project it was evident that the student progressively became more assured and independent. This, taken together with the fact that the project required him to work on his own and at his own pace, suggests that it is quite appropriate to use the term 'Independent Learning' to describe the project.

3.3   Autonomous Learning

When considering an independent-learning activity, it is appropriate to ask to what extent autonomy is exercised by the student. The student may be free to assume responsibility for his/her own studies in areas such as objectives, content, method, pace, assessment and support.

The project under discussion was severely constrained as to its objectives, which were preset by the author, its general method, its assessment and the support provided. However, the student exercised autonomy in the content and pace of work and was able to limit himself to what was possible. His behaviour rapidly became highly proactive and independent, but it is not clear that he fully reached the integrative stage of learning (see Brundage and MacKeracher (1980)). In this stage, as a result of integrating his/her activities with others, the learner develops a sense of balance between him/herself and them and between group and individual tasks.

Apart from the stage-testing phase the nature of the project denied the student the opportunity of interdependent and cooperative behaviour and yet the project could not be described as being only individual-centred (Boud (1989)). Although the needs of the student were taken into account, the requirement to produce useful software was central. Boud describes this project-centred learning in terms of a situation where "students exercise considerable initiative and engage in individual learning in association with the problem, but it is the project itself which ultimately defines the area of learning".

Another criterion for judging the extent to which this type of project develops autonomy is the extent to which the learner is able to exercise judgement in relation to a given body of knowledge and skills. This is an essential ability of the practising engineer. In this case study there is evidence to suggest that the student did, to a certain degree, exercise such epistemological autonomy (see Boud) in relation to the subject areas covered by his project.

3.4 Experiential Learning

It is also appropriate to consider the extent to which experiential learning took place. It has been argued that there are three dimensions of experiential learning: the degree of learner control, the degree of correspondence of the learning environment to the real environment and the degree of involvement of the self (Boud and Pascoe (1978), quoted in Boud (1989)). The type of project under examination should possess significant characteristics of at least one of these dimensions if it is to be described as experiential learning. It is usual for experiential learning activities to show a mix of all three.

Figure 2 constitutes an attempt to place the project in the three-dimensional framework postulated by Boud and Pascoe. The year's activity is thus clearly indicated to be an example of experiential learning.

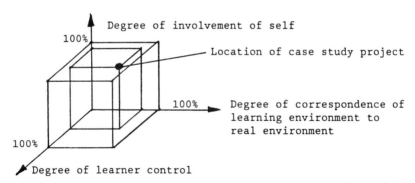

Fig. 2. Dimensions of experiential learning - case study project

In using these dimensions the emphasis is on goals, purposes and content. More important perhaps are the processes involved when experiential learning is taking place. Reflection is the key concept to be promoted when aiming to turn experience into learning.

The author believes that, in the case study project, the student devoted sufficient time to reflection on what he was doing and benefitted accordingly. However, this was not systematically monitored. In future projects of this nature this will be an interesting aspect to evaluate.

3.5   Peer Tutoring

Peer tutoring has been described as "a system of instruction in which learners help each other and learn by teaching" (Goodlad and Hirst (1989)). This is close to Cornwall's notion (1980) of proctoring. If this approach were to be developed on a larger scale, it is possible that there would be some savings in resources. The project student, although not physically present, through his software will become an individual tutor for students in the years to come. This is an unusual but appropriate use of the concept of peer tutoring.

4   SUMMARY AND CONCLUSIONS

A case study in 'Independent Learning through the Development by the Student of Independent-Learning Software' has been described. The student involved was engaged in a form of experiential learning and exercised autonomy over some aspects of the learning process in an area new to him. He was also participating in an unusual form of peer tutoring. Moreover, material produced through this medium could form the basis of independent-learning software of benefit to future students. The type of project exemplified by this case study has considerable potential for developing independent learning and encouraging autonomy and responsibility in learning. Indeed, it may offer greater scope for encouraging the latter than the more traditional student projects in engineering.

The significance of the case study project is that it points the way to a new approach to engineering education. Students must be encouraged to exercise autonomy and to assume responsibility for their learning. In this manner, proactive, independent-minded engineers, able to exercise judgement and responsibility in solving real engineering problems, will be developed.

REFERENCES

Burden, T. (1990) **Developing Independent Learning**, Monograph prepared for the Training Agency funded Enterprise in Higher Education Initiative. Department of Social Studies, Leeds Polytechnic.

Brundage, D.H. and Mackeracher, D. (1980) **Adult Learning Principles and their Application to Program Planning**, Ministry of Education, Toronto, Ontario.

Boud, D. (1989) Some Competing Traditions in Experiential Learning, in **Making Sense of Experiential Learning: Diversity in Theory and Practice** (ed. S.W. Weil and I. McGill), SRHE and OUP, Buckingham.

Goodlad, S and Hirst, B. (1989) **Peer Tutoring: A Guide to Learning by Teaching**, Kogan Page, London.

Cornwall,M.G. (1980) **Students as Teachers: Peer Teaching in Higher Education**, COWO, University of Amsterdam.

The assistance of Dr A. Brew, of the Educational Development Unit, University of Portsmouth, in the preparation of this paper is gratefully acknowledged.

The Use of Computers in the Teaching at ETH - An Overview of Project IDA (Informatik Dient Allen)

W. Schaufelberger

Swiss Federal Institute of Technology, Zürich

Abstract
ETH is a Technical University with emphasis on Engineering and Natural Sciences with about 11,000 students. A large project for the integration of computers into the teaching process was carried out at ETH during the last five years. The outcome of this project is briefly summarized in the paper by discussing the organizational aspects and some of the results.
Keywords
Computer based teaching, Hard- and software for teaching, Simulation in teaching.

1   Introduction

Strongly supported by the Swiss government, ETH was able to carry out a large project for the integration of computers into the teaching process in all departments during the period of 1986 to 1991. The goal was to acquire one workstation per five students, thus allowing each student about eight hours of work on computers per week. The change from about two hours of work on computers to about eight in only five years is certainly a major teaching experiment. The contents of many courses, exercises and student projects had to be adapted to the new situation.

2   The Project IDA

Goals: When the project started in 1986, one of the first questions was what kind of tasks the students should solve with computers. Decisions were taken to support the following activities (Schaufelberger 1992):

- *Document processing:* Report writing including graphics.
- *Information access:* Inquiries into databases.

- *Calculations:* Solving equations, optimizations.
- *Graphics:* Technical drawing.
- *Modelling and Simulation:* Technical and environmental modelling.
- *Computer Aided Design:* VLSI, mechanical, architectural.
- *Laboratory Automation:* Measurement and control of experiments.

It was decided to provide most support for every day work and not for special learning environments. However, development in this area was also to be followed, with emphasis on
Test and drill programs of the multiple choice type,
Information access and browsing programs,
Simulation and analysis of complex systems,
Intelligent tutoring systems.

Organizational aspects: Responsability for the project was delegated to a committee chaired by the Rector of ETH, Prof. H. von Gunten. A center (Projektzentrum IDA) with five positions was created as a support and consultation unit for all staff members. All staff members were invited to send in applications for hardware and software for teaching. 400 applications were handled during the five year period and the following numbers of workstations were acquired and integrated into the teaching process during the period of the project:

	1986	1987	1988	1989	1990	1991
IBM-compatibles	130	160	92	29	105	66
Macintoshes	250	80	150	91	265	31
Workstations	60	40	90	73	206	44
per year	440	280	332	193	576	141
Total	440	720	1'052	1'245	1'821	1'962

Table: Computers acquired for teaching during the IDA project

Most of these machines are used in the laboratories of the different groups for student projects. Only about 400 machines are in public rooms with open access. Because of the fact that about fifty percent of the students have access to private machines this is sufficient for general work.
A major problem encountered was the question of software. Few vendors understand the operation of a university and are willing to offer reasonable licensing conditions for use on a large number of stations, where the software must be available for highly parallel use during organized exercises but is used very little otherwise. The general packages most in use in engineering education are Matlab, Mathematica and Maple.

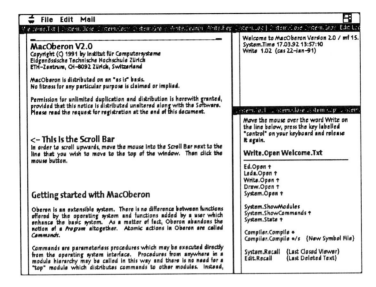

Fig. 1: The Oberon environment used for program development.

CAD centers: Three main centers for the teaching of design in different areas were created by the University and supported by means from the IDA project:

The *CAAD* center in Architecture is equipped with Macintosh and SUN computers. Autocad and Lisp are used as a standard environment. Students learn how to do architectural work at different levels successfully with computers. The *CADETH* center for mechanical engineering students is based on a high powered IBM environment with CATIA, CADAM and CAEDS, where even freshmen get their first introduction to CAD. SUN workstation are used in the *VLSI design center in electrical engineering*. Every third year student does a small design project in the studio.

Pilot projects: Whereas the centers are mainly based on powerful commercial environments, five pilot studies were carried out to investigate the possibilities of more modest solutions in teaching in the following areas:

*   *Architecture:* Design and construction.
*   *Civil Engineering:* Planning with spreadsheets.
*   *Mechanical Engineering:* Technical mechanics.
*   *Electrical Engineering and Environmental Sciences:* Modelling and Simulation.
*   *Agricultural Engineering:* Automation of food processing plants.

It was shown in these projects that good teaching material can also be developed on small computers (IBM compatible PC's and Macintoshes).

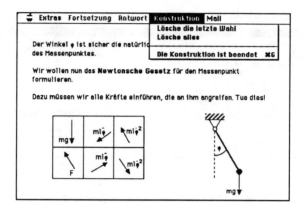

Fig 2: Screen from a MECA exercise.

3   Examples of hard- and software development for teaching

Four examples are given here to provide a better insight into the approaches used:

Computer Science: Prof. N. Wirth and J. Gutknecht developed a new machine (Ceres 3) and a new object oriented programming environment (Oberon) that is very well suited for teaching of computer science basics. 100 Ceres-3 computers were manufactured and 60 of them put at the disposal of the first year students of computer science by the IDA project. Fig. 1 shows the Oberon development system, in this instance running on a Macintosh. Outstanding features of the system are its clarity and simplicity achieved through a regular and purpose-tuned structure (Wirth 1988). One of the consequences is the fact that all windows can be used as editors for communication with the system, thus providing a powerful modeless environment (Reiser 1991).

Technical Mechanics: All exercises of the three term basic education in Technical Mechanics can be done in a multiple choice type environment that is especially suited for drill and practice exercises, helping the students to acquire basic skills in the area. The system MECA has been developed in the mechanics group and consists of a program, where the teacher develops the material (no knowledge of computer science required) and a run time system for students. A typical screen is shown in Fig. 2 (Kaufmann and Sayir, 1992).

Control Engineering: A set of so called minitools has been developed for the teaching of basic methods in Control Engineering (Kessler and Schaufelberger 1991). It consists of:
- *BDESim:* Block diagram editor and simulator for simulations that are based on the typical block diagrams of control engineering.

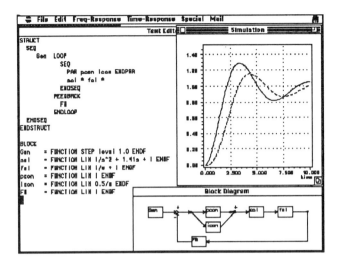

Fig. 3: The BDESim environment.

- *DESolver:* A program to numerically solve differential equations.
- *Frequency:* A program for Bode- and Nyquistplots, root loci etc.

All programs run on Macintoshes and IBM PC's (using GEM) and are easy to understand, needing little or no introduction. A typical simulation for verifying controller settings in a classical two term controller is shown in Fig. 3.

Environmental Sciences: A full grown simulation environment (Model-Works) has been developed and is freely available to all students of ETH (Fischlin et al. 1990). It is based on the Modula-2 system developed for the Macintosh by Prof. N. Wirth and used in several departments for teaching of dynamic systems. A typical assignment for students is the investigation of the famous world model (World2) by Forrester and Meadows (Fig. 4.). The students are asked to study the model and to find and verify good operating conditions.

4 Experience

Staff: Several hundred staff members were involved in one way or another in the project. As a final report on the project a 200 page book has been edited, where some 25 projects in all areas are briefly described (Domeisen et al. 1992).

Students: 4.000 students were interested in our final inquiry, but only 650 returned duly filled in forms, so that we do not have accurate statistics. Most students agree, that use of computers has considerably increased during the five years of the project and that the goal of about eight hours of

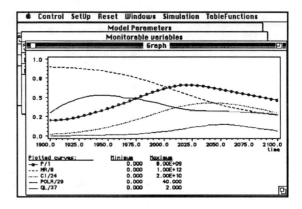

Fig. 4: Standard run of World-2.

work on a workstation during the week has been reached for most
(Domeisen in Domeisen et al. 1992).

References

Domeisen, H. et al. (1992) Computer im Unterricht an der ETH-Zürich.
    vdf.
Domeisen, H. (1992) Die Studierenden und die Informatikmittel im
    Unterricht. In Domeisen et al 1992, 183 - 196.
Fischlin, A. et al. (1990) ModelWorks An Interactive Simulation
    Environment for Personal Computers and Workstations. ETH Zürich.
Kaufmann, S. and Sayir, M. (1992) Unterrichtsprogramme am Institut für
    Mechanik. In Domeisen et al. 1992, 55 - 66.
Kessler, P. and Schaufelberger, W. (1991) Minitools for Education in
    Control System Design and Analysis. IFAC CACSD Swansea.
Schaufelberger W. (1990) Educating Future Control Engineers. 11th IFAC
    World Congress, Tallinn.
Schaufelberger, W.: Educational Simulations with ModelWorks.
    Proceedings CALISCE 91, Presses Polytechniques et Universitaires
    Romandes, 15 - 24.
Schaufelberger, W. (1992) Erfahrungen beim Einsatz von Computern im
    Unterricht - das Projekt IDA. In Domeisen et al. 1992, 7 - 16.
Wirth, N. (1988) The Programming Language Oberon.
    Software - Practice and Experience 18, 7, 671 - 690.
Wirth, N. and Gutknecht, J. (1989) The Oberon System.
    Software - Practice and Experience 19, 9, 671 - 690.
Reiser, M. (1991) The Oberon System.
    User Guide and Programmer's Manual. Addison-Wesley.

Computational Recipes for the Future of Engineering Education

G. Akhras

Department of Civil Engineering, Royal Military College of Canada, Kingston, Ontario

Abstract

Since the advent of computers, computing has been introduced gradually in many fields of the engineering curriculum. The rate of transforming the curriculum to reflect and adopt all the new computing techniques is not following the fast rate of their evolution. Consequently, many engineering educational programs are lagging behind, and very often, it is left to the individual faculty to incorporate the required changes to the courses.

The undergraduate education must undergo the necessary changes to incorporate all of the new technologies. To do so, new approaches are needed. One such approach is the concept of computational recipes. In this paper, the above issues are discussed in detail and the new concept of computational recipes is presented with examples.

Keywords: Computers, Engineering Education, Curriculum.

1 Introduction

Many if not all the engineering educational programs accredited in North America (ABET, Accreditation Board for Engineering and Technology, U.S.A.; CEAB, Canadian Engineering Accreditation Board, Canada) include computing as an important and integral part of any engineering curriculum. Teaching computing consists primarily of developing the computer programming, expertise and know-how of the student. Implicitly, this requirement consists of learning how to develop, write, debug and run a program, as well as how to properly use and run existing programs and software. In both cases, the student will learn not only how to get the right results but exactly how the computer reaches the solution. Until recently, the attempt to reach this idealistic objective was more or less successful. Nowadays, it is extremely difficult, if not quite impossible, to perform this task in a satisfactory manner. Despite this fact, the above requirement is still present in all the curricula.

On the other hand, the miniaturisation of the hardware and the introduction of the microcomputer produced a drastic change of computing and of the way we deal with computing. What was expensive, remote and inaccessible, is now available and cheap. Suddenly, many, if not all, the complex numerical and computational techniques developed specifically to reduce cost and effort, lost their "raison d'être" and consequently their value for the educational purpose. This situation is deemed to repeat itself because the computer technology is evolving in a very fast fashion.

To deal with the above concerns, a reassessment and a reorganization of the teaching of computing has to take place, and new approaches have to be developed. In this paper, the concept of

computational recipes is introduced and compared to the present
approach of teaching computing. This new concept, if adopted, will
greatly influence the computing part of the engineering curriculum.

2   Description of the present approach

In a conventional engineering curriculum, computing is introduced to
the student throughout the full academic program and can, in general,
be divided into three separate but interrelated courses.

2.1 Introductory course

All the engineering schools and universities have in their programs,
for their preparatory or first year, a general computer course to
introduce the student to the computing world. The contents of this
course varies tremendously and can be described by one or more items
of the following:
1) A general introduction to computing and computing methods for
   engineering problems;
2) An introduction to computing languages with emphasis on a particular one. Traditionally, the most learned language is still FORTRAN,
   but PASCAL, APL, BASIC or even C may be taught;
3) An introduction to numerical methods and analysis;
4) An introduction to, what the author defines as the basic utility
   software: Spreadsheets, Word Processors and Graphics, via well
   known commercial software, i.e., Lotus, WordPerfect, AutoCad, etc.

2.2 Numerical analysis course

This intermediary course is a follow up to the previous course and is
taught in the middle of the curriculum program. It consists mainly of
exposing the student to the numerical techniques required in the
various disciplines of engineering. The basic objective here is to
provide the numerical expertise, and practical experience with systems
and devices, so that the student will progress easily and comfortably
in the computing manipulation of the succeeding engineering courses.
   The content of this course includes many topics: from matrice
operations and equation solvers on one side, to system approaches on
the other side, with differential equations, eigenvalues, regression
analysis, finite difference, finite element and other topics in
between.
   The computer is used systematically in teaching these topics. At
least five or six of them constitute the basis of this course. The
selection of a particular topic versus another depends solely on the
teacher's background and ease in teaching the subject. Also, courses
have been set and organised differently form one university to another
to complement the particular need of a curriculum program.

2.3 Advanced computer/numerical analysis course

In the final year of the curriculum, an advanced computer/numerical course is normally devoted to a particular discipline; for example, the computer analysis of structures is adapted for civil, mechanical, aeronautical and aerospace engineering. Usually, this course is considered an important one and is heavily oriented to using and manipulating computer programs and software. In practice, computer manipulation is included in each assignment and class work. This includes reading, writing, debugging, and manipulating computer codes and graphics, etc., assuming that the student is comfortable and familiar with the programming languages, techniques and styles used for this course.

3   Assessment of the present approach

The field of computing is evolving very rapidly due to the fast growth of new ideas, methods and approaches. To take advantage of the expertise and knowledge accumulated, more and more software development groups tend to be multidisciplinary. These groups are formed of individuals with different backgrounds such as computer science, numerical analysis, mathematics, optimization, etc., each providing a specific expertise to the team.

Consequently, many computer programs are the products of the knowledge, experience and expertise of more than one developer. They incorporate a great deal of the collected expertise on a specific subject in order to assist and guide the user in solving problems and in reaching the right results. The sophistication of the computer programs has evolved so fast and in such a way that it is more and more difficult, if not impossible, to perceive how the results are produced when you use a computer program. This process is so time consuming that more and more of these programs are used without knowing the complete details of the computing process.

If, as expected, teachers are continuously updating and adding to the contents of their courses to reflect the new technologies, how will an "average" student cope with all the extra information and pressure ? Unfortunately, not very well.

With all the added complexity and sophistication to computing, most of the students are lost between learning the subject of a particular course and learning the computing related to that subject. Optimistically, they would be learning both. In reality, they end up learning a little bit of both and not very well. Worse still, because computing is "fun" and "in", they may end up learning the computing part of the course rather than the course material.

3.1 A typical example

The following example, related to numerical analysis, will help explain the situation described above and facing educators in all the fields of engineering. Many recent textbooks of structural analysis (Holzer, 1985; Wang, 1986; Melosh, 1990; Chadrupatla and Belegundi; 1991) include a detailed chapter or appendix on two or three different equation solvers with corresponding programs and subroutines. One may find, for example, a routine for a straightforward resolution of a system of equations, another for the solution of a system of banded equations, and another using the active column approach, etc.   The authors of these textbooks expect educators and students to spend some time in writing codes, as well as debugging and thoroughly understanding these routines; otherwise they would have not included all the details in their books.

On the other hand, every computer centre in any educational institution has a commercial engineering/scientific/mathematical software with one or more versions of the above equation solvers (IMSL, NAG). These commercial programs are structured and written by professional programmers and/or computer scientists, and may outperform, in space requirements and resolution time, the corresponding programs written by the academic engineering community.

An undergraduate student obviously has a fixed amount of time to spend on learning structural engineering.   So, what is the best alternative for him/her :
- developing the computing expertise of structural engineering versus developing the computing know-how, assuming that there is not enough time to learn both;
- Is it better to spend time on deciphering computer programs or to learn the course material by manipulating these programs, assessing their intrinsic values and selecting the right and appropriate program for the application at hand ?

The academic community may surmise that manipulating computer codes is a good learning exercise.   The same can be said of structural analysis and design, which is more appropriate to the civil, mechanical, aeronautical and aerospacial engineering profession.   It may be a better approach to teach structural analysis by using appropriate computer programs (Jayachandran and Leblanc, 1987; Akhras, 1990) and leave programming manipulations to advanced graduate courses and to the research community.   Another approach is to use computational recipes.

4   Computational Recipes

The idea behind computational recipes is based on the fact that the ultimate goal of teaching some of the numerical and mathematical topics mentioned above, is to learn their capabilities and limitations, and to exploit them as tools to solve problems .   All the available technological means should then be used to reach this goal. A computational recipe is a intelligent tutorial system (ITS, Wenger, 1987) which encapsulates all the available expertise concerning a particular topic and offers the user a judgment and an advice on his/her particular application.   It is divided in three parts: a preprocessor, the core programs and a postprocessor.   The preprocessor is an expert system which will capture the information from the user, process it and make recommendations on the nature of the problem. Then with the help of the user, it will select from the core programs, the best procedure to solve the problem, and run the appropriate programs.   The postprocessor, another expert system, will help the user digest the results.   Different levels of complexity can be included in the recipe.

An attractive feature of this approach is that the student can use the recipe at increasing levels of sophistication as his/her experience grows. The pre and post expert systems will provide all the necessary explanation to allow the novice and the expert users, to manoeuvre with ease at his/her own pace.

The real advantage of this approach is that the student will concentrate their efforts on exploiting the recipes to define, circumscribe and solve the problem at hand instead of manipulating programs and computer codes. Moreover, the intimidation and overload of computer instructions will be replaced by developing the ability of the student to exploit available computer software as a tool.

The basic idea of computational recipe may appear controversial but it is a very simple and efficient way to continuously upgrade the computing of the numerical methods in engineering.

4.1 Examples of recipes

To illustrate this concept, let us assume that a computational recipe of the example "equation solver" presented above has been developed. The preprocessor of the recipe will analyse the topological properties of the matrice (density, bandedness, etc) and after providing the user with all the alternatives and the corresponding explanations, the system will guide the user to the appropriate action.

For example, if the matrice is symmetric and sparse, the system may propose 1) to reduce the bandwidth before solving the equations with a band-solver; 2) to use a frontal solver; 3) to reduce the profile of the matrice before using a skyline technique; or 4) to use any other appropriate program. All the different programs and routines will constitute the core part of the recipe. The postprocessor will present the results and provide any appropriate analysis: i.e. precision, roundoff errors, etc.

Another good example for a computational recipe is statistical analysis. Many users of statistical analysis are ill-prepared and not very comfortable with the collection and analysis of data. Users may drop a few odd points or select tests where assumptions have been violated and carry on their analysis unaware of the consequences of their decision. The expert systems of the recipes will tell the user what is the nature of data at hand, and provide advice on what to do, why and how, with all the necessary explanations. This will help increase the awareness of the student to the sensitivity of the data.

5 Conclusion

A proposal for using a new approach in teaching numerical methods to various engineering disciplines is introduced in this paper. The concept of computational recipes is presented and explained with examples. If adopted, this new concept will greatly change the computing part of the engineering curriculum.

References

Akhras, G. (1990) Teaching Structural Analysis with Computer Programs,
    International Journal of Applied Engineering Education, 6, 461–464
Chadrupatla, T. R. and Belegundi, A. D. (1991) Introduction to Finite
    Elements in Engineering, Prentice Hall, Englewood Cliffs, N. J.
Holzer, S.H. (1985) Computer Analysis of Structures; Matrix Structural
    Analysis; Structural Programming, Elsevier Science, New York.
IMSL, International Mathematical \& Statistical Library, Problem
    Solving Software Systems, Houston, Texas, U.S.A.
Jayachandran, P. and Leblanc, S.G.B. (1987), Structural Analysis using
    Microcomputers and Graphics, Proceedings, ASCE Congress, Computer
    Applications in Structural Engineering, Florida.
Melosh R. J. (1990) Structural Engineering Analysis by Finite Elements
    Prentice Hall, Englewood Cliffs, New Jersey.
NAG, Numerical Algorithms Group Inc, Downers Grove, Illinois, U.S.A.
Wang, C. K. (1986) Structural Analysis on Microcomputers, Macmillan
    Publishing Company, New York.
Wenger, E. (1987) Artificial Intelligence and Tutoring Systems,
    Morgan Kaufmann Publishers, Inc., Loas altos, California.

Information Technology in Learning: Exploring Electronics Through a Modern, Interactive Learning Enviroment

A.G. Cartwright

Centre for Engineering Educational Technology, University of Surrey

Abstract
Modern Computer and Information Technologies provide the means of radically rethinking and revising methods of teaching and learning in education. This paper describes on-going work in the Centre for Engineering Educational Technology at the University of Surrey focused on the development of innovative computer-based learning methods which challenge traditional lecture-based teaching. Through modelling, simulation and the 'what-if' approach, the learner can more effectively develop a deep understanding of course content, principles and practice. The paper describes such a learning environment in a first-year undergraduate course in Electronics for Mechanical Engineers at the University of Surrey. The course has been in place for 2 years and to date 140 students have passed through it. Lecture content is minimal with the predominant delivery method being self-paced interactive computer simulation with tutor support.
Keywords: Interactive, Multimedia, Simulation, Modelling, Teaching, Learning, Engineering

1 Introduction

It is well recognised that Engineering Undergraduate courses, as currently formulated, are far too heavily biased towards the presentation of 'knowledge' with insufficient emphasis on the acquisition of skills and the development of a real understanding of the subject material. These concerns are the subject of national debate and are considered in depth in, for example, the EPC (1991) occasional paper.

The debate arises from a growing feeling in Engineering education that the way we teach is simply not effective. Recognising that engineering is of crucial importance to the future wealth and prosperity of the UK, the supply of well educated engineers and well trained technicians is essential. It follows that if the quality and effectiveness of engineering undergraduate courses are to be improved then a radical rethink of delivery methods is critical. This is even more the case as we seek to expand student numbers and broaden intake into engineering courses from both traditional and non-traditional sources.

1.1 Current Teaching Practices

The primary method of delivery in Engineering undergraduate courses is the lecture and although its contents are regularly subject to revision, the delivery method itself has remained virtually static. Whilst the lecture is relatively *cost*-effective, it suffers from significant *educational* deficiencies. In particular the lecture is essentially a one-way interaction between the teacher and the learner in which information is *passively received* by the student - not *actively discovered*. The essence of the learning experience, personal discovery through curiosity driven exploration, remains virtually dormant.

The major educational deficiencies associated with the conventional lecture are:-

• the whole class must proceed at the same rate

With a single delivery source (the teacher) all members of the class must attempt to assimilate information at the same rate. It is not possible for an individual to influence significantly the rate of delivery. If delivery is too slow interest will be lost and if too fast the student will be lost. In either case the educational process is clearly not optimal.

• the route taken by each student is the same

The route is chosen by the teacher and cannot be modified by the student. If free to choose then the route taken would depend upon individual strengths, weaknesses and level of understanding.

• the student passively receives the information - it is not actively discovered

From where the student sits, the lecture is a very passive affair. Information is simply (and hopefully) absorbed from the source. The student is not actively involved in the discovery and exploration of the knowledge itself and as such the essence of the learning experience, personal discovery though curiosity driven exploration, remain virtually dormant.

1.2 The Potential Role of Information Technology

Over the last decade there have been sporadic efforts to develop technology in the support of teaching and learning in Higher Education. More recent developments in modern computer and information technology, including authoring software and multimedia devices, have presented the potential to extend that role beyond simple 'support'. For example, breakthroughs in generic software such as National Instrument's LabVIEW now provide cost-effective modelling tools within which powerful, interactive learning methods can be developed.

The advent of the modern personal computer and its associated information technologies can provide the means of radically rethinking and revising current delivery methods - harnessing the power of computers to establish new learning environments in which the student can more effectively develop a deep understanding of engineering principles and practice. The incorporation of information technologies into the learning process enable the integration of the major learning ingredients of self-pacing, self-guided discovery and small group tutorial. This integrated approach is applicable across the full subject base of engineering - technology, commercial and management skills. Properly applied, technology breaks the mould of traditional teaching and enables the exploration of new and flexible approaches that more effectively realise educational goals. Students no longer need remain the passive absorbers of knowledge; they can become active thinkers and investigators. Modern technology has provided tools that allow us to gather and access information and to manage and transform that information to create knowledge and understanding in innovative ways. Modern technology enables us to make a shift from predominantly lecture-centred delivery systems to interactive, self-paced, self-guided, student-centred learning.

Such learning environments naturally arise through the exploitation of interactive multimedia. Multimedia is the bringing together of information, ideas and concepts from a variety of sources and in a variety of forms at one central control point - the student's personal, desk-top computer. For the undergraduate engineer such sources include manuals, books, periodicals, example sheets, drawings, presentations, data sheets etc, whilst the forms include text, diagrams, graphs, tables, simulation, video, and sound. For the student, multimedia technology provides an unprecedented degree of control over and interaction with the subject matter whilst for the teacher the constraints associated with the traditional lecture are significantly reduced. Multimedia blurs the demarcation between the lecture, the tutorial and the lab because it naturally encompasses all three. In this respect one of the major implications for teaching is the ultimate breakdown of the traditional course structures and the infrastructures that have developed to service them.

Through the Centre for Engineering Educational Technology at the University of Surrey, interactive, computer-based courseware is being developed to support Level 1 technical courses in the University. The first module, now in routine use, covers an introduction to Analogue and Digital Electronics.

1.3 Interactive Learning in Analogue and Digital Electronics

Previous teaching in Electronics in the Department of Mechanical Engineering at the University of Surrey has been traditional with a typical 10 week course being divided into 70% lectures supported with 30% laboratory/tutorial. The new computer-based course reverses those divisions with 70% laboratory/tutorial work and 30% (support) lectures.

With routine technical content (see Fig.1) available on screen and presented largely through active simulations exploiting the 'what-if' approach, the teachers' role is now almost entirely that of 'tutor' rather than that of 'information deliver'. Typically 70 students undertake the course and work in pairs at each workstation. Whilst such an approach is resource intensive (if such classes are not to be repeated several times a week) the benefits are significant. Students are able to investigate subject matter in their own time and follow their own routes. Simulations permit the modelling of concepts impossible with 'real' devices - eg. op-amps with infinite slew-rate and bandwidths can be investigated with 'real' characteristics added later (see Fig.2). It is only necessary to bring students together in the lecture environment to present an overview of each stage of the module and to set targets to be reached. With the student centrally involved in the discovery of knowledge and the development of skills and understanding, learning becomes more effective. In addition, the teacher's role becomes equally more effective - through that of tutor, to reinforce understanding and support individual difficulties.

It is of significance to note that since each workstation is equipped with standard word-processing, spreadsheet and drafting packages the student has full access to professional word-processing and data-processing tools as a matter of course. The very existence of this level of technology means that each student has, on a freelance basis, access to professional resources for data and information processing and thereby naturally acquires expertise, competence and literacy in the tools which are already part of the professional engineer's everyday life.

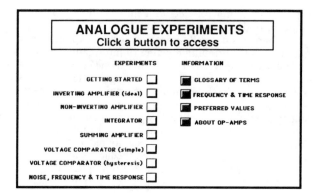

Fig.1 The initial screen is the student's window into the courseware. From here the complete range of experiments, background information, mathematical treatments, glossary of terms and additional peripheral information is accessible. An introductory 'getting started' feature is also included. This relieves the teacher from time consuming routines and enables the student to 'self-start'. Navigation is intuitive and simple - a 'point and click' selection being used. This selection method is common to all courseware material.

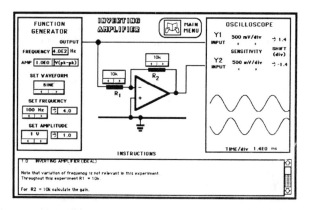

Fig.2 A typical experimental arrangement shows an 'ideal op-amp' simulation. The op-amp, with resistor feedback, is shown in the centre of the screen with a function generator on the left and dual-beam oscilloscope on the right. By pointing and clicking the student interacts with the instruments, changing waveform, frequency, amplitude etc. and monitoring the results on the 'scope. Resistor values can be likewise changed. Operating instructions appear in the lower scrolling window. Screen-based instruments behave EXACTLY like real instruments in every respect but being created in software they may possess characteristics that their 'real' counterparts cannot. Such simulations present enormous potential for learning.

References

EPC (1991) Engineering Professors' Conference occasional paper 'The Future Pattern of 1st Degree Courses' - no 3, Feb.1991

The Use of Computers for Teaching a Thermofluid Engineering Course

N.C. Hay, T. Muneer

Department of Mechanical, Manufacturing, and Software Engineering, Napier Polytechnic of Edinburgh

Abstract
This paper describes the authors' experience of using computer software to enhance learning of thermofluid engineering. Examples demonstrate how the chosen software packages were used and the types of problem tackled by the students. Comparisons with conventional methods and advantages are presented.
Keywords: Thermofluids Engineering, Engineering Education, Computers, Software.

1   Introduction

In the education of engineers, much time is spent providing undergraduates with the computational and manipulative skills to be able to use the theoretical tools which will enable them to function as qualified engineers. However, it is the hope of industry that engineers be creative; be able to identify the nature of problems; identify and generate the information necessary to solve problems; synthesize solutions and be able to make decisions. Unfortunately, the main teaching technique in many courses is lecturing where teachers use most of the time in delivery, as they sometimes do also in tutorial or seminar where the objective of the activity is student interaction and participation(Powell, 1973). This style of teaching fails to impart the above engineering skills and there is a need to give students more opportunity to learn rather than using up time ineffectively(Sparkes, 1988).

Often the engineering content of topics is swamped by mathematics which some students will have already mastered but for others has still to be digested or studied elsewhere in the course. Alternatively, the topic being studied depends on a secondary skill which the student has to master to comprehend the engineering objectives. These act as noise and distraction, making learning objectives more difficult to achieve. The objectives of some learning situations are also often mistaken because the student is concentrating on the secondary skill or because time is wasted by pretending to listen to a lecturer, punching at keys on a calculator, or defacing pages of thermodynamic property tables.

These distractions occur in thermofluids engineering. A basic skill in mathematics and proficiency with a calculator should be sufficient in the early years of a such a course but the effort required by some problems means that the student only has time to consider one or two specific solutions rather than general relationships or the implications of altering parameters. Navigating through steam tables for example, is a skill which is learned gradually as the concepts and language of properties of pure substances is absorbed. Thus learning about energy balance in steam plant can be impaired if the necessary skill to use steam tables is underdeveloped.

Limitations in time mean that single solutions for problems are often all that can be attempted rather than realistic engineering situations where time is needed to define problems, gather information and explore solutions. Graduates from engineering courses, unlike those from a social science or arts courses, are often left with the impression that all engineering problems have unique solutions!

There is therefore a need to improve the teaching of engineering courses to reflect the real world by giving the student experience of real problems (Cawley 1989). The authors are attempting to address this problem by using computers and commercially available software. This reduces the computational and manipulative burden on the student who will develop these skills elsewhere, allowing time to concentrate on the engineering. Examples in this paper demonstrate how software was used to improve learning in a thermofluids course.

2   Thermodynamic property software

Presently the authors are using three software packages to improve thermodynamic property evaluation for student-oriented problem solving. These packages respectively evaluate properties for steam (Intercept Software 1986), refrigerants (Software Systems Corporation 1988), and moist air (Elite Software 1990). Previously, property evaluation used thermodynamic property tables (e.g. steam tables) or charts (e.g. Mollier diagram for steam or pressure-enthalpy chart for refrigerants). These are still presented elsewhere in the course. It shall be demonstrated herein that the tedium of using tables or charts may be beneficially obviated by using packages, resulting in significant time savings!

Firstly, we shall deal with the software package for the steam/water substance. The International Association for the Properties of Steam (IAPS) is the recognised authority on thermodynamic formulation and the current IAPS standard is the one due to Haar, Gallagher and Kell (1984). It must be noted that the new standard makes all previously published property tables and charts obsolete. The authors have therefore, in addition to acquiring the HGK software, also produced a new T-s chart for steam (Muneer 1991).

A time and motion study was undertaken to compare the relative performance of the software package (mounted on a PC 386), the T-s chart and steam tables. The performance was judged on the basis of time taken and accuracy of results while obtaining the properties, which require interpolation, for the following problem.

Consider the two-stage steam turbine with interstage heating shown in Fig. 1. The data are as shown on the diagram. Assuming a constant pipe diameter in the interstage heater, and reversible adiabatic turbines, determine:
(a)   The power rating (kW) of the turbine.
(b)   The rate of heat transfer (kW) in the interstage heater.

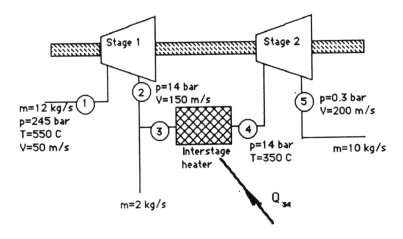

<u>Fig 1 Two Stage Steam Turbine</u>

To give an indication of the relative performance of each tool, a student of above average ability was asked to solve this problem. Table 1 provides the details of our observations.

TABLE 1 Time-Accuracy Assessment for Steam Property Evaluation

Activity	Time to evaluate state points 1,2,4 & 5 (Fig.2)	Average Accuracy of estimates	Remarks
Steam Tables	32 minutes	98%	Tedious Interpolations but better accuracy
T-s Chart	11 minutes	95%	Faster but less precise
Software Package	3 minutes	100%	Best of both worlds !

Similar time savings are obtained when evaluating refrigerant properties (R12) for solving a problem on energy flows to a compressor using the refrigerant property software referred above. Similarly in estimating the properties of moist air using the psychrometric software in a design exercise on an air-conditioning plant, the time savings were again found to be significant. Note that the routine task of evaluating properties is not fundamentally important to the learning objectives. Rather the stage which follows evaluation of properties, i.e. the analysis of the first and second laws of thermodynamics, is the core activity.

3   Analysis Software

The objective of using analysis software is to speed up computation and improve the presentation of solutions. This can be viewed as part of the continuing development of computational aids, from logarithms to slide rule and to electronic calculator. At each stage of development, processing speed has improved and this has changed the style of problems from mathematical manipulation of a limited number of specialised problems to reproduce elegant proofs by reasoning or rote, toward the evaluation of a wider range of problems and practical applications. This means, of course, that comparing the quality of engineering courses and engineers, past and present is invalid because there are different styles and objectives.

All computational aids require training but it is the authors opinion that the time devoted to mastering this particular analysis software (MathCAD 1989) is little more than that required for a hand calculator performing similar tasks. There is however, greater potential which students are keen to exploit.

Unlike a hand calculator, the software displays the logic and calculation of solutions on computer graphics. This shows mathematical symbols as they appear in written work and so writing the solution is similar to typing text on a word processor but with the advantage that expressions are evaluated. The validity of equations, erroneous keystrokes or the correctness of data are easily checked because the solution is displayed in this form. Any deficiency in a solution is due to the engineering and is more easily identified. Also, the software processes expressions from left to right and top to bottom. Thus if an expression cannot be evaluated because of missing data, this is immediately flagged. Feedback to the student is instantaneous, prompting re-examination to assign values to missing data or to restructure the solution.

The solutions to many engineering problems require the roots of equations to be determined or simultaneous equations to be solved. Even when the equations are linear, these solutions can take a significant time or entail specialized mathematical techniques. For example, it is unreasonable to expect more than two or three simultaneous linear equations to be solved in tutorial and this severely restricts the number and content of problems tackled. However, numerical solution of equations by the software eliminates computational errors and reduces the time required to achieve solutions. After a solution has been developed, alternative values for parameters can be used to investigate alternative configurations for the problem.

The advantages of this type of software are illustrated in the following problem on pipe flow (Fig 2) in which liquid is raised from one reservoir to another by a pump. In the conventional problem, a relationships between flow rate and head is provided for a pump and the student is required to compute the discharge rate at the operating point of the system. A graph of friction head loss in the pipe is drawn which requires the Reynolds Number and friction factor to be determined at several values in a range of flow rates. The friction factor is determined by formula or from a Moody diagram. The solution is the intersection of the curves of head plus friction loss against flow rate with that of the pump characteristic.

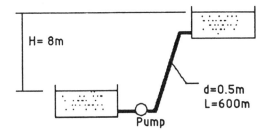

Fig 2 Pump Discharge Problem

Expressions for the relevant parameters are presented in Fig. 3 as they appear on the screen or in a print out. One expression determines values for the parameter at all flow rates. Writing these formulae requires similar skills to data entry on a calculator and so they were used in training and familiarization with the software. In practise formulae can be presented as a software formula sheet from which alternative expressions can be cut and pasted. For example, in this topic alternative expressions for friction factor can be used. Students can therefore examine the effect of assumptions such as smooth pipe by using cut and paste to select appropriate expressions.

$$c_i := \frac{q_i}{A} \qquad Re_i := \frac{c_i \cdot d}{\upsilon}$$

$$f_i := \frac{1.325}{\left[\ln\left[\frac{\varepsilon}{3.7 \cdot d} + \frac{5.74}{Re_i^{0.9}}\right]\right]^2} \qquad Hf_i := \frac{f_i \cdot L \cdot c_i^2}{2 \cdot g \cdot d}$$

Fig 3 Expressions from MathCAD Screen

The software also handles text as a basic word processor and can import sketches. This allows skeleton solutions to be presented, complete with diagrams. These solutions can be presented in a form in which the student only has to interrogate the question and assign values to parameters, or, for more advanced students, the skeleton might be notes of guidance on how to formulate the problem. Graphs can be plotted for functions or subscripted variables allowing instant interpretation such as in Fig 4. As an alternative solution, to this problem, the operating point can be found by writing the governing equations as functions and the software used to solve these non-linear simultaneous equations.

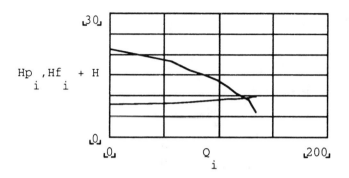

Fig 4 Pump and System Characteristics

Once the calculation is complete, values are easily altered to investigate other geometry or conditions. The time saved in this example, is used for more interesting questions. For example a range of pumps and pipes at various costs was offered and the students asked to use their calculation sheet to decide on the best configuration and to justify their decision with an economic analysis. These are alternative objectives but certainly more realistic in the education of engineers.

4   Conclusion

It is natural for engineers to carefully and selectively choose the best tool for each job. Students can also appreciate these computer tools as superior to those used by their previous generation and are willing to make use of them. The software described here provides tools which give the students time and confidence to understand and learn the engineering in their course and meet with decision making situations without the distraction of secondary skills.

References

Powell, J. (1973) Small group teaching methods in higher education, Educational Research, 16, 163 - 171.
Sparkes, J. J. (1988) Quality in Engineering Education, Engineering Professors Conference, Occasional Paper No 1.
Cawley, P. (1989) The Introduction of a Problem-based Option into a Conventional Engineering Degree Course, Studies in Higher Education, 14(1), 83-95.
Mathsoft Inc. (1989) MathCAD Users Guide, from Adept Scientific, Letchworth Herts.
Intercept Software (1986) NBS/NRC Steam Tables, Campbell California.
Software Systems Corporation (1988).Thermodynamic Properties: Gasprops,Refrig,Steamcalc,John Wiley & Sons,Chester UK.
Elite Software (1990) PsyChart Program V1.2, Fullerton California.
Haar,L., Gallagher, J. S. & Kell, G. S. (1984) NBS/NRC Steam Tables, Hemisphere Publishing Corporation, New York.
Muneer, T. (1991) Temperature - Entropy chart for steam, Napier Polytechnic, Edinburgh.

Design, Manufacture and Test of a CAD/CAM Generated Centrifugal Pump Impeller

A.J. Addlesee, J.B.C. Davies, G. Simpson

Department of Mechanical Engineering, Heriot-Watt University

Abstract

A Second Year undergraduate project involves Mechanical Engineering students in the integration of design, manufacture and testing of a range of centrifugal pump impellers.

Each impeller profile is designed using the in-house CAD system, and an integrated NC machining package generates the manufacturing program for transfer by DNC link to a 3-axis machining centre.

The finished impellers are performance tested in a rig which allows the speed to be varied and the head, flow and power to be monitored. Analysis of the data is an important part of the exercise.

Keywords: Engineering Applications, CAD/CAM, Pump impeller.

1 Introduction

A developing repertoire of projects is a necessity for an Engineering Applications course if staleness by repetition is to be avoided. The centrifugal pump project arose from on-going efforts to extend the range of available exercises, and a large part of its educational value is due to the fact that the student is responsible for the entire progress of a selected component from the initial specification through to the analysis of test data.

The component under consideration is the pump impeller, which is a highly suitable subject because of the large number of geometric variants that are possible within the fixed overall dimensions determined by the test rig. After an initial lecture on the principles of pumping, CAD/CAM technology is used in the design and production stages. Three cycles of the project have now been completed and it is still evolving in the light of accumulating experience.

2 Design

Following the lecture on basic centrifugal pump theory, students are provided with a standard drawing which specifies the blank material dimensions and the outline of the pump impeller, Fig. 1. The general specification calls for a single-shrouded impeller carrying blades which taper uniformly from 10mm width at 40mm inlet diameter to 4mm width at 100mm outlet diameter. The impeller is thus nominally designed for uniform radial velocity. The shroud and blade thicknesses are specified, as are standard hub dimensions.

Individual variants specify the number of blades to be used (4-12), and the required value for the inlet angle β_1 in the range $40°$-$90°$. The blade shape also depends on a second parameter, namely its radius of curvature, which can be varied to produce a wide range of both backward-facing and forward-facing blades. The outlet blade angle β_2 is required in subsequent analysis and can be determined by either calculation or measurement.

Using the dimensional data along with detailed CAD and CAM instruction sheets, simplified in Figs.(2,3), each student produces an individual detailed drawing, Fig.4, and an associated program of CNC (Computer Numerically Controlled) machining instructions. Extensive use is made of the CAM visualisation facility and on-screen editing package before transferring the program to the machining centre through the DNC (Direct Numerical Control) link.

3 Manufacture

The impellers are manufactured on a Wadkin V5-10 CNC machining centre. Although originally manufactured from aluminium, the impellers are now produced from UPVC which drastically reduces the distortion induced by large area-clearance machining operations.

4 Performance testing

After manufacture, each impeller is fitted into a purpose-built pump casing with an easily removed suction end cover. A stud in the shaft end is tightened to grip the impeller hub against a shoulder on the shaft, so that the impeller can be driven by friction. The pump is driven by a variable speed motor so that a series of tests can be performed at different speeds with a view to checking the pump similarity laws.

The rig is instrumented to measure shaft speed (optical tachometer), flow (rotameter), pressure rise (mercury-water manometer), and electrical power input. The shaft power is estimated as the difference between the electrical power under test and the power at the same speed but without an impeller fitted. It was initially found that the maximum obtainable flow was severely limited by the pressure drop round the test circuit, but a booster pump, installed in series with the test pump, now enables the full operating range from zero flow to zero pressure rise to be investigated.

5 Analysis

The overall efficiency of the motor and the pump can be calculated, and results are required in the form of graphs of pressure rise and overall efficiency against flow rate, for several constant speed tests. The significance of dimensional analysis is demonstrated by replotting this data in terms of head and flow coefficients.

Experimental and theoretical results can be compared by calculating the manometric efficiency, which is the ratio of the observed pressure rise to the pressure rise predicted by Euler's idealised turbomachine equation. The aim is to illustrate the influence of blade geometry through the use of velocity vector diagrams to describe the flow. With the notation shown in Fig.5, the Euler analysis gives:

$$\Delta p_{ideal} = \rho \cdot U_2 \cdot V_{w2}.$$

To use this result, the blade velocity U_2 is set to $\Omega \cdot R_2$, and the whirl velocity V_{w2} is determined by the interaction of the geometry of the outlet velocity triangle with the volume flow condition:

$$V_{w2} = U_2 - (Q/A_2) \cdot \cot \beta_2.$$

The significance of the vector diagrams is further emphasised by using the geometry of the inlet velocity triangle to find the relation between flow rate and rotational speed required to minimise the inlet shock losses.

The results produced from all the individual impellers are correlated by a member of staff and a further exercise is issued, based upon the the collated performance figures. These exercises vary from year to year, but a typical activity would be choosing a pump to achieve a particular performance, or predicting the impact on performance of varying the angles of the impeller blades.

6   Conclusion

During the project students use computer techniques to design and manufacture a centrifugal pump impeller, which they then test. Analysis of the experimental and theoretical performance, associated with subsequent attempts to predict the effect of modifications, provide the student with excellent practice and help to generate a realistic understanding of engineering problems.

7   Symbols

Suffices 1,2 denote values at impeller inlet and outlet respectively.

A	Flow area = Q/V_r
Q	Flow rate
R	Radius
U	Blade velocity
V	Fluid velocity
V_r	Radial component of V
V_w	Whirl component of V
β	Blade angle
Δp	Pressure rise
ρ	Fluid density
Ω	Rotational speed

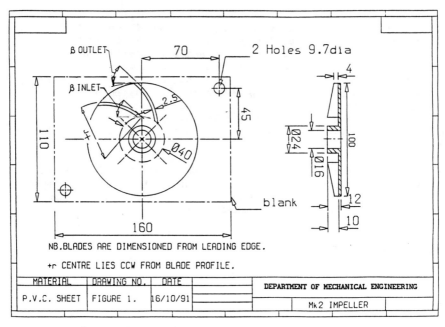

Figure 1:   Impeller Outline

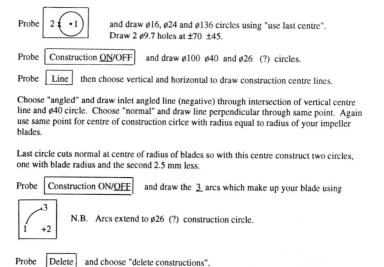

Figure 2:   CAD Guidance Sheet

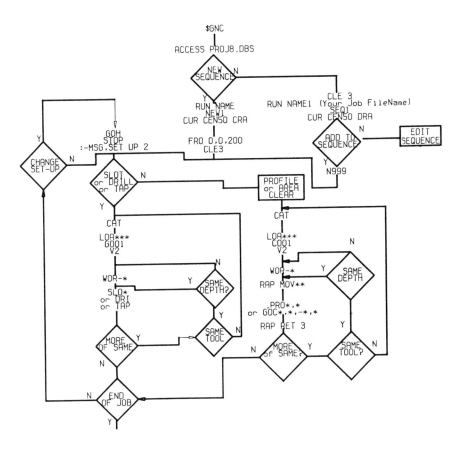

Figure 3:   CAM Flow Chart

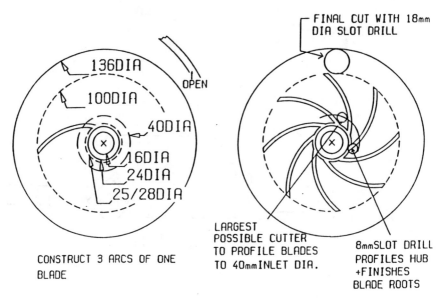

Figure 4:   Detail and Manufacturing Drawings

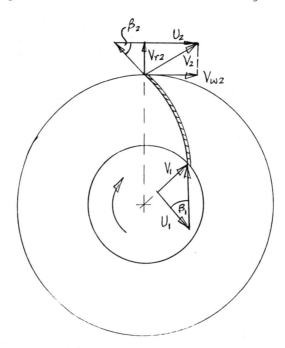

Figure 5:   Velocity Vector Diagrams

Restructuring Circuits and Systems Curricula in Electrical Engineering

J. Choma, Jr

Department of Electrical Engineering, University of Southern California

Abstract

A redesigned circuit and systems (CAS) curriculum that promises to offset many of the observable problems that beset the CAS component of an undergraduate electrical engineering (EE) program is presented. This new curriculum has been partially implemented. It entails an intimate relationship between systems and circuits courses, as well as laboratory pedagogy that requires students to design experiments that verify theoretical contentions proffered in the lecture hall. The paper also addresses the pragmatic roles played by the personal computer and the requisite technical complexion of CAS faculty and support staff.

Keywords: Circuits and Systems, Circuits Laboratory, Circuit Simulation, Circuit Analysis And Design.

1   Introduction

The purpose of undergraduate circuits and systems (CAS) classes is to establish an analytically strong foundation that supports design-oriented courses taught in the electrical engineering (EE) upper division. But there is compelling evidence to suggest that fundamental CAS course objectives are not achieved in modern EE curricula. A form of such evidence is the generally accepted argument that the recent EE graduate who is able to assume significant design responsibility in industry or in the graduate laboratory is an exception, not a rule.

One reason for the failure of CAS courses to provide meaningful support for the upper division curriculum is that basic CAS classes have not kept pace with advancing technology. The past four decades have witnessed an electronics progression from the vacuum tube and discrete component transistor era to hybrid (combined analog and digital) VLSI monolithic chips. While various aspects of these technological advances have been incorporated into advanced coursework, modern CAS course textbooks and syllabi remain similar to those of four decades ago.

The most serious problem with the majority of CAS courses is that neither their content nor their pedagogy exploits the basic fact that insightful circuit analysis is the mother of creative circuit design. Circuit analysis applies the fundamental laws of charge and energy conservation to the problem of determining the mathematical equations of equilibrium for circuits. Interpreting the solution of these equations in terms of the circuit response characteristics they imply is the second step toward circuit design competence. This interpretation underscores parametric factors that define and limit achievable circuit responses. The analytical insights that resultantly accrue lead to parametric optimization exercises aimed toward enhancing circuit response attributes. When optimization fails to deliver acceptable circuit performance, new circuit topologies must be conceived. Topological innovation separates competent circuit designers from circuit analysts. It demands a thorough understanding of the interrelationships that circuit analysis highlights among desired circuit performance, the volt-ampere characteristics of circuit branches, and the equilibrium charge and energy equations dictated by circuit topology.

The CAS component of the undergraduate EE curriculum teaches the mechanics of circuit analysis well, but it generally fails to promote student design creativity. To be sure, design competence is promoted by relevant professional experiences. But design skills in engineering students can be nurtured by carefully integrating circuit and systems concepts in a contiguous curriculum that recognizes electrical and electronic circuits as the fundamental building blocks of practical engineering systems.

2   Proposed Restructuring Of The CAS Curriculum

A significant restructuring of the basic circuits, undergraduate systems, basic electronic circuits, and upper division circuits and systems design courses is necessary to offset the foregoing problems in EE education. The motivation for this change is that basic CAS courses must offer more than a mere collection of theoretic concepts and analytical tools whose practical utility is demonstrated only in the upper division. Students learn theories and retain them longer if their relevance to practical passive and active circuits and systems is demonstrated in concert with their rigorous definition and derivation. For example, Kirchhoff's Current Law and Thevenin's theorem can be exemplified by using them to analyze the small signal equivalent circuits of amplifiers encountered formally in electronic circuits classes. To be sure, these models must be offered without proof to sophomore EE students. But by qualitatively rationalizing signal amplification in the context of familiar electronic systems (e.g. a stereo amplifier), the pertinent equivalent circuits become tools for reducing vague and obscure theories and analytical techniques to engineering issues with which students can identify.

A methodical demonstration of the utility of all theoretic concepts and analytical techniques addressed in the undergraduate CAS courses makes the lecturing pace slower than that of the present day norm. This fact, coupled with the necessity of enhancing CAS subject matter, suggests a need for three or four, semesters of CAS study. By carefully integrating system concepts with basic circuit theory, the revitalized EE curriculum responds positively to the basic fact that it is system architecting that defines specific circuit requirements. In return for an avoidable curricular expansion, the first electronic circuits course becomes an elective option, as might several other presently required courses.

Since design proficiency is developed only through continuing practice, design must be implicit to the restructured CAS sequence. Design need not involve system intricacies that are beyond sophomore and junior comprehension. It can entail such simple problems as room wiring, an audio-activated on/off switch, a simple counter, etc. To be sure, these designs might involve the application of devices to which students have not been exposed formally. But just as students learn to use complicated software without knowing programming and without reading every page of a voluminous software manual, so they can learn to use unfamiliar components through an investigation of the trade journals and component catalogs. A laudable by-product of requiring design early in the EE curriculum is that it forces students to extra curricular reading.

Since engineering is synonymous with laboratory work, CAS labs must be carefully contrived, and they must afford students access to relevant measurement equipment and computers. Moreover, the lecture discussions must embody measurement practices that complement the presentation of theoretic material. A particularly beneficial type of laboratory assignment is the kind that forces students to design an experiment to validate (or possibly disprove) contentions made in the lecture hall.

In the circuits area, a universally accepted circuit simulation package is SPICE. SPICE is particularly useful for assessing an integrated circuit (IC), since most design proposals that ultimately become ICs cannot be evaluated realistically by characterizing their discrete component realizations. As such, circuit analyses based on SPICE simulations are supplanting laboratory characterizations of circuit breadboards. SPICE simulations can be used to investigate the prudence of an approach proposed for the laboratory. But just as breadboard experiments must be carefully planned if potential problem areas are to be revealed, circuit assessments predicated on SPICE analyses must likewise be designed meticulously. And by requiring students to design sets of SPICE simulations for complicated laboratory test circuits, the relevance of cognate circuit theories to actually observed circuit responses is unavoidably illuminated.

Another beneficial application of personal computers is their use in developing small programs that solve specific CAS problems . The objective here is not the development of elegant software. Rather, the objective is to use the computer as a teaching tool. A student who writes a technical program must exercise logical and organized thinking which, in turn, are limited by his or her understanding of the problem at hand.

In order to place the lower division CAS classes in proper design-oriented perspective, a capstone senior circuit and system design elective is imperative. This senior offering must mirror the industrial development and graduate research environments in which graduated EE students are expected to function creatively. A likely form of this elective is a two semester course focused on promoting the entrepreneurial talents of interested students. Students electing to take this laboratory-oriented class would be charged with the responsibility of innovating practical new electronic products or improving existing products. Students would be graded on the thoroughness with which they execute their product and theoretical research, circuit analyses and simulations, and laboratory experimentation aimed toward verifying analytically derived circuit performance predictions. Their comprehension can be assessed through project reporting and oral presentations made to a committee comprised of faculty, representatives from local industry, and graduate students working in related technological areas.

3   Proposed Syllabus For The Restructured CAS Curriculum

A partial list of suggested topics for the revised sequence of three -to- four CAS courses is offered below. The material is not necessarily listed in the preferred order of presentation, and the lack of space prohibits an itemization of specific topics within a particular subject area.

Engineering Model Of The Atom	Current Conduction
Circuit Branch Elements	Analysis of Memoryless Circuits
First Order Circuits	Convolution Integral
Analysis In Transformed Variables	Second Order Circuits
Sinusoidal Steady State	Multi-Order Circuits
Circuit Theorems	Two Port Networks
Differential Networks	Operational Amplifier Circuits
Circuit Simulation	Topological Concepts
Passive and Active Filters	Canonic Electronic Cells
Communication Circuits	Signal Processing Concepts
Estimation Of Steady State Response	Circuit Partitioning

4   CAS Faculty And Staff

The same faculty need not be involved in each course of the proposed CAS sequence of courses. However, the faculty group that teaches the sequence must continually communicate with one another to ensure thoroughness of presented subject material and continuity between courses. The faculty must also be sufficiently senior so that their cognate engineering experience can properly accommodate the challenges implicit to the proposed new sequence.

Teaching assistants for the laboratories and discussion sections must be carefully screened. In addition to having a demonstrable competence in circuit and system theory and design, they must possess an avowed interest in teaching.

5   Conclusions

The youth of today can handle an ambitious restructuring of the CAS curriculum. To be sure, aspiring engineers need help to bolster their mathematical skills. This help can be provided by a carefully selected staff of teaching assistants and a compassionate faculty devoted to helping their students over significant technical hurdles.

Today's students are not inferior to those of our generation, but curiously enough, they have been impoverished by rapidly advancing technology. Students in the 50's and and 60's appreciated electronics by building, debugging, and disassembling electronics hardware having such recognizable components as vacuum tubes, resistors, and capacitors. Present day electronic systems, with their flat packs and TO5 cans that render monolithic versions of these components indistinguishable, are much more sophisticated than those of yore. They are not given to clandestine experiments in the garage and, in fact, most of these systems defy disassembly. Thus, present day students - even those blessed with a sincere interest in electronics - come to sophomore CAS courses with minimal, if any, exposure to practical hardware. Instead, their reality is computers. It is reasonable that electrical engineering can capitalize on this proficiency by integrating the computer into virtually every aspect of the theoretic discussions and laboratory exercises implicit to CAS offerings. Of course, such a redirection requires new textbooks, new lecturing methods, and a re-outfitting of the laboratories that complement CAS lecture classes.

6   Bibliography

Rohrer, R. A. (1990) Taking circuits seriously, IEEE Circuits and Devices, 6, 27-31.

Rohrer, R. A. (1991) Our worst enemy, ASEE Prism, November, 48.

Olds, B. M. and Miller, R. L. (1991) Departments are obsolete, ASEE Prism, December, 56.

CAS workshop on future directions - Circuits, Systems and Signal Processing (1990) IEEE Circuits and Systems, 1, 10-22.

Desoer, C. A. and Kuh, E. S. (1969) Basic Circuit Theory, McGraw-Hill Book Company, New York.

Huelsman, L. P. (1991) Basic Circuit Theory, Prentice-Hall, Inc., Englewood Cliffs, New Jersey.

Van Valkenburg, M. E. (1955) Network Analysis, Prentice-Hall, Inc., Englewood Cliffs, New Jersey.

Black, T. M. (1982) Straight Talk About American Education, Harcourt, Brace, and Jovanovich, New York.

Teaching Digital Control Engineering Using New Methods and Concepts of Controller Design

H.M. Schaedel, F.J. Hilger

Department of Information Technology, Fachhochschule Köln

Abstract

This paper presents a new concept for a transparent controller design combining time- and frequency-domain methods which is applied in the course of digital control engineering at the Fachhochschule Köln. In a step by step procedure based on the time response function of the process PI- and PID-controllers may be optimized. Several approaches are given. They can be evaluated using simply a pocket calculator. The methods demonstrated are supported by the CAE-tool SIMID for use on Personal Computers which is available to the students of the course and to industry.

Keywords: Digital Control Engineering, Controller Design, Discrete-Time System.

1. Introduction

Controller design is the central part of control engineering. Textbooks usually start with a given model of a process or plant (Isermann 1987, Ogata 1987). For this given model a controller is designed using special design criteria. Modelling is based on the frequency response of the plant. For laboratory experiments this may be convenient. For practical applications this will turn out to be rather unrealistic for various reasons (no appropriate equipment, process may not be interrupted or disturbed for a longer period of time etc.). So the step or pulse response of a system will be the only information available, that may be obtained easily. Teaching situation in digital control engineering is quite unsatisfying in our opinion with regard to methods taught and methods beeing really applicable in practice. It is therefore not surprising that trial and error methods are wide spread in industrial applications. The paper shows a way worked out during a research project at FH Köln making use of information only obtained in the time-domain and applying design procedures combining time and frequency domain knowledge and methods.

2. Didactic Aims

For teaching purposes a transparent design algorithm is important. There should be a simple relationship between the parameters of the process model and the parameters of the controller. Modelling should for practical reasons be based on time response functions of the process which may easily obtained in practice.

Basically during teaching the design procedure should start with measured data of the process and not with a given model. From this in a step by step design modelling and controller design should be carried out. Closing the circle the result of the design should be shown by simulation of the control circuit. In this respect it is very helpful, if the course is asssisted by a CAE-tool like SIMID (Schaedel (1991a)), which allows the whole design circle to be done on the PC and thus preparing the way for the laboratory experiments, which also may be carried out using SIMID.

3. A Step by Step Controller Design Combining Time and Frequency Domain Methods

Let us look at the basic configuration of a digital control circuit in Fig.1. Most control circuits are time domain systems. The controlled variable should follow the command variable as fast and closely as possible . For the frequency domain this means unity gain approach over a range as broad as possible. As proposed by Schaedel (1991a and 1991b) the controller is splitted into a correcting filter (lead network) and an integral controller (Fig.2) . The series connection forms a PI(D)-controller. During the design procedure the correcting filter and the original process are regarded as a resulting process. The intention now is to create a fast process with a prescribed damping ratio by the correcting filter. The correcting filter thus will be designed to perform a resulting process with a minimal response time. In the next step the integral controller then has to be designed for the resulting (fast) process.

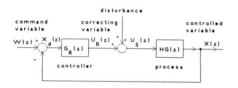

Fig.1 Digital control circuit

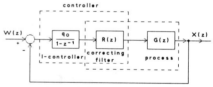

Fig. 2 Correcting filter and resulting process in a digital control circuit

The plant may be described by the step response h(t) and/or the pulse response g(t). As an example we will take a fourth-order process with the time-response functions given in Fig. 3 and Table 1.

For a given sampling time T_0 the weighting sequence results as $g(k) = h(k) - h(k-1)$ at the normalized sampling instants $k=t/T_0$. The process is described by the pulse transfer function G(z). The closed loop pulse transfer function then will be (see Fig. 1 and 2)

$$\frac{X(z)}{W(z)} = \left[1 + 1/G_0(z) \right]^{-1}, \text{ where } G_0(z) = G_R(z)\,G(z) = \frac{q_0 R(z)}{1-z^{-1}} \sum_{i=1}^{m} g_i z^{-i} \quad (1)$$

is the open-loop pulse transfer function with $z = \exp(-T_0 s)$. Applying bilinear transform $z = (1-w)/(1+w)$ with $w = j\Omega T_0/2$ we can investigate the control circuit in the frequency (Ω) domain.

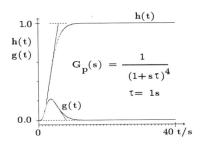

Fig. 3. Step response h(t) and pulse response g(t) with inflection tangent

Table 1. Step response of the process $h(k)$ and momenta s_i

$h(0) = 0.000$	$h(8) = 0.958$
$h(1) = 0.019$	$h(9) = 0.979$
$h(2) = 0.143$	$h(10) = 0.990$
$h(3) = 0.353$	$h(11) = 0.995$
$h(4) = 0.567$	$h(12) = 0.998$
$h(5) = 0.735$	$h(13) = 0.999$
$h(6) = 0.849$	$h(14) = 1.000$
$h(7) = 0.918$	$h(15) = 1.000$

$s_0 = 1 \qquad s_1 = 4.5 \qquad s_2 = 24.33$

$T_0 = 1s$

In order to design the integral controller for unity gain approach of the control circuit a multi-order approximation is made using Taylor-series approximation for the denominator term of the pulse transfer function.

$$\frac{X(w)}{W(w)} = \left[1 + \alpha_1 w + \alpha_2 w^2 + \alpha_3 w^3\right]^{-1} \qquad (2)$$

The coefficients α_i turn out to be a function of the controller coefficients and the time-weighted sums (momentums of the weighting sequence) of the samples of the pulse response g(t) respectively the samples of the step response h(t) of the process

$$s_0 = \sum_{i=1}^{\infty} g(i) = h(\infty) \qquad s_1 = \sum_{i=1}^{\infty} i\,g(i) = n\,h(\infty) - \sum_{i=1}^{n} h(i) \qquad (3)$$

$$s_2 = \sum_{i=1}^{\infty} i^2 g(i) = n^2 h(\infty) - 2\sum_{i=1}^{n} i\,h(i) - \sum_{i=1}^{n} h(i) \qquad \text{,where } nT_0 \text{ settling time of the step response.}$$

3.1 Design of an I-controller for a Multi-Order Lag Process

In order to find a design condition for the single coefficient q_0 of the integral controller we need a second-order approximation for the closed-loop frequency response. For unit gain approach we obtain $\alpha_1 = 2\,\alpha_2$, which is equivalent to a damping ratio $D_0 = 0.707$ for a second-order system. From this the coefficient of the discrete-time I-controller is found as

$$q_0 = \left[2s_1 - s_0\right]^{-1}. \qquad (4)$$

3.2 Design of a PI-controller for a Multi-Order Lag Process

The I-controller may be designed for the original process, but the time-response of the control circuit in general will be too slow. As discussed above a correcting filter can be used to make the process fast. Applying our design rule to this resultant process we now have to consider the weighting sequence of the resultant process. There are various ways of designing the correcting filter which in general is represented by a lead term

$$R(z) = 1 + a_1 z^{-1} + a_2 z^{-2} = (1 + r_1 z^{-1})(1 + r_2 z^{-1}) \qquad (5)$$

for PID-controllers. Let us at first confine the problem to PI-controllers which are dominant in industrial application

$$G_R(z) = \frac{q_0 R(z)}{1 - z^{-1}} = \frac{q_0(1 + r_1 z^{-1})}{1 - z^{-1}} . \qquad (6)$$

3.2.1 Method of Inflection Tangent for the Design of the Correcting Filter in the Time Domain

The filter parameter r_1 may be determined rather easily on the basis of the pulse or step response of the process. The point of approach m is predicted by the inflection tangent to the step response h(t) or pulse response g(t) of the process in Fig. 3. Table 1 gives the values of the step response.

$$r_{1h} = \frac{h(\infty) - h(m)}{h(\infty) - h(m-1)} \quad \text{step response} ; \qquad r_{1g} = -\frac{g(m)}{g(m-1)} \qquad \text{pulse response} \qquad (7)$$

The coefficient q_0 has to be determined for the resulting process considering r_1 as

$$q_0 = \left[s_0(r_1 - 1) + 2 s_1(r_1 + 1) \right]^{-1} \qquad (8)$$

For the fourth-order process under test (Fig. 3 and Table 1) we obtain

$r_1 = -0.571$ and $q_0 = 0.437$ for the step response (m=6) and
$r_1 = -0.568$ and $q_0 = 0.431$ for the pulse response (m=8).

There are only slight differences in the results. The pulse response for the resulting processes with $r_1 = -0.570$ is shown in Fig. 4.

3.2.2 Method of Unity Gain Approach for the Design of the Correcting Filter in the Frequency Domain .

Using Taylor series expansion the frequency response of the control circuit now is approximated by a third-order system allowing two parameters to be optimized for unity gain approach.

Case I . The conditions for unity gain approach are

$$\alpha_1^2 = 2\alpha_2 \quad \text{and} \quad \alpha_2^2 = 2\alpha_1 \alpha_3 \qquad (9)$$

Expanding the denominator in a Taylor-series we find the coefficients α_i. From this the design equations for the PI-controller for unity gain approach are determined as

$$K_1 = 2\sqrt{\frac{s_2}{s_0} - \left(\frac{s_1}{s_0}\right)^2} \ ; \ r_1 = \frac{1 - K_1}{1 + K_1} \ ; \ q_0 = \left[s_0(r_1-1) + 2s_1(r_1+1)\right]^{-1}. \tag{10}$$

This is equivalent to a damping ratio of the resulting process and the control circuit of $D = 1/\sqrt{2}$. For the process under consideration the controller parameters follow as

$$r_1 = -0.603 \text{ and } q_0 = 0.509.$$

From Fig. 4 (b) we see that there is a slight undershoot of the pulse response due to the damping $D_1 = 1/\sqrt{2}$ of the resultant process. The step response of the control circuit to command signals in Fig.5 (a) has the typical overshoot of about 5 to 6% according to the damping $D_0 = 1/\sqrt{2}$ of the control circuit.

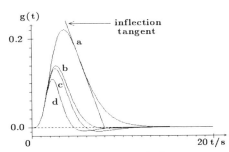

Fig. 4. Pulse response of the process (a) and the resulting process (b,c,d)
a) $r_1 = 0$ b) $r_1 = -0.570$
c) $r_1 = -0.603$ d) $r_1 = -0.687$.

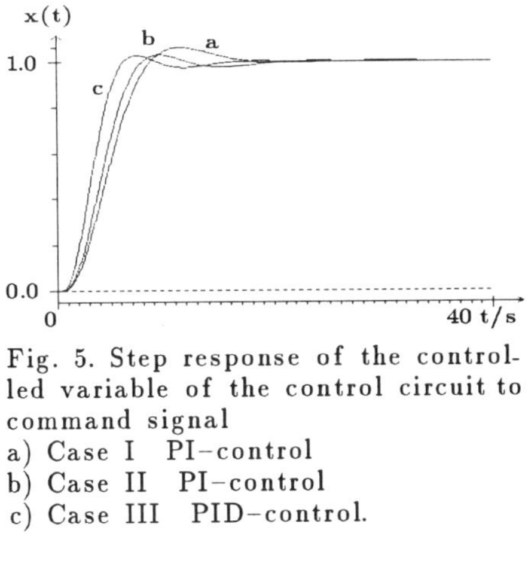

Fig. 5. Step response of the controlled variable of the control circuit to command signal
a) Case I   PI-control
b) Case II   PI-control
c) Case III   PID-control.

Case II. Providing a lower damping ratio for the resulting process by $D_1 = 0.5$ and a higher damping ratio $D_0 = \sqrt{3}/2$ for the closed loop leads to the modified conditions

$$\alpha_1^2 = 3\alpha_2 \text{ and } \alpha_2^2 = \alpha_1\alpha_3, \tag{11}$$

which give for the design of the PI-controller

$$K_1 = \frac{s_2}{s_1} \ ; \ r_1 = \frac{1 - K_1}{1 + K_1} \ ; \ q_0 = 0.75\left[s_0(r_1-1) + 2s_1(r_1+1)\right]^{-1} \tag{12}$$

This condition results in the controller parameters

$$r_1 = -0.687 \text{ and } q_0 = 0.664.$$

Due to the lower damping of the resultant process there is a significant undershoot of the pulse response as to be seen from Fig. 4 (c). By these means the response time of the control circuit is reduced compared to the design for optimal unity approach (case I) as shown in Fig. 5 (b).

3.3 Design of a PID–Controller for a Multi–Order Lag Process

Case III. Case II for the PI-controller may be taken as basis for a PID-controller design. Having chosen a damping ratio $D_1 = 1/\sqrt{2}$ for the resultant process with a first-order correcting filter an additional filter with the parameter r_2 for a damping ratio $D_2 = 0.5$ for the resulting process can be designed. Inorder to avoid uneccessary overshoot of the step response of the closed loop for command signals the coefficient of the integral term q_0 is evaluated for a closed loop damping ratio $D_0 = \sqrt{3}/2 = 0.866$. Under these conditiones the controller parameters are

$$r_1 = -0.603, \quad r_2 = -0.508, \quad q_0 = 1.755.$$

The step response of the control circuit due to a change of the command signal in Fig. 5 (c) shows a significant faster response than for PI-controlling.

4. Concluding Remarks

Using these new concepts of controller design and those of process modelling presented by Schaedel (1991a) a course on digital control engineering has been developed and started with the beginning of the winter semester 1991/92 in the department of communication engineering. The students are supplied with a text book (Schaedel 1991b) including a students version of the CAE-package SIMID (identification, controller design and simulation of digital control circuits on the PC) supporting the methods outlined above. The lectures are accompanied by written exercises and laboratory experiments. Problem solving is done using the pocket calculator assisted by SIMID. SIMID enables the students to check the design and to see how the controller behaves under various conditions in the control circuit. The expanded version of SIMID is used for the laboratory experiments.

References

Isermann, R. (1987) Digitale Regelsysteme, Springer Verlag.

Ogata, K. (1987) Discrete-time Control Systems, Prentice Hall Inc.

Schaedel, H.M. (1991a) SIMID: A CAE Tool for Process Identification, Controller Design and Simulation of Digital Control Circuits in Engineering Education, Autralasian Journal of Engineering Education, 2, 237–254.

Schaedel, H.M. (1991b) Einführung in die Digitale Regelungstechnik (Grundlagen, Identifikation und Regleroptimierung), published as text book, FH Köln.

A Systematic Approach to Electrical Circuits*

A. Métioui(*), C. Brassard(**), J. Levasseur(***)

(*) Dépt. de Génie électrique, Université de Sherbrooke

(**) Dépt. de Technologie du Géni électrique, Collège Lionel-Groulx

(***) Dépt. d'Électrotechnique, Collège André-Laurendeau

Abstract
As seen in most popular textbooks, the traditional method of teaching analog electronics, which is rooted in the study of the physical properties of components, remains in favor. The systemic approach, which is widely used in digital electronics, is also applicable to analog electronics, and offers an alternative teaching approach. This systemic, or "black box" method, introduced by the electronics industry to deal with the increasing complexity of present day systems, may provide a far superior foundation for the engineering curriculum, for reasons which are discussed in this article. The epistemological foundations of the systemic approach are compared to those of the traditional method, and some results which indicate its superior performance are discussed.
Keywords : Engineering, Education, Systems, Systemic, Electrical Circuits, Circuit Theory, Models, Electronics, Analog Electronics, Black Box, Curriculum.

1 Introduction

Studies conducted worldwide converge to indicate that students experience serious difficulties with the basic concepts related to electrical and electronic circuits. For example, Closset & Viennot (1984) have found that second year university students retain naïve representations with respect to the properties of electrical circuits. These authors indicate that the students' reasoning follows the current, disregarding the effect of components which they consider as downstream. Fredette and Lochhead (1980) proposed simple experimental situations, and observed that some university students refer to a unipolar model when asked to light a bulb using wires and a battery. These students believe that, since current flows from the battery to the light bulb, the return conductor is unused and therefore superfluous. In a research involving high school students and their teachers, Cohen et al. (1982) concluded that the teachers, all of whom had a degree in physics, experienced major difficulties with simple circuits. Finally, the authors have conducted research involving students (ages 17-20) enrolled in electrical engineering technology programs in Québec, including a group at the first year university level (Métioui et al, 1992). Their results indicate that the students' representations of current and voltage are erroneous .

Such disturbing results must be considered in the light of the overall situation. Environments of extreme diversity and complexity have emerged from the recent advan-

*Research supported by the Programme de recherche-développement pour les formateurs (RDF) and the Direction générale de l'enseignement collégial (DGEC), Ministère de l'Enseignement supérieur et de la Science, Québec.

ces in microelectronics, especially around microcomputer hardware and software. As a result, the number of teaching hours devoted to the basic theory of electrical circuits, in any typical electrical engineering curriculum, is decreasing constantly under the combined pressure of software and of digital electronics. The situation is presently considered as critical by many. In particular, Rohrer (1990) warns that engineering students are likely to be disoriented, when they graduate and realize that present day electronics is composed essentially of *"black boxes inside black boxes inside black boxes"*.

The systemic or "black box" view has been adopted by the electronics and the software industries to deal with the exploding diversity and complexity of present day systems. In most teaching situations however, the traditional view of analog electronics endures, while showing evident signs of fatigue. In this traditional view, which is basically rooted in the physics of devices, the characteristics of components derive from an analysis of their internal behaviour. On the contrary, in the systemic view a device is characterized by a functional model, according to tests conducted within a known environment.

In view of the major teaching difficulties mentioned above, it is disturbing to realize that little or no information is available in the literature with regards to the application of the systemic approach in engineering education.

The words "model" and "systemic" are used by many authors in different contexts. We clarify herein our meaning of these terms, in reference to electrical and electronic circuits, and compare the teaching approach based on the systemic view to that which is rooted in the analytical method.

2   Epistemological foundations of the traditional view of electronics

In their book titled "La nouvelle alliance", Prigogine & Stengers (1979) remind us that traditional disciplines such as physics and chemistry are mechanistic, reductionistic and confined to linear developments. The reader may recognize the well established analytical method, which isolates the individual parts of a physical system in order to study it and to describe it. In this view, each individual part is studied separately, and the whole is described thereafter in terms of the interaction of the parts. The study of the structure of matter represents one example of the analytical method. We owe our understanding of electromagnetic phenomena to the experimental and theoretical works of Maxwell, Faraday, Hertz, Ohm and other scientists of great prestige, who adhered to the analytical view. In addition, the study of the electronic properties of materials has made possible the development of many useful devices, especially semiconductors. These research efforts exploited the analytical method with impressive success.

The major advances in certain areas of science which were accomplished through the analytical method do not prove it to be universally applicable, however. Research areas in biology, economics, and sociology have adopted alternative methods (De Rosnay, 1975), in order to deal with their respective complex situations. This alternative view is called "systemic", because it addresses the system as a whole, rather than as a collection of interacting elements.

The environments emerging from digital electronics and computer software could, in principle, be reduced to their internal structure and described analytically. However, this view is no longer favored at the user level, and it has been superseded by a systemic view. What are the underlying principles of this new paradigm (Kuhn, 1970), and is there a potential benefit of using it in the teaching of analog electronics?

3   Epistemological foundations of the systemic view of electronics

What happens when components increase in number, or when their mutual interactions become extremely complex? Sometimes, the interactions can be treated statistically, as in the case of the kinetic theory of gases. In other situations, statistics offers little relief, and the analytical method may well become impractical. The systemic view then offers an alternative to the analytical method.

Recent advances in electronics and in computer science are dependent on a process called *encapsulation*, through which a system is designed to execute a simple function, and to show a simple interface to its user. Reading a file from mass storage, on a computer system, is an example of such a function. Under encapsulation, the internal behaviour of a system may become increasingly complex, while a simple model still accounts for it functionally. In software engineering, encapsulation is at the root of object oriented programming. Consider for example the following model of an ideal operational amplifier :

"the inputs draw no current, and if the amplifier is not saturated, then the two inputs share the same potential".

In its magnificent simplicity, this model is far more meaningful to the systems designer than a detailed description of the internal circuit of a specific operational amplifier.

What is meant exactly by a model? The word "model" is used herein to mean an abstraction constructed for the purpose of describing and predicting the behaviour of a device (component, sensor, circuit, software program, system...) in certain applications. It offers a level of explanation which remains independent of the actual internal behaviour of the device. It is not expressed in terms of the actual internal construction of this device. The model is the capsule in the process of encapsulation : it serves to hide the interior.

In the case of analog electronics, models usually take the form of mathematical statements of the idealized relationships between current and voltage waveforms associated with a device. Elementary models are generally represented by the same symbols as the physical components which they model most closely. For example, the symbol of the capacitor is used to represent the capacitance, and the symbol of the resistor represents also the resistance. The ensuing ambiguity often generates confusion in the early learning stages of circuit theory.

There is no direct relationship between the internal complexity of a device, and the complexity of its model. A priori, since the evolution of devices tends to increase their internal complexity while bringing them closer to an ideal, complex systems end up having the simplest models. A signal generator may be represented by a simple Thévenin model (a time-varying voltage source in series with a resistance), whereas a coil (a single inductor) may require an inductance, in series with a resistance, the combination of which appears in parallel with a stray capacitance. At the limit, a simple coaxial cable calls for an infinite number of capacitances and inductances in its RF model.

Table 1 summarises what the authors consider as the major differences between a systemic approach to the teaching of electronics and a traditional approach.

Actually, both the analytical and the systemic methods make use of models. However, they diverge fundamentally on the basis of the role played by models within the theory. Section 4 elaborates on the systemic definition of what models are.

Table 1. Differences between the systemic view and the traditional view
as applied to the case of electrical and electronic circuits

The systemic view	The traditional view
Values the communication network more than devices : the network carries energy and information, it supports standards and protocols.	Regards devices as more important than the network of conductors.
Addresses primarily the interactions of components through the network.	Focuses on the analysis of the internal construction and behaviour of devices.
Emphasizes models, and distinguishes them strictly and explicitly from physical devices.	Keeps physical devices in primary focus and tolerates that models remain implicit.
Considers a device or a circuit as an imperfect implementation of a model. Circuit synthesis becomes the dominant process.	Considers the model as an approximate description of a physical device or a circuit. Circuit analysis remains the dominant process.
Disregards any distinction between components and circuits. The same models are used consistently, at all levels of system integration.	Supports a clear distinction between discrete components, integrated circuits, circuit modules, complete circuits and systems.
Structures the discipline according to the types of models involved : linear or non-linear, time independent or time dependent, etc.	Structures the discipline on the basis of devices : there are textbooks on transistors, on operational amplifiers, etc.
Attributes currents and voltages to the network ("current in a conductor...").	Attributes currents and voltages to components ("current in a resistor...").
Supports encapsulation : The functional properties are expressed in terms of models which ban any reference to the internal structure of the device.	Violates encapsulation : The functional properties of a device derive from an analysis of the physics of this device and are expressed in relation to its internal construction.

4 Models

In view of their high level of abstraction, models defined within a discipline of engineering can be exported to other disciplines, including to disciplines outside of engineering. This facilitates the learning process and helps in multidisciplinary work. The paradigm supports the combination of frameworks in order to bridge the gap between disciplines, such as electrical and mechanical engineering; for example, sensors and actuators can easily be modelled.

The framework of Fig. 1 could be applied to any engineering discipline. Models are linked through their ports by a communication network. Two types of variables are defined on the links of this network : flux variables and network state variables. Other variables are needed to describe the internal state of the model. All of these variables may be discrete or continuous. In the case of analog circuits, the network variables are current I (flux variable) and potential V (state variable). We coin the word "port", as a generalization of "terminal", or "connection".

The nature of the variables depends on the discipline, but all disciplines eventually deal with matter, energy and information. In analog electronics or in electrical circuits, matter is represented by an electrical charge (usually electrons), energy is related to potential and information takes the form of signal or data. Precise rules are needed to express transfers of matter, energy and information in terms of the network variables. These rules are normally characteristic of the discipline, and independent of the par-

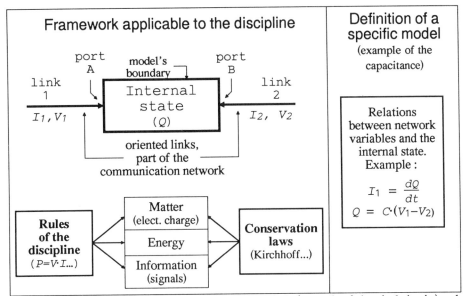

Fig. 1.   Framework applicable to the discipline as a whole (example of electrical circuits) and definition of a specific model in this framework (example of the capacitance). A model may have any number of ports (a minimum of two in the case of electrical circuits).

ticular model under consideration. For example, energy transfer in electrical circuits (power flow P) is calculated according to the rule $P = V \times I$.

Conservation laws are stated with respect to these network variables : Kirchhoff's laws on current and on voltage apply to the case of electrical circuits. A different conservation law could also be defined for information : it disappears from the internal state when it is internally destroyed, not when it flows out through a port.

Rules are defined on the state variables to describe storage of matter, energy or information. For example, the charge stored could be used as the internal state variable for the capacitance. The resistance does not need any variable in its internal state : it does not store any charge, energy or information.

Defining a particular model then consists in specifying its internal state, and the specific rules which link this internal state with the network variables at its ports. For example, the capacitance model C may be defined using the stored charge Q as the internal state, and the applicable rules $I_1 = \dfrac{dQ}{dt}$ and $Q = C \cdot (V_1 - V_2)$.

5   Conclusion

In the digital electronics databooks, gates, flip-flops, counters and shift registers are described in terms of explicit models. Microprocessors use both electronic and programming models. It is impossible, however, to find a model of the operational amplifier or a model of the transistor in typical analog databooks. This is disturbing, because many of the technical specifications in analog databooks rest on implicit models, and would gain in significance if these underlying models were stated explicitly.

The engineering community fully realizes the pertinence and the power of the systemic approach, and the experts in the field use it almost exclusively when dealing with digital electronics and computer software. In analog electronics, the systemic view is supported partially in databooks. What is the situation with regards to teaching?

In the teaching of digital electronics, the systemic view is widely used, but in analog electronics, as well as in software, the approach to teaching usually remains analytical. Why? The authors have failed to find any justification, other than purely historical, for this rather disturbing situation.

Considering the success of the systemic method in the electronics engineering practice, it seems only natural to utilize this view to structure the conceptual framework in electronics (Brassard et al., 1992) and to guide the student's learning process. In itself, however, the success of the systemic method in professional practice implies neither its effectiveness in teaching, nor its suitability to the learning process. It does, however, make it very tempting to investigate.

A systemic approach to the teaching of analog electronics has been implemented since 1985 at Collège Lionel-Groulx, by one of the authors, in collaboration with L. Beaulieu. After seven years of experimentation, the results prove to be excellent. In a qualitative research, Métioui et al. (1992) found that students exposed exclusively to the systemic approach demonstrate a better assimilation of the basic concepts of the theory of circuits than students taught with the analytical method. Other institutions in Québec presently move towards the systemic approach.

The use of a systemic approach does not decrease the importance of eventually understanding the physics of components, such as semiconductor physics. The need remains. What it does accomplish, however, is a decoupling of this need from the problem of learning circuit theory. Also, because the abstract models of the systemic method are rooted in mathematics, they are applicable to all branches of science and engineering. It is in the ensuing transferability that precious learning time can be saved, not in the elimination of the teaching of the underlying physics principles.

References

Brassard, C., Métioui, A. & Levasseur, J. (1992) Modèles utilisés dans une première approche des circuits électriques, **Proceedings of a Canadian Conference on Engineering Education,** Université Laval, Sainte-Foy, Québec, Canada.

Métioui, A., Levasseur, J., Brassard, C. & Lavoie, M. (1992) **L'assimilation des concepts de base de la théorie des circuits chez les élèves du collégial professionnel,** Ministère de l'Enseignement supérieur et de la Science, Direction générale de l'enseignement collégial, Québec, Québec, Canada.

Rohrer, R.A. (1990) Taking Circuits Seriously, **IEEE Proceedings on Circuits and Devices,** July 1990, 27-31.

Closset, J.L. & Viennot, L. (1984) Contribution à l'étude du raisonnement naturel en physique, **Communication information,** 6, 339-420.

Cohen, R., Eylon, B., & Ganiel, U. (1983) Potential difference and current in simple electric circuits : A study of students' concepts, **American Journal of Physics,** 5, 407-412.

Fredette, N. & Lochhead, J. (1980) Student conceptions of simple circuits, **The Physics Teacher,** March 1980, 194-198.

Prigogine, I., & Stengers, I. (1979) **La nouvelle alliance,** Editions Gallimard, Paris.

De Rosnay, J. (1975) **Le macroscope,** Éditions du Seuil, Paris.

Kuhn, T.S. (1970) **The Structure of Scientific Revolutions,** 2nd ed., University of Chicago Press, Chicago, IL.

Problem Oriented Language for Education of Inverse Problems of Electromagnetic Field Theory

J. Korytkowski(*), H. Kraus(**), J. Sikora(*), J. Starzyński(*), M. Stodolski(*), S. Wincenciak(*)

(*) Technical University of Warsaw, Electrical Engineering Department
(**) RWTH Aachen

Abstract
    Description of the problem oriented language named **FIELD ANALYSIS TRANSLATOR (FAT)** and its application for teaching the Electromagnetic Field Theory has been presented in this paper. Three kinds of problems: shape designing, sizing and placing certain subregions are described. Some of the new design possibilities of **FAT** useful for students are illustrated.
Keywords: Inverse Problems, Electromagnetic Field Theory, Finite Element Method.

1 Introduction

In the years of 1986-1990 there was developed a problem oriented language named Field Analysis Translator (**FAT**) in the Institute of the Theory of Electrical Engineering and Electrical Measurements. The main subject of **FAT** language is to solve the electromagnetic boundary problems using the Finite Element Method (**FEM**) i.e. FAT (1991).

Recently, such problems as the optimization of geometric boundaries, placement of conductors and/or sizing of ferromagnetic shims to achieve specific design goals are most important in computational electromagnetism i.e. "VECTOR" (1990), Haslinger and Neittaanmaki (1988). Optimization is now available in most major **FEM** commercial codes like **NASTRAN**, **ANSYS** and **MagNet**. Analytic gradients are available in most cases. The **FAT** language also poses an "optimizing environment" that allows the user to design a field shape (imposed distribution of potentials, electric field intensity vectors or magnetic field density vectors).

As a result the new shape, new dimensions or new location of specified subregions are obtained.

Using the **FAT** language one can solve three kinds of problems:
- determination of the boundaries geometries (each nodes belonging to boundary lines can be moved independently i.e. Wincenciak (1990),
- determination of the dimensions of certain subregions (the whole boundaries or some parts of the boundaries can be moved i.e. Sikora (1990),
- determination of the location of selected subregions (the subregions can change their positions only).

In FAT language, geometry of the region is defined by the homogeneous (material or source function homogeneity) subregions - macroelements. The shape of the region will be optimized by the choice of the position or parameters characterizing the shape of the objects, such as segment, chain or macroelement.

The objective function in FAT language is defined as follows

$$OBJ = \sum_{i=1}^{N} w_i \int_{\Omega_i} (X_i - X_{io})^2 d\Omega_i + \sum_{j=1}^{K} w_j (U_j - U_{jo})^2$$

where Ω_i - subregions in which the state variables are controlled.

X_i - directional components or length of the vector

(electric field intensity or magnetic field density).

U_j - node potential

X_{io}, U_{jo} - imposed values.

The BFGS, the most effective method of minimizing objective function, subject to "box" constraints is implemented in FAT language.

FAT was developed as a very convenient tool for teaching Electromagnetic Field Theory. Its main purpose is to help senior students with subjects like electrical machines, high voltage technique, electrical heating and the others. Especially it is helpful for diploma work. But FAT language could be implemented in the basic course of Field Theory in the case when the most important are interpretations of physical phenomenon. The easy way of defining the geometry of the region, rich postprocessing which allows the students to observe not only distribution of fields but also the integral values like force, electric charge, magnetic flux, energy etc., and the possibilities of interactive work make it the flexible tool for teaching.

In order to illustrate educational possibilities of FAT language several inverse problems will be presented.

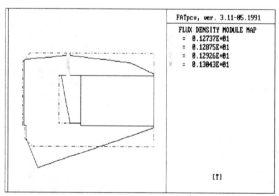

FATpcv, ver. 3.11-85.1991

FLUX DENSITY MODULE MAP
= 8.12737E+01
= 8.12875E+01
= 8.12926E+01
= 8.13043E+01

[T]

Fig.1. Loudspeaker's shape before (dashed line)
and after (solid line) optimization.

2   Optimal shape design of loudspeaker's magnetic circuit

Let us consider the problem of finding an optimal shape for loud-speaker's magnetic circuit. The target is to achieve maximal and at the same time homogeneous magnetic field in the air gap. Results of optimization are presented in fig.1.

3   Crack identification

In order to meet requirement for safety, various methods for non-destructive testing materials have been developed so far i.e. Iwamura and Miya (1990), Ratnajeevan et-al (1991). For example in nuclear power plants it is regularly required to inspect tubes of a steam generator to prevent troubles due to cracks.

Using the FAT language we would like to present some results of shape reconstruction based on the electric potential measurements.

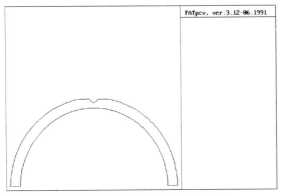

Fig.2. Upper part of a cross section of the tube - results
of shape reconstruction

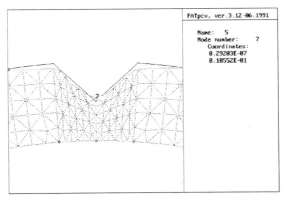

Fig.3. Prediction of a defect; solid line - original shape, dashed
line - numerical results

In order to verify the ability of the language, the numerical
simulation was performed. Result of this simulation is shown in Fig.3.

By inspecting this figure we can see, that the crack was located
precisely, and a very good agreement between original and reconstructed
shape was achieved.

However, when information from the measurement is limited, or
measurements are polluted by noise, it is difficult to predict a
correct shape i.e. Iwamura and Miya (1990).

4 Optimal location and dimensioning

The examples presented in section 2 and 3 belong to *Optimal Shape*
design problems. The designer has to determine the geometry of the
boundary. If the boundary line is located inside the region we have the
so called *Interface Problem*.

The Optimal Location and Dimensioning belong to the broad class of
optimal shape design problems. Both are characterized by small number
of design parameters, usually no more than ten. Now we would like to
present an example concerning the optimal location and dimensioning.

In order to identify the position and the dimensions of the boundary
line (see Fig.4) a vector of potentials on the electrodes placed on the
perimeter of the region was measured. Results of identification are
presented in Fig.5.

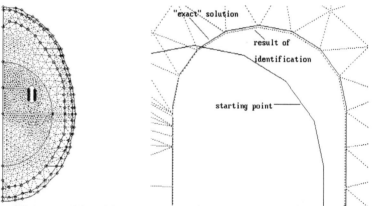

Fig.4. Region under consideration   Fig.5. Results of identification

In each iteration step the position and dimensions of the boundary
line have been changed at the same time. That has allowed us to achieve
such good results (Fig.5) in only thirteen iteration steps.

5 Free boundary problem

Let us consider nonhomogeneous region composed of two materials. The
difference between electric conductivity is not more than 20%. The

problem relies on determining the boundary line position under assumption that measurements could be made only on the surface of the body. Such problem is very common in the industry for nondestructive testing materials.

The region under consideration is a simplified tooth of the wheel presented in Fig.6.

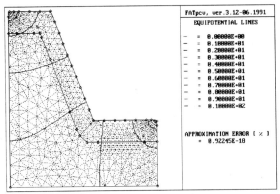

Fig.6. Considered region

In order to collect measurements of electric potentials (positions of the measuring points are marked on the upper surface), electric voltage source was detached as indicate equipotential lines in this figure.

The FE discretization (carefully done around the electrodes to assure exactness of the numerical model) and the starting position of the interface line is also indicated in the Fig.6.

The results of identification achieved after 20 iteration steps and so called "exact" position of the interface line, are presented in Fig.7.

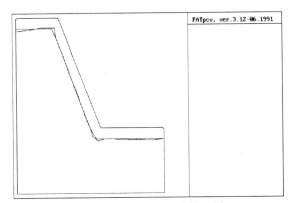

Fig.7. Results of identification

The main difficulties of simulation was a small difference between the electric properties of material coefficients in this case. Nevertheless result of numerical experiment presented in Fig.7 are very promising.

6   Conclusion

In this paper some students examples of optimal shape design based on Finite Element Method were presented. In all presented cases good results have proved FAT optimization ability and it usefulness for teaching Electromagnetic Field Theory. Due to the efficient method of gradient evaluation (Adjoint Variable Method) FAT is able to solve optimization problem with large number of design parameters. It is very important especially in shape reconstruction problems (the crack identification example had 73 design parameters).

References

Field Analysis Translator FAT: Reference Manual and User's Guide (1991) IETiME, Technical University of Warsaw.
Sikora J. (1990) Inverse problems in electromagnetic field theory: Identification and designing. Warsaw Technical University Publisher.
Wincenciak S. (1990) Shape designing methods using electromagnetic fields numerical models. Warsaw Technical University Publisher.
Electromagnetic News Letter "VECTOR" (1990) vol.6, No2, Autumn 1990.
Haslinger J., Neittaanmaki P. (1988) Finite Element Approximation for Optimal Shape Design: Theory and Application, John Wiley & Sons LTD.
Iwamura Y., Miya K. (1990) Numerical Approach to Inverse Problem of Crack Shape Recognition Based on the Electrical Potential Method. IEEE Trans. on MAG, Vol. 26, No2, March.
Ratnajeevan S., Hoole H., Subramariam S., Saldanha R., Coulomb J. L., Sabonnadiere J. C. (1990) Inverse Problem Methodology and Finite Elements in the Identification of Cracks, Sources, Materials, and their Geometry in Inaccessible Locations. IEEE Trans. on MAG., vol. 27, No3, May.

ADA - an Initial Programming Language for Engineers

T.G. Morgan, C.B.Lovett

School of Systems Engineering, University of Portsmouth

Abstract

This paper sets out the reasons for selecting Ada as an initial teaching language for engineering students at Portsmouth, describes the experiences with its use, and outlines future plans.

Keywords: Ada, Learning Needs, Software Engineering, Teaching Materials, Platforms, Assessment, Costs, Programming

1   Introduction

The high level language Ada has been taught within the School of Systems Engineering at Portsmouth for a period of 4 years. This paper outlines the reasons for choosing this language and our experiences to date in using it as a main stream computing language.

2   Courses Involved

The School of Systems Engineering at Portsmouth has a wide range of modular, credit rated and inter-related engineering courses. These courses are at diploma, first degree and post graduate levels. The first degree courses, with which this paper is primarily concerned, cover the engineering spectrum from electrical and electronic engineering, communications systems, electronics and computing through engineering systems, integrated engineering, manufacturing, materials and design, to mechanical engineering. For some of these courses - particularly those with an electronics basis - computing and software engineering are important strands throughout all three or four years of study. On all courses, the students study at least the fundamentals of computer program design.

3   Students Learning Needs

There is no longer a need for students simply to be able to solve equations; specialist mathematical packages and CAE suites are now widely available to perform these functions.

One of the primary needs in computing today is for the writing of software that will be embedded in larger systems such as those for aircraft flight control or the control of plant processes. Many new issues are raised by modern software requirements, including:

Correctness. Predictable performance for any software is essential particularly for safety critical applications.

Understandability. Larger systems inevitably result in more than one person being involved in the production of its software. Team members must be able to understand readily each others program segments.

Maintainability. With the increasing size of software projects the emphasis, for financial reasons, is changing from re-writing to the maintenance of previously produced programs. It is realistic to expect that those writing the original software will not be providing the maintenance service for it.

Testability. The scale of some projects is such that it is not feasible to test a total system before delivery. Special measures are thus needed which allow system components to be tested in isolation.

Modularity. Software production is costly and it makes good economic sense to introduce modularity into designs to increase the prospect of producing re-useable software modules or using existing modules.

Team development. Only the very small or highly specialised projects are still developed by individuals today. Most software development is now much more of a collaborative team enterprise.

Students also need an awareness of the capabilities of modern languages. The growing need for the economic development of robust and fault tolerant software has revolutionised languages. It is necessary to understand data as much as algorithms. Data types, structure and abstraction can be topics in themselves. There is a need to understand about closed control structures, parameters and information hiding. At the more advanced levels, the need for dynamic data types and parallelism must be studied. A clear understanding of the issues involved with large scale software projects has to be addressed together with the associated topics of modularity and re-usable code.

The teaching of programming alone is not sufficient. A positive connection needs to be established at an early stage between the pre-requisite for a systematic analysis of a problem, the design of a software model to resolve it and finally the implementation and maintenance of the solution with the appropriate programs. It is essential therefore to teach both computing and software engineering as complementary subjects. Initially, there is a need to know how to analyze a problem and, structure a program which takes advantage of the features of the language. Later on, specific analysis methods and structured design methodologies need to be introduced together with formal methods of evaluation. Practical computing therefore must be supported by the application of good software engineering techniques.

4   Why was Ada chosen?

The selection process in choosing the language was undertaken in two stages; firstly a requirement specification was established, then a choice was made from the several contending options. The criteria established for the choice were that the language needed to be in widespread use outside academia and available on a range of platforms. It needed to be useable both at an introductory level for all students, some of whom arrive without any computing experience. It should also provide advanced features for use in later years. It must encourage good programme practice and be useable for embedded systems. A short list was drawn up of the main contenders for the language.

Pascal. This is a good introductory language with access to cheap compilers. However, the lack of more advanced features means a switch to another language would be needed for other than introductory courses.

C. This is well suited for embedded systems and is widely used. Compilers are readily available and cheap to purchase. However, it is not that easy to read and not good for encouraging good programming practice.

Basic. There are numerous variants, some with modern features but some without. It is cheap and widely available, good for solving simple or small problems but poor for encouraging good programming practice.

Ada. The language is standardised and available now on a variety of platforms. It tends to be a bit expensive for embedded systems although costs are falling. A Pascal like subset can be taught for the introductory courses. It then provides the necessary advanced features for the more advanced courses.

5   How was Ada teaching introduced?

A phased approach was adopted for the introduction of Ada. This is outlined below.

Phase 1. Initially, Ada was offered as a final year option for electrical and electronic engineering students who had already studied Pascal and C and were familiar with the Unix operating system. The course was based on an initial rapid introduction to the language syntax itself and in particular it included the use of packages. Emphasis was then placed on parallel software, with graphics to show task operation.

Phase 2. A year later, Ada was introduced as a second year course for engineering systems students who had already studied Pascal, but not under Unix, in their first year. This group also included a few direct entry students who had no programming experience at all. The course was based on an introduction to the Ada syntax for 11 weeks and then concentrated on the use of packages and tasks for a further 15 weeks.

Phase 3. Finally, Ada was introduced to all those courses having a computing module in their first two years. The range of platforms was also extended to include PC's as well as Unix workstations.

6   What is taught?

Ada is taught in two parts; one part being used for each year. Each part is divided into a number of discrete topic based units which are sized to enable them to be completed in a single laboratory session. In so doing, the Ada course presentation can readily be adapted to other forms. For example, as short courses for industry.

The first part of the course introduces the operating system and the Ada compiler environment to give proficiency in the use and management of the individual's account. Study continues with the syntax for the design of procedure and function modules using simple types and the sequence, condition and repetition constructs. The provision of temporary storage using arrays and records is then introduced. This is followed by use of library modules in the form of a maths and graphics package. Finally, methods of providing permanent storage are explored using the standard input output library packages provided by the language.

The second part of the course starts with the notion of fault tolerance through the use of exception handlers. Experience is gained in using both predefined and user defined exceptions. The subject of library units is then taken up with the study of packages and generic packages. Small packages are designed by the students in each category. Next, the topic of dynamic data types is studied so that the design principles for the construction of stacks, buffers, queues and trees can be introduced. Finally, the concepts of parallelism are studied with the design of single and multitasking programs.

All practical computing activity is complemented by series of software engineering lectures with a particular emphasis on real time systems. In the first year, use of structure charts and pseudo code to produce well ordered code is emphasised. In the second year, use of data flow, state transition and entity relationship diagrams to analyze larger problems and generate effective solutions is taught.

7   How is Ada taught?

The first part of the course is taught as a series of 12 x 1.5hr laboratory sessions spread over a period of 2 academic terms. The second part of the course is similarly taught as a series of 10 x 1.5hr laboratory sessions over 2 terms. Each course is split up into laboratory groups of up to 12 pairs of students. Sessions follow a similar pattern. Firstly, the topic is briefly introduced by the lecturer together with the salient features of the syntax concerned. This is then followed by hands on work by the students as each unit topic concludes with one or two exercises. These are aimed at testing their understanding of the syntactic aspects of the topic in the context of simple problems. A tutorial style is adopted with individual assistance being provided as required by the supervisor.

Two networked platforms are used for teaching Ada; firstly, the Alsys Ada compiler mounted on a distributed Apollo Domain network connecting HP workstations running under Unix and secondly, the Meridian Ada compiler running on Opus 386 PC's.

Initially, text book material for supporting the course was very limited as it was unsuitable in one way or other for our purposes. It tended to be rather expensive for students to purchase. Some texts were comprehensive, but assumed proficiency in another high level language and were too 'heavy' for an introductory text. Others were good introductory texts but unsuitable as all of the material required was not covered. It was necessary therefore, to write the supporting material for the course. This needed to contain sufficient introductory information for each topic and to provide the kernel of the necessary Ada syntax. In this way it could be suitable as an introductory text and act as a stepping stone to the fuller cover provided by more comprehensive texts. Each of the two parts followed the same booklet pattern. The booklets contain a number of Units, each covering a single topic. The topics have clearly defined learning objectives, contain the essential syntax to support the topic and conclude with simple programming exercises to reinforce the subject matter. References are also provided to the subject matter in the more comprehensive textbooks.

The courses currently use the assignment method of assessment to test the application knowledge of the techniques that have been learned. This method has its limitations and we have yet to find an entirely satisfactory method of assessment. A formal written examination usually provides a reasonable indication of ability but cannot allow students to tackle complex problems. There can be doubt about whose work is being presented with assignments. Individual interviews, whilst being sound for assessing ability are very time consuming to administer. The assessment method is still an ongoing topic for debate but is likely to end up as a combination of assignment and examination.

The running costs of these courses must be considered. The class size, supervision arrangements and method of assessment are all inter-related and have cost impacts. For example, some of our courses at Portsmouth have up to 120 students which necessitates 5 repetitions of each laboratory session. We have found that students working in pairs with no more than 12 pairs at a time is a reasonable compromise between running costs without starving the students of individual attention as and when it is needed. These laboratory sessions are always high activity events for the supervising lecturers.

8   What other languages are taught?

Whilst Ada is the main stream language for all courses, it is not taught exclusively. C and 68000 assembler are taught particularly for embedded system use. Occam is used for the course option studying transputers. Prolog is used in an option on Expert Systems and C++ is about to be used in a new option on object oriented programming.

9   What does the future hold?

The experience we have gained with Ada has encouraged us to extend its field of influence. We soon hope to adopt Ada for use in embedded systems to widen its use for individual project work in a student's final year. Also, we hope to demonstrate the use of Ada's specific capabilities for use in large scale systems and provide experience similar to that which a student might expect to meet in industry.

Multiciel (Logique Séquentielle): A Computer Learning Enviroment Using Metacognition

M. Lavoie, A. Jaques, M. Gagné

Département de mathématiques et d'informatique, Université du Québec à Rimouski, Québec

Abstract

" Multiciel (Logique séquentielle)" is an instructional software using knowledge bases. Its subject is the sequential logic in the context of electronics at the pre-university level. It has been conceived from a didactical model. This model coordinates six modules : the knowledge module, the metaknowledge module, the tutor, the student's profile, the evaluator and the specificator. This paper presents first the problem situation that led to the conception of the software; then, it gives the aims of the software. The actualization of each of the six modules is also presented. Special attention is given to computer and didactical principles used to conceive and realize the software. More precisely, the advanced organizers in the knowledge module together with their representations is displayed. The learning theory working at the level of the metaknowledge module and the artificial intelligence techniques applied to operate the tutor, the student's profile, the evaluator and the specificator is likewise portrayed. We present also the software engineering approach that we adopt to realize the software. This approach plans the realization of a software into functional stages. This feature permits us to assess and adjust the software during its completion. The results of the experiments in class context of professional training at the pre-university level of the province of Québec is also presented.

Keywords: Computer learning environment, Knowledge basis, Metacognition, Professional training, Sequential logic.

1 Problem situation

The main problem of sequential logic in the context of professional training is its sudden extension into the technological curriculum. It turns out that this quick extension is due to rapid technological developments, in Québec as everywhere else in the developed world, and the need for training new technicians able to support those developments.

The first resulting problem was a shortage of adapted didactical material. There are some didactical tools used to learn sequential logic, but they are mainly manufacturer's instruction material. This material is excellent if used as extra didactical tools, but their large scale utilization leads to fragmentation of knowledge and does not contribute to the organized thought concerning sequential logic. Generally, the pieces of theory shown with this kind of material are too close to hardware representations. When sequential logic is exclusively presented within a particular technology, a pneumatic or an electronic one (Transistor-Transistor Logic - TTL -, Complementary Metal-Oxide Semiconductor - CMOS -), it produces specific learning that does not naturally organize into an idiosyncratic structure.

Another learning problem of the students lies in the fact that this corpus of matter shows a specific learning difficulty : the dynamic aspect of sequential logic basic concepts. In fact, to have an operational understanding of these concepts (flip-flops, registers, counters, etc.) one has to simulate them in his own mind. This simulation is difficult when not supported by good didactical materials, especially when students have not yet achieved the stage of formal thought. Micro-computer gets a top place here. This tool is the only one that offers the interactive animation needed to permit transfer from theoretical knowledge to applied understanding.

2 The instructional software

To correct in part the preceding problems, an instructional software : Multiciel (Logique séquentielle) was designed and realized. It ensues from a research project granted by the " Direction générale de l'enseignement et de la recherche universitaire " (DGERU) cf. Lavoie (1986).

The didactical approach of the instructional software is founded on a progressive abstraction of the main concepts of sequential logic. Students are led to abstract hardware representations of sequential logic in representing them as advanced organizers cf. Ausubel (1968). These abstractions transcend hardware representations without excluding them and emerge onto a structuring of sequential logic that permits transfers to actual working situations. We have reinforced this structuring of the matter by grouping it into a corpus and by organizing it into a hierarchy as autonomous as possible. Moreover, the kinetic nature of sequential logic led us to produce interactive animations that respect, as often as not, the rhythm, the style and the learning process of the student.

To realize this software, we used a method called "Evolutionary Delivery Method " cf. Gilb (1988). That method makes the software progress through many functional stages leading to a final goal. It is a software engineering method that operates by successive approximations and, against others, permits software testing during its realization.

Table 1. Experiments results

Institution	Grade	No.	$\overline{\Delta X}$	t	Prob.
CFP (Rimouski)	secondary 6	12	53	12	,0001
Cégep (Rimouski)	college 1	15	42	14	,0001
Cégep (Rimouski)	college 1	18	33	8	,0001
Cégep (Baie-Comeau)	college 2	12	54	17	,0001

The first version of Multiciel (Logique séquentielle) has been tested at Baie-Comeau and Rimouski colleges and at the " Centre de formation

professionnelle " (CFP) of Rimouski cf. Lavoie (1991b). These experiments aimed
to :

1) Check the appropriateness of the objectives achieved by the instructional
software and those shown in " Ministère de l'Enseignement supérieur et de la
Science " (MESS) program book.

2) Check the learning products flexibility generated by the instructional
software.

3) Check the software functionality in classroom situations.

To realize these experiments, the pretest/post-test paradigm has been used cf.
Lindquist (1956). A t-test has been conducted on the differences between post-test
and pretest results. 12 students of secondary school grade 6, 33 of college grade 1
and 12 of college grade 2 have been tested. Table 1 shows the results. As can be
observed, there is significant learning in each case. All three objectives of the
experiments have been achieved.

3 Actualization of the didactical model

The software Multiciel (Logique séquentielle) is based on a tested didactical model.
This model can take into account all kind of situations where learning hierarchies
are applicable cf. Lavoie (1991a).

This software groups six interrelated modules joined together : the knowledge
module, the metaknowledge module, the tutor module, the student's profile
module, the evaluator module and the specificator module.

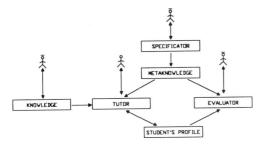

Figure 1. Software schema

Figure 1 shows a graphical representation of the software structure. An
exhaustive description of the model can be found in Lavoie (1991a).

To help to understand the model, let us recall briefly module objectives and
give some illustrations of modules.

The knowledge module cover the whole knowledge that the instructional
software has on a particular subject matter. This matter is subdivided in learning
situations that have specific objectives and prerequisites.

There are three types of learning activities : subject appropriation activities,
learning strengthening activities and those assuring learning transfer to problem
solving situations. An actual learning situation screen is shown in figure 2.

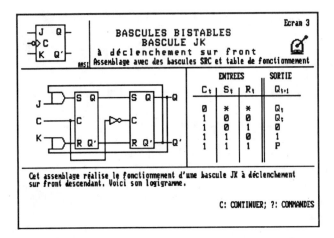

Figure 2. A learning situation screen

The purpose of the metaknowledge module is to structure the knowledge with regard to final, specific and global learning objectives.

It groups the following structures : a learning objective hierarchy, a study plan and a set of prerequisite structures of the learning situations. The learning objective hierarchy and the prerequisite set help to reach the final and global learning objectives. The study plan ensures achievement of more specific objectives.

The tutor module manages interactions with the user by mean of various strategies. It aims to give a student the control of his learning. As a metaphor, we could say that the student becomes a master apprentice directed by the tutor. To achieve this function, various tools are provided. So, the student can use menus, three tutor operating modes, real-time feedbacks about his learning, personalized information and, above all, an access to the metaknowledge. Figure 3 shows the tutor screen interface.

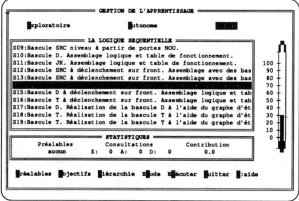

Figure 3. Tutor screen interface

The student's profile module is a data base collecting information about the student's interactions with the tutor and the knowledge modules. It allows the tutor to have an individualized approach.

The evaluator module selects and structures information on student-software interactions. It enables, both the tutor and the teacher, to question the student's profile. The information is structured according to the subject matter and the software metaknowledge of the learning.

```
Connaître la norme ANSI de représentation graphique des logigrammes.
Connaître la norme ISO de représentation graphique des logigrammes.
Associer le nom, un logigramme et la table de fonctionnement de la bascule SRC.
Connaître un assemblage logique de la bascule JK à déclenchement sur un front
descendant.
Connaître un logigramme de la bascule JK à déclenchement sur un front
descendant.
Connaître la norme ANSI de représentation graphique des logigrammes.
Connaître la norme ISO de représentation graphique des logigrammes.
Associer le nom, un logigramme et un assemblage logique de la bascule JK à
déclenchement sur un front descendant.
Connaître la section maître de la bascule JK front.
Connaître la section esclave de la bascule JK front.
Savoir que l'état d'une bascule est imprévisible à sa mise sous tension.
Savoir qu'une condition prohibée d'une bascule SRC nécessite une validation
d'horloge.
Savoir que les sorties d'une bascule en condition non prohibée sont
complémentaires.
Savoir que les sorties de la section maître de la bascule JK sont
complémentaires à la mise sous tension.
Savoir que la section esclave de la bascule JK reproduit les valeurs
complémentaires de la section maître.
```

Figure 4. Example of learning objectives

The specificator module is the part of the instructional software allowing the software producer and/or the manager to insert and change metaknowledge of the subject matter. Moreover, it gives the possibility of specifying some other options. The specificator enables the instructional software to adapt itself to real learning-teaching situations. This gives greater flexibility to the instructional software. Here is a detailed analysis of the specificator module.

4 Functional analysis of the specificator module

The specificator is composed of a set of submodules enabling its user - software producer, software manager, teacher - to deal with learning objectives.

Its first submodule helps the user to record each objective of a learning situation screen. These are the specific objectives. We call this submodule "editor".

Its function is to ease the formulation, not only of the specific objectives, but of the terminal objectives of each learning situation as well as the global objectives of the instructional software. It gives a data base like structure to the objectives.

The editor parallels the learning situations. One can see at the middle of figure 4 the specific objectives corresponding to the learning situation screen displayed in figure 2.

A second submodule aids the user to define equivalent classes of learning objectives. For instance, a learning objective worded at the screen M of the situation X can be the same as another one expressed at the screen N of the situation Y. The system has to know, to be efficient, that those two objectives are in fact the same. The " analyzer" is the part of the software which helps defining equivalent classes.

To construct those equivalent classes, a thesaurus of keywords is built. To accelerate its access, it is structured as a B+ tree. The objectives are compared one to another using their keywords. The comparison of two objectives can be strict, that is each objective has the same keywords, or it can be fuzzy, that is a certain level of discrepancy can be allowed in the list of their keywords. This fuzziness is obtained by using a percentage of congruence of the number of keywords into the two objectives. This fuzzy search permits the comparison of nonidentical objectives that can have identical meaning.

A third submodule assists the user to grade and organize the learning objectives. This organization takes the form of a prerequisite structure. It is possible to create easing objectives or deriving objectives from any objective. In this way, one can construct by degrees the connected components of the learning hierarchy. Here also, one has access to fuzzy comparison of objectives. The principle of fuzzy comparison is the same as the one explained before, but instead of using keywords we used the characters. This substitution of keywords by characters refines the comparison precision. It is then possible to use the result of a comparison to form an easing objective from a set of objectives that almost have the same meaning.

In the software, we graphically represent the set of connected components or branches. At the beginning, one has a completely dispersed cloud of points. Then, more the connected components become related, more the points agglomerate, and doing so, increase the condensation of the cloud. At the end, the hierarchy of the learning objectives is composed of only one connected component. In this way, the starting cloud of particles condenses into a large planet. This tells instantly to the learning hierarchy designer the state of progress of the hierarchy.

Moreover, one can consider graphically each connected branches of the hierarchy. After entering easing or deriving objectives, the submodule verifies the consistency of the new structure and indicates, if needed, the problem and its nature. It even gives the possibility to correct the problem with the help of the graphic display. We call this submodule " organizer ". It has also the function, once the learning objectives are entered, analyzed and structured, to assist the user in conceiving the study plan.

5 Global operation of the specificator

Even if, for the sake of the specificator analysis, we have presented the editor, analyzer and organizer submodules in that order, it does not infer that the metaknowledge conceiver will use these submodules in this sequence. Probably, and it was the case for us, he will start by entering objectives tied to learning situations. After a period of time, when the number of objectives will become too large to be managed only by memory, he will have to use the analyzer. Then, there will be a backward and forward motion between the editor and the analyzer submodules. Next, he will use the organizer submodule to structure a little bit more the objectives. Finally, he will resume entering and analyzing objectives. As one can see, the submodules and their underlying structures have been conceived to be used by the end user - software manager, teacher - in his own fashion and at the time he chooses to utilize them.

6 Conclusion

Multiciel (Logique séquentielle) is an instructional software using knowledge bases. Its architecture has been conceived such that its manager - teacher - can change completely the actual software. In fact, the software manager has the tools enabling him to change the learning objectives, the equivalent classes of objectives, the contribution of each element to its equivalent class, the learning hierarchy, the relative weight of each objective of the hierarchy, the study plan, the threshold of fulfillment of each learning objective, the threshold of fulfillment of each prerequisite objective, the prerequisite structure of each learning situation and the way the assessment is done for each learning objectives. Furthermore, the teacher can add new learning situations. To do so, he will have to use, however, an authoring language, an authoring system or any computer language. And then, he will be in a position to enter metaknowledge linked to the new learning situations and to proceed with the specification of the assessment of each new learning objective.

The specificator module, although a component of the software Multiciel (Logique séquentielle), is intrinsically a software system that can be classified into the category of software supporting specific class of activities (computer aided design - CAD -). Here, the class of activities concerns the conception, the elaboration, the organization and the assessment of learning objectives. The help given by the specificator module is interactive. Moreover, the software really assists the instructional software conceiver or manager in his conceptual pursuit. Finally, the specificator module can be used alone to produce the objectives of a corpus of matter, a course or even an instructional program.

References

Ausubel D.P. (1968) **Educational Psychology : A Cognitive View,** Holt, Rinehart and Winston, New York.

Gagné R.M. and L.J. Briggs (1979) **Principles of Instructional Design,** Holt, Rinehart and Winston, New York.

Gilb T. (1988) **Principles of Software Engineering Management,** Addison-Wesley, Don Mills, Ontario.

Lavoie M., M. Gagné, A. Jacques, D. Dufour and V. Beaulieu (1986) **Un logiciel ouvert et complet concernant l'apprentissage de la logique séquentielle,** DGERU, Québec.

Lavoie M., M. Gagné and A. Jacques (1991a) Specifications of a Software System which Assists in the Design and Construction of Knowledge-based Instructional Software, in **Proceedings of the IFIP TC3 International Conference on Advanced Research on Computers in Education** (eds. R. Lewis and S. Otsuki), Elsevier Science Publishers B.V., North-Holland, 307-316.

Lavoie M., A. Jacques, D. Dufour, and V. Beaulieu (1991b) Expérimentations en situation de classe de l'orientation professionnelle d'un logiciel éducatif, in **Recueil** des résumés de communications, 59e congrès de l'ACFAS, Université de Sherbrooke, Québec, 59, 97.

Lindquist E.F. (1956) **Design and Analysis of Experiments in Psychology and Education,** Houghton Mifflin Company, Boston.

Torkia-Lagacé M. (1981) **La pensée formelle chez les étudiants de collège 1: objectif ou réalité ?** Rapport de recherche, DGEC, Québec.

Access to Computing Skills

G. Burns, T. Westwood

School of Engineering, Glasgow Polytechnic

Abstract

The provision of educational opportunities for practising engineers to update or improve their skill and knowledge is often undertaken as a short term course. At best these can only provide an introduction to new ideas and concepts. The short course concept is not a practical method to introduce completely new technology such as software engineering. This paper describes the use of a modular approach to the delivery of computing skills in (1) a course leading to a nationally recognised qualification, (2) as an integral part of an access course, and (3) within the context of a learning contract for a post graduate qualification. The content for each course is chosen to reflect both basic and applied elements in the computing skills area. The relationship between entrance criteria and performance is examined and delivery of the course including flexibility in presentation is discussed.

Keywords: Computing, Access, Modules, Credits,

1 Introduction

Many institutions now recognise the importance of software engineering in the training of the modern engineer whether mechanical or electrical, however there is a need to provide suitable training for engineers in post, at a postgraduate level for those who find they require skills not taught in undergraduate courses and those seeking access to undergraduate courses with non-standard educational backgrounds. The development of individual courses to address this need would require significant resources. The use of modules in courses developed in the School of Engineering at Glasgow Polytechnic has provided the ability to address the range of content required within a reasonable resource base. The courses in which computing skills are taught using a modular system are (1) Multi-Skills Engineering (MSE) , (2) H.N.C. Engineering Computing (EC) and (3) Specific units within a Learning Contact for Teaching Company Associates. For both MSE and EC it was considered important to develop basic skills e.g. word-processing and identify Software Engineering as a discipline concerned with the production of efficient, effective software. The post graduate Learning Contact is different in that specific skills are identified e.g. Data base design and addressed through established modules hence in this case the integration of ideas is more related to a wider engineering perspective rather than the directed aim of the MSE or EC courses.

2 Entry Qualifications

2.1 Multi-Skills Engineering

This is an access course that is intended to give students a basic set of skills in a
variety of engineering topics. The course has two aims (1) to prepare students for
work by giving them a set of electrical , mechanical and computing skills that
employers may find attractive or (2) provide a degree of articulation into the
School of Engineerings BSc/HND programme in Computer Aided Engineering or
Electrical Engineering. The definition of entry requirements was therefore
addressed in experiential and motivational terms since it was anticipated that few
applicants would be able to offer formal qualifications.

2.2 Engineering Computing

Engineering Computing is a structured course that leads to a Higher National
Certificate in Engineering Computing. The award is obtained by achieving 12 credits
based on 480 hours of instruction. The course was originally planned as a 1 year full
time programme but was also offered in a part time mode to industry. Entrance to the
course was available under three criterion (1) Formal Qualifications (2) Prior
Learning and (3) Motivation and Capability.   Practising engineers were expected to
offer a range of qualifications hence the entry requirement were written to provide the
course management team with a degree of discretion. Significant among the entry
requirements was the acknowledgement that experiential learning would be
recognised provided it could be adequately quantified. From the outset the course
team considered that all to often engineers in industry who have "grown into " a
computer based job description feel inhibited from applying for courses that result in
formal qualifications because they lack conventional entry requirements. Experience
with this course has shown that recognising experiential learning is a positive step to
reducing the impact of this barrier. Results so far (see later) have shown that this
discretion when applied sensible does not result in poor performance, indeed rather the
opposite has been the experience.

2.3 Post Graduate Learning Contract

In a post graduate learning contract learning outcomes are identified as part of an
overall strategy to improve the operation of a company. Typically participants in this
type of study are highly motived, professionally qualified engineers or employees
who have been deemed to have gained sufficient learning from there work
environment to qualify for entry to the programme. Software Engineering Learning
Outcomes that can be adequately met using modules already established provide a
resource efficient manner for delivering part of the leaning contract.

3 Course Structure

A number of software engineering courses are available from nationally recognised
bodies, for example NCC/IEE initiative, the British Computer Society and
SCOTVEC modular courses were considered. Unfortunately both the NCC/IEE
initiative and the British Computer Society start by assuming a qualification level
well above that which it was considered appropriate for encouraging individuals or
industry to participate. The SCOTVEC modules offered an opportunity to construct a
course which could have available modules addressing software and hardware issues

in self contained units. The course team for MSE and EC considered that it was appropriate to use a selection of these modules in developing both courses.

3.1 Multi Skills Engineering

Four modules, Introduction to the Computer Resource, Word Processing, Databases and Spreadsheets are taught in this course. The content of the modules was directed towards using software associated with the various heading e.g. how DOS operates , using a word processor to prepare C.V.'s etc and through the use of the software some basic elements of software design are developed. An optional module, Pascal Programming was offered for students who were considering application to the BSc/HND programme thus providing a degree of articulation within the computing element.

3.2 Engineering Computing

In this course the student must gain 12 credits to qualify for the award of the H.N.C. in Engineering Computing. The units chosen for the course are shown in Table 1. For full-time study the student must complete the core subjects and then choose from the optional modules to complete the 12 credits required. Students by careful choice of the optional units were able to direct their studies into either hardware or software areas. The integration of these units to provide a structured view of software engineering is the responsibility of the course team. Discussion with industrial partners led the course team to select core units that provide a balance between software engineering, applications such as data base systems and hardware giving a realistic mix of educational experiences for students. The units identified in Table 1 as core units deliver this basic content and all students were required to achieve these units before qualifying for the award.

3.3 Post Graduate Learning Contract

The development of specific software engineering skills as determined from a learning outcome may be encompassed by a single module, require study of a number of modules or require study of a single module plus more advanced study. In the first two of these the material is already available, the third makes use of existing modules to develop the basic understanding which is followed by more advanced study under the direction of the students supervisor or an appropriate member of staff with the necessary experience.

4 Mode of Delivery and Assessment

4.1 Delivery

The MSE and EC courses are delivered using a combination of lecture , laboratory , demonstration and programme development. Both programmes require the student to complete a number of modules satisfactorily but in the EC it is essential for the award to be made that the student achieve the core units. Optional units are chosen in a full-time delivery of the EC course allowing the student to pursue a definite interest such as software engineering to hardware structure. Experience has shown that the part time mode of the EC course must be delivered as a package of defined units, choice would inevitable lead to the course lasting longer because students would have to wait for the units they have chosen to be taught. Delivery of material in a postgraduate

learning contract is less structured and requires the supervisor to provide direction
through discussion, directed studies, and where appropriate arranging for students to
attend lectures. The methodology employed here is much more akin to that used for
typical research students.

4.2 Assessment

Assessment in both the MSE and EC is competence based that is the student is
required to demonstrate the ability to complete specific tasks that match the
performance criteria in the module descriptor. In courses assessed using performance
criteria there is a very real danger of over assessment if each performance criteria is
assessed independent of all others. The course teams for MSE and EC therefore took
a decision to combine assessments wherever possible subject to a combined
assessment being able to demonstrate clearly the performance criteria being assessed.
By this means the assessment exercises on the course were reduced to a manageable
level for both the staff and students. Teaching strategies varied from individual
performance to group work, the latter being used extensively in the core module
software development life cycle of the EC course.

4.3 Multi Skills Engineering

Each of the computing modules has a set of performance criterion that the student has
to achieve in order to qualify for the award of the module. Assessment is by the
student demonstrating that they can perform the task described in the assessment
schedule.

4.4 Engineering Computing

Assessment techniques used included written exercises, development of complete
software solution, construction of appropriate design documentation, demonstration
of hardware skills and maintaining documentation appropriate to the development of
a piece of software from requirements definition to completed software. Analysis of
the individual performance criteria required for the units in table 1 shows that
approximately 230 assessments would be required for satisfactory completion. By
adopting a combined assessment policy this was reduced significantly.

4.5 Post Graduate Learning Contract

Assessment of leaning outcomes in this type of study is based on a CATS scheme for
Scotland. Credit points are achieved for the satisfactory completion of each
assessment related to a learning goal. The assessment may be completed by written
report, demonstration of satisfactory development of software, submission of design
material or any other practical means that demonstrates the learning goal has been
achieved. In this process of assessment the academic and industrial supervisors are
involved in judging the progress of the student in learning in relation to a defined set
of assessment crieria and not by formal examination or the completion of
competences.

5 Summary

In the case of the MSE and EC courses it is evident that both courses provided opportunities for the students. MSE has now had some 70 students in 4 courses, of whom 30 have progressed to the BSc/HND programmes offered by the School of Engineering. It is worth noting that this year a student will graduate with a BSc who started on a multi-skills engineering course. The balance of students have had reasonable success in the jobs market with approximately 60 % achieving employment. The EC course has had one full-time year with 20 students, of which 2 withdrew after a short space of time indicating that the course was not what they had imagined. The remaining 18 students completed the course with 17 achieving the award of the Higher National Certificate and 1 student currently repeating a module. A further two courses are currently under way for industrial groups on a part-time basis. Neither course is completed but the results to date show that of some 34 students who started 28 will complete the course and achieve the Higher National Certificate. Currently there has been one student on a learning contract who required to study the use of database system. The student successfully demonstrated the achievement of the learning goal by describing the design of a database system and the demonstrating the working system.

6 Conclusions

The development of the courses and assessment materials has provided the opportunity to structure a students experience of computing skills and software engineering in a series of programmes with links. The first or beginner level in the MSE course emphasises acquiring keyboard skills , the confidence to use application packages and develops some basic software design skills. The study of a coherent set of units leading to a national qualification develops skills in both theoretical and practical software engineering appropriate to a technician software engineer. Finally the use of the modules to provide a basis for industrially based students to develop relevant solutions to software engineering problems or as a springboard for further advanced study within the learning contract framework demonstrates the utility of this approach. The availability of a core set of units from SCOTVEC has considerably eased the development of this series of courses, any suitable set of modules would serve the same purpose. The structure of these courses suggests that a similar approach could be developed for software engineering within BSC/HND and BEng programmes. Once developed a ciriculum composed of common and differentiated modules would provide for increased articulation between the two programmes, easing the transfer of students from one to the other.

The MSE and EC courses have demonstrated that assessment of prior learning is a useful tool for students who are not able to offer standard entry qualification. Part-time industrially based courses have also shown that motivation together with assessment of prior learning is no less an indicator of success than normal entry qualifications.

Table 1
Software Engineering Modules

Module Title	Core Module	Optional Module	Credit Value
Communication Skills	Yes (40 hours)		1
Software Eng. (1)		Yes (40 hours)	1
Software Eng. (2)	Yes (120 hours)		3
Systems Develop (1)		Yes (40 hours)	1
Database Management		Yes (40 Hours)	1
Computer Resource	Yes (40 Hours)		1
Data Communications	Yes (40 Hours)		1
Microprocessor Sys.	Yes (40 Hours)		1
Prog. Logic controllers		Yes (40 Hours)	1
Telecom. Networks		Yes (40 Hours)	1
Systems Develop. (2)		Yes (80 Hours)	2

Note 1

Software Engineering 1	:- Static Abstract Data Structures
Software Engineering 2	:- Development Life Cycle
Systems Development 1	:- Software Tools and Techniques
Systems Development 2	:- The System Development Life Cycle

SECTION 2: PROJECTS, DESIGN AND MANUFACTURE

Engineering Design - 'An Integrated Programme for the Development of Confidence in Technical Decision Taking'

J.E.E. Sharpe, A.J. Adey

Department of Mechanical Engineering, Queen Mary and Westfield College, University of London

Abstract

Given the wide range of engineering careers and the rate of technological change to be experienced by today's students, the core role of Design in integrating engineering education within our degree programmes is re-emphasised. The ability to find problem solutions, make technical decisions and assess risk and effectiveness is achieved mainly through a series of carefully structured weekly assignments in the second year which build on core material from the first year and lead to project work and option subjects in the third year.

Keywords: Design education, Engineering integration, Assignment learning.

1 Introduction

Aspects of engineering design feature in each year of the MEng and BEng degree programmes offered by the department. The approach to the teaching of Design has been developed over the past 15 years and predates the Finniston, Lickley and other reports, whose views the authors generally support.

Following a first year introductory course in Engineering Method, two second year courses entitled Engineering Design Methods and Engineering for Manufacture build on the student's early foundation in Mathematics, Engineering Science, Technology and Practice. These courses are characterised by a series of weekly assignments that are carefully related to the lecture programme and develop the student's critical awareness and ability to make decisions with confidence. Engineering Design Methods culminates in a sizeable design study on a concept chosen by the student which introduces him/her to project work and allows him/her to try out ideas which may form the basis of subsequent work. This opportunity when taken often leads to excellent final year project work and occasionally even to further research. These two compulsory courses, together with Operational and Financial Management, provide experience in problem solution and synthesis techniques particularly valuable for their third year individual project, and subsequent careers.

In the well integrated degree programme, aspects of engineering design are also introduced to many courses in engineering science such as Stress Analysis, Heat

Transfer and Fluid Mechanics particularly by the use of Computer Aided Design Education (CADed) learning packages. These enable the students to explore the design implications of the subject and constraints imposed by manufacture, etc.

2 Course structure and objectives

The individual design courses taken by students during each of the years of their degree programme are carefully integrated to provide a wide experience of real engineering problems which are not tied to any one specific branch of mechanical engineering. Whilst the design examples given make use of material normally taught to engineering undergraduates, adequate background information or references are always given, enabling students without the necessary prerequisite courses to take part fully, including those from other departments and, occasionally, other faculties.

The object is to assist students in thinking objectively and critically, thus enabling them to make technical decisions with confidence and understanding. The design exercises in the second year give the opportunity to develop communication skills, both graphical and verbal. The weekly tutorial periods encourage students to ask the right questions and form an integral part of thinking through the exercises. The marks given are on the basis of the reasoning over a particular solution rather than for its technical correctness and after marking, a full discussion takes place with particular reference to known existing solutions to the question.

3 The courses

3.1 First year: "Engineering Method and Practice"

The first year course, Engineering Method and Practice, covers not only design and workshop practice, but also a series of lectures, Engineering in Practice, given by visiting lecturers from industry. Others might prefer the title 'Fundamentals in Design and Manufacture'. The formal design teaching in the first year should have three elements. Beginning with the nature of engineering design which embraces creativity, decision taking, the complexity of real problems, the nature of risk and the cost of safety, this introduction also considers the engineers' responsibility and role in society, and the organisation of engineering, including manufacture, sales and research and development, as well as the need for profit and the constraints imposed by finance. A topical case study is used to illustrate the points made, which could be researched by the students and presented through a poster competition.

The second part of the course deals with 2- and 3-dimensional graphical construction and the principles of engineering drawing. Students undertake exercises on the drawing board and compare them with computer graphics.

A third part deals with design appreciation which is linked to the development of descriptive skills. Students are expected to identify components from their manufacturing drawings and to describe their form and function, materials and method of manufacture as well as the relevant areas of engineering science needed for their design. The parts and drawings are taken directly from industry, who generally are enthusiastic to support such teaching methods.

Finally, the students prepare detailed drawings to BS 308 of simple components and systems, using parts and assemblies taken from industry.

3.2 Second year: "Design Methods and Engineering for Manufacture"

These courses use the College's two semester teaching year, with three lectures in the mornings, and one afternoon per week given over to a combined tutorial and seminar period. The weekly assignments are closely related to the lecture topics. Students are encouraged to think about the problem beforehand and should come to the afternoon tutorial/seminar well prepared with questions. This tutorial session has, first, a reiteration of the problem and a presentation of background information and, second, a question and answer session before the students break up into small groups, ideally with other members of staff or research assistants to continue the discussion informally. Students are encouraged to discuss with their peers and on appropriate assignments, to work in groups. The finished assignments must be handed in on the due date, with reduced marks for late work and none at all if later than the next seminar when feedback is given.

In addition to the nine weekly assignments in each of the two courses, students are expected to undertake a design study of their choice over Christmas, which may be completed in the final two weeks after the vacation. Ten marks are awarded for each assignment and twenty for the design study. In determining the coursework mark, the worst assignment is ignored, allowing a student to have an 'off' week without being penalised. The requirement of having to meet weekly deadlines is an important aspect of the courses and is designed to develop self-discipline. Ideally, each weekly assignment is marked and returned to the students in the following seminar with both whole class and individual feedback from the lecturer; the latter whilst the students are working in their small groups. This means the lecturer must set aside an undisturbed day for the marking in his personal timetable. The options here are:

Day 1 - hand out new assignment, collect previous assignment students' work,

Day 2 and 3 - lecturer marks previous assignment, students prepare questions,

Day 4 - seminar; hand back previous assignment, discuss new assignment,

Days 5, 6, 7 (including the weekend) - students work on new assignment.

Alternatively, some lecturers may be prepared to use the scheme with which we have most experience where days 2 and 3 in the above are the weekend. The practice of giving feedback during the seminar saves time overall since it reduces the demand on the lecturer to provide extensive written comments when marking each script.

3.3 Engineering Design Methods (taken in first half of second year)

The course is divided into four broad topics. The first deals with Design
Philosophy, including aspects of Product Liability and other legal and economic
constraints. The second looks at design Optimization and Technological Systems,
including failure mode analysis, reliability and safety. The third looks at materials
and component choice, whilst the final part considers real design problems and
their solutions. After introducing the role of the designer and the Morphology of
Design as shown by different national standards and individuals, initial lectures
cover the analysis of need, constraints on design, preliminary design, brainstorming
and design evaluation, followed by a topic of historic interest. The students' first
assignment is on examples of good and bad design from their own observation; the
second on Needs Analysis and Design Evaluation has used an emergency braking
system for an articulated truck as a typical problem. These open the students'
eyes to artefacts, needs, constraints and the assessment of many different
approaches. Next comes legal constraints to design such as safe working, reliability,
health and safety legislation, followed by commercial factors, such as profit, cash
flow, intellectual property law, industrial design, consumer attitudes and the
growing importance of product liability. The third assignment evaluates, for
example, the design of an industrial storage cabinet for solvents, including the
production of a one-page sales leaflet.

The second part deals with the design of technological systems, introducing
the concept of the performance function in which optimization is an amalgam of
science, mathematics and experience, especially in specifying the problem correctly
in the first place. A typical problem is the position of the wheels on an articulated
semi-trailer to minimise the maximum bending moment. The problem is further
complicated when the legal requirement relating to overhang is introduced. Next,
the design decision - making process proceeds to the choice of manageable
elements with appropriate divisions and interfaces. The traditional concept of the
black box is not encouraged. Considerable emphasis is placed by the use of Bond
Graphs on the transfer of energy through the system and its environment with
particular reference on energy storage, dissipation and the implications of the laws
of Thermodynamics. This encourages the student to identify the behaviour of the
system and to develop graphical methods at both the macro and micro levels.
Complex system analysis using Bond Graphs also assists the identification of
potential failure modes. The question of reliability, warranty and design is
considered not only from a technical point of view but also in relation to profit.
The systems lectures conclude with the machine matching problem, identifying
prime mover and load characteristics including non-linearities. Here, it may be
convenient to introduce students to technical papers which they will be expected
to read, understand and above all to criticise and apply.

The final part of the course develops further the commercial aspects of design,
including Value Engineering and is again based on 'learning by doing'.

3.4 Engineering for Manufacture (taken in second half of second year)

This course studies the optimization of the manufacturing process by improving effectiveness, productivity and quality, both through better design and operation of the production system and through the implications of processing decisions for the detail design of products. It is divided into four parts dealing with i) the Product and Manufacture, ii) Manufacturing Processes, iii) the Design and Control of Manufacturing Systems and finally iv) Value Analysis, Idea Generation and Product Quality. Ideally the programme concludes with the Technological Audit and the Design Review to draw the two courses together. The weekly assignments include experimental studies on material cutting carried out on CNC machines. It is hoped to introduce computer terminal assignments of the CADed type in the Design for Assembly, production scheduling and Quality Assurance parts of the course.

First, the course reviews the production problem, its life cycle, its production specification and the effects on cost of quantity and tolerance. Manufacture is seen as a system which itself must be designed, operated, controlled, costed and optimized; comprising raw material processing, primary and secondary manufacture, including their constraints in terms of resources and energy, as well as assembly. Following examples such as metal cutting conditions and tool life optimization, the third part focuses on the design of a production facility, including its physical layout and control. Aspects such as the use of Flexible Manufacturing Systems, Group Technology or dedicated flow lines are included and as a further assignment students are asked to prepare a process layout for a typical engineering product such as a gearbox. Production and inventory control, including MRT, JIT, OPT and the use of simulation, are covered. The Idea Generation section, including such techniques as brainstorming, lateral thinking and the systematic approach to analogy, helps to build the students' confidence for innovative work without having to be a genius. The engineering skill to be learnt is the power to recognise the good idea which is lying around waiting to be grabbed. Quality Assurance covers the latest techniques on Total Quality Management, the implementation of BS5750, the implications of Company Mission statements and concludes with statistical process control and the consequences for design, manufacture and assembly of a zero defects policy.

4 Assessment Methods

Overall, the coursework (assignments, etc.) has the same weighting as the end of year examinations. The students have good feedback from the continuous assessment which includes group work and ideas from others as in the real life situation, whilst their individual ability is assessed by the examination. In the Design Methods paper students can choose a single 100 mark design question or the appropriate number of 25 or 50 mark questions on various aspects of the design process. In general, about 40% of the students opt for the 100 mark question; usually the best students, who do extremely well and the worst students who will never become designers.

5 Future Developments

A further attractive innovation is to introduce a Computer Aided Design Make and Test activity for all students, relieving the load on the teaching workshop used in the first year which currently requires considerable scarce technician support. Pairs of students will design, draw, manufacture and subsequently test objects to perform some prescribed function. At present preparations are in hand on five projects, viz, the design of a Cam and Follower, a highly stressed rotating Shaft, Cooling Fins for an Electronic component, Blading for a centrifugal fan and a Cantilever to carry an offset mass with the aim of high torsional and bending natural frequencies.

This second year activity will involve the use of computer aided engineering wherever possible. First, students will explore the engineering science of the object and seek an optimal design. Then, the component and its testing assembly are drawn using a Computer Aided Draughting programme. The programme for the CNC machining is then prepared and validated by a computer simulation. The parts will be made by technical staff on CNC machines before being checked for dimensional accuracy by the students. Finally, the parts will be assembled and tested with relevant test data being logged and processed by suitable computers. The various modules for this activity can be developed through third year student projects.

This exercise is aimed to give students an early taste of the total activity of engineering of which Design is central. It will also introduce some element of competition. Marks will be awarded on the basis of the quality of the written report, not just on how good the final test was. This should encourage students to literally 'learn from other's mistakes'.

6 Conclusions

The courses that have been described are unique in a number of ways. They are set in a course-unit structure - they stress the role of technical decision taking, while presenting the students with a wide range of practical problems - they are structured towards learning by doing - and introduce a commercial discipline, where decisions must be made within a given time and based on the limited amount of hard information available.

The course attempts to put Engineering Science in context and to develop the students' confidence whilst at the same time giving them experience of a wide range of carefully structured problems that introduce the whole complexity, challenge and excitement of real engineering design.

The Integration of Design, Materials Selection and Product Manufacture in Undergraduate Courses in Manufacturing Engineering

N.P. Fletcher

Course Tutor Product Design and Manufacture,
Department of Manufacturing Engineering,
Loughborough University of Technology

Abstract
Today's consumer driven market calls for a vast array of innovative and updated products to be on offer to the public. The ever increasing demands on product quality, reliability, competitive price and customer appeal means that the manufacturing and design engineers of today need to be astute and professionally competent to be successful. This is particularly important when competing with overseas manufacturers of consumer products for a place in world markets. At Loughborough University of Technology a degree course in Product Design and Manufacture is offered which integrates design, materials selection and product manufacture in all years of the course. The aim of this paper is to show how industrial engineering concepts have been married together with those of engineering design and related areas, through project work, to stimulate creativity at undergraduate level.
Keywords: Engineering Education, Product Design for Manufacture and Function, Quality and Reliability.

1 Introduction

The best method of understanding any subject area is through its application, this being particularly true of those subjects related to engineering. Group and individual project work lend themselves ideally as vehicles to test out the acqiuired knowledge of the undergraduate and are particularly useful where ideas culminate in a manufactured product. A well thought out project should draw together as wide a range of subject material as possible to reinforce in the students mind that subjects are not taught in isolation, but are complementary in their application. Group projects are particularly useful during the early stages of a student's development since they enable limited individual knowledge and subject understanding to be pooled together. In this way students learn from one another with no loss of face. The group environment also introduces students to the concept of team work and encourages team spirit. This is a positive step towards cooperation with others, and a natural lead in to the concept of concurrent engineering, which is widely practiced in industry. Individual projects are best tackled by students when they have gained confidence and competence in applying engineering knowledge. This is usually at second or final year level of an undergraduate course. By final year most students are well able to produce reasonably sophisticated designs which incorporate mechanical/electrical and electronic requirements, aesthetic and ergonomic requirements, and apply sound methods of manufacture for ease of assembly and maintenance.

At the start of any project a clearly defined route is needed which students can take in order to produce a satisfactory solution to the set problems, be it undertaken individually or in a group. Typical guidelines for tackling a project are given below in figure 1.

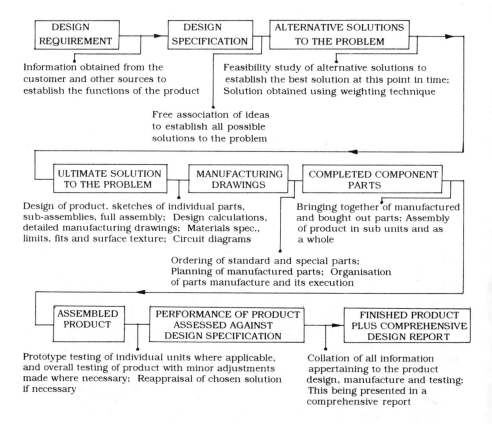

Fig. 1.   Guidelines for tackling a design and manufacture project

2 Formative Stage of Product Design for Manufacture and Function

One of the most important requirements for any design engineer is to be able to communicate ideas to others. This is accomplished through formal engineering drawings which are either computer generated or produced on the board. Product designers also need to be able to create concept drawings that highlight the aesthetic and ergonomic features of a product as well as functional and manufacturing requirements. These aspects of design teaching are service taught from first year onwards by the local college of Art and Design and the department of Human Sciences at Loughborough University. As well as having an input in design and manufacture projects they carry their own coursework and examination requirements. Whilst materials science is taught in first year as a subject in its own right, the application of materials selection has been reinforced through manufacturing design, which brings together formal drawing techniques, freehand sketching, and design for function and manufacture. The mediums for teaching this subject are case studies and practical exercises. To engender a better understanding of the interaction of engineering subjects, formal laboratories in first year have been replaced by group mini-projects. These bring together the basic principles of engineering science, manufacturing processes and materials, computing and design. This approach allows students to develop and apply their knowledge through experimentation at a more leisurely pace than that afforded by standard laboratory exercises. It also encourages them to research information necessary for the successful completion of each set task. To consolidate the knowledge that the students have acquired by the end of first term, group design and manufacture projects are undertaken.

At first year level the design and make project is used as a vehicle to bring together the engineering and design knowledge, and communication skills of students in the design and manufacture of simple products. Whilst at this stage of their education students have acquired a basic understanding of engineering science subjects, a prime aim of the project is to give students the chance to be innovative rather than apply engineering science knowledge to any great depth. Having said this, the project does require them to demonstrate their understanding of basic engineering principles. To ensure, as far as possible, that the project topics are realistic, products are chosen that encourage the students to seek an end user outside the university environment. One good source for customers is that of local schools, who generally have limited budgets for buying educational equipment and are willing to liase with design groups in the development of products. One theme that has been adopted for the past two years is for groups to design and make educational toys and equipment that demonstrate specific scientific or physical principles. With the development of the National Curriculum for schools, the physical principles that five year olds and upwards should know are clearly defined, and afford an excellent shopping list for project topics. Typical projects that have been undertaken are analogue and digital clocks for telling the time, balancing and weighing equipment, products that demonstrate centripetal and centrifugal force, and the conversion of potential into kinetic energy. All products that have proved to be successful have been donated to the participating schools.

The requirements set on each group have been to design and develop their particular product so that at the end of the project period, which spans second and third term in first year, each group has produced a formal report, a set of working drawings and a finished product. The principal materials available to students from which to manufacture their products are plastics, which are easily formed into relatively complex shapes, can be purchased in a variety of colours, and are relatively cheap. The drawings and sketches which record product form are produced by a mixture of computer and hand generated means, and cover functional, aesthetic and ergonomic requirements. The report covers the development of the product from conceptual stage to proto-type proving, including relevant methods of manufacture and materials selection. The last stage of the project is to present the work at a formal seminar before peers and members of staff, and defend decisions taken. By the end of first year the students have become familiar with the concepts of project management, the application of engineering and design principles, and working together in groups. They are then ready to tackle the more demanding rigours of design and manufacture project work in second year.

3 Secondary Stage of Product Design for Manufacture and Function

Product design and manufacture at second year level constitutes a larger proportion of time than at first year, and accounts for one quarter of second year credit. It is examined entirely through a major group design and make project. The design requirement in second year is more searching than at first year level and requires students to produce full design analyses of the intended product including relevant mechanical and electrical calculations, circuit diagrams, aesthetic and ergonomic considerations, materials selection and manufacturing strategies. Running alongside the project are taught subjects which are called upon as tools to support the project work. Industrial Engineering gives an input of aesthetic design concerned with product presentation and company image. Ergonomics includes a computer design package that enables the designer to try out conceptual ideas of products on a computer generated manikin, proportioned to be representative of the population for whom the product is intended. Design of Machine Elements covers mechanical requirements of products, and Electronics and Electrical Technology covers electrical considerations. An in-depth study of materials and their processing capabilities is accomplished through Manufacturing Process Selection. Design and manufacture projects in second year are again complemented by group mini-projects, where knowledge assimilated through the lecture program is applied.

Major constraints on design and manufacture type projects are those of limited resources of money, manufacturing facilities and technical back-up. These problems can be alleviated by designing projects that accomodate group sizes of between six and eight students, using standard bought-out components that can be recycled for future project work when existing products are no longer functional or required, and steering product manufacture through those processes that are readily available within the department. Taking these factors into consideration a good project brief should stretch the imagination of the students, be enjoyable,and above all be able to be accomplished within the allotted time.

Whilst it is said that large group sizes are to be avoided, since demotivated students will rely on others within the group to carry out the work, with careful structuring large groups can work efficiently with everyone taking part. This is best accomplished through the "small company" concept. A product is identified who's structure can be divided into sub-units that can be designed as independant entities. The sub-units can then be combined to produce the overall product. In this way teams of students can be split up into two or more sub-groups. Initially the whole team analyses the set problem and allocates the individual design tasks to each sub-group. The sub-groups then design and manufacture their portion of the product, bearing in mind that ultimately everything must operate as a single unit. A further means of encouraging enthusiasm is to create an element of competition between each "small company" by giving the same product requirement to everyone. A prize for the best result is a sure means of creating healthy competition!

The requirement on each group is to produce a product that meets the agreed original design specification, this proved by a clearly defined means of product evaluation, produce a comprehensive report with appropriate calculations and drawings, and present the product in a professional manner consistent with good marketing practice.

A current second year design and make exercise that has proved to be popular with the students was to design a vehicle capable of recovering "unidentified flying objects" on Mars, and produce a 100th scale radio controlled model to prove out the design. Three "small companies" of eight students per company were asked to tender for the contract of supplying such a vehicle and were given a model of a UFO in the form of a spinning top. The full-size vehicle was to be presented in concept form only, through sketches and accompanying notes. These were to cover mechanical and electrical requirements for travel between base camp and the UFO, and UFO recovery;   life support systems for the two operatives of the vehicle, vehicle body design, selection of materials and manufacturing processes to be used.   The scale model had to be accompanied by appropriate design calculations, concept sketches and manufacturing drawings. A range of standard materials were made available and each team was given a budget to buy parts that they thought appropriate. Each team of eight was sub-divided into two teams of four. One team concentrated on the travel requirements whilst the other team concentrated on the recovery requirements. Sub-teams then recombined to consider the overall design of the vehicle.

The effort each "small company" put in was impressive. Information was obtained from American and Japanese space agencies, major car manufacturers on advanced materials and their influence on future vehicle design, and British Aero Space on vehicle design for use in space. The ensuing designs and models presented by the students were a credit to them.

4   Tertiary Stage of Product Design for Manufacture and Function

At final year level all students carry out a major personal design project that in many cases culminates in the manufacture of the designed product. The project originates in one of three ways. Either the student puts forward a proposal, a member of academic staff puts forward a proposal or the project can be industrially generated. A further consideration for inclusion in the project write-up that is not expected in earlier projects is that of financial implications of the design proposal adopted. Many of the projects carried out by students reflect the subject options chosen by them in final year. Product Design, which is a compulsory subject for all students, consolidates knowledge gained from previous years and has further inputs of human factors in product design, and the application of engineering and industrial design techniques using conventional and CAD approaches. Topics from this subject form a complementary input to the project work to those chosen by the students as options. The design and make project is an ideal vehicle for students to try out their design flair and bring together their accumulated knowledge of materials, processes and engineering principles.

Areas which lend themselves to the design of consumer products are special purpose equipment for the D.I.Y. market, household products, leisure and sporting equipment, and toys. One final area worthy of mentioning that has proved popular as a vehicle for design and make projects at final year level is that of special purpose equipment to aid the disabled.

5   Conclusion

The input of project work into degree courses, particularly of a design and manufacturing nature, is a sound platform for the creation of practically minded potential professional engineers.

Computer Integrated Manufacturing Teaching - A Case Study in Real Life Simulation

F. Schmid, P. Broomhead, R.J. Grieve

Department of M&ES, Brunel University

Abstract

Environments for the successful acquisition of engineering knowledge and skill can be created in many different ways. They range from the early engineering apprenticeships of Watt's times to personal computer based learning systems. However, depending on the aspect of the engineer's role which is to be developed, e.g., analytical ability or synthetic thought, one environment may prove more suitable than another. Each environment though requires its own range of methods for teaching and forming the aspiring engineer. Apprenticeships would use learning by imitation and correction, supported by much practice, while the most modern systems may use virtual reality to let the learner 'experience' and resolve problem situations. In this paper the authors describe a course aimed at creating team work skills for an advanced technology future. They present a case study and illustrate the features which distinguish the approach from role–play and simulation.

Keywords: Education, Teamwork, Computer, Integration

1 Introduction

Concurrent engineering and other modern project management techniques rely on multiskilled teams working in an integrated manner to achieve success, as outlined by Cummings and Blumberg (1987). More and more engineers have to carry out their professional activities in such teams rather than working by themselves in hierarchical structures. Unfortunately, the 'classical' methods of engineering education fail to address the problems inherent in teaching interdisciplinary problem solving. Although analytical skill and factual knowledge are still very important in designing and operating advanced manufacturing systems engineers' communication abilities, management and motivational skills have assumed greater relevance.

Different methods for helping students acquire such skills are being used on many engineering courses. They range from lectures on management to role–play and the simulation of team situations. Yet even a sophisticated simulation can never be expected to model reality in a convincing manner since, of necessity, it must be limited to a short duration, up to a week, perhaps. The depth of experience provided is similarly limited because of the difficulty of sufficient detail and enough options,

Lodbrock and Appert (1992). As an alternative Züst and Büchting (1991) describe an industry based teaching environment for CIM which is designed to give students an appreciation of the problems of integrating different technologies. However, their approach does not involve the young engineers in the process itself – they do not experience the problems inherent in successful teamwork. Students simply watch designers and production operatives carry out their tasks using computer systems.

2   CIM at Brunel University

When staff at Brunel University were faced with the problem of teaching CIM to their students they decided to use an approach they describe as 'real life simulation'. The 4th year course in computer integrated manufacturing (CIM) is designed as a double option for two complementary undergraduate courses, the Brunel Manufacturing Engineering (BME) and Special Engineering Programmes (SEP). The course is an extension of the Manufacturing Design and Practice course in years one to three of the BME course, where students' work is restricted to the use of individual machine tools and stand alone computing facilities.

A wide range of teaching methods is used on the course, including lectures by course staff, presentations by experts – on human centred design, scheduling and strategy – and, as the major element, a large group project involving all the students on the course, organised in a management matrix, co–ordinated by the students and supported by the staff acting as experts.

The course environment is provided by Brunel's Advanced Manufacturing laboratory. Most of the capital intensive equipment already exists in this laboratory, together with a range of powerful personal computers. The configuration of the system though and additional equipment are determined by the students. The work in the laboratory is, as far as possible, closely related to the environment which will be experienced by graduates in industry. The facility developed as part of the course may well be a prototype for the future subcontract machine shop, capable of competitive tendering via direct computer links.

The CIM course was first introduced in the academic session 1987/88. This was an experimental year although a substantial amount of work was carried out on the implementation of a flexible manufacturing cell for the production of small machined parts. During this period management concepts, assessment procedures and marking schemes were evaluated. It was shown that a large group project can provide a teaching tool which goes beyond simulation but which can still be managed successfully by students.

In each of the academic sessions of 1988/89 and 1990/91 over forty students formed what became known as the CIM company. It was decided to change the cell arrangement in order to be more in line with current industrial practice. The system became much more realistic and useable and progress over the two years was substantial, though mostly directed at hardware development. However, foundations were laid for a computer based business system for the CIM company, but this was not integrated with the system hardware.

In 1991/92 the business information systems and real time systems have been linked up successfully for data interchange and feedback. Today computers are used to carry out all the functions necessary in a manufacturing company, such as order taking, order processing, planning (including parts explosion and materials requirements), accounting, cash flow analysis and forecasting.

As the above summary indicates, this course is closely modelled on an industrial situation, a claim made for many project based courses. In contrast to most classical undergraduate university projects, however, it has two 'real–life' deliverables:

- the results of software and hardware developments must be to industry standard.

- the system as a whole must be demonstrated to sponsors and local industry at least twice a year and must operate reliably regardless of changes which may have been necessary.

The following diagram depicts the course matrix for 1991/92. It indicates the responsibility (R) of senior co–ordinators for skill group leaders (SL) and task leaders (TL) as well as the allocation of personnel to tasks.

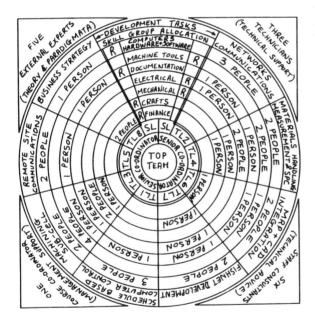

The targets for the teams and their managers are tough and immovable while the constraints are absolutely realistic:

- limited financial resources.

- reliance on teamwork with limited personnel resources.

- management by members of a peer group (seniority no longer confers status in industry).

- group members' recorded performance is affected by that of the team as a whole.

The combination of targets and constraints creates an atmosphere very different of that on an 'ordinary' course. The wish to succeed engenders commitment which manifests itself in the way in which students communicate with each other and with academic staff, the creativity invested and the emotional involvement in the process, as well as the number of hours worked on the project.

The course management expect that students work on their tasks for three to four hours per week, with a limit of about five hours. Most students work far more hours than this, though not on an 'as needed' basis but according to clear schedules set by task leaders. While some students work excessively long hours there appear to be virtually no 'freeloaders', a result perhaps of the fact that the mutual assessment system used on the course would penalise such behaviour.

The following case study serves to illustrate the atmosphere of the course and the variety of learning situations. The pressures to which the teams are subjected are highlighted and discussed.

3   Case Description: The Fishnet

The 'Fishnet' is a communications network based on a reduced wiring specification to RS485. It requires only 4 wires, 0V, V_{cc} and the two signal lines, but ensures good noise rejection and allows data transmission rates of up to 200 kbit/sec between addressable nodes. The Fishnet concept was introduced into the CIM course in 1990/91 by a lecturer who wanted to benefit from the generally high level of commitment existing on the course. At the time he did not provide a clear rationale for the need for developing this type of communications back−bone, since all the necessary control information could already be transmitted by RS232 while CNC data was provided on node computers.

A team of students undertook to work on the Fishnet, motivated by personal interest and, in one case, in the hope of gaining information for a final year project. The task was perceived as marginal and therefore received attention only when all other tasks had been completed. The team's objective was 'to have something, anything working by presentation day'. This was achieved by a period of very hard work immediately before the target date. A minimal configuration network was demonstrated in a 'dummy' mode but no reliable system was available. The system was, in fact, only working unidirectionally and only at a much reduced speed. This disappointing outcome resulted despite the high intrinsic interest of the task.

In 1991/92 the network development task was fully integrated into the CIM company project and discussions about its potential contribution to communications between system elements were intense right from the start. The team assigned to the fishnet was given and accepted clear deadlines aimed at completing a working system within the project span, with trial transmission of NC data as a target. This well defined aim with a clear 'deliverable' engendered a completely different attitude amongst the group members: they divided the task into manageable elements which could be tackled by teams of two engineers, with two major intermediate milestones, namely, testing of a breadboard system and testing of a pair of purpose built prototype printed circuit boards (pcbs). Right from the start the leader of the group encouraged the team to plan for a production run of node units once the hardware had been proved. This production was to be subcontracted to technicians and was completed during a holiday period. There was thus a further controlling deadline linked to the 'real' world of limited resources.

Progress on the Fishnet task was good although the members of the team were at times slowed down by poor documentation relating to previous work and also by lack of 'instant' response from consulting staff. Development of hardware and test-software went hand in hand and led to completion of the prototype pcb's only two or three weeks behind schedule. However, at this late stage it suddenly became clear that no decision had been taken about the communication protocol to be used for sending messages between nodes. This was a very fundamental question since the RS485 bus does not prescribe the method of controlling data flow. The leader, together with the key software engineer of the team, therefore, called a meeting involving one of the non–executive managers of the CIM company (a lecturer). The group was well prepared and able to discuss the issues at a high intellectual level.

Although all the members declared that they would accept any group decisions it became clear that the senior software engineer had already committed substantial effort to one particular solution. The meeting was chaired by the task leader who stated that he was neither an expert in the hardware nor the software area but that his task was one of project management. He allowed an initial wide ranging discussion of the possible solutions but then guided the group to adopt one of the solutions. The lecturer found himself in a difficult position since he was championing what he considered a workable solution while attempting to leave the choice of options as open as possible. Eventually the group settled for a compromise between the ideal, but virtually untestable, system and the solution proposed by the software engineer.

After the meeting the lecturer discovered that the task leader felt he had detected that the former was critical of the group's performance. It was difficult to dispel this view which was endangering the previously very positive attitude of the group. The meeting was therefore analysed and the task leader realised that he and the team had performed very well. The next day the senior software engineer told the lecturer that he too had gone home after the meeting, totally disheartened, since he felt that all his effort and thought had been wasted. Again it was necessary to rebuild a more positive attitude, this time by showing, at a purely technical level, where the work already invested could be used in the solution chosen by the group. This process allowed the engineer to regain his old enthusiasm.

4   Analysis

In common with the other practical tasks on the CIM course the 'Fishnet' development had features which made it both challenging and risky:

–   the task was based on an outline specification which defined its aims and the technology but not the method of implementation. Work to specification.

–   the task had many elements which were interdependent and could not all be carried out concurrently. Breadboard testing, prototype pcb design / make / proving, test software development and evaluation, parts procurement, pcb manufacture and production software development had to be followed by the combined test. Parallel vs sequential work.

–   the cost of the first stage production system was high for an academic context since it required a number of working pcb's built to a professional standard. Significant and visible cost implications.

–   an immovable deadline determined by the need to interface with a large number of other system elements which all had to be ready for a particular day at the end of the 9 month project period. Time pressures.

The team used concurrent engineering techniques with good project management to complete the task within the time scale defined by the overall project aims despite the group's resources being stretched. An industrial development task of the kind undertaken by this group of students would have attracted a wage and component bill well in excess of £ 20,000. It was carried out at a component cost of less than £800 for the ten units and taught the team members new skills in communications engineering, electronics, micro-processor development and, of course, management.

Similar group dynamic processes could be observed in many task teams of each year of the course. In most cases the problems would be resolved by the two students who were acting as co-ordinators and team counsellors. In general, it was found that disagreements in the group did not affect the fairness of the assessment process.

5   Conclusion

Experience at Brunel leads the authors to believe that CIM and its management should be taught in a project based environment with clear and real targets and real constraints, offering students challenges which can only be realised through close and creative team work. The form of task execution should be left largely in the students' own hands. A high level of "consultant" type support is essential, allied to an assessment scheme which promises the individual fair treatment.

At Brunel students undertake assignment work alongside their practical tasks. The marks of the reports carry about equal weight to that of the students' mutual assessment. Students are thus exposed to a great variety of teaching and learning methods stimulating discussion and the development of a problem oriented engineering approach.

References

Cummings, T. and Blumberg, M. (1987) in **The Human Side of Advanced Manufacturing Technology** (ed T.D. Wall, C.W. Clegg and N.J. Kemp), John Wiley & Sons Ltd.

Lodbrock, P. and Appert, MG. (1992) Zentralstelle Plan-spiele Schweiz, **io Management Zeitschrift**, 61(5), 23

Züst, R. and Büchting, F. (1991) Wie wird CIM-Ausbildung attraktiv? **io Management Zeitschrift**, 60(7/8), 43-47

Visualisation of the Decision Making Process in a Maximum Flow Algorithm

P.M. Nobar

Computer Assisted Teaching Unit, Queen Mary and Westfield College, University of London

Abstract

Rational decision making is the most common feature of the daily activities taking place in the field of engineering management. In the last four decades a great deal of research and effort has been focused to explore the mechanism of decision making process from psychological, philosophical, sociological, economical and political points of view. At present, the decision making process has been taught in universities in different areas such as operations research, cognitive psychology, artificial intelligence and economics. The primary aim of this paper is to describe the role of the rational decision making in connection with the operations research algorithms. Secondly to describe the process of visualising the decision making process as it happens during the execution of a typical algorithm. The Ford and Fulkerson algorithm for determining the maximum flow has been used to illustrate the visualisation process.

Keywords: Rationality, Rational decision making process, Problem solving process, Algorithm visualisation, Visualisation of the Ford and Fulkerson method, Maximum flow problem, Problem solving process.

Rational decision making

Rational decision making process has attracted a broad range of interest from philosophers, psychologists, sociologists, economists, political scientists and anthropologists among others. In psychology rationality is defined as an act in accordance with the laws of logic. It has been shown that modern logic consists of a vast number of logical systems of which the prepositional calculus is just one. So it would be unrealistic to pick this particular type of logic and call it the laws of logic. Some theorists argue that people do operate in accordance with some rational principle, but some theorists do not accept that people operate in this fashion all the time. They state that people are rational, but rational in principle rather than in practice. That is, given sufficient time, the motivation and a light working memory load people will reach at valid conclusions. A decision is a choice among alternative courses of action. If there are no options or alternatives, then there will be no decision to be made. However, decision making is more than the final choice. There is a lengthy process of exploration and analysis which precedes the final choice. Rational decision making is at the centre of management activities. The decision making function in management is a task which involves choosing the right course of action at the right time. The idea of using science to improve rational decisions is not a new one, but there are many to whom using science in management is an alien concept. To argue that management is an art that cannot be reduced to a special science ignores an important point that, the judgement aspects of the decision process may be augmented by applying the logic and methodology of science.

Decision making and problem solving

Decision making involves problem solving and visa versa. One of the early theories on problem solving suggested by members of Gestalt school of psychology. Ohlsson[1] has summarised the theory in terms of the following propositions:
•problem solving behaviour is both productive and reproductive;
•reproductive problem solving involves the use of previous experience and can hinder successful problem solving;
•productive problem solving is characterised by insight into the structure of the problem;
The concepts of insight and restructuring are both attractive because they are easily understood. However, as theoretical constructs they are radically under specified. The information processing approach for problem solving was suggested by Newell&Shaw &Simon[2]. It involves transforming an initial state by a set of operations into a goal state. It has also been proposed that when people solve problems, they pass through correlative knowledge states in their heads. They begin at an initial knowledge state and search through a space of alternatives states until they reach a goal knowledge state. Moves from one knowledge state to the next are achieved by the application of mental operators. If a problem has a large number of alternative paths, people use heuristic methods in order to move from the initial state to the goal state efficiently. Although the exact details of how human mind processes information are still subject of active research, it is already known that the mind is a very inferior to modern computers in its data processing capacity. It can picture or grasp only seven or eight elements at any instant, therefore, a human mind can be characterised as a low information processing capacity system with a vast storage. Attempts at problem solving are often hindered by the low processing capacity of human mind. Most practical problems have more than seven or eight elements. Thus the elements of a problem must be combined together until the total number of newly formed elements are small enough to be conceptualised simultaneously.

Typical stages of problem solving

While decision makers do not follow any one procedure in arriving at decisions, there are clearly defined common stages in the decision process as follows:
Problem definition
In defining problems, a decision maker usually seeks to answer:
What is the problem to be solved?
Problem definition is based on identifying the true needs and formulating them in a set of goals.
What are the environmental and boundary conditions?
Identifying the criteria for evaluating various courses of action is an important part of the decision process. In one situation a decision maker may seek a satisfactory but not necessarily the best possible solution. In another situation, a decision maker may seek an optimum solution or one which maximises attainment of an objective and satisfies a set of constraints which limit the decision maker choice. Thus an optimum decision requires that the objective be expressed as a value function, i.e., the expected gain or loss which can be maximised or minimised.

What are the criteria for ultimate choice?
The transformation of goals into criteria for evaluating alternatives is one of the difficult problems in the rational decision making process. Decision makers may not clearly define goals and in some situations it may be desirable not to define goals too precisely.

Evaluation of alternatives
Because of limitations on time and resources, it may be impossible to explore every feasible option. Predicting the outcomes of an alternative may require a great deal of data collection and analysis. As a result, much of the work in management science and decision theory has been concentrated on finding ways to facilitate decision analysis. Operations research algorithms are among the methods which have been used extensively in this area.

Selection of a course of action
A decision maker faces the moment of choice when a selection option becomes available. Occasionally, one alternative may stand out as clearly superior to the others, but in most cases there will be factors which cannot be quantified and uncertainties which must be resolved. The decision maker must use his or her judgement to solve the problem.

Decision making under certainty

Decision making under certainty is a vast area. Under this condition it is assumed that only one state of nature exists which is known. In addition it is assumed that our prediction about future events is perfect. Such an assumption simplifies the rational decision making process, but may lead to wrong decisions in situations where the assumptions does not hold true. Kaufman[3] suggests three primary methods which may be used to select an alternative under conditions of certainty:

Enumeration of all feasible solutions
In this method all the feasible solutions will be specified and one which yields the optimum solution will be selected. Decision making under certainty may seem trivial, but problems may arise when there is a great number of possible courses of action to choose. In these situations the process of searching through the alternatives may be impossible because of excessive number of searches or comparisons.

Progressive improvement
In this method a feasible solution is found first and then search is made for another solution which has a better value. It is the most widely used approach to decision making and scientific discovery. It is used when one does not have a sufficiently complete model to permit locating directly an optimum solution and there is not enough time for enumeration. The methods of progressive improvement do not necessarily yield optimum solutions. With these methods, one can observe that a better solution has been obtained, but it may not be possible to tell whether or not one has reached an optimum solution.

Use of optimisation techniques
There is an increasing interest in applications of optimisation techniques to management decision problems. A perusal of the management science and operations research literature of the past three decades reveals that many models have been developed to determine optimum solutions to complex administrative problems. These methods include applications of the differential calculus and computational algorithms. Some algorithms such as linear, non-linear and dynamic programming use iterative procedures to arrive at optimum solutions. Typically, decision making under certainty can be set out as: Given a set of possible options choose one that optimises some given index. Symbolically, let $\mathbf{x}$ be a generic act in a given set $\mathbf{S}$ of feasible acts and let $f(\mathbf{x})$

be an index associated to **x**. Determine x_{opt} in set S which yield an optimum index $f(x)$ for all **x** in **S**.

Visualisation of the decision making process

Paivio[4] shows that in general the visualisation of phenomena increases understanding. The aim of this paper is to visualise the decision making process in one of the OR algorithms in order to improve the teaching process of mathematical algorithms and strengthen Paivio's claim. To make the presentation more productive a brief description of the steps will be provided prior to the display of the graphical frames.

The maximum flow problem

Consider a network with n nodes which includes a single source and a single sink. For convenience the source is labelled as 1 and the sink as node n. Furthermore, let: c_{ij} be the capacity of the arc (ij) and x_{ij} be the amount of material flowing from node i to node j. The mathematical formulation of the maximal flow problem can be expressed as

$$\text{Maximize} \quad f(x) = \sum_{k=1}^{n} x_{1k}$$

Subject to

$$\sum_{i=1}^{n} x_{ik} - \sum_{j=1}^{n} x_{kj} = 0, \quad k = 1, 2, 3, \dots\dots\dots\dots, n-1$$

$$0 \le x_{ij} \le c_{ij} \quad i, j = 1, 2, 3, \dots\dots\dots, n$$

The mathematical formulation of the problem shows that, it is a linear programming problem which can be solved by any of the simplex-like algorithm. However, the linear programming approach is inefficient and in practice algorithms such as Ford &Fulkerson[5] labelling algorithm are used. The steps of this algorithm are as follows:
(1)-Enumerate the nodes such that 1 is source and n is the sink,
(2)-Complete the network by drawing the directed arcs and assign their capacities c_{ij}. The excess capacity is defined as

$$d_{ij} = c_{ij} - x_{ij} + x_{ji}$$

(3)-Form the set N_1 of all nodes which are connected to the source by an arc with positive excess capacity. Now label each node in N_1 with the ordered pair of numbers (e_k, p_k), where $e_k = d_{1k}$ = excess capacity of the arc from the source to node k and p_k is the node which led to node k. If the node n has been labelled then go to step(7).
(4)-Choose the node in N_1 with smallest index k_{min}. Let N_2 denotes the set of all unlabelled nodes which are jointed to node k_{min} by an arc with positive excess capacity. If there are no such unlabelled nodes, the next smallest index from the set N_1 is selected and a new set N_2 will be formed. If the index m is used for each node in N_2, label each unlabelled node in N_2 with the ordered pair (e_m, p_m), where

$$e_m = \text{Min} \{d_{km}, e_k\}$$

$$p_m = k_{min}$$

(5)-Repeat step(3) and step(4) with N_i replacing N_{i-1}. After a finite number of steps either the sink is not labelled and no other nodes can be labelled or the sink has been labelled.
(6)-If case (a) has happened, then the current flow can be shown to be maximal, thus the algorithm terminates.
(7)-If case (b) has occurred, then flow will be increased as follows:
If the sink has the label (e_r, p_r), the e_r indicates the amount by which the flow can be increased and p_r gives the node that led to the sink making it possible to move

backwards along this path to the source. Let d_{st} denote the excess capacities of the arcs in the path P. To increase the flow by e_r the excess capacities are calculated as:

$$(d_{st})_{new} = d_{st} - e_r$$
$$(d_{ts})_{new} = d_{ts} + e_r$$
$$(d_{ij})_{new} = d_{ij}$$

(8)-Go to step(3).

Assuming that the maximum flow exists, it can be shown that the algorithm terminates after a finite number of iterations. At this stage the net flows in each arc can be obtained as follows. If $c_{ji}=0$, then flow cannot take place from node j to node i. Hence, the flow in the arc from i to j is

$$x_{ij} = c_{ij} - d_{ij}$$

where d_{ij} is the most recent excess capacity calculated as described in step(7). If both c_{ij} and c_{ji} are positive, so the flow can take place from i to j as well as j to i, note that

$$c_{ij} - d_{ij} = x_{ij} - x_{ji}$$
$$c_{ji} - d_{ji} = x_{ji} - x_{ij} = -(c_{ij} - d_{ij})$$

Hence, $c_{ij}-d_{ij}$ and $c_{ji}-d_{ji}$ cannot both be positive. Let

$$x_{ij} = c_{ij} - d_{ij}$$
$$x_{ji} = 0 \qquad \text{if } c_{ij} - d_{ij} \geq 0$$
$$x_{ji} = c_{ji} - d_{ji}$$
$$x_{ij} = 0 \qquad \text{if } c_{ji} - d_{ji} \geq 0$$

The program illustrates the steps of the algorithm and by showing flow through each route visualises the details of the algorithm. Two of the frames have been shown in Fig(1) and Fig(2)

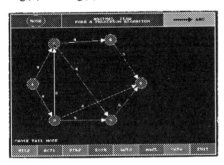 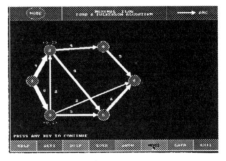

Fig(1)-Construction of the network   Fig(2)-Flow through the arcs of the network

Development of the computer program

The program MAXFLOW has been written in Turbo Pascal (version 5.5). The program runs in two different modes. These modes have been designed for the novice and experienced students. The duration of animation can also be adjusted depending upon the users requirement.

Summary and conclusion

The decision making process has been investigated and the relations between different modules as shown in Fig(3) have been established. The program has been used in the management and operations research courses for the last two years. Our observations are encouraging. Overall, students have shown enthusiasm towards using the package. A large number of them have stated that using the program make the learning process easier and they can remember the details of the algorithm for a longer period. The full statistical analysis will be published later.

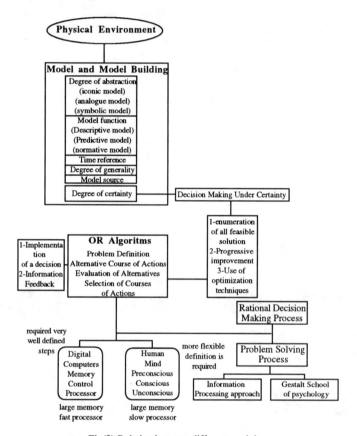

Fig(3)-Relation between different modules

References

[1]-Ohlsson,S., (1984) "Restructuring revisited I: Summary and critique of Gestalt theory of problem solving. **Scandinavian Journal of Psychology,** 25.
[2]-Newell,A.,Shaw,J.C.,Simon,H.A. (1958) "Elements of a theory of general problem solving", **Psychological Review,** 65, P(151-166).
[3]-Kaufman,A., (1968) "The Science of Decision Making", **New York, McGraw-Hill Book Company.**
[4]-Paivio,A. (1979) "Imagery and verbal processes", **New York:Holt ,Rinehart** and Winston, 1971. Reprinted by Lawrence Erlbaum Associates Inc.
[5]-Ford,L.R.,Fulkerson,D.,R., (1957) "A simple algorithm for finding maximum flow and an application to the Hitchcock problem", **Canadian J. Maths.,** Q92.

CIM-Course for Electric and Electronic Engineers

A. Laurs

Hogeschool Eindhoven, Sector of Technology,
Department of Electrical and Electronic Engineering

Abstract:

   CIM(Computer Integrated Manufacturing) is a concept that should create new possibilities to improve efficiency, flexibility and quality aspects in a manufacturing process. It is considered as a way to let manufacturing enterprises be more competitive in their market segments. Implementation of CIM has strategic importance for a company and will involve every staff member. It needs people with "helicopterview" combined to their normal skills in their jobs for product design and engineering, logistics, preparation of production, production planning and the supervision and execution of production.

   Educational institutes will have to consider the importance of CIM in industry and should introduce this topic in their curriculae.

   This paper will discuss how aspects of CIM, applied in the electronic industry, have been introduced in the curriculum for Electrical and Electronic(E&E)-engineers at Hogeschool Eindhoven. New modules have been developed for basic education at bachelor level and for postgraduate training of staffmembers of industrial enterprises.

   The new curriculae are products of the ECIM-project that was executed from 1987 until 1990. Partners in the project have been the Dutch government, several enterprises and Hogeschool Eindhoven.

1. Basic aspects and objectives

   In 1987 the Dutch government (the Ministry of Education and Science and the Ministry of Economic Affairs) concluded that CIM was an important topic to improve the performance of the manufacturing industry, especially in the electronics branch.
A project was launched to develop a curriculum for ECIM (Electronic Computer Integrated Manufacturing).

   Objectives of the ECIM project were:
- to develop a CIM-course for electronic engineers for full-time education at bachelor-degree level and for postgraduate education.
- to initiate a continuing process for acquisition of expertise in CIM-related fields.

Partners in the project were the Hogeschool Eindhoven, the Dutch government and some major companies (Philips, Baan, Silvar Lisco, DEC and HP-Apollo).

Hogeschool Eindhoven is an Institute of Higher Professional Education. It has sectors (faculties) for Technology (6000 students), Business Administration (2500 students), Health (1500 students) and Welfare (1500 students).

The ECIM project has been situated within the Department for Electrical and Electronic Engineering(1400 students) from the Sector of Technology.This sector has also departments for mechanical engineering, information technology, industrial management, chemical technology and physical technology.

2. Curriculum planning and development

The curriculum for ECIM engineers (bachelor level) was structured as follows:
- 2 years of basic education in physics, Dutch and English language, basic electrotechnical knowledge, analog and digital electronics, computer architecture, programming in assembly language and Pascal, organisation and control of manufacturing processes, electrical power applications.
- 1 year of practical training in a product design or production environment in electronic industry or a related organisation.
- 1 year of intensive ECIM-specific education, divided into two semesters:
  * 6 theoretical and practical ECIM training modules;
  * a graduation research project.

The six theoretical and practical training modules, during one semester in the final year, are:
- a SSE(Systems and Software Engineering) module, in which students learn how user requirements or market/product requirements can be translated into precise, verifiable and cohesive specifications for hardware and software components in an electronic system.
- a CADES(Computer Aided Design of Electronic Systems) module, where students learn top-down design of electronic hardware (sub)systems, using professional CAD tools.
- an AMES(Automated Manufacturing of Electronic Systems) module to give students basic knowledge concerning the principles and methods of automated production of electronic systems.
- a MNS(Manufacturing Network Systems) module, to acquire knowledge at user level of datacommunication systems in a manufacturing environment.
- a MCL(Manufacturing Control and Logistics) module to teach students principles and methods of management and organisation of a manufacturing system.
- a CIM(Computer Integrated Manufacturing) module to teach students how departments for marketing, product design, production preparation, logistics, production, distribution and service in a CIM-organised manufacturing system must function, in order to realise general objectives such as: zero-defects in delivered products, just-in-time manufacturing and delivery, small series production and flexible response to market changes.

The development of the curriculum took 6 man-years, and was done in 1987, 1988 and 1989. A first postgraduate ECIM course was based on the developed graduate curriculum; it is intended for electronic engineers who need a working knowledge of ECIM.

Hogeschool Eindhoven has the intention to develop also an advanced post-graduate curriculum on special ECIM subjects, for those who need a broader and deeper knowledge of ECIM than that provided by the standard graduate course. This development will start in the near future.

The necessary expertise in ECIM-related fields was acquired in several ways:
- ECIM project staff members were recruited from industry and from several Hogeschool Eindhoven technical departments: information technology, industrial management, physical technology and E&E.
- the staff followed an intensive updating course, presented by industry and specialised training institutes.
  Furthermore, selected staff members spent five months each on sabbatical practical training in appropriate industries.
- Hogeschool Eindhoven made contacts with several national and international institutes and companies to exchange experiences on CIM topics.

3. Laboratory planning and realisation

Practical training is an important part of the ECIM curriculum. Therefore, the following 4 ECIM laboratories were set up for practical activities and research:
- the SSE(Systems and Software Engineering) lab, with 14 workstations and 6 PC's. Available is software for CASE, general software development (Pascal, Fortran, C, LISP), demonstrations of graphical items (GKS), database functions (ORACLE), and network development and network performance monitoring (NCS).
- the CADES(Computer Aided Design of Electronic Systems) lab, with 12 workstations and CAD software for top-down design of electronic systems including PCB layout.
- the ECAM(Electronic Computer Aided Manufacturing) lab with an automated line for PCB assembly and functional product tests.
  The line has an entry station that produces barcode labels which are used to identify PCBs; a PCB transport system with barcode readers and several switchpoints; a SMD pick and place system; a wire-components mounting system; an automatic in-line soldering station; and a test station. The line control system is set up according to the Philips-CFT CAM reference model, with a DEC MikroVax 2000 Line-controller computer system.
  Off-line is in the ECAM-lab available a NC-PCB-drilling system.
  Four PC's are available for development of product test programs.
- the CAL(Computer Aided Logistics) lab, with a Philips P 9050 computer system with 12 terminals and manufacturing control software for MRP (Manufacturing Resources Planning), capacity planning and production control, and generation of management information.

The four ECIM labs each have an internal data communication system (LAN or multi-user system). The labs are interconnected via an Ethernet backbone LAN for data interchange, to create a hardware implementation of a total ECIM structure(see figure).

4.Involvement of industry and authorities

The Dutch government took the initiative to launch the ECIM-project for development of an ECIM curriculum, and sponsored it with a grant of 0.95 MECU. The Hogeschool Eindhoven invested 1 MECU in the project. Several industrial companies and computer hardware and software houses (Philips, HP-Apollo, Baan Info Systems, DEC, Silvar Lisco and GEI) participated; this can be valued as a total investment of 1.65 MECU in the project.

The Commission of the European Communities granted a substantial contribution for a postgraduate training activity under the COMETT program. Under this program a subproject to execute four short courses on CIM in the electronic industry is defined. In this project are cooperating Newcastle Polytechnic (UK), University of Erlangen/Nuernberg (Germany) ,Hogeschool Gent (Belgium) and Hogeschool Eindhoven and several companies from the participating countries.The courses will be held in Autumn 1992.

5. First results and conclusions

In September 1988 56 students started their first year of the ECIM course. In September 1989 there were 102 first year students; at the same time, 15 students from the standard E & E course started on the final year of the ECIM course, as a pilot group. In September 1990, a second group of 24 students started on this same program.

The ECIM postgraduate training program started in September 1990.In 1991 the Department of E&E had 132 students in the full-time ECIM-course and 21 persons attended postgraduate training.

ECIM-labs are also in use for practical training activities of other departments than E&E within and outside the Hogeschool Eindhoven.

Promotion of the ECIM-courses took place with free publicity in several general and specialised papers and journals, brochures and presentations at seminars, congresses and fairs.

First conclusions are:
- ECIM has strategic importance in the European and Dutch industrial economy. There is a need for adequate educational programs for engineers involved in the design and manufacturing processes for electronic systems.
- a reasonable number of students is interested in ECIM.
- there is no standard way to define ECIM and to introduce it in an educational program.
- continued research is needed to develop and maintain an ECIM curriculum.

References:
1."Automation, Production Systems and Computer Integrated Manufacturing" M.P.Groover Prentice Hall   1987
2."Managing the Engineering Design Function"
   R,J.Bronikowski Van Nostrand Reinhold Company
3."Open System Architecture for CIM:CIM-OSA"
   ESPRIT-Consortium Amice Springer Verlag   1990
4."Bausteine fuer die Fabrik der Zukunft,eine Einfuehrung in die rechnerintegrierte Produktion(CIM)"
   L.Kronjaeger u.a. Springer Verlag   1990
5."CIM,der computergesteuerte Industriebetrieb"
   A.W.Scheer   Springer Verlag   1990
^Za

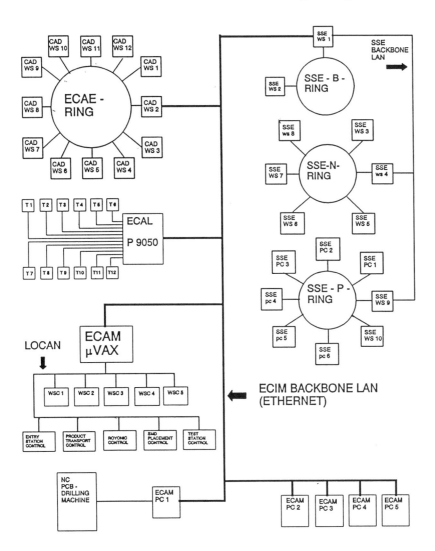

ECIM Networkconfiguration

Engineering Design Education - A Unique Facility

P.J. Hicks

Secretary of SEED (Sharing Experience in Engineering Design), Engineering Design, University of Portsmouth

Abstract

This paper identifies the unique contribution to Engineering Design Education offered by SEED. The Curriculum for Design is explained. The direct relevance for industry is identified. Publications information is presented.

Keywords: Design Education, Interdisciplinary, Industrially Relevant, Curriculum Development, Unique Publications, Continuing Education.

1   Introduction

The strategic role of Design in industry is well recognised for many reasons and there is a **fundamental need** for academia to:-

* Identify Design as a discipline in it's own right, and as an integrating activity.
* Educate students to problem solve and design successfully, both within specialisms and across boundaries.
* Provide the firm foundations for the achievement of effective Design Education through the provision of publications for academics' and students' use.

It is acknowledged that "learning through doing" is a very effective mode of education - also that engineering students need to have experience in critically appraising real problems and solving them efficiently and economically.

Engineering education should therefore be concerned, not only with the knowledge base of engineering science and technology, but with the application of that knowledge in a well managed way to the understanding and solution of problems and to the production of well designed artefacts and systems.

The underlying approach, together with the detailed strategies and techniques available needs to be meaningful to students and usable with confidence - also realistic in the context of industrial practice.

SEED members have developed "The Curriculum for Design" and from this have generated a series of integrated publications, with many more to come.

These publications present proven and non-esoteric approaches to Engineering Design. They are trans-disciplinary and appropriate both to the Developing World and to 21st century engineering.

2   SEED - A Unique Facility

SEED - Sharing Experience in Engineering Design - is an association of some 300 Design educators from all branches of engineering. Founded in the UK, it now has membership throughout the world. The initial philosophy was to provide a forum in which to share problems encountered and successes achieved by those directly involved in design teaching in higher education through informal low cost seminars. This soon led to annual conferences which revealed the existence of a wealth of experience and expertise amongst Engineering Design academics which was widely scattered across the UK. Within a few years SEED was able, in a unique way, to bring together a range and depth of knowledge from these academics, many of whom have practiced in industry, and continue to practice as consultants, and to harness and distil it for the benefit of aspiring engineers.

Annual conferences develop and enhance consensus views on good practice in design teaching, with information disseminated via conference proceedings. A publishing programme is progressed through working parties and specialist authors - with advice sought from industry where appropriate.

Recognition of the potential of SEED to effect improvement in Design education over the past decade has been shown through the award of grants by The Department of Trade and Industry, The Fellowship of Engineering, The Partnership Awards and in particular The Smallpeice Trust.

The aims of SEED are:
* To encourage the sharing of experience by design educators.
* To arrange visits to design teaching departments.
* To provide a forum for the discussion of matters of concern.
* To represent the collective and informed view of members.
* To further a better understanding of design and quality of design education.
* To publish relevant material and conference proceedings.

3   SEED Curriculum For Design

Coursework and project experience should provide the student with a disciplined and creative approach to the analysis and solution of problems:-
* From the project brief; discovering, accessing and assessing relevant data, literature, theory and advice.
* Specifying the requirements and constraints effectively in the Product Design Specification (PDS).
* Generating viable alternative solution concepts and evaluating them against the

criteria in the PDS.
* Developing the detailed engineering of the chosen concept.
* Communicating the proposal convincingly.

With this in mind, a working party was constituted to recommend a coherent curriculum for design. Much consultation, development work and discussion at SEED Conferences generated the agreed final **Curriculum for Design - Engineering Undergraduate Courses** report which contains:
* A design activity model - figure 1.
* A proposed teaching curriculum.
* A glossary of associated terms - necessary for commonality across disciplines.

The activity model builds the "experience" identified above, into an understandable activity model incorporating feedback and inputting relevant strategies and techniques. It has been found to be applicable, at appropriate levels of sophistication, across all years of courses. Furthermore it has been used to great effect across a spectrum of industry, thus strengthening mutual interaction.

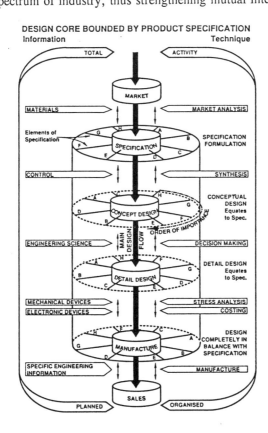

Fig 1   Design activity model

4   The Spectrum of SEED Publications

The initial intention was for SEED publication to disseminate information to design teachers, thus helping them to improve the quality of their teaching. The means used was to share tested, proven approaches rather than suggest esoteric, untried hypotheses. Prices were to be kept low in order to increase availability. Although the initial target was academia, industry has shown considerable interest in the literature, both for training and professional use.

The SEED 'model' of design in Fig. 1 is applicable to any product, system or service which may be desired or devised. Design is seen as the 'total activity which is necessary to provide a 'product' to meet a market need, commencing with the identification of that need and culminating in the resulting 'product' in use, giving an acceptable level of satisfaction'.

Four aspects of the model illustrated in Figure 1 are:
* a succession of **'core phases'**, through which the project will proceed from the recognition of need to final product in service
* a **body of information**, opinion, experience and knowledge which is relevant to the particular product required
* **techniques**, strategies and skills which aid the transformation of information and knowledge into forms which allow the project to proceed
* **management** of resources to achieve a satisfactory result within given constraints of money, time and other influences

For each aspect above, a series of publications has been identified. Thus an integrated overall matrix of publications exists, yet each topic is dealt with in a single publication. This has the following advantages:
* It enables individual topics to be dealt with more comprehensively.
* It facilitates the use of experts to deal with their own particular topics.
* It permits users to purchase booklets on those topics of interest to them.
* It allows users to put together selected publications to form a reference book appropriate to their own individual needs.

A further series entitled Design Projects and Assignments and the Proceedings of Annual Conferences make up the spectrum of SEED Publications.

5   Publications Currently Available

5.1   Curriculum for Design - Engineering Undergraduate Courses
The core material and its inter-relationship, how it should be taught and implemented throughout the undergraduate course.

5.2   Core Phases Series
It is important to remember that these phases are highly interactive and form the basis of a fully integrated design activity.

Specification Phase, Manufacturing Phase.

5.3   Information Series
This series guides the user in procedures for the design and selection of components, assemblies and systems.

Rotary Power Transmission, Electric motor, Shaft coupling, Gearbox, Belt drive, Seals, Rolling element bearings, Design of shaft for strength and rigidity, Design of shaft with fluctuating loads, Planar mechanism, Spring selection, Gear selection.

5.4   Technique Series
Information Retrieval, Communication, Costing, Quality and Reliability.

5.5   Compendia of Engineering Design Projects and Assignments
Three compendia comprise sixty-six tried and tested student projects.

The concept involves the provision of a "project brief" given to students, and "project guidelines" to enable the academic to effectively implement the project.

All projects contain educational objectives, estimated student time required, relevance to engineering or other disciplines, information made available to students, facilities and other resources required, assessment scheme, other comments and the contact address of the academic who submitted the project.

5.6   Conference Proceedings
SEED '88 - Project work and industrial links in the teaching of design.
SEED '89 - Design, the way forward.
SEED '90 - Interdisciplinary engineering design.
SEED '91 - Assessment of students' engineering design activities.

6   Publications in Preparation

The ongoing programme of publications for academics' and students' use includes the following:

Market investigation phase, Conceptual design phase, Detail design phase, Sales phase.

Clutch selection, Oil hydraulic systems, Threaded fasteners, Bolted joint design, Cam mechanisms, Spring design, Operational amplifiers, Tolerances and Fits, Journal bearings.

Aesthetics in design, Idea Generation, Evaluation in design, Modelling and simulation, Ergonomics considerations for designers.

Planning techniques, Budgeting design projects, Design reviews and audits.

7   Future SEED Activities

It is clear that users of the SEED publications - be they students or people in industry - understand and can apply the material to advantage. The excellent attendance figures at annual conferences are proof of the leadership and support SEED is seen to be providing.

SEED will endeavour to develop these and other activities, through the support of its members and with appropriate financial support.

One recent development, in partnership with The Institution of Engineering Designers, is the mounting of continuing educations seminars for people to update themselves in aspects of Engineering Design.

8   Conclusions

Engineering Education is the better for this unique formula provided by SEED and its integrated system of Design literature; which directly addresses the achievement of effective, higher quality engineering education.

Design is considered across the spectrum "from requirement to retirement" through an easily comprehended generic activity model and major support documentation, which also finds application within industry.

There is an ongoing need to consolidate on this work and to continue to "share experiences" across the disciplines and across nations.

The Integration of Design and Manufacture: A Project Based Approach to Learning

A.P. Jarvis, N.J. Quick

School of Manufacturing and Mechanical Engineering, The University of Birmingham

Abstract

Product design and manufacture are becoming increasingly integrated. As a result of this, manufacturing engineers need to understand the whole process of product introduction and be able to work in teams. This paper describes a special student project which has been set up to address not only these broad issues, but also some specific educational needs of the undergraduate programmes of which it is part. This project is believed to be unique in its duration and scope.

Keywords: Commercial exploitation, Communication, Design, Leadership, Manufacture, Market, Peer moderation, Product, Project, Project management, Self-disciplined, Simultaneous engineering, Transferrable skills, Team, Team-building, Total design.

1 Introduction

The undergraduate project described below was originally developed to meet two specific educational objectives. Firstly, it was to be a vehicle for integrating the wide variety of material taught on undergraduate programmes in manufacturing engineering. Secondly, it was to provide an opportunity for students to experience the total design process; from identifying a market need, through design, to manufacture.

Whilst tackling these specific course related issues, the project also addresses some of the changes in industry which are affecting the way in which manufacturing engineers work. Product design and manufacture are being drawn closer together in many companies. Increasingly, a team based and integrated approach to product development is being adopted. It is appropriate that students should have experience of this.

In fact, within the context of the project much more emphasis is now being placed on various transferable skills. Experience of working together as a team, development of leadership skills, team organization, time management and presentation skills are increasingly being seen as very beneficial aspects of the project.

The project is carried out over three years by students working in teams of about seven members. All teams in a particular year group, or cohort, are given the same starting scenario of a fictitious company. The student team represents the engineering team within this company. Over the three years the team has to identify a market need, design a product to meet that need and design the manufacturing system to make the product. It should be noted that members of the project team have to take into consideration many aspects of business operations, but they do not have to design the whole business.

2 Operation of the Design Project

The second cohort has now reached the end of the project, so what follows is a brief description of how the project has been operated to date.

The selection of the teams is the first important aspect of the project. This is done on a semi-random basis. Names are drawn from a series of "hats," so that each team contains some sponsored and some non-sponsored students. Each team also contains students from the three different Manufacturing Engineering programmes run by the School. In this way the teams should be comparable, with a good mix of students within teams. The interaction of students from different programmes is seen as a particular benefit.

Using a team size of about seven members leads to some difficulty in finding sufficient academic staff to supervise the 30 plus teams undertaking the project. A staff-student ratio of this order is considerably better than the overall ratio with which the School has to work. However, given the great educational benefits of the project, and the relatively small number of hours of staff contact at this rate, this "cost" is currently considered acceptable; a higher cost may not be.

The organisation and supervision of teams is done by a combination of staff and team members. Each team is required to elect its own leader and secretary. Some teams allocate other administrative tasks. A member of academic staff is assigned to each team as a supervisor. A cohort director is in overall charge of each cohort, and follows it through the three years of the project.

The project is divided into three phases, corresponding to the three academic years over which the project takes place. These three phases are:

Year 1 -   Identify a market need
Year 2 -   Design a product to meet this need, with an
           initial consideration of manufacture
Year 3 -   Design the manufacturing system to make this product

This approach was derived from the total design concept of Pugh (SEED, 1985; Pugh, 1991) and the Institution of Production Engineers Management Guide (IProdE, 1974). Students are required at all times to consider the needs of subsequent phases, so that the project remains simultaneous, rather than serial in nature. The three phase approach does not follow the simultaneous engineering model rigidly, but it was felt necessary to have a clear end point or objective for each year, especially for assessment purposes.

In the first year of operation, assessment consisted of a verbal presentation by all members of the team, and a written portfolio submitted by the team, with a section provided by each team member. Individual and team marks were given for both of these elements. For the next two years this was supplemented by an element for the contribution of the individual through the year. This was primarily assessed by means of an individual interview and comments from supervisors. Within the last year a system of team marks with peer moderation has been introduced.

3 Benefits Obtained from the Project

The general principles of the project have been very well received by the students. (The difficulties that have been found are discussed in the next section). It has been seen as beneficial to have a vehicle for integrating disparate course material and an opportunity to apply lessons learnt elsewhere. The project is widely viewed as a way of working which is interesting and generates more enthusiasm than other learning methods.

The project has also been enthusiastically received by the majority of staff of the Manufacturing Division within the School; all of whom are now involved in team supervision.

The general level of student performance has been above that anticipated. In particular, in their first year, cohorts have done work which would not ordinarily have been expected of them. The most notable feature has been the quality of the verbal presentations given by these teams.

Many students have shown considerable initiative; for example in extracting information from diverse sources and in making industrial contacts. Several companies have shown an interest in commercial exploitatio. of the ideas being generated. A number of teams have undertaken patent searches and two products were patented by teams from the first cohort to complete the project.

The project has very obviously introduced the students to team working, of a long term and significant nature. This is generally viewed as beneficial, though there have been attendant difficulties - due mainly to the large size of some teams.

Students have been forced to address very open ended questions, for which there is no right answer, only a range of compromise solutions. For some students this has evidently been a new experience; and an initially daunting one. As well as having to tackle open ended questions, students have had to formulate their own questions for solution and their own targets for achievement. They have had to get used to a more self-disciplined way of working with less direction from external sources. It is essential that graduate engineers should be able to perform in this manner, but it is perhaps an area which has been neglected in the education of some engineers.

4 Difficulties

The main problem area has been assessment. The problems are associated with establishing which members of the team have been satisfactory contributors and which have not. This problem was originally compounded by the large size of the groups, but this has been largely overcome by reducing the size of the teams to 7 or 8. The introduction of individual interviews was very favourably received by students, as it was seen as a means of allocating marks on the basis of students' contribution to the progress of the team throughout the year. However, this approach was very expensive in terms of academic time and has therefore been replaced by peer moderation. The team mark, as provided by the supervisor, represents the mark for the average team member. This mark is combined with the score from the peer moderation to arrive at a mark for the individual. It is too early to make conclusive comments on this approach, but early indications are that it is a positive motivator.

Team size has already been mentioned as a problem. At one time the initial team size was set at 10 and the problem was made worse by the addition of students admitted directly into the second year; who then had to be integrated into existing groups. (After admission of second year direct entry students, some teams had as many as 13 members). Communication within such a large team was found to be a great problem. This resulted in time being expended by one or more team members purely in the task of communication and coordination. Now that groups have 8 members or less such problems seem to have been eliminated.

Another difficulty associated with large student teams is that some of them have difficulty in usefully employing all their members at all times on parallel activities. Some teams overcame this by splitting into smaller sub-groups, to concentrate on particular aspects of the whole task.

Problems of assessment, communication within the team and useful employment of all team members are likely to occur in teams with more than eight members. Hence it is vital to have sufficient supervisors in order to keep teams to this size.

Lastly, the supervision of teams needs to be adequately uniform. Supervisors may adopt various styles of working, from the interventionist to the laissez faire. This can result in some teams perceiving themselves to be at a disadvantage.

5 Lessons

Many lessons have been learnt from the first four years of operating this project, some of which have already been mentioned.

The principal lesson is the need to be, and be seen to be, fair in assessment; both within teams and between teams. A major part of this is giving marks for the contribution of the individual through the year, not just for an end of year presentation and written submission. Work done during the year, for example organizing meetings and coordinating the team, or carrying out patent searches, can often be valuable, but produce little in the way of tangible results. Members of a team are better placed to know the true contribution of their peers and it was with this in mind that peer moderation was introduced.

Students need to be equipped with certain basic skills before, or near, the start of the project. The most important of these are basic project management and team-building skills. A pilot course in team-building and leadership skills was run in January 1992 at the University's Outdoor Pursuits Centre at Lake Coniston. This was very successful and will hopefully become an integral part of the first year of the project, when teams are going through the initial forming phase. The aim is to teach something of the process of team working and to help teams to "gel."

Supervisors need to be thoroughly briefed about their role, so that students feel that all groups are being treated as equally as possible. This was implemented before the second cohort started the project.

Interim presentations, made at the end of the autumn term, have been found to be a useful spur to action. These have not been assessed, but have nonetheless been a valuable motivator as they require the teams to account for their activities.

6 Wider Implications

Team working, especially in inter-disciplinary teams, is becoming more common in industry. If this is to be done successfully, then it is not sufficient to merely put together a group of people and expect them to function as an effective team. In particular one would see the need to provide team members with the basic skills and tools for team working.

In the academic context one could take the team working concept further by forming multidisciplinary teams. (This would come nearer to the task force approach adopted by some companies.) The authors have some experience of this, but only in the context of a short 12 hour design assignment. Even in that situation one can see the benefits of the interaction of students from different disciplines (electrical, mechanical and materials engineering).

Amongst both engineering students and academics, there is a widely held set of unspoken assumptions about the nature of the early employment of graduate engineers. It is generally assumed by both groups that young engineers will work for someone else, in a large company, probably with high technology, on purely technical problems, presented by someone else (McPhun, 1981). In contrast to this, the starting scenarios for the three year project have been based on small to medium sized companies and the task facing the students has been very broad in nature. This approach has been adopted deliberately to help change the way graduates view their early years of employment.

Through this project it is hoped that students will be better equipped to tackle broadly based tasks, perhaps within a smaller business,or even as the employer of other people rather than as an employee.

7 References

Institution of Production Engineers. (1974) A Management Guide: From Concept to Production ,
    IProdE, London.
McP hun, M.K. (1981) Teaching Appropriate Technology in the Engineering Degree, Appropriate
    Technology , 8, 3, 22-24
Pugh, S. (1991) Total Design , Addison Wesley, Wokingham.
SEED (Sharing Experience in Engineering Design). (1985) Curriculum for Engineering Design ,
    SEED, Loughborough.

Teaching Design Through Project Management

I.S. Gibson

Department of Industrial Engineering, University College, Galway

Abstract
This paper describes the parameters affecting the teaching of design
as part of existing educational and training courses for engineers
attending third level institutions. Not only is there little
substantive design input to be found in these programmes but also
there are severe restrictions on the introduction of additional
material. This is due, in part, to the nature of design and to
external constraints imposed on the curriculum. This paper describes
an innovative project-based course that can be accommodated within
existing curricula. The course allows students to learn at their own
pace, tailor their work methods to their own timetable and contribute
positively to their own learning environment.
Keywords: Engineering, Education, Design, Universities, Curriculum,
Accreditation.

1   Introduction

It is acknowledged, Pugh (1991), that there is little substantive
design input in the educational and training courses of engineers in
third level institutions. In Ireland, as in many other countries, full
undergraduate degree courses are run under severe manpower
constraints, both teaching and technical - a situation that more often
than not leads to conveyor-belt teaching methods and single
end-of-term examinations. And since many teachers in these
institutions have little or no professional experience outside
academia these teaching methods are seen as adequate - and even
preferred. In this environment, studying design is seen simply as
studying another subject heading rather than what it is: a highly
conceptual and participatory activity that requires exposure to a wide
variety of material and thought processes.
  The structure of engineering degree programmes throughout the world
is largely predictable and similar; even where they differ, they are
converging. Indeed, the comparability and similarity of syllabi is
perceived as a factor which contributes to a successful outcome of the
professional accreditation process. This process, it is suggested,
ensures that engineering educational standards will be maintained and
worldwide reciprocal recognition of those standards will be realised

through appropriate national bodies. This, in turn, will guarantee an acceptable and recognisable level of education within the engineering profession. The organisation of the medical profession is often selected as a comparative model to emulate.

Whilst there are many laudable arguments to support this general view, there are also dangers. It must not be forgotten that the professional bodies only specify minimum academic standards, they do not generally specify how they are to be attained; although in engineering it is usual to have theoretical subjects assessed through a formal examination process complemented by a series of laboratory-based practicals and/or project work. Some of the more "progressive" degree programmes often require a period of work experience which, whilst compulsory, is not usually part of the assessment process.

Any degree programme that does not conform to this model is quickly identified as requiring special attention – simply because it is different. By implication, and indeed in practice, a programme that conforms to the standard format is given a comparatively less thorough review. The standard, then, gradually becomes one of conformity rather than one of excellence. The immediate and obvious casualties of this process are innovation, thinking and design.

In Section 2, which follows, a brief illustration is given of the static and hierarchical structure of a fairly typical undergraduate curriculum in engineering from which it is possible to identify the major parameters affecting the introduction of (more) design into the existing structure. Section 3 begins with a description of the content and methodology of a compulsory design course introduced to Industrial Engineering students in their penultimate year of study at University College, Galway.

2   The curriculum

2.1 Present structures

Whenever there are discussions or recommendations that involve change there is always a strong lobby to maintain the *status quo*. And nowhere is the resistance to change more hard-fought than when the topic is teaching curricula. At universities, where teaching staff have a large degree of independence in regard to course content and structure, one might expect a high degree of innovation. But this is simply not the case. Any changes that do come about are usually the result of a gradual percolation of material from higher level courses down through the hierarchical teaching structure. Additional external demands of professional accreditation bodies simply add to this resistance to change.

Table 2.1 presents an abbreviated extract from a university Calendar which lists some fairly typical subject headings of the first two years of a four year undergraduate degree course in engineering (Electronic Engineering, in this case).

Year 1		Year 2
Mathematics	---->	Mathematics
Mathematical Physics	---->	Mathematical Physics
Experimental Physics	---->	Experimental Physics
Chemistry		Strength of Materials
Computer programming	---->	Numerical Analysis
Engineering Drawing		Electrical Circuits
Years Work		Hydraulics
		Electronics
		Years Work

Table 2.1: Undergraduate curriculum - the first two years
(source: Calendar 1990/91, University College Galway)

The partitioned structure of the curriculum is clearly in evidence, as is the predictability of the content to any engineering educationalist. The assessment of each subject is generally by written examination. Practical or skill-based subjects usually contain laboratory sessions of the conveyor-belt type: alphabetically-assigned groups of students repeat the experiments, drawings and computer assignments carried out by generations of predecessors. Students quickly recognise the sheer tedium and irrelevance of the teaching and assessment methodology and soon learn to devote their energies to mimicking the highest scoring products of past students. Furthermore, the participative or practical element rarely counts for more than 20% of the overall assessment in any year.

To compound matters, the supervision and assessment of practical work in the form of laboratory reports and assignments is a relatively time-consuming activity. As a consequence, it is often delegated to graduate students who, more than likely, underwent the same tedium only one or two years previously. That such a situation continues to regenerate itself on an annual basis is adequate testimony to the inertia of those institutions involved and, indeed, of the accreditation bodies.

Quite often, though not always, students undertake a definable project in their final year which tends to boost the participative element to somewhere in the region of 30% of the overall assessment. In regard to the activity of design, the overall picture is much worse: since the project-based activities occupy only 30% of the overall assessment then, at best, this is the maximum proportion that can be identified with design. Normally, however, the design element is but a small fraction of these project-based activities.

As already stated, one of the main obstacles to the introduction of design into an undergraduate teaching programme is that the curriculum is seen, overall, as fixed and compartmentalised. This perception illustrates the generally held but unstated view that knowledge can be bundled under separately identifiable headings, i.e. it illustrates a false epistemology, Rand (1979). In consequence, any suggestion that design (or more design) be introduced into the curriculum is reduced almost immediately to a question of which other course(s) it might replace. Design is perceived simply as another subject heading rather than a synthesizing activity. Moreover, the introduction of any additional continuous assessment/assignment-based material is seen to demand too much time commitment – particularly from academics who can find hope of promotion through competency in research or committee work but not through teaching.

2.2 Learning process
Although there are several conflicting theories on the psychology of learning, Illich (1973), there is general agreement that knowledge and understanding are acquired much more effectively if the subject matter under study has some direct relevance to the student. This relevance may take almost any form: an affinity with the teacher, an overlap with a hobby, or a keen interest in intellectual activities.

   This is recognised in the more enlightened degree courses by the inclusion of projects as part of the syllabus, as noted above. Further, some courses require students to gain outside experience in the form of summer work in appropriate engineering companies or by working full-time for a company for several months. The positive effects of these activities is well known and only inertia prevents further developments in these areas. Other approaches involve the development of enhanced degree courses and of extended degree courses, Crossland (1989). Whilst there are many reasons for these approaches, one very fundamental element is always present: the experience gained in these activities allows the student to develop a more mature attitude towards university studies, i.e. he/she gains in confidence and experience and begins to develop some perspective regarding the relevance of course content. Normally, this provides a spur to learning, particularly if the experience is also seen to have a fun element or produce a personal sense of achievement.

2.3 Summary
From the foregoing observations it is possible to make the some general comments on the introduction of (more) design into an undergraduate engineering curriculum:
▶ There is a general lack of understanding about the nature of design which is compounded by a false perception of the structure of knowledge.
▶ To teach design effectively, it must be introduced as a project-based activity and continuously assessed; the student must be allowed to develop through a regular and meaningful feedback mechanism.
▶ Design projects must be seen to be challenging and as far as possible, fun. Neither teacher nor student will gain anything if the same projects are repeated year after year.
▶ The activity of design should be presented through as wide a range of material as possible. Design projects which involve their everyday surroundings will encourage students to learn that the activity of design extends beyond the classroom.

3   Project management

3.1 Introduction
Following the evaluation of the effectiveness of several pilot and

partial programmes spread over a number of years, a continuously
assessed project-based course on design was introduced in October 1989
to Industrial Engineering students at University College, Galway in
their penultimate year. In a design context, one of the attractive
elements of the Industrial Engineering course is that it covers a much
wider range of material than more traditional engineering courses.

3.2 Course format

During a first introductory lecture, students are informed that the
course differs from other more conventional courses in three important
and fundamental ways: (i) The teaching methodology involves occasional
specialist lectures rather than the usual two hours per week, (ii) the
overall assessment is continuous rather than by a single end-of-term
examination, and (iii) student participation is active rather than
passive. Additionally, the course demands the widespread use of
computing facilities, not just as an end in themselves but as part of
the overall professional training. The assessment methodology also
demands the submission of typewritten reports at the end of each
project. Much to their surprise they receive their first assignment at
the end of this first lecture.

As a follow-on, during the second week, the author's view of design
is outlined briefly. The role of problem solving, inquisitiveness and
thoroughness in preparation, planning and presentation are
highlighted. This second lecture ends with the specification of a
second assignment which is intended to get students to synthesize
concepts and broaden their terms of reference. Examples of topics for
these early assignments are: "What is design?", "What role has a
University?", "What is a Professional Engineer?".

During the third week, the class is allowed to split into four
groups of approximately equal size, i.e. about ten per group. This is
normally the first time they have ever been allowed to exercise a
choice in the matter of their co-workers, since it is a common
practice amongst teachers to lump students together from an
alphabetical list of the class. These relatively large groups are
allowed to choose from a short list of projects such as waste
recycling, parking and traffic problems on and off campus, sick
building syndrome, pedestrianisation, and student timetables. Since
one of the primary objectives of the course is to encourage students
to identify problems and propose solutions, the groups are generally
left to organise themselves according to their collective abilities,
interests and inclinations. Some groups splinter into smaller factions
and others remain as a fairly cohesive whole. During this period, the
class are introduced to word processing and document preparation, and
assessment is based on individual project reports and interviews. Also
during this period, students are exposed to a complementary and
continuously assessed Project Reporting course.

As these projects come to an end students have, for the most part,
already formed self-determined sub-groups which are then asked to
select their next project from a prepared list or to suggest projects
of their own. From this latter option there have emerged two excellent
project reports: the first on the problem of birdstrikes for aircraft,
the second on an automated football management system for secondary

schools. Usually, however, a choice is made from the prepared list; each group consisting of two to four individuals. These projects cover a wide range of material and demand the acquisition of new knowledge, techniques and skills appropriate to the scope and depth of the project itself. For example, areas covered include the design of a car refrigerator, the design of a self-powered road sign, the role of a university, the design of a boat trailer, the design of a satellite dish, computer control of analogue devices (in robotics, NC machining and experimentation, for example), the design of experiments and database development. Over the remainder of the academic year students may undertake up to three or four projects -- all of which are assessed on the basis of written reports and, if appropriate, oral presentations.

3.3 Course Director

From a teaching viewpoint, all projects are managed and directed through regular meetings with each group. This is very time consuming - as is the assessment of reports. There is also a heavy demand for the provision of both computing and laboratory facilities. In other words, this type of course demands a much greater intellectual, resource and time commitment from the teacher than other courses. On the positive side, the teacher can see first hand that students are both learning and, by and large, enjoying the process. And since projects may continue from one year to another, larger tasks can be progressed over a period of time.

4   Conclusions

Despite the short period that this course has been running, the consequences are already becoming noticeable: a significant increase in the demand for computer facilities, the development of laboratory and classroom facilities and, indeed, a complete review of the undergraduate curriculum has begun within the Department. Not least, undergraduate students are involved in many diverse subject areas which are seen to progress from year to year. A limited intake optional course on design was introduced in October 1990 to Final Year students organised on a similar format, and a graduate course on design is planned to commence in October 1992.

References

Pugh, S. (1991) Total design, Addison-Wesley Publishers Ltd., Wokingham.
Rand, A. (1979) Introduction to Objectivist Epistemology, Mentor Books, New American Library, New York.
Illich, I. (1973) Deschooling Society, Penguin Books.
Crossland, B. (1989) The life-long education and training of mechanical engineers, in Proceedings Institution of Mechanical Engineers, Volume 203.

The Teaching of Design of an Engineering System

R.E. Koski(*), A. Akers(**)

(*) Sun Hydraulics Corporation
(**) Department of Aerospace Engineering and Engineering Mechanics, Iowa State University

Abstract

Software, suitable for use with a P.C. and which will enable Engineering students to learn how to design Mechanical Engineering Systems, is described. Reasons for requiring such software are discussed together with ways in which the broad objectives may be attained. The overall algorithm showing how the software will be used will be described and ways in which the software can be generated are outlined.

Keywords: Engineering design education, Design elements, Analytical layers, P.C. Software

1   Introduction

The ASME is engaged on a program of development of software to perform design of an engineering system. The eventual aim is to introduce fluid power teaching into engineering curricula at 4-year schools. Currently in the U.S.A. Manufacturing, Mining and Agricultural Technology are the only curricula where fluid power is included and then only done so on a need-to-know basis.

The problem is not confined to the U.S.A. In FRG Dr. Wolfgang Backé, who leads the largest and most eminent research academic organisation in Europe, states that fluid power is thought of merely as a means of changing mechanical advantage, i.e. like a gear system.

There have been put forward a number of reasons why fluid power is not taught as much as it should be [1]. The Systems and Design Group of ASME assigned one of its constituent Divisions, namely the Fluid Power Systems and Technology Division, to spearhead the software development initiative. The software is envisioned by considering that the mechanism design separates naturally into four layers of mathematically described machine design elements. These elements are: 1) the work that needs to be performed; 2) the structural system to carry the loads performing the work; 3) the motoring mechanism that moves the structural parts (actuators); and 4) the power control system. The three analytical software layers that link these elements will simulate and analyse mechanism performance bi-directionally (top-to-bottom and bottom-to-top), running on desktop computers.

The software to be developed will have as its prime purpose therefore the provision of "hands-on" experience to a mechanical engineering student to perform correct optimum design. We are getting as many people as possible to express the need for the software. We also are soliciting suggestions as to how best to get the software written, and, at least as important, how to support the software when it has been developed. Our real objective, therefore, is to change the way in which engineers study and learn mechanism design and when we have convinced Deans of Engineering at 4-year schools that there is a void in their curricula (i.e. insufficient fluid power instruction), then our job will have been completed.

2   Brief Review of the Design Problem

Suppose we require to perform work with a particular device and have at our disposal a diesel engine of adequate power. There are three generic ways in which the power may be transferred. In the first way power can be communicated through gear boxes and pulleys, modulation being provided by means of clutches and mechanical brakes. The second way would be to connect the engine to an electric generator and convert current through wire to electric motors, linear or rotary. Modulation would here be provided by the magnitude of electric current being used. In the third way, the engine may be connected to a positive displacement oil pump. The pressurised oil would be conveyed by means of hydraulic tubing to hydraulic motors, again linear or rotary. Modulation can be provided in this case by fluid power valves. Since fluid power systems are harder to describe or envisage than the other two (mechanical and electrical), fluid power systems and control is not taught properly at Universities and therefore fluid power is not used as a power transmission medium in most designs.

On looking at an already designed mechanical system it is often apparent that a better design would have resulted had fluid power been used as a means of power transmission in at least part of the device. There are tasks which cannot be performed other than by using fluid power. For instance, it is the *only* transmission medium that can provide for modern aircraft a source of electrical power with a constant frequency coping with the large changes in input rotational speed and in power demand experienced. It is also the *only* medium that can be considered capable of driving control surfaces operating in the atmosphere at supersonic speeds.

The reason for developing the software is that since engineering graduates have not been exposed to fluid power, the industry suffers in particular but in addition also the Engineering profession suffers in general. It follows that the competitive advantages of using fluid power as the means of power transmission in part or all of an engineering system is never recognised. The fact is that if power has to be transferred with minimum volume and weight for a given power, if movements required are slow and forces required are very high, if instant reversibility and use in hazardous environments with remote control possibilities are needed then fluid power will be a superior manner in which the power may be transmitted.   A principal purpose of this project therefore is to create software that will allow analysis and design comparison of mechanical, electro-mechanical, hydraulic and pneumatic actuation and control systems.

This paper gives, in summary form, more details of the proposed software and what it should contain.

3   The Software
3.1   The engineering system
It has been previously stated that, for convenience, the engineering system to be designed consists of four layers of mathematically described machine elements regarded as independent entities.   They are linked by three analytical software layers.   This postulation, which is the result of many discussions between interested parties ad the authors, is the structure which has been received with most approval by Industry and Academia alike.

The system is shown diagrammatically in Figure 1, where the four elements are shown and described.   A typical piece of construction equipment is given as an example in addition to a human being model; the appropriate parts of these two devices are also indicated for the elements.

3.2   Composition of the work environment element
The mathematical description of the work environment should include at least:
  - mass and structural properties
  - the work path;
  - velocity, acceleration and jerk constraints
  - end point and possibly mid-path orientation

3.3   Composition of the structural system element
The mathematical description of the structural system should include at least:
  - structural mass added to work load
  - FEM/FEA links for flexural and stress analysis
  - mechanical efficiency

3.4   Composition of the motoring mechanism element (actuators)
The mathematical description of the actuators should allow:
  - interchangeable descriptions for mechanical, electro-mechanical, hydraulic and pneumatic alternatives
  - transmission elements such as gearing

3.5   The control system element
Due to the large (and daily increasing) numbers of strategies used to control the output of an engineering system or device, it is not possible to give a list of techniques for this element in this paper due to space shortage.

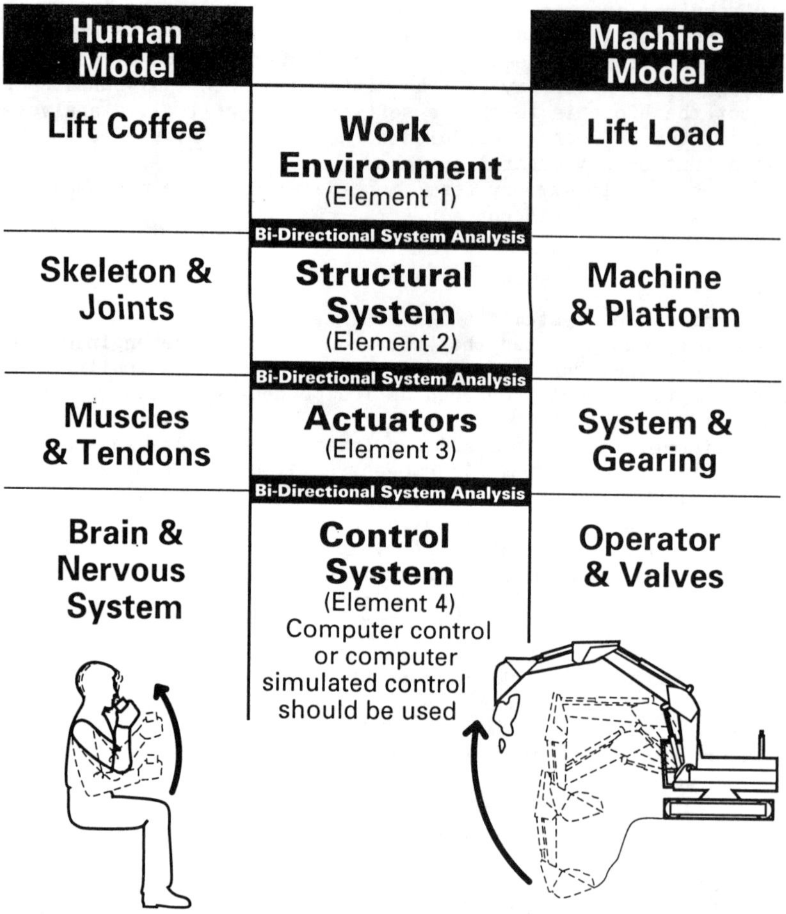

Human Model	Work Environment (Element 1)	Machine Model
Lift Coffee	**Work Environment** (Element 1)	Lift Load
	Bi-Directional System Analysis	
Skeleton & Joints	**Structural System** (Element 2)	Machine & Platform
	Bi-Directional System Analysis	
Muscles & Tendons	**Actuators** (Element 3)	System & Gearing
	Bi-Directional System Analysis	
Brain & Nervous System	**Control System** (Element 4) Computer control or computer simulated control should be used	Operator & Valves

Fig. 1. Juxtaposition of machine design elements and analytical layers.

4   Analysis Procedure

Figure 2 gives the four elements in a type of pie chart showing connecting analysis. It should be emphasised that each of the elements is an independent entity and the analysis in each case is bi-directional. Note also that the information feedback is unidirectional. Engineering judgement will be learned by students using the software.

5   Concluding Remarks
5.1   This project should result in the development of significantly improved design tools which can influence the teaching and the practice of fluid power system engineering.

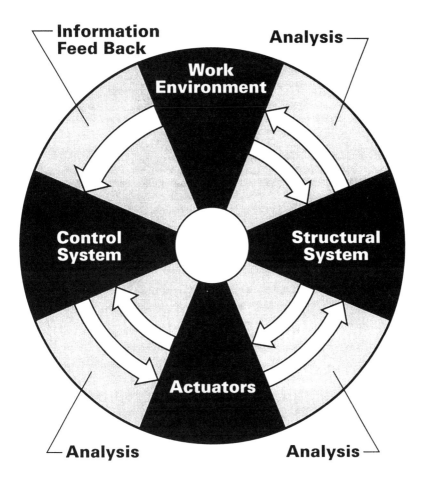

Fig. 2. Design procedure.

5.2 When the software is used to compare the different modes of actuation in a particular design, it will be concluded that transmission of power using fluid power techniques is in many instances competitive with other power transmission techniques.

5.3 This project will produce software which will be of great interest to industry and can also serve as a model of how industry and academia can work together to better prepare our future engineers.

References

Akers, A. (1988) Prospects of a fluid power engineering curriculum,
    International Journal of Applied Engineering Education, 4(2), 97-102.

Acknowledgements

Gratitude is hereby expressed to the U.S. organisations and companies
who have supported the ideas generated and discussed above.   These
organisations include Eaton Hydraulics Corporation, The Fluid Power
Distributors Association, The Fluid Power Educational Foundation, The
Fluid Power Society, The National Fluid Power Association, Parker
Hannifin Corporation, and Vickers Corporation.

Project Based Methods in Engineering Education

A.C. Patterson

School of Electronic and Manufacturing Systems Engineering, Polytechnic of Central London

Abstract

This paper describes the use of project based methods for delivering engineering science in a new Product Design (Engineering) course. It contrasts the traditional delivery of engineering science in an axiomatic structure, which is unsuitable for project based teaching, with a restructured approach used in project based teaching. An example of a project for teaching simple beam theory is outlined with a general comparison of results between traditional and project based approaches. A objective comparison is difficult due to the predominately art backgrounds of the students and the fact that project based methods also develop additional generic or transferable skills in the student.

Keywords : Engineering, Education, Projects,Beam Theory.

1 Introduction

In the 1990/91 academic year the Polytechnic of Central London started a new course in Product Design (Engineering). The course is run jointly by the School of Electronic and Manufacturing System Engineering and the School of Design and Media. It was decided to adopt the project based teaching methods common in Industrial Design education throughout the course. The course is studio based, each student has their own workstation (desk) and the bulk of student time is spent within the studio working on projects. This has required a rethink in the way we deliver the engineering and in particular the engineering science content.

Project based methods are based on students working independently on problem solving exercises with open ended solutions. If project based methods are to be used for delivering engineering science, students have to be in a position where they can apply their knowledge almost from the start. The traditionally structured axiomatic approach (i.e. a systematic development from first principles) for teaching engineering science is unsuitable for this type of course delivery for two prime reasons. Firstly students have to acquire a relatively large amount of knowledge before they can start any real applications. Secondly, the rigorous applications of first principles to real systems often leads to intractable mathematical problems (e.g. static indeterminacy) particularly at the early stages. As observed in the CNAA report, Technological Change and Industrial Design Education, the delivery of engineering and technology in a Product and Industrial Design context requires restructuring. In this paper I outline our rationale for restructuring engineering science for project based teaching with an example project. I will start by outlining the traditional approach to illustrate it's difficulties and then a project based method for delivering similar material.

2 The Traditional Approach

The traditional structure of subject delivery in a lecture-tutorial-laboratory is an essentially axiomatic one which is reflected in the format of most text books. The starting point is the mathematical definitions and first principles of the subject under study e.g. Newton's Laws, Kirchoff's laws, conservation laws etc. The subject is then developed in a logical progression until possible applications are reached. In the early stages it is difficult to demonstrate practically this theory except in controlled environments where equipment is contrived to match the theory (e.g. laboratory experiments). I will illustrate this by simple beam theory where the ultimate engineering objective is to enable the analysis of beams for rigidity and failure. The traditional development of the subject (starting from scratch) could well be in the following steps:

1. Resolution of forces;
2. static equilibrium of a particle;
3. moments and static equilibrium of a rigid body;
4. free body diagrams, connection forces and moments;
5. internal shear force and bending moment;
6. shear force and bending moment diagrams for point and uniformly distributed loads;
7. direct stress and strain, Young's Modulus, yield stress;
8. second moment of area and parallel axis theorem;
9. bending stress;
10. slope and deflection of beams.

The specific problems in this order of delivery for a project based approach are:

(i) If the student succeeds at each stage then they will be competent to analyse any constant section beam under any loading condition. However, failure at any stage can lead to complete faiiure in achieving the overall objective. This is particularly significant for applications based courses when (exam) success is measured at 40% achievement in about 50% of the content.

(ii) There are few possible meaningful practical applications until step 9. The student is required to embark on what is essentially a piece of mathematics under the promise that it will subsequently be useful. (At the same time they are probably also engaged in a separate Maths programme on much the same basis).

(iii) When an applications stage is reached, stages 9 and 10, students can have difficulty in applying their knowledge to the arbitrary practical situations that can arise from the open ended solutions to problem solving exercises. This I believe is due to a number of factors. Through a formal development of the material students, not unreasonably, acquire a "single right answer" attitude. Examples to date have convenient geometry and given data such as moments of inertia or centres of gravity which somewhat disappointingly are not marked on real objects. Additionally the rigorous application of first principles can lead to intractable mathematical problems to the student. Students do not have the experience or confidence to make appropriate approximations. Nor have they yet had the opportunity for relating actual physical situations to the schematic diagrams analysed to date. At this stage I think we are asking too much of the student, still wrestling with the mathematics, to additionally apply their minds to the application of it **and** look for innovative solutions to practical problems. It has been my experience that the student is stifled into finding solutions that are easy to analyse rather than solutions to the original problem.

3 Project Based Approach

The Project Based Approach centres on a Project Brief which defines a specific problem to be solved. Project briefs define active needs defined in real world terms such as "Design a minimum weight structure to support an engineer's vice", rather than a passive analysis in technical terms such as "Determine if the simply supported beam fails with a 10kN end load". The brief also contains a broad structure for solving the problem. This is important in the early stages to give students a direction and stop them floundering whilst trying to get to grips with the problem. Finally the brief contains the assessment criteria for the project. The students are expected to work autonomously on the project within a support structure of lectures and studio supervision with personal support and seminars supplied on a needs basis.

The example presented here is reduced from one completed by the students. Since projects are delivered in an overall design context they also cover other course material including design methods, aesthetics and manufacturing. We will only deal here with the structural aspects. The project should be also seen in the context of a series of projects in the same style. It was preceded by a project concerned with developing an understanding and comparative use of a wide range of intrinsic material properties and at the start of the project the students were familiar with properties and calculations involving direct stress and strain.

The project was run for one full day per week of student time for four weeks. This included about four hours of formal contact time (e.g. lectures and tutorials). The remaining time was spent in the studio partly supervised by an external designer.

For the students to start independent working immediately the traditional order of engineering science delivery is reversed. Our rationale is to start from a particular case (a simply loaded cantilever) and build, through reference sources, to the general case based on first principles. Our aim is to ultimately end at first principles rather than start from them.

Project Brief
    "Redesign a Cantilever Desk Frame in a new Material (NOT Metal or Wood)"

Project Structure
Stage 1 Specify the structural requirements of the desk frame.

In the design context this is part of the functional analysis of the problem. It requires the students to make the intuitive association between a real physical system and it's representation within a schematic diagram. The students are required to determine what loads the desk frame should support both in terms of failure and rigidity. They are expected to find numerical values for acceptable loads and deflections based on their experience of the desk and the environment it is used in. A good starting point is to get them to consider the number of people that could reasonably be expected to stand on the desk and how the desk should respond. A cantilever desk is deliberately chosen because it is a physical system within their experience as opposed to traditional examples like bridges and jib cranes.

Stage 2 Analyse the desk frame

With reference to fig 1 the students are given the following formulae to conduct the analysis:

$$\text{deflection } v = \frac{W.l^3}{3.E.I}; \quad \text{max. stress } s = \frac{W.l}{I}; \quad I = \frac{bd^3}{12} - \frac{hk^3}{12}; \quad E = 209 \text{ GN/m}^2$$

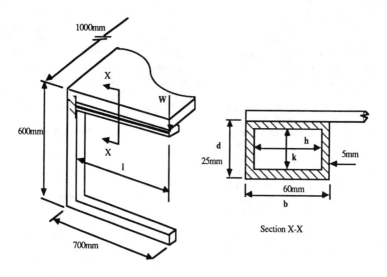

Fig 1 - Cantilever Desk Analysis

The significance of the second moment of area I as simply a "geometrical factor influencing rigidity" is displayed at a qualitative level by demonstration. Remedial maths is covered by needs based tutorials (many of the students on this course come from an arts based background). The formulae are simply quoted at this stage and produce (for our desks) surprisingly good results. The students now have a tool and a degree of confidence in using it. They are also in a position to continue independently with the project by researching new materials either by searching the literature or by conducting their own tensile tests on "found" materials and exploring and testing design solutions.

Stage 3
Refine the Analysis Using Reference Sources

Having gained confidence in the technique and established it's shortcomings for their initial design solutions particularly with regard to the nature of the loading e.g. is five people standing on a desk a point force acting at the end ? and their own solutions with differing beam sections, an appropriate reference source is introduced (Machinery's Handbook). This contains an enormous range of beam solutions for failure and deflection in the same format as originally presented to the student.

The problem is now finding the most suitable case in the reference source for analysing each individual problem. It is of course not complete in every detail, stylish designs with non-constant sections being a particular difficulty, but it does begin to develop the practical skills of appropriate (in this case conservative) approximation.

Stage 4
Demonstrate the Design Feasibility

It is not practically feasible in all projects, especially engineering based ones, to produce individual working prototypes. In Product Design (Engineering) we use the concept of demonstrable feasibility. The student is expected to show by drawing, calculation and research of manufacturing processes that a potential design solution is realistic. In the case of the cantilever desk the student is expected to produce adequately detailed and annotated sketches (not necessarily complete engineering drawings at this stage); supporting calculations and presentation drawings.

4 Assessment, Assessment Criteria, and Learning Outcomes

Assessment is based on the pre-defined and published assessment criteria. We have found by experience that assessment criteria are of fundamental importance to project based teaching. Their attainment is the primary goal and motivation for most students as well as clarifying to the student precisely what is expected. The assessment criteria covering structural aspects of this project are :
- Technical specification of structural requirements.
- Suitability of structural specification.
- Selection and application of appropriate analytic formulae.
- Demonstration of the correspondence of analytic formulae with design drawings.
- Practicality, as demonstrated through calculation, of the result.

The ultimate learning outcome of this project is the effective use of a reference source for beam analysis. The following project of designing a collapsible stand to support a television monitor for exhibitions is a vehicle for introducing and developing free body diagrams for establishing loading on the individual components in a structure. At the same time buckling as a mode of failure is introduced again by quoted equations. The project described here is also intended to provide an initial previous experience and need as an introduction to the subject matter of the following project.

On completion of this series of projects, as well as projects in other subject areas, we would not claim that the student has (ideally) acquired the same knowledge as (ideally) by the traditional approach. However we believe that they are equally competent to act in the vast majority of practical situations. The next stage, which we have yet to reach in the current course, is engineering theory. It is a return to the formal approach but in a different context. The role of engineering theory is to use first principles and the subsequent mathematical development to provide a theoretical framework to the so far unstructured body of knowledge that the students have received. We hope that the experience gained through the project work will give a basis for, and make students more receptive to, their theoretical background.

5 Experience To Date

Comparisons of attainment between traditional and project bases methods are difficult. The Product Design (Engineering) course recruits at GCSE level for maths and science, many students coming from an Arts background. We estimate that the best 50% of students attain the same practical competence as for the equivalent material in a straight engineering course, although we have not dealt with the theory yet. Objective comparison is further complicated since project based methods also develop additional generic or common skills not normally required by the traditional approach. However, whatever the attainment the student has gained some useful ability. They can deal completely with 50% of problems, rather than being 50% able to deal with all problems.

The amount of material delivered per unit contact time is undoubtably reduced but we believe the students learn a higher proportion of it. How much of this is to do with our inexperience is difficult to tell (in the worst case a 20 hour project delivered the equivalent of a 1 hour lecture!)

Students are generally better motivated although there is strong tendency in our course for them to concentrate on visual aspects of design at the expense of the technological or scientific. For design based projects intended to develop scientific or technological skills and knowledge it is vital to ensure that the technological aspects are completed. Without care in formulating project briefs it can happen that students "cut their losses" and only concentrate on the non-technological aspects of the project. As a consequence the project as a vehicle for developing technological knowledge becomes useless. The assessment criteria are a crucial method of controlling this. In some cases we insist that all criteria are satisfied for a project to be satisfactory.

Our other concern is the integrity of assessment and consequently the actual range of knowledge acquisition. There are no formal exams in the course so we can only be sure that the student has satisfactorily exercised an ability and knowledge for a particular project in which they have been closely guided.   We cannot be sure, at this stage, whether they can transfer that same knowledge to general situations e.g. do they understand beam analysis ? or do they understand the beam analysis of cantilever desks ? Examinations are at least a method of testing knowledge by cases that are new to the student.

6   Conclusions

Over the year we have attempted to deliver traditional engineering science in a project based approach with varying degrees of success. We believe in terms of net academic attainment that the achievement in the best cases is reasonably comparable to the traditional method. With our increasing experience this should improve and the student does acquire further skills and knowledge outside of the main subject area. What ever level of attainment the students are still capable of some degree of practical application. Students are generally more interested and better motivated and subject matter across the course as a whole is better integrated.

Engineering science has a historical background as a science and is traditionally delivered as a science. The motivations of science and engineering science are substantially different. The former is concerned with explanation and the latter with prediction Rogers (1983). We believe that the organisation of engineering sciences into theory and practice would both aid delivery and clarify to students in all courses why they are engaged in what can be difficult material, and to what purpose.

References

Technological Change and Industrial Design Education, CNAA report February 1992.
Rogers G. (1983) The Nature of Engineering, MacMillan Press 1983,
    ISBN 0333 34741 2

Student Projects in Mechanical Engineering

C.T.F. Ross

Department of Engineering Systems, Portsmouth Polytechnic

Abstract

The paper describes some of the experiences of the author in supervising over 100 student projects over a period of about 28 years.

The paper describes methods used by the author in motivating project students, especially the high-flying students. The paper describes how these high-flying undergraduates are used for research purposes.

The paper also describes the quality and assessment of project students.

Keywords: Projects, Quality, Motivation, Assessment, Research.

1   Introduction

The present author considers the final year student project for mechanical engineering undergraduates to be one of the most important topics at this level. In the mechanical engineering division of our department, students spend, on average, about one day per week on their project, spread over most of the academic year.

The well-planned student should complete his project by the end of the Spring term, and he/she should write up his/her project report during the Easter vacation. Most students, however, spend some of the first few weeks of the Summer term collating their project reports.

The project reports are required to be typed on A4 paper and bound with the appropriate covers. The polytechnic provides the covers for the project report and assists the student to ring-bind his/her report. Reports vary in size, but are normally between fifty and one hundred pages. For certain reports, where the student has gathered a lot of data, he/she sometimes adds a further report in their submission, the sole purpose of which is to contain the data gathered.

In the final year subjects, the mark allocation between the project and the other subjects is as follows:-

Other final year subjects = 2600 marks
Individual student project = 600 marks

From the above figures, it can be seen that the project plays a major role in the mark allocation, in the final year of the mechanical engineering undergraduate course.

2   Project Numbers

In the mechanical engineering division of our department, over one hundred projects are carried out annually, and as there are approximately 35 lecturers in this division, it is evident that, on average, each lecturer is required to supervise about three projects during each academic year.

In practice, of course, projects are rarely distributed so evenly, because some lecturers have a high priority on research, whereas others spend a disproportionately large percentage of their time on administrative duties. Additionally, some lecturers have considerable industrial and research experience, and in general, such lecturers tend to supervise a larger share of the projects.

The present author has been a lecturer and a researcher in higher education for over 28 years, and during this period, he has supervised over 100 projects. In recent years, he supervises, on average, five individual projects every year, although during one academic year, he successfully supervised seven individual projects.

3   Student Quality and Choice

Like most higher educational establishments, students in our department vary from the very mediocre to the very good, and although the entry qualifications of a student are not a good guide to his/her ability, their pre-final year degree results are a very good guide. Unfortunately, however, their second year results are not available prior to the students choosing their projects, as the students choose their projects before they take their second year summer examinations.

Fortunately, however, the present author takes all the second year mechanical engineering students for computer-aided engineering, which is continually assessed. Thus, the present author is in a good position to judge the industry of a student, if not his/her ability. It must be emphasised that it is very important for the student to choose a project that suits him/her, and very often, the student is not in the best position to decide which project suits him/her the best, so for such cases, a little guidance from the prospective supervisor can be useful.

On some occasions, the proposal for a project will come from the student; very often as a result of the student gaining an idea from his/her earlier industrial experience, and whereas such a proposal can be beneficial to both student and supervisor alike, considerable caution should be exercised when accepting such a project, for the following reasons:-

a)   The necessary equipment for the project may not be available in the department, and although the industrial concern may promise to provide the necessary equipment, the industrial concern may not fulfil their promises.

b)   The industrial concern may have found the problem a very difficult one to solve themselves, thus, the problem may be much too difficult for the undergraduate to solve.

c)   The problem may not have sufficient "meat" for a student project.

d)   The project may have been of interest to the industrial concern at the time of the project proposal, but may be of no interest to the industrial concern once the project has been started ie the problem may have been a troubleshooting exercise, which the industrial concern is no longer interested in, because they have either solved it or alternatively, they have avoided it.

Nevertheless, the present author has enjoyed direct collaboration with industry in supervising may student projects over the years, and he hopes to continue in such joint ventures in the foreseeable future.

4   Research Projects

Currently, over 50% of the projects supervised by the present author are research projects, and this percentage has increased over the years, largely because of the difficulty in attracting suitable postgraduate research students to engineering research.

On graduating, most engineers prefer to seek employment in industry, rather than research for a higher degree. This is partly because industry pays engineers salaries which are far in excess of SERC awards, and partly because industry prefers to employ a newly qualified first degree graduate rather than a newly qualified PhD, and most modern engineering undergraduates are well aware of this trend.

According to a report in "The Times Higher Educational Supplement", in 1991, British industry is not too keen on newly qualified PhD engineers, partly because their expectations are higher than newly qualified first degree engineers, and partly because a first degree graduate with three years of postgraduate industrial experience, is in general, much more useful to industry than a newly qualified PhD engineer with no industrial experience.

The present author realised this tendency about fifteen years ago, and also noticed that a clever, highly-motivated final year undergraduate, working one day per week on his project, would very often make more progress than a less talented full-time PhD student. Sometimes the undergraduate would not only show more imagination than the PhD student, but very often, the undergraduate would be a better engineer.

Hence, because of this, the present author has increasingly used undergraduates to support his research, with varying degrees of success. Some undergraduates have shown a very mature and imaginative approach, while others have done well only after much prompting. Naturally, of course, some of the research carried out by undergraduates has had to be discarded, and whenever possible, for such cases, the projects have been repeated.

In the academic year, 1990-91, the present author supervised six projects, and the research from three of these projects has been accepted for publication in international journals. It must be emphasised, however, that the present author has the backing of a full-time experimental officer, whose contributions to supervising student projects has been very considerable. Additionally, it should be emphasised that the supervision of such projects needs very careful monitoring.

5   Student Motivation

Some students need very little encouragement, while others have to be carefully nursed. One way of motivating a talented student is to promise him/her the co-authorship of a research paper in an international journal, if his/her project warrants it.

Other ways of motivating students are as follows:-

a)   Inform the students that when he/she applies for his/her first job, the potential employer is likely to be more interested in the student's final year project than on his/her other final year subjects.

b)   In the event of the student's examination results being on a borderline, the external examiner often recommends an up or down movement, depending on the quality of the student's project.

c)   One of the CNAA's regulations requires that the project must be conducted satisfactorily for the award of a degree.

So far the present author has not failed a student for his/her project work; in fact four of his former project tutees have won awards for their projects.

6   Student Assessment

The department holds a poster session early in the Summer term, when the student's are required to demonstrate their project with the aid of a poster. The poster is of a pictorial nature, on which the student is expected to display his/her project. Each student is visited by his/her supervisor and a first and second assessor, and these three members of the lecturing staff attempt to assess the quality of the project. Additionally, many potential employers are invited to attend the poster session and very often, many employers take the opportunity for "head hunting".

The student's project is formally marked in the middle of the summer term by his/her supervisor. Supervisors often allocate their marks in the following ratio:-

a)   Project work throughout the year = 150 marks
b)   Project report = 100 marks

These two items are broken down as follows, although the allocation of marks for each individual item is left to the supervisor's judgement:-

a)   Project work -   Initiative
                        Planning
                        Motivation
                        Theoretical work
                        Experimental work
b)   Project report -   Presentation
                        Conclusions and discussion

After the supervisor has marked his/her student's project, the project report, together with the supervisor's report are sent to the first assessor. If the first assessor disagrees with the supervisor's marking of the project, the project report is sent to the second assessor for his/her comments. Additionally, the subject group of lecturing staff discuss all the estimates of the recommended mark at a formal meeting, prior to awarding the student his/her final project mark.

7   Conclusions

Although the supervision of student projects are very labour intensive, the present author believes that they are amongst the most important of the topics in the final year of the first degree course.

It is very important for the student to choose a project that has the potential to motivate the student, and for the student and the supervisor to be compatible.

If the project has a good combination of theoretical and experimental work, it gives the student a good opportunity of consolidating his/her engineering skills.

Projects often lead to the student developing other common skills, such as getting on well with their peers, and acquiring social skills when working closely with technicians and other supporting staff. Additionally, students acquire communication skills when they present their poster session and when they write up their thesis.

8   Acknowledgements

The author would like to thank Miss Sharon Snook for the care and devotion she showed in typing the manuscript.

His thanks are extended to Terry Johns for his assistance, and to Prof John Boardman and Dr Jim Byrne for encouraging this work.

The Design of a World Champion's Solar Car as an Example for Engineering Education by Project Seminars

B. Cramer

Institute for Electromechanical Design, Technical University of Darmstadt

Abstract
The paper introduces to engineering education by project work in small teams, as practiced by the Institute for Electromechanical Design of the Technical University of Darmstadt, Germany. In order to train students also in cost- and time management and cooperation in a bigger team, a solar-driven vehicle was made subject of a seminar. It was designed and built in two semesters and became the most successful car of it`s kind.
Keywords: Project seminars, Electromechanics, Solar Energy, Solar car, Motivation.

1   Introduction

The education in electrical engineering is one of the major branches of the Technical University of Darmstadt, Germany. Every year approximately 400 students start their studies and the total number presently amounts to 2500. During the first two years education is concentrated on theoretical basics such as mathematics, physics and theory of electricity. This program is identical for all students in electrical engineering. It is concluded with examinations, which have to be passed before studies may be continued. After this the student chooses one out of eight specific branches of electrical engineering, in which he or she is most interested. These branches concern:
- general electrical engineering
- theory of electromagnetic fields
- telecommunication
- electrical energy
- process control
- data processing
- semiconductors and
- electromechanical design.

2   Project Work in Electromechanical Design

The education in electromechanical design differs in some distinguished details from the more traditional ways of studying engineering. The differences arise from the insight, that innovation depends more and more on the combination of an interdisciplinary variety of technologies. This means that modern engineers must not restrict themselves to their narrow fields of specialized expertise alone. They should also develop an understanding for neighbouring areas and be able to solve technical problems by combining differing tools. Moreover innovation is more and

more the result of teamwork. Especially in electromechanics, where mechanical, electronic and optical components interwork as closely as in
compact disc players or laser printers and where know-how from all of
these fields is needed in order to achieve optimal results. Training in
teamwork is therefore of increasing importance in engineering education.
The two major characteristics of the education in electromechanical
design are:

Firstly only a small number of fundamental courses is mandatory to
all students. There is, however, a minimum total number of courses,
which have to be chosen from a menu. In order to prevent students from
concentrating on one narrow field, the menu is devided into branches,
from which again minimum contributions to the total number have to be
chosen. Menu branches are for instance telecommunication, mechanics,
control theory, mathematics and economy. The remaining number of free
courses between the mandatory contributions from the menu branches and
the total is used by the students to concentrate on focal points of
their interests. Figure 1 shows an overview of this menu scheme.

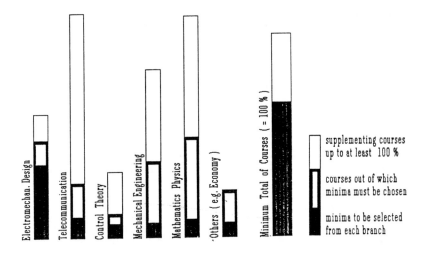

Fig. 1. Menu scheme showing minimum and maximum contributions from
        different branches

Secondly all students have to participate in so-called project seminars in four subsequent semesters. In these seminars four students,
guided by one tutor, form a team with the objective to solve a product
development problem from specification to an operating model. The tasks
are of very different kinds. Some are defined in cooperation with industry, others concern pieces of equipment which are needed by the institute and some may originate from the hobbies of the tutors. All projects
are carried through only once and they are new to tutors and students.
In addition to the use of pure technical knowledge, it is also subject
of the seminars to adopt and to use methods, which support creativity,
motivation and realistic planning of time and resources. Attention is
also spent to the students` training in reporting. The seminar teams
have to present two major progress reports in front of a large auditory

and finally they have to submit written documentations of their projects. Over the years a wide variety of products have been created with
more or less success. From medical instruments to speedometers for surf-
boards. Some of them went into industrial series production. The complexity of tasks is steadily increased in the subsequent four semesters. After each of the semesters tutors and teams are mixed, in order
to give new rolls to the group members.

3   Problems with Project Seminars

In spite of a relatively high workload, the project seminars seem to be
the students` most important reason for choosing electromechanical
design as their specific field of training. As a matter of fact, the
number of students has to be limited considerably every year, due to
limitations in capacity and resources. Away from the success, the project seminars turned out to suffer from two drawbacks: After three turns
the students` enthusiasm and motivation for a forth seminar is partly
exhausted and, moreover, none of the seminars disclosed the many problems which are connected with bigger research or development programs
in industry, such as communication between working groups dealing with
different partial tasks or working under a severe time pressure. Therefore it was proposed by some of the tutors, to organize a bigger project, comprising two semesters` time and all students of the third and
fourth project seminar turns starting summer 1989. By this a total team
of 40, including the tutors was available for an ambitious task. Looking
for a suitable subject which would fit the resources and technical
abilities of the Institute for Electromechanical Design, the Swiss Tour
de Sol was detected and it was decided to design and build a solar-
driven car and to participate in the solar competition of the following
year 1990.

4   The Tour de Sol

The Tour de Sol was first held in 1985 in order to promote the use of
solar energy. It is still the world`s most important event of its kind.
The tour successfully pushed solar technology and made Switzerland the
leading country in this field. News media report in full length and the
tour enjoys greatest publicity. The regulations are permanently adjusted
according to the actual state of the art. In 1990 three categories of
vehicles were allowed:
- Battery powered electric cars from series production,
  which are recharged from a stationary solar generator.
- Prototypes with the same technical characteristics as the
  first category, but not from series production.
- Racing solar cars, which carry solar panels with them and
  which are not allowed to charge batteries from other
  energy sources during the race.
The competition is carried through on public roads and under normal
traffic conditions over a total distance of approximately eight hundred
mountainous kilometers. The regulations make sure that most efficient
use of energy is the key condition of success.

5   Project Seminar Solar Car

It was decided to compete in the third category, because it offered the widest field for experimenting and optimizing. In october 1989 the team was devided in subgroups, according to the particular tasks of the project. Figure 2 shows the organisation chart and the manpower in the subgroups.

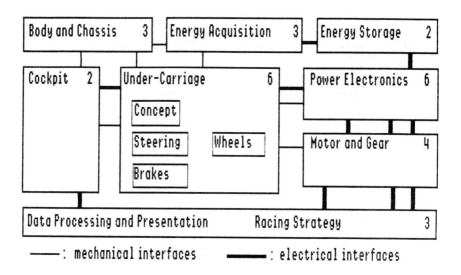

Fig. 2. Organisation chart of the project team

During the following winter semester the groups collected know-how in their specific fields, defined specifications for their tasks and interfaces to the other activities. A time schedule for the whole project was discussed and agreed and many make-or-buy-decisions were made. During this semester only theoretical design and planning work was done. The target was to optimize the vehicle in each of it`s details, because the analysis of the competitor`s cars of former years showed, that a single decisive improvement was impossible. The activities became very similar to industrial product development. The students were encouraged to think first before any hardware realisation was started. Very early it became obvious, that the project was too expensive to be financed from the regular budget of the institute. Sponsors were found, who supported the project with approximately 100 000 DM in money or material. Other institutes of the university contributed specific know-how, e.g. in the fields of aerodynamics and automobil kinematics. By the end of the winter semester the design was essentially frozen.

The technical target specifications of the vehicle were:
- Electrically driven 4-wheel car for one person
- Total weight: 410 kg max.
- Engine: 3-phase induction-type motor, maximum power 12 kW
- Storage battery: Lead-acid-type, 4,8 kWh, 120 volts
- Solar generator: Monolithic silicon panels, 540 W, 5,6 sqare meters
- Undercarriage: Front wheels seperately suspended, rigid rear axle
- Brakes: 2 independent systems, one providing energy recuperation
- All safety equipment according to Swiss regulations
- Air drag coefficient: 0.16 max.
- Maximum speed 130 km/h

Figure 3 shows the layout of major components and the size of the car.

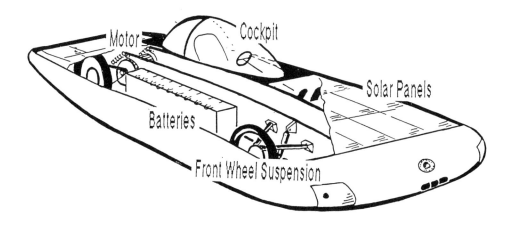

Fig. 3. Component layout of the solar racing car

During the pause between winter and summer semester some of the most
motivated students and tutors went on working. They completed the more
time-consuming preparations for the assembly, such as building a reduced
scale model of the car for wind tunnel measurements, measurements on the
selected motor and fabrication of difficult mechanical components.
    Available time between the official restart of the work of the whole
team and the start of the Tour de Sol was only ten weeks. The components
of the car were now fabricated under the responsibility of those teams
who had done the design. The size of the teams was only slightly adjusted according to the expected workload. During this time all of the students contributed much more of their time than they are expected to

spend in normal project seminars. The car body, consisting of two shells of carbon and glass fibre composites, was built from scratch. Mechanical components, such as wheel suspensions were built with the assistance of the institute`s modelshop. Final assembly was performed round the clock according to a tough time schedule, because only a limited number of persons could work in and around the car at one time. Rollout was only five days before the start of the tour. Very few test rides were done on the professional Opel test course near Darmstadt. They showed, that the car generally met all specifications. Away from painting only little modification work had to be done as the result of the test. There was anyhow no time left to correct major shortcomings of the concept before the start of the competition. The car was named EMcar, due to the similarity with the name of the originating institute.

6   Project Results

The car passed the approval procedure of the Swiss authorities without major problems and participated the Tour de Sol with greatest success. After one week and 800 kilometers the EMcar was world champion in it`s category, best newcomer, best foreign competitor and champion in mountain-climbing. As a matter of appreciation all team members were invited to travel to Switzerland at low cost and to stay there during the tour. The whole project was documented by film and copies of the film were made available to all team members.

With the end of summer semester 1990 the project was finished. The Institute of Electromechanical Design finished the solar car activities, but supported the foundation of an academic solar association, in which students, university collaborators and professors successfully continued the development of solar-powered vehicles.

7   Conclusions

Modern engineering education must not restrict itself to teaching science and technology alone. What we really want is the development of something we might call action competence; to control the process of creating a simple product or a technical system of highest complexity from the first idea to its pefection. The ability to solve mathematical equations is only one - without any doubt very important - component of this competence. But there are other factors of similar importance. The ability to proceed systematically, to communicate in a team, to present status and results of a project (sometimes in a foreign language), to motivate others in the case of problems, to think in terms of milestones and money and, last but not least, to create ideas. The traditional education of engineers makes the student believe that engineering restricts to the quick solution of mathematical calculations. This part of engineering competence is easiest to teach under normal university conditions. Project seminars give at least an insight, how products are made in real industrial life. The seminars are demanding in terms of time and effort for everybody involved. The teachers must have own experiences in practical product development.

In addition to knowledge, the project seminar "Solar Racing Car" caused a lot of emotions with all participants. None of them will forget it during a lifetime. We also had a lot of fun together and I think that fun in education is not against the rules.

An Interdisciplinary Design Project: A Course for First Year Engineering and Design Students

R.W.G. Cloutman

Division of Electrical Engineering, Hatfield Polytechnic

Abstract

This paper describes a one semester interdisciplinary design project that provides a student-centred learning experience. Student teams are required to design build and test a prototype electronic product.

Preparatory lectures and briefing documentation for the project are summarised. Progress monitoring and assessment methods are discussed.

The participating students are either studying at Hatfield Polytechnic as part of a first year B.Eng honours degree in Electrical and Electronic Engineering, or for an Industrial Design Higher National Diploma at the nearby Hertfordshire College of Art and Design.

Keywords: interdisciplinary design project, electronic product design, documentation, assessment methods, team management.

1 Introduction

It has long been recognised that engineering design should play an important part in the education of tomorrow's practising engineers. The Moulton Report [1] indicated that courses should expose students to a proper mixture of analysis, synthesis, conceptual design and other wider issues. Prof JJ Sparks states in his paper 'Quality in Engineering Education' [2] that the goal in engineering is to create successful artefacts and systems to meet people's wants and needs.

At Hatfield we run a two semester engineering design course for first year Electrical and Electronic Engineering Undergraduates that represents about 25% of the first year contact loading. This course has been described in detail in a previous paper [3]. During their second semester students are provided with a realistic interdisciplinary product design project which has now been successfully undertaken for four years.

2   Educational Aims and Objectives

The principal aims of the design course are to equip students with a number of key skills including; prototyping, construction and test, problem solving and decision making when presented with an outline specification, planning and team management, also general interpersonal and communication skills. The key aims of the second semester project are to;

a) provide experience of a realistic product design exercise,
b) provide exposure to inter-disciplinary team work,
c) present a project that is open-ended enough to allow imaginative solutions,
d) encourage industrial involvement.

3   Preparatory Lectures

A series of twelve one-hour lectures is presented during the autumn term, by staff from Hatfield and a local design consultant, to provide a suitable introduction to product design concepts and project management techniques. In particular the SEED design model [5] is discussed, this provides the opportunity to practise drafting a Product Design Specification (PDS). Product design awareness and related issues are also be covered. To conclude, two specific briefing sessions are given to prepare students for the design project that commences at the start of the spring term.

4   Team Selection Process

Originally for the first year, the course organiser (the author of this paper) grouped participants into teams comprising six electrical engineers and two design realisation students. The selection process was made by randomly placing names together from the course register. It is worth noting that in previous years when similar group work had been undertaken staff had tried to select teams based upon knowledge of the individual students. Neither method proved particularly successful, so for the past three years students have been allowed to select their own teams. Whilst this approach can produce cliques and always leaves a small residual unable to select a team without the course organiser's intervention, it generates the least number of student complaints about their fellow team members.

For the last two years it has been found that five seems to be the optimum size for a team, comprising four electrical engineers and one industrial designer. This apparent imbalance in disciplines is dictated by enrolment numbers but the arrangement works well with the industrial designers able to present what might seem like a minority view.

5 The Project Briefing Document

Each student is given a twelve page brief [5] outlining the aims and requirements of the project. The booklet presents the specific design requirements for the proposed product in the context of an industrial marketing scenario. Three potential marketing areas have been identified for a range of products all based around a universal counter/timer module. These are;

    a) sports/leisure
    b) agriculture/industrial
    c) transport/automobile

Once the team selection process has been completed each team is allocated one of the above areas. Originally a wider choice of markets was given but it was observed that these created conceptual difficulties for some students. The above have been found to provide a good mix of end-user environments with sufficient scope to generate enough original electronic circuit designs for the intended applications.

An outline specification lists a number of particular technical requirements; the product must for instance be battery powered, utilise an Intersil 7224 universal counter integrated circuit with an associated Liquid Crystal Display and be of modular design. Specific limitations include an overall cost ceiling of £25 and the manufacturing capability to only produce single-sided Printed Circuit Boards (PCBs).

A requirement to provide supporting product documentation is discussed along with information for draughting an initial team work plan. A short discourse on top-down design methods is also presented.

Each team is provided with a list of components available ex-stock from the divisional stores, data sheets and proformas for progress reports, [6]. Students are expected to make full use of the division's technical reference library and the main campus library to research their design proposals.

6   Project Timetable

The project commences with a one-day Design Seminar, when all the participants meet for the first time, this has always been located away from both college campuses, and has proved to be an enjoyable day for staff and students. The day starts with an introductory talk from an industrially based product designer. Teams then play a 'survival game' serving as a get-to-know-you exercise. The afternoon session allows the teams to informally brain-storm their ideas to produce an initial team plan (which must be submitted for assessment) and to draft a PDS.

A timetable is included as an appendix to the briefing document [5] and important project milestones are highlighted. These must be observed by students in their team plans to enable them to meet PCB production deadlines and, ultimately, the final assessment deadline in early May.

7   Progress monitoring and the role of supervisory staff.

The role of supervisory staff is explained to the students as a mainly consultative/senior management one. As teams are expected to initially seek out their own solutions some form of monitoring mechanism is needed to ensure that targets proposed on team plans can be realistically achieved.

A number of monitoring mechanisms has been tried with weekly team meetings between staff (the team managers) and students as the preferred method for the first two years the project was run. This approach proved to be rather too formal, inhibiting some students from admitting to their actual state of progress. This year a new approach has been tried, getting the teams to complete weekly progress reports on standard proformas. All team members must agree the contents of the report and sign it accordingly. Once completed these forms must be handed in to the project co-ordinator by a set weekly deadline. The forms are then distributed to the team managers who will use the information provided as part of a short informal feedback session the following week. (A report on the outcome of this approach will be given at the conference.)

An interim appraisal is held about halfway through the project at which teams present their design proposals in front of their peers and staff. The proceedings are recorded on video tapes that are then placed in the campus library for student self appraisal.

8   Assessment Criteria

As already mentioned an initial team plan, PDS and weekly progress reports must be submitted for assessment. During the penultimate week of the project separate formal assessments are made of the electrical and industrial design students' work. On the final day a Product Exhibition is held, enabling teams to display their assembled designs and supporting documentation.

Final marks are awarded to the electrical engineering students in three main categories:

a) Electronics; design concept, construction and execution
b) Supporting documentation;
   Product Design Specification (PDS)
   User Manual
   Technical manual
   Individual project log-book
c) Team Presentations
   Team plan and progress reports

The log-book mark is unique to the individual student, the remainder are team marks (unless the students elect to indicate otherwise) hence all team members will receive the same mark. The team mark is then weighted using the results of a peer group assessment exercise to produce an individual student's mark.

Particular attention is given in the assessment to the presentation, style and content of the supporting documentation, which should all be produced on a word-processor. Detailed estimates for both component and labour costs should be provided along with the original team plan and an amended version indicating the actual sequence of events. A short written summary and conclusion are also expected.

To provide a degree of uniformity when making their final judgements the assessors are looking for a number of the points:

a) for the hardware;
   what is the level of understanding of the circuits designed?
   what is the quality of construction and layout of PCBs?
   how does the final circuit compare with the original PDS?
   does it meet the parameters quoted in the technical manual?
   if the circuit works, what level of ability is shown to demonstrate the design functions; if the circuit does not work, can a bread-boarded prototype be demonstrated, can a clear explanation of what went wrong be given?

b) for the supporting documentation;
   what level of communications
   skills, regarding clarity, brevity and presentation, are demonstrated?
   how well does the documentation relate to the final product?
   will the User Manual make sense to a non-technical user?
   will a technician be able to fully service & repair the product based on
   the information given in the technical manual?
   is the parts list complete and reasonably costed?
   is the students' effort fully detailed & costed?

9   Summary and Conclusions

At the end of their first year of study our Electrical Engineering students will
be prepared for the challenge of a second year multidisciplinary design
project and further project related work at later stages of the course. Upon
graduation, students should be more aware of the needs of industry and be
prepared for the demands of their future employment.

The first year interdisciplinary design project has now been run for four
successive years. All the main educational objectives have been met,
although the level of local industrial involvement has not been as great as
originally anticipated. Apart from minor changes made each year the project
has been run as originally envisaged, meeting with favourable comments
from all participants.

References

[1] Design Council (1976) *Engineering Design Education, the Moulton
    Report.*
[2] Sparks JJ. (1989) *Quality in Engineering Education,* Engineering
    Professors' Conference, Occasional Paper No. 1, pp 3.
[3] Cloutman RWG. (1992) *Teaching Electronic Engineering Design -
    a course for first year BEng students,* Proceeding of sixth conference "The
    teaching of Electronic Engineering Degree Courses", Hull University.
[4] SEED (1985), *Curriculum for Design - Undergraduate Engineering
    Course*, Proceedings of working party, SEED Publications Loughborough
    University.
[5] Cloutman RWG (1992) *A Design Project for Electronic Engineers and
    Industrial Designers* , student briefing information, 4th edition,
    Hatfield Polytechnic, UK.

The Development of Transferable Skills in Engineering Design

T.J. Mulroy, J.W.K. Rowe

School of Engineering I.T., Sheffield City Polytechnic

Abstract

This paper describes a common design thread which runs throughout the three undergraduate and one postgraduate engineering degrees in the School of Engineering Information Technology at Sheffield City Polytechnic. The paper also discusses the methods used to enable effective student centred learning and group working in the area of Digital System Design.

Keywords: Microprocessors, Case Study, Electronic Engineering Education, PSQ, Transferable Skills.

1. Introduction

The school of Engineering Information Technology run the following degree courses:

BEng. Electronic Systems and Control Engineering.
BEng. Electronic Systems and Information Engineering.
BSc. Engineering Information Technology.
MSc. Engineering Information Technology.

In the first year of each undergraduate course, the students are introduced to the concepts of digital systems; traditional combinational and sequential logic. In the second year of each undergraduate course, students are introduced to aspects of digital system design, namely system specification, system analysis, system synthesis and system implementation.

The students learn general sequential circuit design, which is reinforced by a substantial grounding in Algorithmic State Machine (ASM) design. By the end of this year, the students are able to design and implement moderately complex digital machines in a variety of target technologies (SSI, MSI, PLD, Gate Array).

The Masters course attracts students from a wide variety of backgrounds. This requires a fairly intensive introduction to the fundamentals of digital systems at the start of the course, so that the students can apply this knowledge in the design of such systems. It is important that the students are able to take a design problem, and use a suitable design methodology, to enable them to produce a correct solution.

Over the last ten years, there has been pressure from employers for universities and polytechnics to add practical content to engineering degree courses. In addition, employers require graduates to fit easily into multi-disciplinary teams, and to be skilled in presenting and communicating information.

To satisfy the practical content requirement, the Electronic Systems and Control Engineering course became an enhanced degree course, with an Engineering Applications (EA1 and EA2) content. To improve transferable skills, a series of lectures were given to the students in the first year of their course, which developed the student's understanding of communication processes, and enabled students to develop their own communication skills.

To allow students to make greater use of these skills, a series of mini-projects or "case studies", that ran during the first and second term of the final year, were developed. These case studies were intended to give the closest possible experience to a "real" industrial design.

2.   Case Study Exercises

It is important to devise exercises of sufficient complexity so that students can realise all the disciplines involved in the successful completion of such a task. Both authors of this paper have had industrial experience of the design and manufacture of Integrated Circuits, and this helped in the development of the following case studies.

2.1   4-bit Microprocessor

This mini project involves the design of a 4-bit microprocessor to be implemented on a semi-custom gate array. The students are allocated three hours per week of timetable time, with the opportunity of using any spare time as they wished. The software used in the task is a commercial package (MCE BXDESIGN), which can run on IBM-PC compatible computers, or advanced graphics workstations. The students are split into groups of four, and are given a specification and two briefing sessions, to ensure that they are heading in the right direction.

The groups are led by a group leader, nominated by the groups themselves. The selection of tasks within the group is left to the students, but to ensure fairness and that all members of the group put in equal effort, the group members are required to declare that they agree on the split of the group's marks. An informal viva voce is held to support this mark split at the end of the case study.

Paper design continues over the first half of the term, with the development of a team strategy amongst the groups. By week 5 the better groups are ready for schematic capture and simulation. Towards the end of term the simulation is complete, and staff assist in

putting together the final designs and layout. Successful designs are
then sent to MCE for fabrication, and when they are returned to the
Polytechnic, the students test the samples to verify their designs.

2.2 Neural Network

This mini project, which is allocated two hours per week for a term,
gives the students the opportunity to examine implementation methods
for hardware neural networks. The project is carried out on a group
basis and reflects interest in the school of a number of academic
staff and succesfully draws together a number of subject areas. Neural
network applications are taught as a mainly software/algorithmic
subject within the expert systems portion of the course and hence many
students have a grounding as to the capabilities of networks
implemented on standard microprocessor systems.

The requirement to implement neural networks in algorithm specific
hardware opens up the possibility of utilizing skills learnt in a wide
spread of subject area within the course, and focuses them onto a
specific problem. The student's first problem is to relate this model
to the models presented in expert systems and to consider potential
prototype implementation methods. Implementation methods which could
be considered are very varied, as the neuron is amenable to both
analogue and digital implementation methods.

Analogue methods range from relatively crude operational amplifier
approaches to sophisticated CMOS sub-threshold methods. On the digital
side again a relatively crude bit parallel approach can be applied but
an alternative bit serial method could be employed to provide an
efficient circuit. Signal types should also be considered and hybrid
designs are possible. The advantage in such a rich solution set is the
requirement to integrate approachs to system design from analogue,
digital, computing, mathematics and control.

2.3 Integrated Circuit Fabrication

In one final year undergraduate course option, namely IC design,
students are exposed to clean room (better than class 100) training
and integrated circuit fabrication methods. This facility is provided
by SCP School of Science, and involves the student in a twelve hour
programme over four weeks.

From previous coursework, the students have knowledge of the structure
and behaviour of Metal Oxide Semiconductor (MOS) transistors. To give
an appreciation of how the individual layers of a transistor are
fabricated, the students are given a small n-type silicon wafer. They
photo-engrave the wafer to produce the gate source and drain regions,
and the contacts. The aim of the project is for the student to produce
a working digital logic function.

The process available is metal gate PMOS, so the students are given a
mask set that will allow them to fabricate a 3 input NOR gate with

test inserts. Following fabrication, electrical performance is tested
by use of probe stations and associated test equipment. The rigorously
controlled process stages and continuous quality checks involved in
such a laboratory, contributes to the development of a precise and
methodical approach to a task.

3.   Transferrable Skills Development

The three case studies described above are more than simply teaching
students about these topics. They are also intended to improve their
skills in organisation and presentation, to learn the value of working
methodically and accurately, and to be able to bring together aspects
of different subjects to enable them to achieve a successful design.

The 4-bit microprocessor case study aims to improve the students
awareness of team work, project planning, and the importance of
working to deadlines.

The Neural Network case study aims to improve the students ability to
make use of different design techniques, and combine different design
methods to produce an effective system implementation.

The IC Fabrication case study aims to improve students techniques in
terms of accuracy and care in producing a design in silicon. Different
transistor layers **must** be accurately aligned for the device to
function!

4.   Conclusions

From surveys on the employment destinations of the students within the
School of Engineering IT, it is apparent that over 85% obtain
employment before, or soon after graduation. From discussions with
students, it appears that the case study exercises provide good
talking points at job interviews.

The wide variety of employment that the students obtain within
engineering indicates that it is not simply the degree subject that
provides the student with a job. The employer is more concerned with
the personal skills and qualities of the student. The School of
Engineering IT has a firm commitment to enhancing the personal skills
and qualities of students, and these case studies help to achieve
this.

5.   Recommendations

With the increasing difficulty of obtaining employment in the current
recession, it is important to make graduates from Sheffield City
Polytechnic, School of Engineering IT as employable as possible. It is
not feasible to simply add more and more content to the course
syllabus, because the students have such a heavy workload already.
Therefore, the emphasis of the course should be changed so that

students can learn and refine these skills, that will be useful to them in industry. The intention is to offer these case studies in more subject areas, in the first and second years of each course, not only the final year.

6.   References

Mulroy, T.J. Rowe, J.W.K. Yates, R.B. (1990) Semicustom microprocessor: an undergraduate study **Microprocessors and Microsystems**, 14, 251-255.

The Integrated Engineering Programme

M.E. Horsley, J.B. Lord
School of Systems Engineering, University of Portsmouth

Abstract
Final year engineering degree students at the University of Portsmouth have to pursue a group project which spans the whole academic year. The project is a two part exercise - first, the establishment of a consulting company, to give an insight into the formation and operation of commercial engineering activities; second, the discharge of a design contract. The latter also involves making choices and decisions based on market potential. Assessment is continuous, with students preparing working files, making group presentations and undertaking an individual interview. The whole project is generally well-received by students and potential employers alike and there is no doubt about its formative effects on the embryo engineer.
Keywords: Engineering; Education; Degree; Project; Industry

Background

The integrated engineering programme as practised at the University of Portsmouth is a student group project which forms part of several final year degree curriculae within the School of Systems Engineering. It has been designed to aid the students' development and appreciation of the totality and integrative nature of engineering as a discipline which, industrially and commercially, involves far more than the traditionally taught subjects of mainly or solely technical content.

In 1975, the UK government gathered together an advisory body under the chairmanship of Sir Monty Finniston, a noted industrialist, to consider the future needs of engineering education. As a consequence, the Bachelor of Engineering degree courses (and by implication, other courses such as Diplomas) which supplanted the traditional first degree courses in engineering place a greater emphasis on engineering applications and the wider dimension of the business of engineering. This change was given teeth by the involvement at an early stage of the professional institutions, such as the Institution of Mechanical Engineers. By way of example, that body now requires of applicants for Chartered status clear evidence of exposure to and proficiency in Applications of Engineering Technology (AET) and Engineering as a Dimension of Business (EDB). For the present illustrative purpose, these topics may be summarised as including

AET   -   Materials and components; engineering processes; assembly, installation and commissioning; design and manufacture.

EDB   -   Management of engineering activities; financial, legal and commercial implications; personal and interpersonal skills;

The subject of Integrated Engineering Applications (IEA) is one of the main vehicles developed for, and used to complement these topics, and is based on a philosophy which recognises the full engineering dimension of real industrial or commercial engineering problems. The objectives of IEA therefore include

i   complementing and extending the students' present knowledge and developing potential at all honours degree levels;
ii   securing mathematical and scientific principles rigorously;
iii   imparting further technical knowledge and, by extending into the business realm, developing the applications of skills to the business of engineering;
iv   pursuing these aims by practising, as far as reasonably possible within an academic environment, specialised and integrated applications of engineering;
v   reinforcing the fact that professional engineering is an exciting and continuous multidisciplinary challenge.

Items i and ii of this lest reflect traditional aspirations but items ii, iv and v show the new orientation.

The Activity

As practised successfully in our courses for the past seven years, IEA is a final year group project activity allocated some 3 timetabled hours per week for the full academic year. The students (140 or so in the year 1991-2) are separated initially into groups of five or six for the discharge of IEA. There is no choice on the students' part, the separation being entirely within the control of the academic supervisors, of whom there are six. With the progressive introduction of the broader based Engineering and Engineering Systems degree course and the Manufacturing Systems degree course to run alongside the long-standing Mechanical Engineering degree course within the School, there is a major mix of student interests and academic disciplines. Each group is thus chosen from the range of courses to include students with biases towards mechanical, electronic and manufacturing interests. As other courses are introduced into the school, having mainstream management and business features, these too will be integrated in similar fashion.   Much effort is expended in balancing the skills, backgrounds, experience and academic history of the groups and each group is allocated a member of the School's academic staff as mentor.   Typically, a staff member will deal with four groups but this is not an exclusive role, more a focus for the groups.   All staff associated with IEA disseminate their specialist abilities across the whole exercise.

As with other timetabled activities, the students are expected to add time outside the formal schedule and this becomes an input which involves their own time to the benefit of themselves and to others.   With the unavoidable team aspect of a group activity, the scheduling by the students of work outside the formal time enhances the broadening of students' awareness and the development of interpersonal and leadership skills in the engineering context.

The purpose of arranging groups in this way is to reflect the fact that, in the real world, choice of working partners cannot necessarily be made and there has to be capitalization on the team's available skills.   Parallel to this, the topic for the year also reflects the fact that in the real world there is not always a free choice of work area.   The professional engineer is expected to do the task set by the employer or the customer and to discharge that task to the best of his or her ability.

When the teams are established, during the first meeting of the whole student body for the year, the first step for each group is to elect a chairman or coordinator so that a proper team attitude may develop.   Thus individual skills used may be optimised and any information disseminated by the academic supervisors or found separately by the individual group members is more likely to be utilized properly.   As a coherent group, they then have to set up a small consultancy organisation, dealing with its formation, financing, location and technical work area.   Whilst the latter is automatically geared to the year's chosen topic (again set by the staff, not the students) the team is expected and encouraged to take the wider view of future work opportunities, both nationally and internationally.

Since commerce is intended to play a significant part from the beginning, a simple scenario for the students is laid down wherein they are all assumed to have about ten years' professional engineering experience.   They have thus a bank of experience and contacts and have now decided to set up as a consultancy group.   By way of severance pay from their former employers, personal savings and collateral, they are each able to raise a nominal £50000 to start their venture.   This shows that real consideration has to be given to the starting of any commercial venture and that significant prior discussion would have been undertaken.   Evidence of such discussion is required of the groups as part of their progress assessment.

Initially each group is encouraged to determine for instance

i   What sort of organisation will they form and why? A partnership, a limited company?

ii Where is the group based and why? Will they be close to their potential customers? Will they take advantage of any financial inducements to locate in specific areas of the country?

iii Will they rent or buy premises? Will they rent or buy equipment? What is needed?

iv What roles will each group member take? Will the roles be exclusive or rotated?

v   What precisely is being offered to their potential customers?

vi Will banks or financial institutions be supportive?

Parallel to this but initially subordinate, the groups are given a commercial engineering problem to attack for a customer. Topical problems are formulated for this purpose and the subjects change from year to year. Even if topicality remains, the results of an exercise filter down to next years' students and some of the advantages are thus lost if the same topic is used. The topics covered to date include

i   A waste oil fired space heating system;
ii A low volume specialist motor car;
iii An attack on the motor cycle market;
iv A microlight aircraft;
v   A light rapid transit system;
vi A leisure industry product.

Once the type of company, its location and offerings have been decided, along with the roles of the individuals within the team, the emphasis changes to a more technical nature. The groups have to take a broad view of the problem set so that some assessment can be made of what the customer expects of the product and what the market conditions are for the exploitation of a successful design. Professional advice, such as from banks or practising engineers, is brought in for the whole student body as appropriate, but the individual groups are expected to seek out relevant information as and where or when it may arise. It has to be significant that many companies and commercial or industrial bodies have given their information freely and regularly in this context.

With the progressive gathering and analysing of information gained, each team is then expected to investigate the design, manufacture, production facilities, costing, quality control and marketing aspects of the intended product. It can be seen then that the activity provides the students with attitudes which in turn means the wide range of selecting, combining, transferring, converting and manipulating ideas, facts and laws into viable products or systems for commercial exploitation.

Eventually, each group is required to produce a total package for their assumed client. Since it would be most unusual in the real engineering world for there to be a unique solution to any complex problem, then there is no single correct answer to this group topic problem or project, whatever its basis for any given year. Each group therefore has to justify and defend its own decisions or preferred solution and to show an ability to take a critical view of the offerings of others.

Assessment

Assessment is continuous, being spread across the life of the project. There are three main features to the assessment plus some moderating ones. The main features cover the keeping of a working file, presentations of the work in progress and an individual interview.

All students maintain a personal working file which may be reviewed at any time by the group mentor. This file is then assessed more rigorously at the end of the first term by a member of staff other than the group's mentor and at the end of the second term by yet another staff member.

At the end of the first term, each group gives a first presentation of about twenty minutes overall duration, using whatever facilities - video, for example - they choose. The other student groups are invited to carry the bulk of the questioning which follows the presentation. The formal marking however is concluded by the academic staff, several such staff commenting on each group.

At the end of the second term each student undergoes an individual interview with the staff member who is reviewing his or her working file at that time. The file used as the basis for the interview and it is expected that the contents of the file and the conclusions from the interview align.

The final formal assessment is the end-product group presentation towards the end of the academic year. At this time, each group makes a presentation of its overall findings in respect of the product, as though they were presenting to their funding customer. As with the first group presentation, whilst the academic staff make the ultimate judgement, the main questioning comes from their fellow students. It is important to appreciate the degree of group competitiveness which has developed by this time and an impressive amount of expertise and privileged knowledge is displayed by many in the questioning.

There is opportunity in the School's annual open day for project displays for the groups to show their findings also. This is normally a static display of information and decisions but several groups will show models of their design or major items borrowed for the day from industrial bodies. This is an optional part of the exercise but most groups participate and are rewarded by extra marks as appropriate to the quality of their display. It is usual for these displays to form part of the group second formal presentations, so the work involved may have a double benefit.

As individual student marks are finally decided by the staff team from the build-up of continuous assessment, the mentor's overview is added. The total technique employed in IEA thus gives students three formal ways of winning a good mark - the group presentation, the individual interview and the working file - as well as the informal way of impressing the mentor with application and developing knowledge. The rotating of marking duties is also a clear precaution against biased marking, although the team is sufficiently experienced for this to be a political precaution rather than a necessity.

Peer assessment has been introduced at all stages, dealing with both a group's view of others' performance and the views of individual students of their fellows. It has proved most instructive and it is worth recording that, in general, the students' views align with those of the staff. Peer assessment provides a valuable insight for both student and staff and adds further to the students' grasp of the way in which real organisations work.

In conclusion

The whole exercise absorbs a significant part of the students' time an the rewards, in terms of marks proportion for the final year at large, is commensurate. Experience suggests that the IEA exercise is a valuable part of the students' development as embryo professional engineers and they emerge better equipped to select and tackle a career in the outside world. There is positive proof that first appointments have been won by students as a direct result of their involvement in the Integrated Engineering Applications activity and it is the School's intention to continue the activity's inclusion in the education scheme.

Linking Graphics, Design and Materials in the Engineering Curriculum

G. Bitterfeld, A.S. Blicblau

CIM Centre, School of Mechanical and Manufacturing Engineering, Swinburne Institute of Technology

Abstract

The basis of engineering design can be related to the integration of fundamental materials properties and concomitant stress behaviour. Specific teaching areas are described for the areas of graphics, materials and design which result in an integrated approach to the study of design concepts. A description of two methods of teaching in these areas are outlined with special reference to industry liaisons and applications to the education of female engineers in the fields of mechanical and manufacturing engineering

Keywords : Design, Graphics, Materials, Manufacturing, Mechanical

1   Introduction

One of the most important areas for training engineering students is to make them familiar and comfortable with apparently complex areas of modern technology. To be able to communicate effectively with fellow engineers, the students must be able to both comprehend and perform design projects utilising both traditional and advanced techniques. The starting point for this training is during the first year engineering studies where from many different areas the needs of design, graphics and engineering materials are combined to develop a comprehension of the requirements of a finished component. However, there is a large gap in the understanding of the technological requirements by the incoming students. It is only 16 weeks since they finished high school, where the teaching methods and subject content are vastly different to that at tertiary institutes.

The traditional engineering first year subjects of physics, chemistry or, mathematics offer no surprise or apprehension to the students. It is the few remaining 'engineering', subjects which the students often have to come to understand and master in a relatively short amount of time. We will selectively discuss and show examples of teaching methods for three areas which are 'new' to the student, viz. graphics, design and materials. They appear to have no correspondence to their high school studies, and offer a challenge to the student. By linking graphics, design and materials the first year student is prepared for their most important step - their placement in industry in a cooperative education framework. Because the

understanding in these three areas may often be cultural and gender
based, special teaching styles are required to facilitate the
comprehension of these subjects.

2   Linking Students to Engineering

To understand why we are selecting this specific area of teaching, we
first have to examine the type of student population with which we
come in contact. The first year intake into engineering is based upon
how well the students perform in a common statewide exam known as the
Victorian Certificate of Education (VCE). In the normal course of
selection approximately 450 students commence first year studies in
engineering. The students undertake a common first year of
engineering subjects and are not required to select their specialty
field until they finish this first year of studies. Within this
intake there are a number of distinct student groups who require
special attention. These fall into three broad categories, the first
are the foreign students whose first language is not English, the
second are the 'alternate entry' students, who do not have the
necessary pre-requisite subjects for engineering from the VCE exam,
and the third group are the females who encompass both the two
previous groups as well as the general intake (Fig. 1).

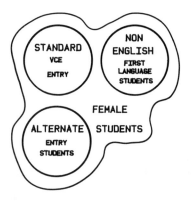

Fig. 1 Distribution of first year student intake

These 'alternate' students are given special tutoring in
mathematics, physics, or chemistry depending on their shortfall in
the VCE. However, there is no introduction to concepts of engineering
or technology nor special tutoring in the 'engineering subjects. We
have found that a large number of students, in particular, females
(approximately 10% of the first year student intake) do not have any
technical understanding or skills. Their comprehension is based only
on scientific understanding. This first year program is intended to
enhance the appreciation and familiarity of 'alternate' students with
the basics of engineering

3   Linking Engineering Concepts to Students

One of the most important subjects for all the first year students
is graphics. The purposes of teaching graphics, which incorporates
design and strength of materials are twofold; the first is to prepare
the students with a solid basis in the areas of design in later years,
and the second is to develop a good understanding of the requirements
of engineering industry. This approach introduces the student to the
first steps of engineering innovation, irrespective of their previous
training.

3.1 Linking Graphics Concepts

The course is divided into two major parts, manual drafting and
computer aid drafting (CAD). This is because industry still has
components of design based on paper (manual) drawings. Each part is
given in alternate weeks, so that the student is simultaneously
exposed to both modern and standard methods of design (Bitterfeld,
1991). By working on a computer with CAD, it appears the motivation
and the interest factor is increased over that of solely manual
drawing. An example of this ability and involvement is given in Fig. 2
which shows how these various first year subjects interact

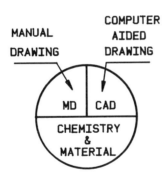

Fig.2. Interaction of first year engineering graphics subjects.

(a) Manual drafting: this is covered by both lectures and tutorials,
and a series of associated class assignments during the first
semester. The theory for each drafting session is given during the
one hour lecture. This essentially covers basic techniques of views,
projections, and sectioning. The student is then required to complete
the class assignment during the following hour tutorial session.
(b) CAD: during these sessions the same topics are covered as with
manual drafting. The session is also divided into a lecture period
and a tutorial period with an assignment required for completion
during the latter session.

(c) Projects: the next step in the linking process is to complete a project at the end of each session. The student now has the basics of drawing and is ready to combine these concepts with a mechanical engineering design activity.

These require a combination of drawing skills and design philosophy. This may involve exercises with screws, springs, gears, or other simple engineering components. The exercise requires information on a parts listing, materials listing, welding or joining, an assembly drawing and any sub-assembly drawings. At the end of these exercises the student has the ability to both design and draw a complex project.

At the commencement of second semester of first year studies, engineering materials are introduced into the syllabus. We are now able to combine the concepts of graphics (and simple design), together with the influence materials has on these processes. The student is given an understanding of why it is necessary to study this subject, by investigating a range of material and learning the difference in materials behaviour and properties. However, the student still has to understand how materials behaviour are related to their utilisation and performance. It is in the following two years of study (Fig. 3) that the principles of graphics, design and materials behaviour learnt in the first year are applied to such areas as Design in Industry (second year) and Design in Manufacturing (third year)

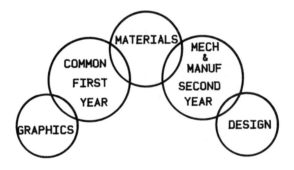

Fig.3. Enhancement of principles of fundamental studies

4   Linking Engineering through Design Applications

To highlight the importance of the design situation, three examples are given to the student to analyse as part of their second year assessment. These require a number of different specification criteria as shown in Table 1, which combine much of the theory they have learnt. The projects involve developing a CAD graphics design together with appropriate selection of materials.

At this stage the student undertakes the first of two six month periods of industrial cooperative training. With the knowledge and experience gained through the design and allied subjects the students will be able to put these into application. This is a major step, because for the most of them it is the first contact with the real life in industry as engineer. It is at this crucial stage that real differences amongst different groups of students, e.g. females, and foreign language students become apparent.

Table 1. Design and specification criteria (Shigley, 1986)

ITEM	CRITERIA	COMMENT
Spur Gear	High Surface stresses	Material dependent
	Hertzian contact stresses	C_p elastic coefficient
		High load bearing capacity
		Metallic - non metallic materials
		Brinell hardness 70-85
Shafts	High Failure stress	Analysis of materials using Sines, Goodman or Soderberg approach
Friction Clutches	Good wet environment properties	Film oil viscosity Thin coating or spray

5 Linking Females To Engineering

If present trends in the number of women enroling in engineering courses continue, then by the end of this decade up to a quarter of all practising engineers in Australia could be women (Sargent, 1991). The face of the future profession of engineering is that of a woman. We can use this conclusion to show the development of initiatives in the way we approach the engineering studies at Swinburne. Because more women now undertake engineering, course structures, subjects and teaching styles need to be reevaluated to accommodate women's interest and experience. The results of these initiatives may also be used to complement the education of other groups of engineering students.

Female students come from high school from both a technical and non-technical background, but with great motivation and willingness, with young conceptions about an "old male profession". We as educators need to receive them with strong open hands and to make them feel equal with all other students in first year .

Graphics is a subject of visualization of life, bodies, and machine parts. For the female students we need to develop a special approach in which visualisation forms a part of the subject rather than a purely technical approach. The subject of graphics is taught using two different teaching styles, although the same topics are covered. For example, in the first style, females may study the same problems and have the same tutorial exercises as the males, but from the practical(visual) point of view , whilst the second style gives the males problems and tutorial exercises from a technical point of view. There is not a division between the understanding capacity of females and males but merely looking at two teaching approaches to the same problem. To discuss drawings from industry and to interpret graphics from real parts in front of a class can help the female students better understand the principles required. This is one way in which the subject of graphics is made interesting.

Using this approach to introduce the principles of graphics and subsequent design to first year female students, other subject areas are also introduced utilising this visualisation manner. Materials studies are undertaken in second semester utilising a combination of lectures, demonstration, and practical exercises for all first year students not only for female students but for all first year undergraduate students. This approach has been found to be a satisfactory technique for providing students with a practical realisation of the requirements of engineering(Blicblau, 1991).

6   Concluding remarks

Integration of materials, stress analysis and engineering design has formed a powerful teaching base for graduating engineers. An industrial liaison programme has proved successful in relating design to operation. The area of female participation in engineering has been successfully addressed by the provision of a special approach to the teaching of graphics, materials and design.

References

Bitterfeld, G.(1991) MM250 Engineering Design Lecture Notes, School of
    Mechanical and Manufacturing Engineering, Swinburne Institute of
    Technology, Melbourne Australia
Blicblau, A.S.(1991) The Modern Engineering Curriculum in Materials,
    Int. J. of Applied Engineering Educ., 7, 15-21
Sargent, M.(1991) Womens' Contribution is a Gain to Engineering,
    Engineer's Australia, 63,15-17
Shigley, J.E.(1986), Mechanical Engineering Design, McGraw-Hill, New
    York, Metric Edition.

Philosophy and Assessment of Final Year Undergraduate Degree Projects in Electrical and Electronic Engineering at Thames Polytechnic

S.M. Vaezi-Nejad, D. Lidgate

School of Engineering, Thames Polytechnic

Abstract
The final year undergraduate projects for the BEng course in electrical and electronic engineering at Thames Polytechnic are devised to provide the opportunity for students to develop and demonstrate individually their ability to carry out design and development tasks similar to those met in industry, in an efficient and well organised manner. This paper discusses the aims, structure, organisation and assessment of these final year projects and the criteria for project progression.
Keywords: Projects, Electronics, Reports, Assessment, Engineering.

1   Introduction

Thames Polytechnic has five faculties each divided into several schools. The School of Engineering is one of three schools within the Faculty of Technology. Full-time faculty academic staff total approximately 90 of which 21 belong to the School of Engineering. The School offers full-time, part-time and sandwich courses leading to BEng Honours degrees in Mechanical, Electrical & Electronic, Electronic, and Manufacturing Systems Engineering, and BA/BA Hons degrees in Engineering and Management; full-time and part-time courses leading to BSc (Hons) in Metallurgy and Materials Engineering; and full-time courses leading to Higher National Diplomas in Electronic Engineering and Mechanical Engineering.

The BEng Hons course in Electrical and Electronic Engineering is vocational in nature and seeks to develop the skills and expertise of the student to the point where he or she can make an immediate and significant contribution as an engineer or design engineer in the areas of communication, control engineering or microelectronics. The overall aim of the course is to provide a programme of study that will develop understanding and knowledge of theory and practice in the broad area of Electrical and Electronic Engineering.

In the following sections we first describe the structure of the course as a whole and then concentrate on the final year project as an important component of the course.

2   Course Structure

The School of Engineering operates a Credit Accumulation and Transfer Scheme (CATS) for all its degree courses. The aim of CATS is to recognise any previous learning a student has so that it need not be duplicated, thus providing a flexible and adaptable method of recognising learning achievement.

At Thames, a Polytechnic wide structure has been implemented based upon a two semester academic year, with either four or six subjects, or units as they are now called, studied in each semester. The School of Engineering has elected to follow six units per semester, commonly known as the 6 + 6 structure. Subjects studied throughout the academic year, as most engineering subjects are, are known as double units.

The assessment takes place either continuously throughout the taught period, at the end of the last semester in which it is taught, or a combination of the two.

Each semester is 13 weeks long; there is a pre-semester week before the first semester, an inter-semester week between the first and second semesters, and a five week post-semester period.

Pre-semester week	Semester 1 (13 weeks)	Inter-semester week	Semester 2 (13 weeks)	Post-semester (5 weeks)

During the pre-semester and inter-semester weeks no formal lectures take place, but other learning activities take place such as industrial visits and design exercises. These two weeks are not reading weeks or holidays but an integral part of the course and attendance is compulsory. The post-semester period is for revision, examinations and meetings of examination boards.

Full-time students study units totalling 60 credits in each semester (ie 10 credits per unit). Generally, each unit consists of a $1\frac{1}{2}$ hours lecture per week and $2\frac{1}{2}$ hours laboratory/seminar (tutorial every 3rd week). Hence, an average week consists of 6 x $1\frac{1}{2}$ = 9 hours lectures and 6 x $2\frac{1}{2}/3$ = 5 hours lab/sem/tut, a total of 14 hours. However, this may vary from week to week and subject to subject. In addition a further 15-20 hours of unsupervised work is expected of each student in order to complete assignments, coursework, homework and to generally keep up-to-date.

3   Final Year Project

The main objective of the final year project is to provide the opportunity for a student to develop and demonstrate individually his or her ability to carry out a design and development task, similar to those met in industry, in an efficient and well organised manner. Additional emphasis is placed on the development of a student's ability to apply electrical and electronic engineering concepts in design, test and analysis and also his or her ability to introduce creativity and innovation into the design.

Since the project topics come from a variety of sources including industry, the students themselves, members of staff and other polytechnic/university departments, the project subjects cover a wide spectrum of engineering problems. At the end of the second year examinations in June, each student is given a copy of the project proposal booklet which contains about 100 separate projects.

The proposal for each project includes a title, objectives, a brief description of the background, the hardware/software required, an outline of the design/construction to be carried out, the major stages to be reached during execution of the project, the expected outcome and in some cases, the minimum acceptable amount of work for successful completion. A student's own proposal is evaluated by at least one member of academic staff.

3.1 Project Selection and Supervision

Students who wish to pursue their own projects see the Project Co-ordinator, in the first instance. Their proposal is then evaluated by a member of staff and if acceptable a supervisor with interest in the subject of the proposed project will be assigned. Other students select a project from the booklet on a first come, first served basis. Each project will be supervised by at least one member of the staff whose name, office and telephone number are listed in the project booklet. In the course of the project, each student is required to write a project plan and specification report (worth 5%), a progress report (worth 15%), a final project report (worth 35%) and to give two oral presentations (worth 15%). The remaining (30%) of the mark will be for the student's overall performance during the project as measured by the supervisor.

In order to score a good mark for the project, students need to demonstrate to the assessors their ability to:

(i)   identify and formulate the main problems and organise appropriate approaches to their solutions.

(ii)   understand any underlying theory and previous solutions in the literature.

(iii) apply theory to the problem in order to determine a solution.

(iv)   design hardware/software to realise a solution with full attention to the technical, manufacturing, cost, reliability and maintenance aspects of the design.

(v)   construct hardware/software to realise a solution.

(vi)   test the resulting hardware/software

In (iv) students should make intelligent use of conceptual engineering and mathematical models and appropriate analysis techniques.

3.2   Timetable and detail of assessments

The timetable for the assessment is as follows:

(a)   project specification and plan (5%): End of pre-semester week.   This report is normally a few pages long plus a flow chart or procedure diagram.   Its main purpose is to ensure that the student obtains a clear grasp of the project. Results of a literature/previous project survey and feasibility studies and other plans of action to carry out the project should, however, be included.   The report will be marked by the supervisor and a second assessor.

(b)   Progress report (15%): End of intersemester week.   As a continous assessment each student writes a progress report which is approximately 3000 words long plus the flow charts, graphs, diagrams etc.   Each student should show that adequate progress has been made.   Students are encouraged to describe in some detail the design, construction, tests and analysis to date and outline their plans for the remainder of the project.

(c)   First oral presentation (5%): End of Spring term.   This presentation is given to the Head of School and the Project Co-ordinator 'on site' so that apparatus can be demonstrated, and should be viewed as a 'trial run' for the second presentation.   Students should ensure that the necessary equipment is available, that diagrams, charts and graphs are set out and that the overall presentation lasts not more than 10-12 minutes.   A further 5 minutes will be allowed for the assessors to ask questions and comment on the presentation.

(d)   Second oral presentation (10%): End of second semester. This second presentation is given to one of the external examiners, and is of a similar content and duration to the first one.   However, at this stage since the project is nearing completion, students often restructure their presentation.

(e)   Project practical work (30%).   The students are advised that normally the practical work should be completed **before the Easter holidays**.   The project supervisor then assesses each students' overall performance in the laboratory.   The mark reflects students' work rate, initiative, achievement and ability.   Allowance is made for the difficulty of the project, unavoidable delay caused by sharing equipment, breakdown, finding the right equipment, etc.

(f)   Final project report (35%): Mid May.   This report, which is the subject of the next section should normally be about 50 pages long (including diagrams, appendices and data sheets) and is marked by both the supervisor and a second assessor.

3.3   The project report

As most supervisors retain copies of project reports, we ask
students to make every effort to take records and present reports
in such a way that they can be contained in one A4 folder. This
facilitates the storage and retrieving of complete reports.

Students must provide two copies of their report in the
folders provided by the School. One copy will be retained by the
School and the other will be returned to the student.

The report should not normally exceed 50 pages including any
relevant drawings, print-outs, etc. and should be typed. It is
the responsibility of the student to organise the typing of the
report.

The School does not wish to see any special layout for the
report, preferring to leave scope for individual presentation.
However, there are some general rules which should be followed:

(i)   the typescript should not extend into the binding of the
folder.

(ii)   pages should be used on one side only.

(iii) all pages should be numbered.

(iv)   the report should have a contents page.

(v)   any table, graph, sketch or photograph which for some
good reason has to be presented at right angles to the
binding, should be arranged with its top towards the
binding.

(vi)   references should be complete, ie author, title of book,
publisher; or author, title of paper, journal, volume,
year and page number.

(vii) many copying machines depend on the presence of carbon
in the original for the copying process. Students are
advised to check that their original is prepared in a
way suitable for copying.

The report has to strike a balance between objective reporting of
the significant work and its outcome, and the record of all work
undertaken during the project. In general, it is found that a
clear statement of the origin and objectives of the project and
its outcome sets the scene for the reader. This part of the
project should be in terms commonly used by engineers and should
not depend on terms which are special to the field of the
project. As the project continues, specialist terms should be
explained and, where symbols are used, these are most easily
followed by a reader if they are explained or defined as they are

introduced and also collected together, preferably, at the end of
the report.

Students often find that the presentation of a main report and
appendices is a useful way of separating the subject matter.

Students ae recommended to make reference to, and make
comparison with, any relevant result from other workers in the
same field. They are told that the purpose of a Report is to
furnish the reader with easily assimilated information, and that
tabulated data or computer print-outs may provide impressive
bulk, but they are of little direct information. Well-annotated
and explained graphs convey information quickly and easily.

Students are also advised to look at their draft reports from
the point of view of the reader. In this connection the reading
of the draft by the supervisor and by fellow students will
frequently lead to constructive criticism.

Students are asked <u>not</u> set tasks for the reader to perform,
such as:

(i)   having to search through the report to locate (separate)
      items of data to which they have been referred (eg "It
      can be seen that ....."), or to confirm statements that
      students have made (eg "Theoretical and practical
      results are very close")

(ii) having to work out the scales of graphs from sets of
      numbers and conversion factors ("2 V/cm", "5ms/cm").

It is also recommended that quantities which are to be
compared should appear together, either quoted, or presented in a
table (not forgetting to give a page reference, if the table
appears elsewhere in the report). Graphs should have a title and
a reference number, and be clearly labelled with the variables,
units, and actual values.

A synopsis or summary, of not more than one side of A4 paper,
should be included at the front of the report.

4   Conclusion

Final year project develops a student's understanding of knowledge
of theory and practice and prepares him or her for entry into
industry with useful skills. We believe that our approach promotes
the students' initiative and creativity and encourages them to
tackle real problems in an efficient and well organised manner.

SECTION 3: ACADEMIC-INDUSTRIAL LINKS

Professional Development in the Mechanical and Manufacturing Engineering Cooperative Degrees

H.T. McGregor, S.F. Johnston

School of Mechanical Engineering, University of Technology, Sydney

Abstract
The commitment to cooperative education remains at the core of the educational philosophy of the Faculty of Engineering at UTS. However, our undergraduate programs have recently been restructured and our academic semester length reduced to bring it into line with a national system. An important goal in the restructuring has been to devise strategies which will integrate professional issues throughout the curriculum and encourage students to take responsibility for their own professional development. This paper describes some of the changes which have been made in the restructured course to achieve this goal.
Keywords: Professional development, Cooperative education, Curriculum development.

1 Cooperative Education

Cooperative education is as highly regarded in engineering in Australia as it is in the UK and USA. Many universities offer various cooperative programs, and even the more traditional universities require a component of work experience. The Faculty of Engineering at the University of Technology, Sydney (UTS) is fully committed to cooperative education. The Faculty comprises three Schools: Civil Engineering, Electrical and Computer Systems Engineering and Mechanical Engineering. Just under a quarter of the 2,600 undergraduates in the Faculty are in the School of Mechanical Engineering, which offers degrees in Mechanical Engineering and Manufacturing Engineering. All the engineering undergraduate courses are cooperative programs, with an integrated structure of study and relevant industrial experience. There are two basic patterns of attendance. In the Sandwich Pattern of attendance, students undertake alternating periods of full-time study and full-time employment. In the Part Time Pattern of attendance, students are normally in full-time employment, but with one or two half-days of study leave per week, so that they attend classes on one or two afternoons and two or three evenings a week. From year to year, students may switch from one attendance pattern to the other as their financial and other circumstances require. Typically about 70 percent of our students attend on the sandwich pattern and 30 percent on the part-time pattern.

There is extensive evidence that cooperative education can work well. The students involved are highly motivated, adapt easily to new situations, are familiar with basic engineering skills, and are productive immediately upon graduation, and frequently for some time before that. Ideally, cooperative education involves much more than simply a particular academic administrative structure (Knowles, 1984). At one extreme, industrial experience may be simply a haphazard matter of students completing tasks set by employers and hoping somehow to learn something of value in the process. At the other extreme, industrial experience may involve a tightly structured, strictly controlled, on-the-job training program. Both extremes have obvious problems. The elements of cooperative education which we have been eager to preserve include:

• the student as the central figure in the learning process;
• the inter-relationship between the student, the institution and the employer;
• the opportunity to transform theory in the context of practice;
• the ability to enter the learning spiral at the concrete experience level.

While a national inquiry into engineering programs (Williams 1988) generally praised the UTS Faculty of Engineering, it did criticise it for 'overteaching'. UTS has always prided itself on the quality of its teaching and student surveys have generally confirmed that rating. However, the Faculty has used the opportunity offered by restructuring to review its teaching practices in the light of modern trends in education.

The Williams report also questioned the effectiveness of concurrent or intercalated work experience. It suggested that there was concern amongst our students that insufficient benefit was obtained from the work experience, possibly due to inadequate communication between UTS and employers, but possibly also due to a failure on the part of students to appreciate the learning opportunities available to them in their work placements.

Traditionally, the cooperative engineering courses at UTS have integrated at least 144 weeks of approved industrial experience with the academic work. The sandwich program consisted of six academic and six industrial semesters. This involved very long semesters to fit in the equivalent of four full-time years of academic material. These long (twenty week) semesters were exhausting for both staff and students. From 1992, the semester length has been reduced to bring it into line with a new national system. The sandwich program has changed to eight academic and four industrial semesters. At the same time, the minimum requirement for approved industrial experience has been reduced to 90 weeks.(Mathews, 1991) The questions confronting us during the restructuring were: what impact would reducing the time spent in industry have on student learning, and what techniques could we adopt to enrich the learning process?

Research indicates that a range of broad, implicit professional skills are developed during the industrial semesters (McGregor, 1984). Through exposure to a variety of role models, and the chance to see theoretical perspectives in a societal context, the student has the opportunity to adapt to a professional standard. To assist the student in this process, in the restructured course the School has developed a stream of professional orientation subjects, designed to maximise the effectiveness of this robust experiential learning program.

2   The Professional Orientation Stream

The important elements of cooperative education listed above were the basis for the design of the Professional Orientation stream. We decided it would need to be student-directed learning rather than teaching centred; it would need to be integrated and problem based. To achieve this, we have incorporated a variety of learning processes such as learning contracts, simulations, traditional tutorials, structured experiences, and case studies, all of which can help students to develop team skills while at the same time refining their own learning techniques.

The emphasis is on an integrated model of education. The professional orientation subjects are to be the focal points of the curriculum, where the knowledge and skills gained during the education process are developed, refined and recognised as relevant to the students' individual needs. To achieve these objectives we felt it was of paramount importance that a team of senior staff develop and remain involved in the subjects in this stream.

We were influenced by research into the kinds of knowledge, skills, abilities and other characteristics that are associated with effective performance in the professions (Kemp, 1977). The most consistent, and unexpected, finding of this research has been that the amount of knowledge acquired in a content area is generally unrelated to superior performance in an occupation. The analysis of successful performers in a variety of occupations has led to the conclusion that cognitive, interpersonal, and motivational factors are the critical elements. Foremost of the cognitive skills required is the ability to conceptualise, organise and present complex information thematically and logically. A related skill is the ability to view issues from a variety of perspectives. The most important skill for sustained high-level professional performance is the ability to learn from experience, by translating observations from work and life experiences into theories that can be used to generate behavioural alternatives.

Many of these educational issues were already being addressed in the Mechanical Engineering curriculum, particularly by three existing professional development subjects: Engineering Communication; Engineering and Society; Engineering Management. Three additional subjects have been introduced to enrich the shorter industrial experience and to enhance student learning processes generally. These are: Introduction to Engineering; Industrial Review; Professional Review. Aspects of professional orientation are also dealt with in many other subjects in the course, particularly in Design 1, 2 and 3, Project 1 and 2 and Commercial Issues for Engineers.

Introduction to Engineering, in Stage One, helps new students appreciate the complexity and diversity of engineering and prepares them for their first industrial semester. It assists students to make the transition from secondary to tertiary education by reviewing various learning and teaching methods and explaining the essential features of the cooperative education courses at UTS.

Parallel to the development of fundamental concepts of engineering practice, this subject develops basic skills in critical and creative thinking, research, communication, and problem solving. This subject introduces a holistic, systems-based approach, emphasising the interdisciplinary nature of engineering. The importance of working as part of a team is highlighted throughout the subject both by team exercises and by presenting a model of team teaching. There is also hands-on laboratory work to encourage students to become aware of the importance of experimentation.

In preparation for their first industrial experience, students will develop the skills associated with applying for jobs. To promote integration of the various first year subjects, letters of application and personal resumes form the basis for an assignment on word processing in the subject *Introduction to Computing*. Students also begin to design their first learning contract. Knowles (1984) recommends learning contracts as a technique for reconciling the needs and interests of learners with the expectations of organisations and professions. In traditional education, the learning activity is structured by the teacher or the teaching institution. The learners are told what the objectives are and how to achieve them. This approach often conflicts with the learners' own perceptions of their needs. In professional practice situations, there may be no clear idea of educational needs at all, merely a set of discrete tasks or projects to be completed. We see learning contracts as a powerful tool for reconciling and expressing the divergent yet complementary needs of the various partners in cooperative education and have included them as assignments throughout the Professional Orientation Stream.

Reflection on the experience is an important part of the learning process. Students are encouraged to keep journals to help them assess the effectiveness of their on-the-job learning. They will also continue the existing practice of writing up a Log Book to provide administrative records of their work. The process of documentation is an important, rapidly developing aspect of engineering practice, and its importance is highlighted throughout the course.

Engineering Communication, taken in Stage Three, emphasises the importance of effective written and oral communication skills and the application of communication concepts throughout engineering practice. It further develops several of the topics initiated in *Introduction to Engineering*. Job application skills are reviewed and extended to a professional level; the treatment of oral and written communication skills includes a wider variety of professional tasks including those involved in conferences, training, manuals, proposals, formal reports and other engineering documentation. The learning contracts and journals produced in previous semesters are reviewed from a communication perspective and the interpersonal communication experienced in the workplace is discussed and evaluated

Engineering and Society, a core subject for Stage Five students, focuses on the inter-relationship between engineers and the community. Topics such as history, economics, politics, philosophy, ethics, the environment, commerce and industry are developed. In this subject students are encouraged to draw on their experience to formulate their own research projects. Tutorial sessions use simulations and games as well as group discussions to help students develop an appreciation of complex issues such as poverty, sexism, racism, conflict and other interpersonal dynamics.

Engineering Management, in Stage Six, prepares students for an appreciation of the complexity of the engineering workplace. It may be helpful to note here that the Institution of Engineers, Australia which is a unified professional organisation with membership of 50,00 of the 90,000 professional engineers in Australia, has highlighted the importance in engineering practice of a range of contextual and other material which it has labelled as 'management'. By 1995, this material must comprise at least 10% of the content of Institution-approved engineering undergraduate courses (IEAust, 1990 and 1991). The Institution has recommended that these topics and associated skills be integrated into subjects across the curriculum, from first year onwards. Our approach has been to focus on the development of broad skills and the appreciation of the social context of the engineering profession in the earlier stages of the course, while specific management theories and their application to engineering are addressed in this subject.

Industrial Review is taken during the industrial experience period following Stage Six. This subject is offered as a distance learning program and draws on the knowledge gained in both *Engineering and Society* and *Engineering Management*. Students negotiate more complex learning contracts with their employing firms, contracts to assist them to understand, analyse and assess the commercial culture of the firm, its context in the Australian and global markets and the appropriateness of its technology. An important consideration is an assessment of future directions for the firm. Students complete a progression of assignments designed to help them appreciate both the process and the product of their learning. The first assignment develops skills of observation and objective reporting; the second , analysis; the third, argument; the fourth persuasion, and the final assignment requires a comprehensive analytical report.

Professional Review, in Stage Seven, is a capstone subject, drawing together the elements of the whole stream. Its goal is to assist students to evaluate their own professional development so far. Emphasis is placed on self-directed learning by having students share experiences with their colleagues. The basis for life-long learning is laid by having students recognise how much they have learned and acknowledge how far they still have to go. Finally, aspects of career development are treated in the context of general futures planning and students devise a range of strategies for their own continuing professional education.

3   A Systems Approach to Professional Education

The report of the committee of inquiry roundly criticised the narrow technical and engineering science emphasis of many traditional engineering courses. Reviews of the Engineering profession have consistently acknowledged the multi- and inter-disciplinary nature of Engineering. In the design of the professional orientation stream we have sought to demonstrate this breadth. Representatives of various specialist areas are involved in both the presentation of material and the evaluation of the educational process. In *Introduction to Engineering*, for example, subject coordinators from maths, chemistry and physics are involved in a focal session, to highlight the relevance of their subjects and to encourage students to recognise the importance of being able to draw on knowledge from a variety of sources to solve problems. A session on critical thinking has been developed in conjunction with specialists from the Faculty of Adult Education.

The curriculum material and presentation methods have been developed in consultation with members of the ESL (English as a second language) team to ensure that the needs of students from a variety of cultural backgrounds will be met, and to emphasize the international nature of the engineering profession. Gender issues have also been considered and the Faculty has recently received an award from the Institution of Engineers, Australia for its programs to encourage women to join the Engineering profession. The Faculty of Adult Education and the Centre for Learning and Teaching at UTS have been the source of extensive input and many creative ideas for the development of these subjects, and several joint research projects will evaluate and test the effectiveness of the program.

The professional orientation stream also addresses the need for provision of some pastoral care (Ramsden et al, 1991). The interactive nature of the curriculum encourages team building and the development of a variety of support strategies. Team members are able to offer each other peer support for both academic and personal problems. Later stage students serve as mentors for entering students. Senior academic staff are more accessible to entering students, at the time when they are most likely to need advice and support. Sheahan and White (1990) emphasize the need to improve the quality of life of engineering students, and an obvious goal of this program is to help students deal realistically with issues such as stress, conflict, goal strategies and personal priorities.

4   Conclusions

The Professional Orientation stream has been designed to enrich the cooperative education process by focusing on the techniques students (and professionals) need so that they can learn effectively by experience as well as by traditional methods. The stream integrates broad skills through the entire curriculum as they are needed, in a JIT (just in time) management style. It embodies an adult learning model, reinforcing the partnership of student, institution and employer in the learning process. This integrated process should develop engineers who are better able to handle the complex problems of the next century. The emphasis on the importance of the human as well as the technical side of engineering, and the location of the engineering profession in its social context, will help avoid the shortcomings associated with the narrow technical and engineering science emphasis of many traditional engineering courses. At the same time, it should make the course relevant and attractive to a much broader cross section of the community.

References

Institution of Engineers, Australia (1990) *Policy on Management Studies in Professional Engineering Undergraduate Courses.* (IEAust: Canberra).

Institution of Engineers, Australia (1991) *Guidelines for Management Studies in Engineering Undergraduate Courses.* (IEAust: Canberra).

Kemp, G.O. (1977) "Three factors of success", in Vermilye D. W., *Relating work and education.* (Jossey Bass: San Francisco).

Knowles, M. (1984) *The adult learner: a neglected species,* 3rd ed., (Gulf Publishing: Houston).

Mathews, C.T. (1991) *Reducing quantity while increasing quality of the industrial experience .* World Conference on co-op Education, Hong Kong.

McGregor, H. (1984) "Perceptions of Cooperative Education in Engineering." *Proceedings of the 3rd World Conf on Cooperative Education,* Melbourne.

Ramsden, V., Schooling, P., Law, N. and McKenzie, J. (1991) *A Survey to Identify Factors Influencing Student Completion of Undergraduate Degree Courses in Electrical Engineering.* (UTS: Sydney).

Schon, D. (1986) *The reflective practitioner: how professionals think in action,* (Basic Books: NY).

Sheahan, B.H. and White J.A. (1990) "Quo Vadis, Undergraduate Engineering Education?" *Engineering Education,* December 1990, pp 1017 - 1022.

Williams B. (1988) *Review of the discipline of engineering.* (AGPS: Canberra)

Partnership in Education? How do we make it Happen?

T.H. Breckell, D.J. Dell, R.D. Gregory, B.L. Wibberley

Division of Mechanical and Aeronautical Engineering, University of Hertfordshire (formerly Hatfield Polytechnic)

Abstract
This paper describes the setting up and initial operation of a Partnership Centre within the university. The centre is sponsored by industry to provide a focus within the university of the partnership between the college, industry and students in engineering education. The paper describes the evolution of the original concept and the development of the integration of a place for company/student communication and the provision of open access learning and peer tutoring.
Keywords, Education, Engineering, Partnership, Open Learning,

1 Introduction

The idea of engineering education as a partnership between industry, college and students is not new. The Division of Mechanical and Aeronautical Engineering has a long history of relationships with industry through running sandwich degrees and consultancy and research. A Vehicle option on the Mechanical BEng has given rise to a particularly close relationship in both the original concept and in the subsequent running of the scheme. Students have also been involved in operation and review of schemes through our committee structure and informal and formal monitoring arrangements.

The division has maintained strong relationships with companies through regular visiting of students in industry as part of the monitoring and assessment of industrial training. All these tri-partite relationships have made an important contribution to the educational quality of the engineering schemes.

2 A Fresh Initiative

The Division of Mechanical and Aeronautical Engineers at the University of Hertfordshire took a fresh initiative about two years ago and invited representatives from industry to discuss our informal partnership in a seminar entitled 'Partnership for Training'. The seminar included all the staff from the division, technicians, administrative staff, students and ex-students. This initiative was supported by the Enterprise Initiative funding awarded to the university. Its aim was to formalise and to gain the added benefits of a more stable and committed relationships between the various parties. The aim seemed to be laudable and obvious but the question to answer was how could this be put into practice?

Training was selected as an area of obvious mutual interest both at undergraduate and post graduate level. It was, however, hoped that co-operation in other areas of interest would also evolve.

As a college we recognised the considerable wasted effort involved in finding and assessing new training placements each year and the considerable mutual benefits of having ongoing plans between employers and colleges. We also recognised that to produce a long lasting working partnership there needs to be mutual benefit, tangible outcomes and reasons for the partners to meet each other regularly. No longer could colleges expect to always be receiving help without making an equal contribution to industry.

The Partnership Centre was one of two major initiatives which came out of the seminar to tackle this problem. It was followed by a joint working group and follow up seminar.

3   Evolution of the Concept

The Partnership Centre concept arose out of initial discussions with the Rover Group who have been involved with their own similar ventures in schools and at their factory at Canley near Coventry. The idea was developed by the division to be a partnership with an enlarged group of companies all having an interest in the education of undergraduate and postgraduate engineers at the university.

At the same time as these discussions were taking place a need was identified in the division to provide accommodation and resources for open access student directed learning. There was a need to encourage a more student centred approach to learning and to provide support material particularly in the first year mathematics and mechanics for a student cohort of 140. These subjects are fundamental to engineering courses and are also ones which students often find difficult. Open access learning requires a partnership between the students and the university which can make a contribution to overcoming these difficulties.

The concept of partnership brought these two ideas together in one centre with a recognition that the full partnership in engineering education is between the students, the university and industry. All three benefit from an early close relationship and an ongoing exchange of information. Students are better motivated by seeing, early in their course potential employers involved in the division, companies benefit from being able to recruit and communicate with undergraduates throughout the college course and the university benefits by having a resource which improves the quality of the educational provision. It also brings together both the formal learning on the course and the informal or experiential learning. It is in this latter area that industry makes a major contribution by providing the industrial environment for training .

The companies involved in the Partnership Centre financially support the facility and make use of it for displays and as a seminar room to communicate with students. It is used on a day to day basis for open access learning by all students but by first years in particular. This gives the centre an all year round student presence avoiding any danger of the centre becoming a 'museum'. At the same time it gives our industrial partners a base for recruitment and the presentations of their own recruitment philosophy.

The division took the initiative and provided a room of 125 square meters with comfortable fittings and decor to encourage all the partners to see the centre as a place of quality. This gave the motivation to maintain and use the facility with some pride.

4   Statement of Purpose

A formal statement of purpose was formulated to circulate to prospective industrial partners.

The room was to be a focus for the partnership between engineering students, industry and the university. It provides an area for open access student directed learning and a medium for communication between the partners. The room would meet the needs of the partners in a variety of ways.

For students it provides an open access area for study and mutual support, a resouce for self help materials, a place to arrange self help groups to meet, and a place to obtain company information.

For industry it provides a focus within the university for student contact, early development of links with students, participation with student directed learning and a place to facilitate company/student communication. It also gives companies easy access to other Schools and Divisions within the university.

For the university it provides a place to focus educational support and resources, relationships with industry, student directed learning and the partnership in engineering education.

5   Initial Operation

The centre is jointly financed by industry and the Division of Mechanical and Aeronautical Engineering and managed by all three partners. The initial activities and resources were chosen to emphasise and support student directed learning and the concept of partnership.

Companies join the scheme with an initial fee to support the centre and then a smaller annual fee to cover ongoing costs. Currently seven companies have joined as partners and the final number will be limited to twelve. This number would comprise both large and small companies mostly with an already close relationship with the division. Companies provide such things as display material, a supply of upto date brochures and video films covering technical and training aspects of their work. It is expected that artifacts will be displayed and changed regularly to provide interest. A possible telephone ' hot line' to companies is currently being discussed.

6   Initial Resources and Activities

The Partnership Centre has resources to encourage student   centred learning including a computer based tutor system, video film of course lectures and self study books. The books concentrate in one place specialised support material and thus supplement the university's excellent central library facility.

The video filming of lectures is carried out for mechanics lectures on a routine basis and a video film of a lecture are available in the centre a few days later. The filming is carried out in a specially equipped lecture theatre. The recordings are kept until the following year as an aide memoire to students and as revision material.

The lectures are not given as 'filmed lectures' and are not designed to replace attendance. The computer based tutor system is an interactive package covering the relevant parts of the A level Mechanics and Mathematics to support the first year courses.

Past years examination papers and solutions are provided to assist the students revision.

Extra tutorial assistance in the centre is provided by specially selected second year students who provide 'peer assistance' for the first year students in their learning. The second year students meet together regularly with a staff tutor to monitor progress. The nature of the assistance given is carefully described to all the students involved. The second year students are there as partners with the first years· This assistance is provided in the centre four hours per week and the first year students attend on a voluntary and informal basis.

7   Initial Reactions

The Partnership Centre has been fully operational since November 1991. A pilot open access scheme ran before that. The response from all the partners so far is encouraging.

Students are regularly using the room as a place for individual and group work in a very responsible way. The provision of video filmed lectures is proving popular and providing a useful back up resource to the lectures. The books represent invaluable and specialised support material. They are situated where assistance is available from fellow students on the course and the books are kept in the room on an honesty system which is currently working well.

The peer assisted learning system has so far involved eight student 'tutors' and they have reported enthusiastically in feedback sessions with staff. The encouragement and motivation for first year students to discuss work with second years is appearing to be one of the most important benefits from the system. The second year students are gaining in confidence and improving their communication skills. They are also reporting benefit in their second year courses as they help with the learning of the basic concepts.

All first year students were given a questionnaire at the end of two months operation. Students using the session have reported them very useful and some continue to use them on a regular basis. The numbers coming are small but feedback from other first year students not yet using the system is that the numbers will grow as the year progresses and becomes more demanding.

There are difficulties in finding suitable times when both first and second year students are free at convenient hours. It has become necessary to continually communicate the opportunities for help that exist in the centre. but is hoped that this need will be reduced as the system of peer assistance becomes part of students expectations.

A number of outside lectures have been delivered in the centre again giving emphasis to the industrial partnership in the schemes of study. Rover Group are the first company to use the centre for recruitment purposes by conducting seminars on their Student Placement Scheme for engineers and business studies students. This scheme gives three months training prior to the final academic year and is becoming a major recruitment tool and well suited to the type of partnership for mutual benefit envisaged. The scheme further emphasises partnership by requiring the construction of a formal Learning Agreement between the company, university and student. An agreement is made in which all agree on objectives and the resources needed for the training to be successful.

Companies with very different training needs and methods of recruitment are responding to an opportunity for a presence in the university and in some cases pursuing a relationship with students from the first year through to employment.

8   Conclusions

The Centre has at the time of writing been operational for five months and is showing promise for the future. It is encouraging to find significant support at a time when it is difficult financially for industry. It represents a tangible expression of the partnership which is vital for high quality engineering education. It provides a practical demonstration on a day to day basis linking the needs of all three partners and together developing ways of meeting those needs to mutual benefit.

It is envisaged that there will be further initiatives in the Partnership Centre coming from all three partners. Our student and industrial partners will be particularly important in bringing fresh perspectives to the educational process. The structure, facility, philosophy and now a working model are in place to encourage this in the future.

Links Between Industry and Academia - An Industry View

H.M. Bedalian, J.G. Keer
Balfour Beatty Limited

Abstract
Industry-academia links are examined and the benefits of these to
the education of students, to the academic institution and to the
employer are discussed. The potential for further development is
considered in the light of changes in industry and higher education.
Keywords: Engineering, Construction, Education, Universities,
Polytechnics, Industry.

1   Introduction

The present and future contributions of engineering graduates are
vital to the international competitiveness of companies in the
engineering and construction sector. Reports have shown clear links
between commercial success in world markets and a country's
education and training system (eg CBI, 1990).

It is not surprising, therefore, that industry wants a voice in
the education process of engineering graduates. However, as the
Fellowship of Engineering has stated: 'Engineering education must
now be seen as a career-long process ... First degree courses must
therefore be regarded as but one stage, albeit a vitally important
stage, of the seamless and career long continuing process of
professional development' (F.Eng, 1991).

In Balfour Beatty in 1991, we invested about 0.5% of our turnover
in the education and training of our employees, from general
construction apprenticeships and operative training through to
senior management programmes at international business schools (The
UK average is much lower than this). Although the major proportion
of this investment (and that of industry generally) in education and
training is outside the higher education sector, where government
must remain the principal source of finance, there is much that both
industry and academia have to gain through interaction and links.
This paper examines a number of areas of interaction and the
benefits to students, academic institution and employer are
considered.

2   Background

It is important to consider the background which stimulated many of
the links which have developed, concentrating particularly on the
construction sector of industry in which the majority of Balfour
Beatty's activities lie.

In 1987, the output of Polytechnic and University construction-
related degree courses was as shown in Table 1 (ICE, 1989). However
the number of courses did not correlate with the demand for certain
types of graduates. With building services accounting for over 20%
of new construction work, there was a perceived need for more high
quality Building Services Engineering graduates. Furthermore, there
was a demand for more University graduates educated in the
management of construction, rather than design, and in buildings
rather than civil engineering infrastructure. Though it is
important to ensure that there is a fundamental understanding of the
engineering principles of building structures, such construction and
management-related courses make less demand on the mathematics and
physics knowledge of students, allowing recruitment from a broader
range of able sixth formers.

Table 1. British Polytechnic and University Construction
Degree Courses, 1987

Course	Number of Courses	1987 Graduates approximate number	per cent of total
Building Services Eng	6	120	2.5
Building	11	350	7.5
Quantity Surveying	25	640	13.6
Architecture	35	1300	27.6
Civil Engineering	61	2300	48.8
TOTAL	138	4710	100.0

Note: the numbers include foreign students.

In the 1980's, civil engineering courses were also coming under
closer examination. Not only was the syllabus crammed, it was
crammed with material likely to be of greatest value to those
entering the consulting engineer/ design side of the profession,
even though data on the employment of civil engineering graduates
has generally pointed to contractors employing between 30 and 40% of
graduates. Yet judging by the evidence of many civil engineering
syllabi, contractors have been able to exert little influence on the
content of courses.

One reason is that most contractors are enlightened enough to
appreciate that, broadly, it is Universities and Polytechnics' duty
to educate and industry's to train. A grounding in engineering
knowledge and skills is required and the ability to think logically,
albeit creatively, to solve problems must be developed. Yet

problems of construction which are intellectually demanding, - for example, the planning of a complex sequence of construction activities - are rarely explored in preference to routine design problems. The contracting industry, by involvement in higher education, can bring about the shift in balance that is required.

3   Industry-sponsored degree courses

A number of sponsored degree courses have developed in the construction sector, where a consortium of companies has not only provided sponsorships to students, but has also made financial contributions to higher education institutions to assist with course development and staffing. Balfour Beatty companies have participated in three such consortia.

The B.Eng Honours degree in Building Services Engineering Design and Management was established at the University of Reading because of the under-representation of that discipline in the University sector, as mentioned earlier, and the perceived need to raise the profile and status of the industry. A feature of the course is a special project on a building research topic, supervised and assessed by the University and industry and undertaken in the sponsoring firm.

Closures in building degree courses in the university cuts of the early 1980's had limited the opportunity of a university education for students who would eventually work in the management of the construction process. A pioneering sponsored degree course in Construction Management was established at Salford University in 1988 (Stradling, 1989) and this was followed by a course in Construction Engineering Management at Loughborough University in 1991.

The establishment of University courses in Quantity Surveying and Commercial Management at Loughborough University and U.M.I.S.T., while outside the engineering context of this Conference, are worthy of note. A motivating force in their establishment by contractors was not only the need for more University graduates in that discipline, but also the perception that the University sector, left to its own devices, might well increase the numbers graduating but direct them all into private quantity surveying practices!

Although the extent of academia-industry links varies between the sponsored courses, the education of students has benefited through industry's involvement in the initial course design, ensuring its relevance to future careers. Advisory Boards, integrated project work or industrial experience, site visits and provision of industry staff for lecturing and project work are also a feature of such courses.

4   Industry-sponsored academic posts

Balfour Beatty have sponsored the Chair in Civil Engineering at Portsmouth Polytechnic since 1989. We already had contact with the

department, largely through graduate recruitment. The Chair has
strengthened the link and both sides have successfully sought to
broaden the contact beyond the sponsored post. One benefit for us
has been that we have, through Portsmouth, established links with
the Ecole Nationale d'Ingenieurs in St. Etienne. This has
contributed to our strategy of developing European education and
training contacts and of recruiting in Europe as our business
interests develop there.

We have recently announced sponsorship of a Chair in Building
Engineering and Construction Management at the University of Leeds.
By enabling the University to appoint a new member of staff at
professorial level, we look forward to strengthening the interface
between the design and construction processes, which is a
comparatively neglected area in university engineering education.

In times of increasing student : staff ratios, the educational
advantages of an extra post facilitated by external sponsorship are
obvious. What is less apparent is that a link through a sponsored
post acts as a catalyst to many other beneficial contacts. Within
days of our announcement of the sponsored Chair, one of our
international project managers and an alumnus of the University was
offering his services as a lecturer/tutor. Access to expertise
obviously works two ways and what benefits students one way may help
industry as expertise and advice flows the other way.

5   Industrial Training Placements/Student Sponsorship

Apart from graduate recruitment, industrial training placements and
sponsorships are perhaps the most common link between industry and
academia.

It is generally agreed that a mix in higher education of straight
three year courses and four-year courses including industrial
training placement(s) is a good thing. We recruit from both types
of courses. Educationally it can be argued that it is beneficial
for students to see the practical application of theory and of
personal/communication skills before more theory and skills
development in the final year. A more informed selection of options
can then be made. Also the welcome practice of academic staff
visiting students serves to keep those academics in touch with
developments in practice.

For industry, it gives the opportunity to assess how a potential
sponsored student and employee performs in the work environment. On
joining after graduation, they are able to make immediate
contributions, and, aware of the demands of the job, there is less
likelihood of early dissatisfaction in the employer or the
graduate. By the end of a placement and frequently long before, our
students are not seen as a cost to the project but as valuable
members of project teams. Training objectives are provided, and the
experience contributes to that required by the professional
institutions for chartered status.

It is interesting to note that since the early 1980's there has
been some substantial movement away from full-course sponsorship

towards sponsoring part way through the course, and as a result, industrial placements have assumed a more significant role in the selection of sponsored students.   About one in three final year engineering undergraduates are sponsored (IMS, 1991).   Sponsorship is likely to increase over the next few years and employers are likely to continue to move towards sponsoring students part-way through a course.

6   Research and Development Projects

Our experience of a Teaching Company Scheme has been particularly beneficial in strengthening links with a University.   The Balfour Beatty Construction/Loughborough University Teaching Company successfully developed computer-aided estimating systems.   The close working relationships necessary between Associates, University staff and company staff during the course of the project have been of lasting benefit, supported by the fact that four Associates subsequently accepted positions with the company.

For the University, the Teaching Company scheme occurred when traditional research grants for work in this field were not forthcoming.   The size of Balfour Beatty and our need to remain competitive in UK and international markets offered a development opportunity to progress the concepts to implementation. Following on from the Teaching Company scheme, the University, with company support, secured an SERC grant for the development of intelligent computer systems in estimating.

The Teaching Company scheme has been of direct benefit to the education of students, in this case particularly post-graduate students on the Civil Engineering Department's Construction Management course.   Through related project work and company staff input they have been exposed to 'state of the art' practice in a major field of construction management.   The Scheme also led to the company commissioning the University to write a Construction Management game which is now run annually at national level for the Institution of Civil Engineers.

7   External Lecturers, Examiners, Advisers

It is now common for departments of engineering to have Industrial Boards to advise on course content and new proposals.   The Boards are often the channel by which external lecturers or industry-suggested projects are arranged.   Too frequently the one-off external lecture is the only input students receive in a key area of their discipline.   More effort is needed by both sides to ensure that such contributions are fully integrated into the syllabus so that the full educational benefit of the industry input is realised.

Industrial nominations as External Examiners can provide much needed practical input into the assessment of courses, examination papers and their solutions.   Commercial and cost implications are often lacking in academic papers as are the relationships to actual practice. Industrial input can also ensure that course work is relevant and of value to a student's future needs.

8   Future Trends in Industry-Academia Links

A number of factors will influence the development of industry-academia links as we approach the year 2000:
i.   broader entry qualifications for courses;
ii.   slimmer courses with emphasis on fundamentals, understanding of basic principles and on general skills which prepare students for the world of work and continuing learning;
iii. proposals for two year degrees and B.Tech degrees directed towards the needs of the Incorporated Engineer;
iv.   proposals for a common syllabus in the first two years for construction professionals;
v.   National Vocational Qualifications placing emphasis on competences related to the jobs people do.
   These will lead to less specialisation at undergraduate level and more emphasis on continuing professional development at post-graduate level to develop managerial and specialist technical skills. The challenge to higher education institutions will be to provide and market programmes which will deliver CPD in a flexible, cost effective way suited to the needs of industry.
   Higher education institutions may find themselves in competition with other providers, including major companies themselves with their own existing in-house training programmes. This competition can be turned into cooperation through the accreditation of in-company training as part of nationally and internationally recognised post-graduate qualifications.

References

CBI (1990) **Towards a skills revolution,** Confederation of British Industry: London.
F.Eng (1991) **Framework statement on the future formation of chartered engineers,** Fellowship of Engineering: London
ICE (1989) **The future manpower needs of the construction industry,** The Institution of Civil Engineers: London.
Stradling, D. and March, C. (1989). A degree of partnership, **Personnel Management,** June.

New Modes of Integrating Higher Education of Science and Engineering with Industrial Production and Scientific Research

Y. Xu(*), Ge Hong-han(*), Chen Da-ming(**), Xu Juan(*), Li Jia-bao(*)

(*) Research Institute of Higher Education, HIT, P.R. China

(**) Ministry of Aerospace Industry, P.R. China

Abstract

Today, all the countries throughout the world pay close attention to studying and looking for the ways to solve the problem of integrating universities of science and engineering (especially the first-rate universities) with industrial production units and institutions of scientific research. For Harbin Institute of Technology (HIT), the new effective ways of its integration with industrial production and scientific research mainly include the cooperation with plants or enterprises in establishing and administering a school, the cooperation with institutions of scientific research in imparting education and/or jointly carrying out scientific projects, the cooperation with user units in jointly estalishing scientific research institutes devoted to special research programs, taking part in the development of new high-tech in the districts specially for opening up new high-tech industry, and so on. According to the practical experience of HIT, the principles of mutual benefit and mutual compensation should be followed; both the parties should make and execute an agreement or contract which will be guaranteed by the legislation and the policies of the State.

Keywords: Engineering education, Industrial production, Scientific research, Integration (cooperation), Mode.

Further integrating universities of science and engineering with industrial production units, institutions of scientific research, and user units is one of the core problems in the improvement of the education of science and engineering. Today, all the countries throughout the world are trying to explore actively all possible ways and modes to enhance this integration. HIT is a university of science and engineering, placing great stress on engineering, in combination with management engineering and humanities. It is one of the fifteen universities of the country enjoying priority in nation's investment. (There are totally one thousand and more institutions of higher education in China) In order to improve the education of engineering, raise the quality of its graduates, and enhance its competitive power and capacity in this age characterized by more and more severe competition, HIT, in recent ten years, has tried to make some explorations in the respect of enhancing the integration with relevant industrial production units, institutions of scientific research, and user units, and obtained some exciting achievements. On the basis of summing up the experiencc of HIT, this paper presents some of our conclusive opinions on the new modes of integrating higher education of science and engineering with industrial production and scientific research and also on how to apply these new ways effectively.

1   World Tendency in the Reform of Engineering Education

Today, all the countries in the world pay close attention to studying and looking for the ways to solve the problem of integrating universities of science and engineering (especially the first-rate universities) with industrial production units and institutions of scientific research.

In the late twentieth century, the waves of the world-wide new-tech revolution are pounding heavily the economic and the social structures of all the countries throughout the world. This endows them with vigour and vitality and facilitates their further development.

When the governments, universities of science and engineering, and workers of higher education in science and engineering are facing the challenge of the more and more complex engineering techniques and the new-tech revolution, an historic mission confronts them, ie, how to improve and perfect the higher education of science and engineering, how to train the students to become engineers who can satisfy the requirements of economic and social development in the last decade of the twentieth century and the early years of the twenty-first century, and how to overcome to a certain extent the phenomenon of disjunction between the trained talents of the university and the requirements of the employer unit, so as to further adapt the education of the university to the needs of economic and social development.

In recent years,some of the universities in the former Soviet Union, under the direction of the policy "Integrating Education with Production and Science", have established "Joint Entities of Education-Production-Science" together with factories and institutions of scientific research. They have also established"Affiliate Teaching and Research Divisions" in the factories. In Europe and America, the "Scientific Park" is fashionable in university campus. Besides, in Massachusetts Institute of Technology, USA, there are "Lincoln Laboratory" and "Industrial Liaison Program"; in the UK, "Sandwich Courses" are usually conducted in universities, the "Industrial Centre" can be seen in campuses, and the "Teaching Company" can be found in some enterprises. In Japan, Tsekuba City and Tsekuba University have been built up for the same purpose. At the same time, the Japanese government offered a slogan in the White Book of Science and Technology in 1988: integrating industrial production with education and government, and also in the 1988 its White Book of Education decided that in order to promote the cooperation between the industrial production unit, the institution of education, and the government in helping to give a technical education to civilian technicians and to carry out the scientific research program jointly by the university and the enterprise, a joint research centre would be established in each national university after 1987. In China, the modes and ways adopted by some of the universities of science and engineering to realize the integration of education with industrial production and scientific research are essentially similar to those mentioned above.

2   HIY's Modes of the Integration of Education with Industrial Production and Scientific Research

In the process of integration with the industrial production unit, the institution of scientific research and the user unit, HIT holds that the new effective ways of the integration mainly include the cooperation with plants or enterprises in establishing and administering a school, the cooperation with institutions of scientific research in imparting education and/or jointly carrying out scientific projects, the cooperation with user units in jointly establishing scientific research institutes devoted to special research programs, taking part in the development of new high-tech industry in the districts specially for opening up new high-tech industry, and so on.

2. 1 Cooperation with plants or enterprises in establishing and administering a school

Since 1988, HIT has signed a cooperation agreement with No. 1 Automobile Plant, Changchun, jointly estabishing the school of automobile engineering. Every year this school graduates many students with the Bachelor's Degree majoring in design and manufacture of automobiles and internal combustion engines specially for No. 1 Automobile Plant, Changchun and the country. The mode of the cooperation is characterized by: a) The enterprise provides a certain amount of money for the university as an investment, and both the parties jointly administer the school. b) Both the parties organize a joint faculty of the school, and the school has the right to use the facilities of both the parties. c) A new mode of the "3+1" system is used in education, ie, the courses in basic subjects and the courses in basic technical subjects are offered at the university in the three former years and the courses in specialized technical subjects and graduation theses (designs) are offered and written in the last year of the programs at the factory, of which the engineers and technicians are engaged to be teachers.

In order to meet the need of the partner plant, HIT transferred a number of sophomors and juniors majoring in other specialties to the school of automobile engineering when the school was just established. Now the school has graduated three batches of graduates, amounting to 150 students. Among them 82 graduates were assigned to No. 1 Automobile Plant, Changchun, and their quality of education was highiy praised by the employer.

2. 2   Cooperation with institutions of scientific research in imparting education and/or jointly carrying out scientific research projects.

The astronautics school, HIT, jointly imparts education with some research institutes of space science. According to an agreement. both the parties jointly formulate and coordinate the education plan so as to train students flexibly and adapt it to the practical needs; some research fellows are engaged to be part-time professors of the school faculty; the institutes accept the higher-class students of the school and are in charge of directing them to practise, perform experiments and write graduation theses (designs) in their own laboratories or experimental factories; both parties jointly establish some new specialties, and so on.

The astronautics school, HIT, has jointly established two specialties with the Chinese

Research Institute of Space Science and Technology: manned space engineering and applied satellite engineering. They have also adopted the mode of the "3+1" system in education.

2. 3   Cooperation with industrial production units or user units in establishing scientific research institutes devoted to special research programs

In recent ten years, HIT has made great successes in this kind of cooperation, and attained rapid development in the number, scale, and quality of the cooperation. This has attracted great attention from the relevant authorities, and formed the superiority of HIT. Cooperation with institutions of scientific research, industrial production units, or user units means that the university is entrusted by them or cooperates with them to undertake a certain research project. The two parties will work out the scheme concertedly, carry out the research work cooperatively or separately, and organize the acceptance check, appraisal and extending of the achievement of the research project.

This kind of cooperation has become a new way of effectively integrating the university with the industrial production unit, the institution of scientific research, or the user unit. Practically, in HIT all the disciplines and specialties which have succeeded in this kind of cooperation must obtain remarkable achievements in scientific research and and be rewarded by the government. The cooperation between the specialty of thermo-turbo-machine, HIT, and the Harbin Turbine Machine Plant in the development of bending and twisting the turbine blade, the cooperation between the specialty of electronic instrumentation and measuring techniques, HIT, and the Research Institute of High-Energy Physics, Academia Sinica, in the development of the water-cooled temperature control system of the linear accelerator used in the positive-negative electron collision machine, and the cooperation between the research institute of electronic engineering techniques, HIT, and the Chinese Navy in the development of new types of radar are all good examples.

Among the above-described examples, the establishment of the research institute of electronic engineering techniques is a relativly successful one. This institute is in close cooperation with its user units and obtain great financial support from them in return. Although the institute is affiliated to HIT, it is an economic entity and relatively independent of the university. It has its own regular research fellows and regular staff members, and it also has its own regular research orientation. This institute successfully developed the first new type radar of world level in China, and whereby the achievement of the research project was awarded the first-class Scientific and Technical Progress Prize of the State in 1991. Now the director of the institute, professor Liu Yongtan, has been appointed, by supplemental election, the academician of the technology division, Academia Sinica.

2. 4   Taking part in the development of new high-tech in the districts specially for opening up new high-tech industry

The districts of new high-tech industry are the parts of our country which are established specially for the purpose of opening up new high-tech industry, and to which the government is executing a policy of privilege. The ways of HIT taking part in the development of new high-tech industry are mainly as follows: One is to remodel the campus factories to adapt the production of new high-tech industry. For example, after being remodelled, the electronic instrument factiory is capable of producing new high-tech products such as the high-precision fluid density meter. The other is the cooperation of HIT' s high technology with the money an facilities of the industrial production unit. For example, since 1986 in cooperation with the department of precision instrumentation, HIT, the Mudanjiang Watch Manufacturing Plant has developed a series of new high-tech products and become an enterprise which once had a great loss in business and nowadays its productive value exceeds ten million RMB ￥ and its profits and the sum of taxation increase to more than a million RMB ￥ every year.

From the practices of HIT in its cooperation with industrial production units, institutions of scientific research, and user units, it can be seen that universities of science and engineering (especially the first-rate universties) have to take the road to the integration not only with the industrial production unit but also with the institution of scientific research and the user unit. This is a necessary tendency of history, and also a problem with regularity and common property in higher education. The practices of HIT shows that a university of science and engineering will not raise to a great degree the quality of education to meet the needs of society, will not overcome the phenomenon of disjunction between the trained talents of the university and the requirements of the employer unit and obtain great support from industrial production units, institutions of scientific research, and user units in return, and in a word will not develop fast and healthily unless it keeps on studying and finding the new modes and new ways of the integration.

3   Key Problems in the Integration

From the practical experience of HIT, it can be seen that by comparison the cooperation with a plant, a research institute, or a user in establishing a new school, a new specialty, or an entity of scientific research institution is the most effective way of the integration. And the key problem of how to use the way satisfactorily is that both parties should follow the principles of mutual benefit and mutual compensation, and they should make and execute an agreement or contract which will be guaranteed by the legislation and the policies of the State.

3. 1 Both parties should follow the principles of mutual benefit and mutual compensation
These principles imply that the cooperation should be first beneficial to the education of the university, and then to the development of its scientific research work and the increasc of its income. Of course, these principles should also benefit its partner. The university, the industrial production unit, the institution of scientific research, or the user unit has its own superiority and strong points. Therefore it is very important that they should display their own superiority and compensate each other appropriately in the process of cooperation.

3. 2 Both parties should make and execute an agreement or contract
On the basis of confidence in each other, both parties should make and execute an agree-

ment or contract. This is the guarantee of the cooperation in law.

3. 3 Being guaranteed by thd legislation and the policies of the State

If we hope that the different modes and ways of the integration will develop smoothly, the relevant authorities of the government should take the legislation of the cooperation into consideration and make corresponding policies. Therefore, it is very important to call the attention of the relevant authorities of the government to the problem of the integration and to develop the study and wide discussion over the problem of the integration in theory and practice.

References

He Guang, Yiang Hongye, Li Jiabao, Ge Honghan and He Shaoyuan (1987,6) Integration of higher education with production and scientific research: an analysis of the current Soviet higher education, Foreign Education, Trans, Chinese Society of Comparative Education, Beijing.

Li Jiabao and Zhou Changyuan (1986,2) On the training and improvement of the faculty of higher education in China in light of the experience of faculty growth in HIT, Journal of Engineering Education, Harbin Institute of Technology, Harbin.

Qiang Wenyi and Xu Yang (1989,2) Forecast for the reform of higher education in China, Journal of Engineering Education, Harbin Institute of Technology, Harbin.

Yang Shiqing (1991,1) Promoting cooperative education and improving the reform and development of higher education, Journal of Higher Educatiom, Trans. Chinese Society of Higher Education, Beijing.

Systems Engineering: A Framework for Collaboration

J.T. Boardman, R.F. Wilkinson

School of Systems Engineering, University of Portsmouth and GEC Avionics, Rochester

Abstract

Systems engineering has many definitions. These tend to fall into one of two classes: purely academic (based on a view of general systems theory); or, purely industrial (recognising that the customer requires a system which demands the subordination of technological disciplines to the overall system requirement). The definition adopted in this paper is: 'engineering strategies for managing complexity using a systemic approach'. This definition is chosen in order to establish a framework for collaboration between systems thinking (systemic approach) and systems engineering businesses (where the management of complexity is *the* crucial issue). This framework has been adopted within the School of Systems Engineering at the University of Portsmouth as part of a planned programme of collaboration with GEC Marconi. Its existence is a major catalyst for curriculum and staff development.

Keywords: Process Modelling, Systemigram, Systems Engineering.

1   Framework for Systems Engineering

In business, three entities are key. First is the *customer*, and the prime requirement of any business must be to keep the customer satisfied. Whatever this might mean, the business will be judged by customer satisfaction. The business does not have the right to say that it is doing the right things. Only the customer has this right, and the way in which this right is exercised will say everything that is significant about the success of the business. Second, is the way the business does things. This, what we might call *process*, must be known, understood, communicable, disseminable, adaptable, and in every way provide the articulation for the business to continue its development. It behoves a business to know what business it is in and why; to be able to express this eloquently and in any form that it takes in order to convince the intelligent observer that the business understands itself. Armed with such an understanding, the business can have a reasonable expectation of surviving in its environment and to plan its strategies for whatever is needful - survival, growth, or retrenchment on the basis of this understanding of process. Finally, there are the *people* within the business, those who execute the process that enables the business to satisfy the customer. Investment in people necessarily adds value to a business, since the process is better matched to achieving customer satisfaction.

2   Systems thinking

The systems movement, which has led to the development of 'soft' systems methodology (SSM) is continually searching for new ways of looking at problems. A recent innovation in SSM is the use of systemigrams, an example of which is given in Figure 1.

In the systemigram, ideas are expressed using systemic concepts (holons) which then act as reference models to participants to guide their thinking as to how the particular ill-ease encountered in soft systems problems can be better articulated, understood and, finally, resolved. Technological fixes incline to reflect an oversimplified view of the problem. They tend not to accord due respect for the complexity inherent in human activity systems. Furthermore, they appeal to a management style which itself pays little respect to the subtleties and nuances commonly encountered in complex reality. What a systemic approach does fundamentally is to recognise the complexity of reality and the nature of human activity systems to behave counter-intuitively. It leaves the problem where it belongs in terms of the venue for the analysis and solution.

Systemicity is the watchword in the design of the systemigram and conceptualisation of reference models (holons). This creates a useful sectionalisation for the application of SSM. First there is real-world complexity, exhibiting all its messiness without restraint and giving rise, for any chosen focus of concern, its particular expressions of ill-ease. Then there is the clean, ordered world of systemicity, where idealisation and conceptualisation can proceed uninhibitedly, whilst profiting from the wisdom of those whose case-hardened experiences have been forged in the white hot crucible of the real world. The rôle for the systemigram is to marry these two worlds.

3   Quality Function Deployment (QFD)

Figure 1 states: "Quality Function Deployment (QFD) is a system for linking a strategy that allows the customer's voice to predominate in product development to tactics for controlling process parameters by means of stable, familiar and unambiguous operating instructions". What the systemigram goes on to describe is the broad requirement placed on the system, the strategy and the tactics. The system should avoid two principal obstacles - specification misinterpretation and management paralysis. This may be a truism, but in these days of technology encrustation and supposed infallible management principles, it is dangerous for a dying breed of quizzical analyst to overlook anything and to treat the obvious as unchallengable. For example it is widely agreed that quality is now an essential concept in any business, so total quality management (TQM) is an obvious need. But do people in the business really know what quality means? If not, when TQM is introduced, there is a danger that its deployment will be flawed and business then proceeds smoothly in the wrong direction! The essence of QFD is that people should listen attentively to the customer's voice (even, it is said, to his whisper). Only then can there be confidence that what is specified, as a result of what the customer says he wants, will not be misinterpreted, and that management will be in complete agreement, and therefore not paralysed, as to what the direction of travel of the business. These appendages to the term 'system' in Figure 1, are therefore present to reinforce the central message of QFD. Likewise, the term 'strategy' is required to call for 'management vision' and 'employee rethinking'. These are major issues if we are resolved to eschew rhetoric, and it therefore becomes imperative to place on upper management the need to develop such vision and to address issues like employee perceptions, skills, attitudes and knowledge. The combined effect of qualifying both the 'system' and the 'strategy' is then to accelerate exploitation of product development.

By implication, the business is invigorated to turn out the right product at the right time which cannot therefore fail to create customer satisfaction. That is the 'upper region' in the systemigram's topology. The lower region indicates how to accomplish what is needful. Product development, to which QFD refers, cannot take place without embracing 'Generic product modelling'. What is meant by this?

Generic product modelling is the ability to know the complete architecture of a product, the detailed composition of its constitutive elements, and the process knowledge to assemble a product including the resolution of choice in instantiating specific products relative to particular customer requirements and the environmental conditions in which the product will operate. It is a statement of knowing what you know about the product not just knowing about the product. The customer's 'voice' is captured technically by a system of matrices, planning charts and operating instructions. It is vitally important that these do not predominate. QFD makes the customer's voice predominant in the product's development process. Technicity must not hold sway over systemicity. The latter is the means of respecting complexity, observing reality, maintaining objectivity, and controlling intervention in the real world to accomplish the business's strategic goals.

4. Process management

No business can possibly hope to survive, let alone grow if the processes by which it conducts itself are not well regulated. That means knowing what they are, how they need to be executed, what their resilience is to hostile environments, what the natural lifespan of each is, and a host of other features. In essence they must be known and kept known. How is this to be achieved? A set of action points which bridge strategy for process understanding to tactics for programme management, is organised using the acronym POLCA: Planning, Organisation, Leadership, Control, and Adaptation. The key to effective **planning** at the tactical level is for planners to create a 3-dimensional visibility to their plans. This requires them to mark up their plans in such a way that: various levels of management audience can follow the thread from their own perspective on the plan's mission; those associated with the stages in development of the plan, say with respect to phases in the product lifecycle if that is what the plan describes, can inherit the plan with simplicity and bequeath it as a legacy with equal clarity. Finally, the various technical authorities who must interact with the plan at any given stage can add their own judgments and amendments in a consistent fashion so that the resulting set of inputs leaves the plan in a tidy state. For the **organisational** element of process to be effective it must support communication with the following key features: *declared prerequisites* - when messages are passed around they need to be encased in a 'protocol shell'; *imperative acknowledgements* - this is to ensure that the loop is closed, i.e. that the recipient does what is needed, not what he thinks he heard; *differentiated actions* - this means that the recipient is enabled to differentiate between information on which he need take no action, and information which is an implied directive.

For **leadership** to be successful it must encourage inter-personal skills which give: *assertive direction* - the programme manager must state unequivocally what it is that he requires and must apply commitment for achievement and not seek reasons why it cannot be done. The customer does not understand reasons, he only understands failure; *effective meetings* - actions must be accepted as being necessary, otherwise there is no point in having actions. There must be targets and dates, actions such as 'think about' or 'consider' are unacceptable; *confirmed completions* - this boils down to insisting that things get done and that completions are confirmed by obtaining the evidence for their completion, i.e. "I told Smith to do it" is not completion.

Action points under the **control** heading relate to implementing timely decisions through the following measures: *problem identification* - the programme manager must recognise difficulties and act upon them; *task definition* - the starting point for every programme should be an understanding of what is required with very clear definition of each task; *investigation - action tradeoffs* - referring to terminating the search for more information in order to make a decision.

Adaptation is the 'outer loop' which evaluates planning, organisation, leadership, and control functions in a context-sensitive manner, in order that: *contingencies are seen and not blurred* - the programme manager should steer clear of contingencies and instead put pain at the front of the activity no matter how difficult this may be. If contingencies are used it should be for the things that have not been thought of, not for the things that have been thought of and which are thought may go wrong. These latter items should be tackled within the day to day management through work-arounds and not just by letting the time extend; *centres of gravity impact in known fashion on performance* - the programme manager should recognise the centres of gravity of the project plan and form an opinion as to the key nodes in the plan which have the greatest effect on the performance of the plan, i.e. if the nodes are unlocked, significant work can go on uninterrupted; *problems are revealed up front* - the programme manager should cover all elements and eventualities in the plan and force out the problems, not hide from them, then work through the shortfalls with solutions; and, finally, *programme execution is at all times user-friendly* - the programme manager should run the project in a manner with which he is comfortable. He should plan early in order to allow time for all disciplines to have sufficient time to do their task, otherwise their discomfort will eventually return to him. He should remember that the plan is only as good as its input. It should not be used to prove that the job cannot be done. There will obviously be difficulties in arriving at a plan where there will be consequences of forward and backward passes.After a number of these passes, the difference between success and failure lies in the belief that it can be done and the commitment to do it.

5 .   Human resources

We turn finally to the people in the business, for which we need a human resource model. This informs the strategists as to the nature of the human resource within the corporation enabling deployment of that resource to maximum benefit of the business purpose.The model reflects three key features in corporate **strategy**: development training, process understanding, and customer orientation. An important process in any business is that which resolves specific requests made of the business e.g. projects or customer orders. This resolution generates what we might call the business tasks, and the job of the tactical manoeuvres within the business is to ensure that this particular process is adequately regulated. **Tactics** which establish mechanisms for the control of business tasks include: *work breakdown* -the definition of capsules of work capable of being executed by individuals or groups within the workforce; *people profile* - the definition of people assets, on an individual basis, as a prelude to understanding the depth, variety and resilience of the total people assets of the business as a whole; *performance measurement* - the definition by which business agrees as to how it is reviewing its assets and its inputs, and therefore how it measures the quality of its deliverables. There is a need to link corporate strategy for human resources to operational tactics for controlling business tasks. At the meeting point of these two entities must lie a **requirements identification** defining the specification of tasks and their allocation: *job definition* -in much the same way that a particular customer demand must be resolved into constituent work packages, capsules resulting from this resolution process must be further scoped in order to produce specific jobs that will then be assigned to particular people; *skills definition* - each job can be assessed for the purposes of identifying the skills needed in order to ensure its timely and satisfactory completion. At this point, we have a clear requirement for human resources relative to a customer demand placed upon the corporation; *assignment criteria* -the business must assume corporate responsibility for defining, and reworking on the basis of experience, a system of criteria that admits priorities, dogma and prudence as the climate of customer demand and corporate well-being dictates.

Two further items must now be borne in mind. The first is an understanding of what it means to mobilise the workforce. **People** have a habit of setting and concealing their own personal agendas no matter how much they are viewed as corporate assets. People are dynamic entities; they have unusual mobility and are aware of the value of this to other prospective employers; they interact with their own development training and become different in ways that were not foreseen by the designers of these - a case of emergent properties in action. Job satisfaction is a variable which strongly impacts on the human resources strategy. Employee appraisal (vexed issue or accelerator of change?), is another factor governing workforce dynamics. The real concern of the **enterprise** is to fulfil business purpose. To model this needs: *development motivators* - to tell the corporation what enables employees to be successful to the business and to keep them a success; *cultural contribution* - to determine how business culture is affected by the programmed development and subsequent employee rethinking; *business performance* - measures of performance for the whole business.

6.   Conclusions

This paper addresses the need to produce a requirements specification for effective collaboration between academia and industry. This is expressed by a framework for systems engineering. The challenge facing engineering today is the management of complexity. Computers, the zenith of technological achievement so far, can help. But technology fixes are transient. They often produce new problems. What is needed is better understanding of the processes which give rise to complexity in the first place. Technology plays an invaluable rôle in supporting this.

The intellectual breakthrough for dealing with complexity is the systems approach, exemplified by the process of systemic inquiry. This respects the rôle of problem ownership, acknowledges the nature of human activity systems, and relies on effective deployment of key systemic concepts such as boundary, hierarchy and emergence.

This paper commends the systemigram as a device for attributing problem ownership and capturing problem definition by hierarchical treatment of boundary issues. Emergent features in systemigrams are testified to by problem owners in any given problematique.

The extensive programme of collaboration between GEC Marconi and the School of Systems Engineering at the University of Portsmouth is based on an agreed definition for systems engineering and makes maximum use of the systemigram as a methodological tool. Though the collaboration is still at an early stage, it is already proving fruitful in terms of the development of both the academic staff and the curriculum.

Figure 1.   A mission statement for Quality Function Deployment (QFD)

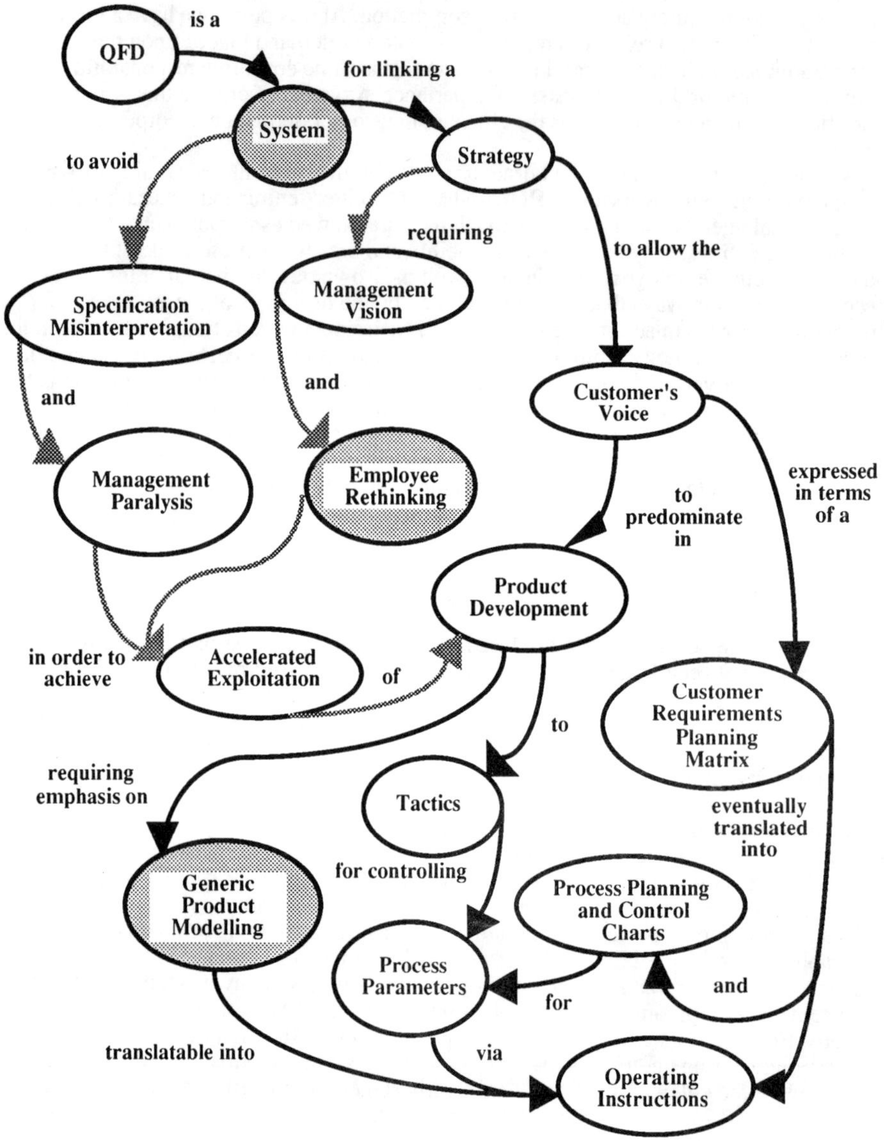

Engineering Education Africa - Differentiating the Cart from the Horse

P.B.U. Achi

Federal University of Technology, Owerri

Africa was "absent" from the industrial revolution and so today relies on theoretical engineering textbooks written by foreigners for its engineering education system. As a result the African engineering education "cart" has been placed before the "horse", thus creating a technological "inertia" against technology acquisition for Africa. The new approach being adopted in the machine design and manufacturing education areas, for example, bases the curriculum on projects - oriented topics using existing local or imported equipment as course examples. With the higher level of engineering development in industrial nations the African market for engineering systems is developing with technical apprentice-ships integrated with formal engineering education. This paper concludes by recommending this "Applications Integral" approach as the proper dynamic differentiation between the "cart" and the "horse" in African engineering education, (AFRED).

Keywords: Engineering Education, Projects-oriented, machine Design, Manufacturing, Technology, Applications - Integral, Industry, AFRED, EDAFR.

1 INTRODUCTION

Traditionally engineering started as technical practices and was learnt as such in industrial nations through apprentice-ship. Pre - and post - industrial revolution inventions were not (and still are not) so much results of theoretical deductions as they are of practical research and development. The technological breakthroughs of the industrial revolution were not achieved so much because of the conscious application of analytic engineering theories as through accidental discoveries, mere "hunches" or in many cases through talents in arts and crafts.

The steam engine, for example, was first invented before the knowledge of the theories of engineering thermodynamics and fluid flow was applied to refine and develop the equipment. It would also have been very difficult to have invented (designed) the steam and internal combustion engines first from pure scientific deductions, analysis and synthesis! Education in engineering, therefore, becomes functional and productive after practical equipment and systems have been invented often by persons less versed in the engineering theories and sciences.

The technologies of the industrial revolution have regenerated and developed to unrecognizable sophisticated machines, processes, systems and techniques today to constitute the present industrial technology of northern countries. Engineering is now a culture of the northern countries and hence textbooks on the subject don't concern themselves with rigorous practical analysis of technological examples required by African countries who were "absent" from the industrial revolution. These textbooks which form the basis of "AFRED" are grossly inadequate for African needs! In comparison with the experiences of the industrial nations in engineering education, African countries have placed the cart in front of the horse resulting in very low productivity of AFRED.

2   HISTORICAL DEVELOPMENT OF AFRICAN ENGINEERING EDUCATION, (AFRED).

Before independence Africa (under colonial rule) relied on importation of manufactured consumer and capital goods using funds from exportation of purely primary (raw) agricultural produce like palm oil, coffee seeds, groundnuts, timber, rubber and minerals. The production of these primary produce was done using manual labour and since very little (if any) processing was done at home, the colonial administrations saw no need to give engineering education to the local people. Whenever engineering skills were required even in road building and similar civil engineering works expatriates were sent to Africa from the home country.

At independence there was hardly any tertiary institution for AFRED. The very few tertiary institutions in Africa before 1960 were mainly for education in the liberal arts to assist in the colonial administration of Africa. As colonial powers made their sudden exit around 1960 engineering manpower vacuum was created in Africa and the new nations established tertiary engineering institutions in a hurry. Without time for proper planning, the tertiary engineering education systems in Western countries were transplanted into Africa. Import - substitution industries were also hurriedly transplanted into Africa and AFRED was thus a "cart" driving the "horse" from its inception!

2.1   AFRICAN ENGINEERING EDUCATION (AFRED) - THE "HORSE"

Africa is rich in cultural anthropology but it lacks the modern technological background experience to benefit from the present methodologies in engineering education. Although Africa is rich in arts and crafts which are the original basis of technology the century - wide gap between African traditional technology and modern technology is hard to bridge (but it is not impossible to do so)! The search for African engineering education "horse" rests at the development of African indigenous technology. Since Africa does not need to "reinvent the wheel", development of African indigenous technology in a modern world is the duty of AFRED. To establish the "horse", Africa has to "invent" local machines, equipment, processes and systems to mechanise agriculture in the peculiar African environment, to process African primary raw materials and support African cultural anthropology in feeding, dressing and general living habits. Nobody is better placed than the Africans themselves to design proper solutions for these problems. That some foreign equipment in advanced states of development exist for these functions is not altogether true. The excessive cost of the existing imported equipment, the low local maintenance skill for running this equipment and the absence of local technology for fabrication of spare parts show clearly that imported technology had failed Africa! That Africa remains impoverished decades after owning this non-functional excessively priced equipment is another pointer to the failure.

It is definitely easier to own this equipment economically if they were designed or at least manufactured in Africa using mainly African skills and labour. It is the duty of AFRED today to make this equipment even without much reference to engineering theories and science. It is when this horse (indigenous technology) has been put in its place that the "cart" would acquire a function. Indeed AFRED is now "tinkering" out equipment for Africa!

2.2   AFRICAN ENGINEERING EDUCATION (AFRED) - THE "CART"

The African engineering "horse" conveys Africa to the world of modern technology in which imported machinery would be reasonably priced, easily maintained and economically operated. The African engineering "horse" therefore acquires the skill needed to put the "cart" in its proper place.

Since the last two decades the zeal for African indigenous technology has enabled Africans to fabricate several equipment and systems to solve some African problems. Nigerian structural adjustment programme (SAP) rendered the cost of imported equipment so high that industrialists had no choice but to seek Nigerian sources for such equipment. The first generation of such equipment are now being refined and developed using the principles of engineering science, the "cart"! The relevance of the extensive theories taught previously in AFRED is now beginning to be understood in this period of "Engineering Education Africa" ("EDAFR"), the "horse" and the "cart" having taken their proper places. The process is only painfully beginning and a lot of way is yet to be covered.

3 METHODOLOGY IN "ENGINEERING EDUCATION AFRICA" (EDAFR)

Engineering Education Africa (EDAFR) does not seek to re-invent the wheel when pursuing the development of African indigenous technology. "Indigenous technology" is defined in Achi (1985) as "the contemporary technological expertise possessed by indigenes (through education) to enable them to find solutions to their problems especially (but not only) the traditional ones". Therefore the indigenous technology being taught by EDAFR does not negate the modern basics for such technology but applies cost competitive practical principles to solve problems peculiar to the society.

EDAFR adopts the method of "projects-oriented" teaching and industrial attachments. In Nigeria engineering lecturers are encouraged to base their teaching on projects and researches undertaken by them and their colleagues especially in the neighborhood at the undergraduate levels. Local teaching aids are obtained from broken down or scrapped equipment. Whenever possible craftsmen and artisans mobilised in local industrial centres assist the engineering students in their projects. In universities of technology, engineering courses are usually accompanied by practical course projects designed to produce marketable items.

In EDAFR industrial attachments are periodically undertaken for periods of three months during the long vacations and one semester under the students industrial work experience scheme, (SIWES). SIWES is treated as a course each year in a process of integrating or inter-weaving classroom "theory" and industrial (workshop) practice until the student graduates. EDAFR is therefore an "Application - Integral" approach to engineering education.

In Nigeria EDAFR is involving the country's research and development centres in the programmed SIWES attachments as a result of which research in Nigeria is now reasonably influencing engineering education. Frequent one-day industrial visits are also programmed into certain courses while group and individual projects feature in the engineering courses.

In the Federal University of Technology, Owerri three
common courses in "Industrial Studies" are taught in the 2nd,
3rd and fourth years in classes combining all the departments
in the school of engineering. The emphasis in the
multidisciplinary course (industrial studies) is the group
projects. Each group consists of a student mixture of all the
disciplines in engineering and thus students get used to inter
disciplinary cooperation. The engineering school curriculum
offers common engineering courses at 100%, 50%, 20% and 0% in
the (1st and 2nd), 3rd, 4th and 5th years respectively at the
faculty level.

4   TEACHING "MACHINE DESIGN" AND "MANUFACTURE" THE EDAFR WAY

Fig. 1 is a sketch of a manual food slicing machine used by
the author in teaching shafting and gear design, and
manufacture, bearings, bushings, and power transmissions.

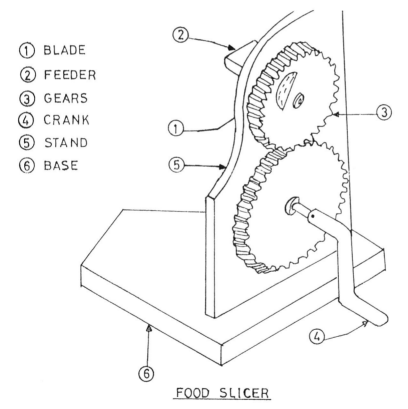

1. BLADE
2. FEEDER
3. GEARS
4. CRANK
5. STAND
6. BASE

FOOD SLICER

The machine is expected to slice local foods like plantains, yams, carrots and cassava with varying forces of resistance to slicing.

The students are required to motorize the slicing process choosing the motor, shaft, bearings or bushings, and gears, configuring and assembling the components. The students designed and manufactured the shaft, bushing and gears, during the study. Because for this project (and generally) proper materials are difficult to find in required sizes and shapes, the supporting frame and gears were manufactured from a special hard wood found locally. The wood was found to be unusually durable as improvised gear material. The gears were manufactured using form-cutters. The use of wood as gear material also prolongs the life of the cutters which are also not easily available.

The first part of the course was the study of a collection of disused motor vehicle components gathered from motor mechanic workshops by the students themselves. This was followed by the fabrication of the manual machine, fig 1, without any reference to theories but purely from sketches.

5   CONCLUSIONS

The use of the "Applications - Integral" approach in Engineering Education Africa (EDAFR) enables the student not only to understand the theories but the applications also. The projects - oriented approach produces practically sound engineering graduates usually preferred by industries for employment.

6   REFERENCES

Achi P.B.U (1985) "INDIGENOUS" AND "APPROPRIATE" TECHNOLOGIES IN DEVELOPING COUNTRIES, paper prepared for Int. Conference on Science and Technology Education, Bangalore.

Teaching Material Obtained From Contracting Experience on the Channel Tunnel

B.O. Corbett

Department of Civil Engineering, University of Brighton (formerly on secondment to Tunnels Construction, Transmanche-Link Joint Venture)

Abstract
This paper gives the background to a secondment to Tunnels Construction, Transmanche-Link J.V.(TML). The flexible management structure of TML brought the opportunity of vast experience in problem solving. Although any one individual could only play a small rôle, in the event the variety and the professional level of the work has meant that a great deal of teaching material has arisen from the project. Following tunnelling experience over thirty-five years since the GPO Tunnels of the 1950s, working with the same engineers, supervisors and foremen, here was the opportunity for the author to obtain material which is unlikely to become available ever again.
<u>Keywords</u>: Tunnels, Construction, Management, Problem solving, Safety.

1   Introduction

'This is actually an easy tunnel. It's just a long, long way'. Those were the words of Peter Bermingham, at the time Superintendent (Land Running Tunnels); Wilson (1991)
   It is not even the largest British tunnelling project of the twentieth century. In man-power terms, the biggest was the tunnelling under the front of the Ypres Salient during the First World War. This work was under the direction of Sir John Norton-Griffiths (Middlemas, 1963) and involved 12,000 men.
   It is true that of all the challenges presented by this project one of the least troublesome is the engineering. Solving the logistical, financial and environmental problems has caused many headaches. In terms of the tunnelling exercise, the fixed link called for little in the way of innovative technology. That is not in any way to under-estimate the engineering achievement. It is from the engineering - Biggart and King (1991); Purrer et al (1991) - that the teaching material for today and the future has come.
   The project consists of three tunnels between Folkestone and Coquelles, of which the outer tunnels carry the trains

running betwen England and France, and the central tunnel
provides access and services to the other two. The main
working sites are at Dover and Sangatte. Trains can cross
from one track to the other on the surface and at two
undersea crossover caverns.

2   Shakespeare Cliff, Dover

There was a certain camaraderie at Shakespeare Cliff that
made one feel that this was not just another job. There was
a determination to complete the tunnelling efficiently and
on time. There was a continuous urge to achieve more than
the next crew.

This could be summed up in the Chunneler Quadrille (Lewis
Carroll, revised Clive Pollard), which was posted at salient
points throughout the offices:-

> "What matters it how far we go?" his scaly friend replied.
>
> "There is another shore, you know, upon the other side.
>
> The further off from England the nearer is to France-
>
> Then turn not pale, beloved snail, but come and
> join the dance.
>
> Will we, won't we, will we, won't we, will we get to France?
>
> Will we, won't we, will we, won't we,
>
> Yes! we'll get to France"

David Denman, Agent first on the Land Service Tunnel and
later on the Marine Service Tunnel said *'One thing that
makes it so interesting is that it's so big. On a normal job
people doing the back-up services and actually working on
the machines themselves would be experienced men. Ninety per
cent of them are people you take around with you from job to
job-experienced tunnellers. Normally you only have to sign a
few new guys up. On this job it's the other way round.
Probably 10 per cent or 20 per cent of the guys are the
experienced men and the rest of the people have come in from
all over the place - bacon slicers from Tesco, lorry driv-
ers, people from other industries. They're all coming in and
somehow we have to weld them all together'.*

This made safety training and the implications of
maintaining safety ever more important - a useful comment
for teaching purposes.

3   Outline of the Project

The system consists of three tunnels. The two outer tunnels,
which will carry the shuttles and trains, are known as

running tunnel north and running tunnel south respectively.
They have a nominal lined diameter of 7.6 metres; they are
separated by 8 metres of Chalk Marl from the smaller central
service tunnel, with a nominal lined diameter of 4.8 metres.
There are cross passages every 375 metres along the tunnel
and pressure relief ducts between the running tunnels every
250 metres.

Two types of lining were used in the tunnels - precast
concrete and S.G. iron.

4   Management

The speed at which it had been necessary to assemble the
technical teams from the five participating contractors and
by recruitment brought many problems with regard to job
specifications. The priority tasks were changing day-by-day.
The way in which flexible teams were built up and demob-
ilised as the work proceeded provides an example for teaching purposes of a management structure which worked. Early
in his secondment the writer was asked to review the management structure in Tunnels Construction, with regard to the
supply and logistics problems, which were acute early in
1989.

5   Logistics

The principal source of teaching material has come from a
study of the logistics problems. At the beginning of 1989,
the Marine Service Tunnel had overtaken the problems of
tunnelling through the adverse ground and was achieving
progress of the order of 200 metres per week. (Ultimately
this tunnel reached a maximum of 295 metres in one week).
The Land Service Tunnel could have achieved even higher
output rates, had the supply system been able to cope. There
were problems with the electric locomotives which served the
Marine Service Tunnel and in the overhead electric supply
system. This shortage of locomotives meant that the Land
Service Tunnel was frequently starved of resources, since
the number of the alternative diesel locomotives available
was limited.

The programme priorities put the emphasis on production
in the Marine Service Tunnel.

There were other pressures in the Marshalling Area at
Shakespeare Cliff at that time, with the completion of the
New Austrian Tunnelling Method (NATM) workings in the shield
chambers for the Land Running Tunnels and with the erection
of the Marine Running Tunnel Boring Machines.

The development at the Lower Shakespeare Cliff working
site was very difficult. The key to increasing the working
area was the placement of the spoil from the tunnels. The
demand for space for the storage of segments, for locomotive
overhaul facilities, maintenance workshops for the tunnels,

for the railway sidings, batching plant, catering facilities, offices, etc. was intense. Plant space at Upper
Shakespeare Cliff was also at a premium. The link between
the upper and lower sites was by a one-way tunnel, which
caused backing-up of traffic; the effects were the more
severe at the lower site.

The 110 metre shaft at Upper Shakespeare eased the access
to the underground works, but whilst the shaft was needed
for lowering the heavy components for the Tunnel Boring
Machines (TBMs), there was only space for one Alimak Man
Hoist.

All this eased by a year later, when there was much more
reclaimed area at Lower Shakespeare, and there were three
Alimak Hoists in the shaft.

6   The Weakest Link

As has already been stated, it was a long, long way. There
was only one way to the tunnel face and the same way out.
Each of the six tunnels was served by twin 900 mm. gauge
railway tracks. However, since work had to proceed concurrently on the cross passages, access was frequently restricted to single track working.(The cross passages had an
important rôle during construction to provide space for
switch-gear, etc.). Should anything go wrong, then the whole
operation in that tunnel stopped.

It was therefore an important part of the rôle played by
the Engineering Team in Tunnels Construction to identify the
weakest link and try to make a forecast of the next pinch
point. This was a continually changing problem, in which the
people at the sharp end had to play the major part in getting the work started again.

7   Underground Problems

Some of the problems in the Marshalling area were not
without humour. There was intense rivalry between the miners
on the separate tunnels. At one stage this was most noticeable between the Marine Service Tunnel and the Land Service
Tunnel. When the ends of the shifts coincided, because of
the limited hoist facilities in the shaft, there were disagreements which could have led to some serious fighting had
not a rapid management response to staggering the ends of
the shifts been implemented.

At times of acute shortage of locomotive power, there was
the occasional incident of hijacking.

8   Safety

Safety training for all personnel was a key priority for
management. Nobody was allowed to work on site before undertaking safety training. Further training was required - for

example the use of the self rescuer breathing filter apparatus - before anybody could go underground.

Apart from the emphasis on personal safety, all operations
were monitored to ensure safe working conditions and methods
by Incident Control. Specially trained and equipped teams
were deployed to cope with any incidents which might arise.

A minor contribution to the dissemination of information on
safety came after discussions in Mainz in April 1989. The
writer returned from Germany with 50 copies of the German
Tunnelling Safety Manual - Tiefbau (1989a). These were
distributed to the construction team at Tunnels Construction. Subsequently, the manual has been produced in
English - Tiefbau (1989b).

9   Graduate Training - on the Job

Recent Graduates played a useful rôle in the Engineering
Team. They were trained in a tutorial and seminar mode. This
on the job training was useful both to the graduates and to
the Senior Engineers. In the writer's case, the experiences
of the problems solved could be taken back to Brighton and
incorporated in the undergraduate course.

10   The teaching material

The writer has used case history material extensively;
Corbett (1991a). The material which was obtained by having
first-hand experience on the tunnelling falls into groups:-

(a)   the factual information on the management structure and
       the way in which the works were controlled.
(b)   the flexible team structure and how this was managed.
(c)   the sequence of construction.
(d)   technical problems on the tunnelling - the TBM
       operations, the NATM tunnels and the cast-iron lined
       hand tunnels.
(e)   the difficulties posed during the design and
       construction of the Crossover Cavern.
(f)   the design and installation of the permanent instrum-
       entation at Dover, Sevington and the Isle of Grain
(g)   the problems of the weakest link
(h)   safety requirements and implementation
(i)   quality control and quality assurance
(j)   on-the-job graduate training
    The significant aspect of the work was the logistics
problems of servicing the tunnelling operations with limited
access, with only one way in and the same way out of a TBM
tunnel, and the weakest link scenario which dictates the
planning behind all these operations.

Good leadership led to high morale on the project. This is evidenced by the record rates of progress which were achieved in the tunnelling. This can be easily demonstrated when taught in a statistical form.

The availability of Eurotunnel teaching material in French and German - e.g. Kent County Council and the Channel Tunnel Group (1991) has helped the writer when working at educational institutions in France, Germany, Czechoslovakia and Poland - Corbett (1991b).

All of this has strengthened experience obtained since 1953 working with the same people in the design office and on site on the GPO Tunnels in London, the provinces and Scotland, on works on the Piccadilly and Victoria Lines and on the Strand Underpass.

11   Acknowledgments

This experience was obtained by personal contact with the Management, Staff and Workforce of Tunnels Construction, Transmanche-Link JV, Shakespeare Cliff, Dover, without whom there would have been no tunnel.

The secondment was made possible by a Leverhulme Fellowship in Engineering Practice, awarded by the Leverhulme Trust on the recommendation of the Committee of Directors of Polytechnics.

Teaching material produced by Eurotunnel and Kent County Council has been useful in providing core factual and visual material.

References

Biggart, A. and King, J.R.J. (1991). Design and Construction of the Channel Tunnel;**Tunnels and Tunnelling**, January.

Purrer.W., King, J.R.J.,Crighton, G., Myers, A., Wallis, J. (1990). Field engineering under the sea: excavating the UK crossover chamber;**Tunnels and Tunnelling**, December.

Middlemas, R.K. **The Masterbuilders** - Sir John Norton-Griffiths (1963), Hutchinson, London.

Tiefbau Berufsgenossenschaft (1989a) **Tunnelbau - Sicher Arbeiten**; Leitfaden für Tunnelbauer, Munchen.

Tiefbau Berufsgenossenschaft (1989b) - **Safe Working in Tunnelling**; for tunnel workers and first line supervision; Munich.

Wilson, D.(1991) **Breakthrough - Tunnelling the Channel** - Eurotunnel and Random Century Group,- London.

Kent County Council and the Channel Tunnel Group (1991) **'Nachrichten zum Kanaltunnel.'**

Corbett, B.O. (1991a) 'Civil Engineering Construction - Teaching by Case Histories'. 20. Internationalen Symposiums, **"Ingenieurpädagogik '91"**, Dresden, Vol.1, p.65.

Corbett,B.O. (1991b) Der Tunnel zwischen England und Frankreich: Nachrichten zum Kanaltunnel. **Lecture at the Technische Hochschule Leipzig.**

An Educational Capacity Planning System for Precast Concrete Production

N.N. Dawood

Division of Civil Engineering and Building, School of Science and Technology, The University of Teeside

Abstract

Junior and even senior production planers in the precast industry have a rather difficult task of planning and controlling the production process. This is because the managers have to rely entirely on accumulated experience and in-house training to achieve the planning process.

The object of this paper is to develop an educational capacity planning system for precast concrete production to educate production managers how to make better planning decisions and explore options open to them. The system is a factory simulator that automates the process of planning and predicts the effect of several managerial strategies before actual production commences. The performance of the system is examined using both real and hypothetical production environments.

The information used by the model is provided by the *ECC Building Products Ltd* and the contribution of the company production managers is highly acknowledged by the author.

Keywords: Planning, Precasting, Scheduling,Computing, Education.

1 Introduction

Junior and even senior production planers in the precast industry have a rather difficult task of planning and controlling the production process. This is entirely due to the fact that the managers have to rely on accumulated experience and in-house training to achieve the planning process. There is little or no formal educational courses to educate students (potential production managers) how to plan in such industry and this is quite understandable because planning practices in the industry is quite unique and even planning the production of one product can be different from another product in the same industry.

   The object of the paper is to develop an educational computer-based capacity planning for precast concrete production to educate managers how to allocate resources, to improving managerial decisions and to explore options open to them. The system automates the production planning process using certain intelligent rules that were extracted from experience production managers. The system acts as a tool to educate managers by passing the knowledge the system holds to users. This is done by automatically producing plans of the work and justifications for resource allocation.

   In a survey of the current production-planning practices in the UK, the author has concluded that the current planning practices are fairly basic and depend greatly on subjective, experiential approaches. Such practices have contributed to poor planning performance that resulted in low profit margins, unfavourable cash flow and carrying excessive stock or running-out of stock for key products. This has promoted the idea of developing an educational planning system for educating managers how to allocate resources and evaluate several managerial strategies before actual production commences. The system is a factory simulator which automates the process of production for six to twenty months using several market and plant characteristics and managerial strategies- i.e. when, which and how product should be produced and on which plant to satisfy certain criteria.

The system is used as experimental tool to test managerial strategies through generating capacity plans. Those plans are then evaluated using four measures of performance: cost of stock, cost of inefficiency and cost of plant changeovers- i.e. adapting a plant to suite particular product and cost of unproduced products. The paper has concluded that managers should be able to detect and learn the advantages and disadvantages of adapting certain production strategies, the effect of inefficiency and plant's changeovers before actual production can even start. The system is equipped with three plant and product selection rules (for illustrating the capabilities of the system) which forms the main production strategies. These rules were developed form both practical and theoretical aspects. The system is also developed to accommodate any number of rules if creative managers wish to apply rules of their own. The following illustrates just entities, process and specification of the system. The software specification and manual is not given due to the restrictions on the size of the paper.

2   The process of the system

The system is basically a " finite rough-cut" factory simulator which develops six to twenty months capacity plans using a backward scheduling technique from middle management level. The model involves the assessment of existing capacity and forecasting future capacity needs over a selected planning horizon under several managerial decisions and as a guide-line for constructing detailed plans. This will help junior or even senior managers to learn how plans are prepared and the consequence of adapting several managerial policies.

The objects of the model are basically entities and attributes. The entities are elements of the system being simulated and they can individually identifies and processed. Plant and products are regarded as entities of the model. Each entity possess one or more attributes to convey extra information about it. For example certain plant can produce a set of products which others cannot. The system educate managers by providing the following information about the production process: a. the ability of the current plant to achieve the required demand within the planning period; b. the consequence of using certain production planning strategy; and c. estimating the monthly stock level and stock cost for each group of products.

Certain terminology has been used in the paper for the purpose of specifying the entities of the model. This is:

Plant: is an independent production line within a factory. Each plant includes a Mixer, Moulds, a Press and Operative. A factory can have any number of plant with similar or different specifications.

Efficiency: is the capability of a plant to reach it's theoretical design output rate. This is expressed in percentage term. For example 100% efficiency mean that a plant is matching it's theoretical output rate and it is 100% utilised, 70% efficiency means that a plant is achieving just 70% of its theoretical output and 30% of the output left without utilisation due to technical reasons.

3   Information needed by the capacity planning model

The information about plant, shifts and demands required to achieve the planning process is: a. plant' attributes information; b. products attributes information; c. demand information; and d. shift patterns.

The plant and products attributes convey the personality of the factory being simulated and can differ from one factory to another. The demand information represents sales forecasting for each group of product for six to twelve months ahead. Figure (1) shows the interaction between the above information and the process of the system.

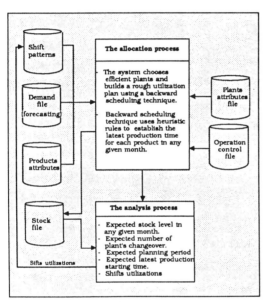

Figure 1
The planning system framework

4   The planning process

4.1   The planning technique
In the system the backward planning technique is applied. This technique uses "backtracking" in the allocation of shifts to plant which starts from the end of the planning period and works backwards. The planning decisions are basically intelligent rules which direct the process of planning. These rules are of two types: *product selection rules* which direct the process of sorting demand before production commences, and *allocation rules* which direct the process of allocating shifts to the running plant and changing the state of the model when certain events occur.

4.2   The product selection rules
These are intelligent rules which are used for establishing the order in which products should be processed in the model. The products selection rules differ from one

precasting factory to another, depending on the management style, type of products and plant, and market. However, general criteria should be satisfied in the planning process, such as maintaining stock cover for products, production efficiency and minimising plant change-overs.

In the system, three product selection rules are developed to model several planning strategies in the allocation process bearing in mind the above criteria. These rules are developed from logic and information gathered from the industry. It should be mentioned that these product selection rules are not the only loading rules possible and the reason for choosing just three rules is to illustrate the use and potentials of the model. The product selection rules which are developed in this research are: a. High production cost rule (HPC rule); b. Long processing time rule (LPT rule); and c. Short processing time rule (SPT rule).

As an example, the logic expression for the HPC rule is:

> IF production cost of one unit of product A > production cost of one unit of product B THEN
> > product A is prior to product B ELSE
> IF production cost of one unit of product A = production cost of one unit of product B AND
> IF volume of product A >= volume of product B THEN
> > product A is prior to product B ELSE
> IF production cost of one unit of product A < production cost of one unit of product B THEN product B is prior to product A

4.3   The plant selection rules

The model selects a plant for a given product with respect to the following rules:

Rule 1 : select a plant that can produce the running product with 100% efficiency and other product with lower efficiency, if it can process more than one product. If this rule has not been satisfied, then rule 2 would be activated.

Rule 2 : select the plant which can produce the running product with 100% efficiency regardless of other products. If this rule has not been satisfied, then rule 3 is activated.

Rule 3: if rules (1) and (2) are not feasible then select the plant which can produce the running product with the best efficiency level.

In the case of rule (1) the idea is to utilise plants which are not efficient in all products and use them as efficient as possible. The plant selection rules can be changed and managers can incorporate their own rules.

4.4   The allocation rules

The allocation rules are developed to direct the process of planning in a logical and sensible way. These rules can be grouped as: a. checking availability of plant and demands; b. searching for efficient plant to be allocated to the running products; and c. updates time and information after each event in the process.

The detail description of the simulation process and the running of the system is presented in reference Dawood and Neale, 1991.

5   The experimental work

The main object of the experimental work is to illustrate the potential and use of the system as educational tool for managers and to investigate the performance of using production strategies under several demand and shifts characteristics. The factory

example used in the experiments is obtained from the precasting company and composed of the following:
a. three production plant, 1,2 and 3;
b. three levels of shift patterns (10, 20, 30) shifts per month are available to each plant for 12 months;
c. nine products, PR1 to PR9;
d. shifts are available for 14 months;
e. demand period is 12 months;
f. curing time is four weeks for all products.
g. cost of capital (interest rate) is 14% per month

All products can be made on all plant, however, the following efficiencies apply:
Plant 1: only 70% efficient on products PR1, PR2, PR3 and PR9;
Plant 2: only 70% efficient on products PR4, PR5, PR6, PR7 and PR8.
Plant 3: 100% efficient on all products.
Output per shift at 100% efficiency for all plant is given below:
PR1: 92 units/shift; PR2:92 units/shift;PR3:54 units/shift;PR4:75 units/shift;
PR5: 75 units/shift;PR6:75 units/shift;PR7:75 units/shift;PR8:63 units/shift;
PR9: 56 units/shift.

In order to study the effect of the production strategies, several experiments have been carried out using the system under different measures of performance. These measures are: cost of stock; cost of under utilisation (that is, cost of using less than 100% efficient plant); cost of change-overs and cost of units left unproduced.
In the experiments, several parameters have been varied for different runs. Due to the limitation of the size of the paper the description and analysis of the experimental work is not given. However, all the information related to the experimental work is documented and available for interested readers. Examples of the results of the experimental work is given in graphs 1 and 2.

6 Summary and conclusions

The object of the paper is to develop an educational capacity planning system for precast concrete production in order to help managers to make better planning decisions and to explore options open to them. The system involves the assessment of existing capacity and forecast future needs over a selected planning horizon using several market and plant characteristics. Several runs of experimental work have been carried out under the three product selection rule, three demand patterns, three shift pattern and four measures of performance. The results have suggested that the system can be used to educate managers about the production process, the utilisation of plant and the consequence of using certain managerial decisions.

References

Dawood, N. (1991) A computer-based capacity planning system for precast concrete production, PhD thesis, Loughborough, UK.
Dawood, N. and Neale R. (1990) A survey of the current production planning practices in the precast industry, Construction Management and Economics Journal, 8, 365-383.

Results of running the planning model, Sine wave demand, 20 shifts per month, Graph 1

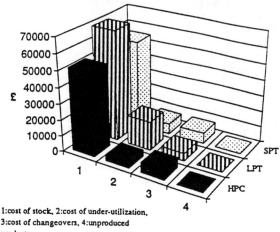

1:cost of stock, 2:cost of under-utilization,
3:cost of changeovers, 4:unproduced
products

Results of running the planning model, Test site demand, 20 shifts per month, Graph 2

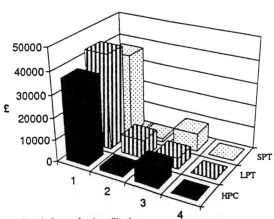

1:cost of stock, 2:cost of under-utilization,
3:cost of changeovers, 4:unproduced
products

Development of Curricula for Postgraduate Training at the Faculty of Transportation Engineering at the Technical University of Budapest

E.K. Gilicze, P. Michelberger, K. Tánczos
Faculty of Transportation Engineering, Technical University of Budapest

Abstract
The faculty offers a number of postgraduate study options after the first qualification, which is the normal Diploma in Vehicle and Transport Engineering obtained after 5 years . Further study of two years duration is possible to obtain an additional Diploma. There are Diplomas in specializations in Transport Engineering and Engineering Economics. Students may also study for Doctoral Degree which can only be obtained after two years of practice in transport engineering. The paper presents the results of recent work on curriculum development for postgraduate education. The authors discuss the programme structures.
Keywords: Education program, postgraduate training

1. Main features of the updated curriculum for graduate training

The training provided by the Faculty of Transportation Engineering ensures the granting of diplomas in mechanical and transportation engineering.

The new curriculum having come in force in September 1991 is one of a modular structure. The modules built up on each other offer a possibility for the students of receiving professional and specialized training by ensuring them the possibility if multiple choice. The modules ensure the possibility of acquiring convertible rudiments of natural sciences, as well as the fundamentals of engineering sciences, the attainment of the general knowledge required for the process-planning in transportation, and intensified study in the field of a certain sub-branch of transportation engineering, or the solution to a particular problem of transportation, respectively.

In the new curriculum, the earlier training separated into sections from the second semester has been replaced by a uniform, fully common engineering training lasting till the end of the fourth semester, then, common in a decreasing measure till the end of the engineering training. The new structure of the curriculum reckons with a scheduled 28-hour occupation per week, which is enlarged by a training in foreign languages of 4 hours per week during the first six semesters. The overall training period includes 10 semesters.

2. Assortment of postgraduate training at the Faculty of Transportation Engineering

The postgraduate training at our Faculty is based on the graduate one. By gaining a two-year engineering practice subsequent to the graduation from the Faculty, a diploma of engineer-specialist or that of engineer-manager can be granted, respectively, or else a degree of "doctor of the university" can be conferred to those taking part in this kind of education. The postgraduate training at the University represents a 4-semester correspondence training including occupation of a scheduled 80-130 hours per semester, as well as individual postgraduate training and writing the diploma thesis. There is a possibility of acquiring the qualification of engineer-specialist, or the degrees of "doctor of the university" within the framework of day-courses in engineering training, too. This lasts for 3 years following immediately the day-training, and is based for the minor part, on a state scholarship, while, for the major part, it is based on a sponsorship offered by companies.

The holders of this latter assistance receive their stipendiate from the companies where they are going to pursue   their activities after finishing their studies   at the University .

Training of engineer-specialists satisfies the demand raised by the special fields. The transportation engineers graduated   from the Faculty can continue their study at the sections of "Transportation management informatics" and "Urban transport".

At the section of Engineering Economy, the training of engineer-managers   for transportation takes places on the basis of an updated curriculum. The goal of this training is that the engineers with the normal Diploma, optained after 5 years, engaged in the different fields of vehicle maintenance for transportation, logistics   and shipment   of goods should obtatin such a management attitude and knowledge by which the completion of technical knowledge   with a feature of venture and business will be rendered possible. The students admitted to this section of the Faculty can make their choice from among the special lines of shipment, transportation, informatics, humane policy and logistics.

In the   following , the updated curricula   of the two most popular lines   of the postgraduate training, i.e. urban transport and transportation management will be introduced below.

3. Training of engineer-specialists for urban transport

3.2 Goal   of training

This section is chosen first of all, by the engineers with   the normal Diploma, graduated from the Faculty of Transportation Engineering who are engaged in one or other part- field of urban transport.

The thorough kmowledge of the characteristics of urban transport requires the special task of providing education and training. In the course of day-time studies, the transportation engineers dealt with the subjects   of Transportation   Technology and Transportation Network Planning, while in the framework of subject "Vehicles" they could acquire a thorough knowledge both in Vehichle Dynamics and Vehicle Construction, besides they could get acquainted   with the sphere of problems associated with   Transportation Development. In the course of writing their diploma   thesis, the students could penetrate into the depth of the sub-branches associated   with the problems to be solved. Naturally, the subject-matter provided by the graduate training enables the transportation engineers with the normal Diploma to pursue their activity with success, however, it can not ensure the advantage of specialization, the re-arrangement of the pieces of knowledge with respect to urban life, or the outlook beyond the restricted knowledge of transportation.

In   recent years, urban transport has becom   more and more determinant of the quality of our   life, and the decisions made on urban transport have their long-range effect on the transportation   policy. Therefore it seemed to be reasonable to organise the training of engineer-specialists engaged exclusively   in this   field. Consequently, the goal of engineering training should cover the specialized knowledge exceeding the subject-matter of graduate training up to the attainment of   the normal Diploma, the disclosure of the demands for urban   transport in the fields of planning, development   and management of urban transport   networks suitable for satisfying the demands with respect   to time and place, with the far-reaching consideration of the possibilities provided by the effective and safe traffic-handling, environmental protection and computing technology.

This   training enables the engineer-specialists, to perform the successful activity of research,   planning,   operation, organization and management, as well as expertise at the institutions of urban transport. It also provides a basis for satisfying the demands of the special fields and those   of the adjoining special lines, as well   as for scientific individual postgraduate training.

3.2 The structure   of the curriculum for engineer-specialists

The   structure   of the four-semester curriculum for training engineer-specialists is shown in Table   1. The total number   of hours   including 14 subjects is: 416 which contains   296 theoretical   and 120 practical-training hours. The number of the obligatory examinations (ex) amounts to 13, and there   is one subject in which the students obtain a mark on the basis of practice (pr). The state   examinations consist of two subjects, and both of them are optional ones. The university training is terminated by writing a diploma thesis   which   can be submitted by the student as a doctoral dissertation, too, if they have achived excellent results, with the restriction that the required set of conditions is fulfilled.

Table 1. Curriculum of the section of urban transport

Description of subjects	Number of hours per semester				Total number of hours for the subject
	1	2	3	4	
Computing Tech-nology	24+16 pr				40
Informatics in urban transport	16+0ex				16
Operational research in urban transport	24+16				40
Town and transport	16+0ex				16
Network planning in urban transport		16+8ex			24
Urban roads, motor ways, junctions		32+8ex			40
Organisation of urban public transport		16+8ex			24
Urban traffic control		16+8ex			24

Description of subjects	Number of hours per semester				Total number of hours for the subject
	1	2	3	4	
Management of public urban transport		24+8ex			32
Modelling of urban traffic flows		24+16ex			40
Urban shipment of goods		16+8ex			24
Urban traffic control and measuring equipment				24+8ex	32
Traffic safety of urban transport				24+8ex	32
Economic problems of urban transport				24+8ex	32
Totally:	80+32	80+32	64+32	72+24	416

4. Training of engineer-managers for transportation

4.1 Goal of training the engineer-economists

Under the changed circumstances   of the market economy, the   national economy   and the special field of transportation raise a demand for engineers trained in economics who are able to make use of the creative technical activity for combining it with the   viewpoint of a contractor-economist, and who will be able - as prospective holders of new information based on their existing technical knowledge - to give a solution to the problems emerged in the fields of marketing,   finance, accountancy, humane policy etc., or fulfil the tasks of management in those fields, respectively.   The training of the engineer-managers for transportation requires the attainment of that special knowledge, and the development of skills and capabilities, respectively.

4.2 Structure of training

The build-up of the curriculum ensures the possibility of acquiring the obligatory fundamentals indispensable for the development of the general culture of engineering economy and management, on the one hand, and for acquiring other more specialized knowledge   in transportation, on the other hand. This   knowledge is provided by the fundamentals and briefing subjects stuffed into the two first semesters,   which are obligatory to read and to sit in for a final examination in those at the end of the course.

The second part of the curriculum is intended to offer a possibility for the students in the second academic year of planning their study to acquire the specialized knowledge indispensable   for practice in their special line, on the basis of their individual interest in selecting the courses from among the great variety of the optional   subjects. This   system   is based on the assumption that the   students may lay claim to acquiring knowledge of a different composition and depth as drawn from the discipline of economy organization, management, technology,   law etc. as a function of the practice gained so far and their future objectives, respectively.

In the fifth semester, backed by the tutor, the students leaving the university will write their diploma thesis to be defended in the course of the semester before a board of examiners.

5. Summary

The Faculty of Transportation Engineering at the TUB intends to meet the requirements of the social-economic structural change as far as possible by developing continuously the curricula for training engineer-economists as a result of updating those to meet the demands of the new market-economy.

With a view to this, even new recommendations for the postgraduate training elaborated in professional discussions can be found in the new curricula.

6. References:

Gilicze, E.K - Michelberger, P. - Tánczos, K. (1991) **A new educational program for transportation engineers at the Faculty of Transportation Engineering in the Technical University of Budapest,** Australasian Journal of Engineering Education, 2, 25-32.

Gilicze, E.K. (1990) **Development of the Education of Hungarian specialists in the field of Transportation,** Journal of Urban Transport, 30, 354-358.

The Development of Teaching Materials from National and International Research and Development Programmes

L.L. Gill, A.J.P. Ward

Department of Mechanical Engineering, Design and Manufacture, Manchester Polytechnic

Abstract

The aim of this paper is to stimulate thought and action in the teaching of engineering fundamental principles in higher education courses utilising national and international development and demonstration material. Many government sponsored programmes exist and by their very nature, produce up-to-the-minute material which could be utilised as case studies in engineering and other courses. A pilot scheme has been tried in the U.K. on the subject of Small Scale Combined Heat and Power and it has proved to be very successful in achieving its aim. This could now be replicated over many other areas.

Keywords: Best Practice Programme, Teaching Material, Combined Heat and Power.

1   Introduction

The modern teacher in higher education is becoming hard pressed in two directions. Firstly, in the amount of time available for material preparation and secondly, in the amount of new material which cries out for inclusion as technology advances.

It was for this reason that the authors looked for likely sources of relevant material for their own teaching and from which search, the present paper arises. Through contacts over several years with the work of the U.K. Department of Energy and its contractors ETSU and BRECSU, the authors were aware that pump-priming activities were being carried out in the energy sector regarding newer technology and its applications. In addition, because of the necessity to use this material for replication of new technologies, it must all be fully tested and fully documented in the public domain.

As a result of the above facts, the information fulfilled their important criteria.

(a)   It was at the leading edge of technology, either as near-market or as applications.
(b)   The results were carefully monitored, documented and proven.
(c)   The information was publicly available.
(d)   It was logically and clearly presented.

It was from this starting point that the Department of Energy was approached to fund a pilot scheme to investigate the use of such material in higher education.

2   Selection of the Pilot Material

The material selected was from the Best Practice Programme (B.P.P.) of the U.K. Department of Energy, which was launched in 1988 to promote the use of good practice in efficient utilisation of energy in the U.K. The good practice guides developed here are the best available information on current thinking. The one which was suggested was on the subject of Small Scale Combined Heat and Power and, as a result, this subject was chosen for trial. It is also a subject which ideally lends itself to the pilot as it is usable in such a variety of areas - see Tables 1 and 2.

3   Applications of the material.

The main problem in any higher education course always seems to be what to leave out rather than "what to put in". It was decided not to attempt to compete with existing material, but to try to augment what would be taught in courses as fundamentals including enterprise and personal development skills. Lecturers usually teach a fundamental principle, then illustrate it as a case study by lectures, student centred learning, or a mini project. This naturally depends on the importance of the particular fundamental principle to the course in question. Unless these case studies are constantly reviewed, they are likely to become outdated.

It is in this application that the authors see the material being utilised, thereby providing lecturers with modern examples and displaying the state-of-the-art results. A student who is subjected to such case studies will become aware of, and absorb, the currently accepted "Best Practice" for that application of the technology. A further positive outcome being the use of best practice engineering principles to either teach or supplement the learning of personal development skills.

4   The Pilot Study

This exercise converted the BPP material into 12 modules, the contents of which are shown in Table 1. The BPP material chosen for the study was basically the results of demonstration projects which had been condensed into two volumes of Good Practice Guides. These were :

No 1 - Guidance Notes for the Implementation of Small Scale Packaged Combined Heat and Power.

No 3 - Introduction of Small Scale Combined Heat and Power.

In addition, there have been about 15 published Case Study reports from the Energy Efficiency Demonstration Programme on Small Scale CHP applications. These publications are typical of the type of documents issued as a result of National and International programmes - see Figure 1.

This material was reviewed and extensively edited to make it suitable for use as teaching material in the appropriate format. The twelve modules were each formatted around a particular subject, the material having a set of objectives as an introduction and finishing with a Case Study which illustrates the point in the module (as near as is possible from previously prepared material). The final sections of each module were a summary of the salient points and then a section which comprises of questions for students to answer called 'Topics for Review'.

Each of these modules was designed to illustrate some fundamental principle of engineering, such as module 6 illustrating economic considerations of a project and module 11 illustrating aspects of contracts and commissioning.

The whole package consisted of:

(a)   a lecturer pack consisting of teaching notes on the twelve modules;
(b)   a student pack (loose-leaf) of the twelve modules, suitable for direct photocopying as handouts, if required;
(c)   a set of original prints for producing OHP slides;
(d)   a set of coloured OHP slides, where required.

The package was designed to be used either as direct teaching material or as student centred learning packs. The loose-leaf notes would enable the lecturer to photocopy the material, either the relevant section, or the full pack. The questions may or may not be included as required. Some of the modules were provided with brief specimen answers as an illustration of what could be built in if it was required on subsequent topics. This is not done for all the modules however, as often lecturers will require answers relevant to the depth to which they pursue the subject with the students.

This package was demonstrated to two groups of University and Polytechnic lecturers, one in the North of England and one in the South. The participants agreed to try out this material, in a variety of teaching modes, to their students, and to report back their findings to the authors of this paper.

In all, 35 packages were issued to a variety of institutions of Higher Education in a number of different disciplines. Table 2 shows the spread of these which was thought to be appropriate to this subject. The main usage from this initial batch seemed to be in courses in Building, Engineering (Mechanical, Electrical and Combined), Architecture, Environmental and Manufacturing Systems.

Feedback received from delegates showed a considerable degree of ingenuity in the usage of the modules. These included direct teaching, student centred learning, group assignments, personal development, and project introduction work at a variety of levels from MSc through degrees to HND courses.

It was fairly clear to the authors that, although CHP was used as the demonstration vehicle for this exercise, there was a readily available source of high quality information, of a depth appropriate to any course up to MSc level, in this type of National and International Demonstration Programme.

The material was, with a number of small reservations, enthusiastically received by students and staff and its application (according to the findings) will consistently increase.

5   Conclusions - The Future

The use of the results from the Demonstration Programme material has been shown to provide a ready source of fundamental teaching information as illustrative cases of fundamental engineering principles in a variety of Higher Education courses. The material was from just one of many Demonstration programmes available nationally and *internationally, and it is clear that the principle of using these sources has been proven.

There are many programmes where the resulting project information is documented fully in the public domain, because it has been publicly funded. A small selection of programmes in the U.K. which are suitable for such investigation are shown in Figure 2. It should be noted that there are many programmes available also in Europe and on the international scene also which would provide appropriate material :

If this information is presented in an appropriate way, it is ideal for use as teaching case study material. It is also a ready dissemination vehicle for the technology and results amongst the rising generation of potential managers in industry and commerce.

Table 1 - Constituent Modules of the Pilot Material

Module Number	Module Title	Fundamental theory addressed in this module
1	Principles of CHP	Technical Principles Economic Principles Major components of a CHP system
2	Buildings Services Interface	Heating systems used Electrical services Effects of cycling
3	Site Appraisal	Selecting correct unit size More detailed calculations Informing the utilities suppliers
4	Selection of CHP system	Choice of generator type Multiple or single units
5	Fuel supplies	Electricity and its tariffs Gas and its tariffs Other fuels and their characteristics
6	Economics of CHP	Compared efficiencies - conventional/CHP Evaluating costs and savings Calculation of cost/benefit analysis
7	Installation and connection with existing boilers	Principles of the heating connection Heat exchangers and pipework Valves, filters drains and test points
8	Electrical installation	Regulations relevant to CHP Switchgear requirements Cables, earthing and testing Notification to supply authorities
9	Fuel supplies and installation	Pipework and sizing Valves, controls, metering, notification Storage of fuels. Fire precautions.
10	Exhaust systems	Technical requirements Clean air requirements Materials required Condensate drainage and silencers
11	Contractual terms and commissioning	Performance guarantees, and acceptance Price and terms of payment Commissioning and subsidiary procedures
12	Plant operation	Operational strategy and procedures Monitoring. Maintenance.

Table 2 - Potential applications of each module

Module No		Finance Management Business Studies	Physical Sciences	Social	Civil Eng Architects	Life Sciences (Env)	Eng Mech Chem	Mathematics Sciences	Elec. Eng
1	What is CHP? The fundamental components of a CHP system	✓	✓	✓	✓	✓	✓	✓	✓
2	The CHP - Building Services Interface				✓		✓	✓	✓
3	Site Appraisal			✓	✓	✓	✓		
4	Selection of the CHP System				✓		✓		✓
5	Electricity, Gas and Computing Fuel Tariffs	✓		✓	✓	✓	✓		✓
6	Savings and Capital Costs	✓		✓	✓	✓			✓
7	Installation and Connection with existing boiler plant				✓	✓	✓		✓
8	Electrical installation				✓		✓		✓
9	Fuel supplies and installation				✓		✓		
10	Exhaust systems	✓			✓		✓		✓
11	Commissioning	✓			✓		✓	✓	✓
12	Operation	✓			✓		✓		✓

The following selection of initiatives contain just some of the investigations and case studies published in the public domain which could be suitable for production of teaching material.

U.K. Department of Energy	Best Practice Programme - a four part initiative.
Energy Efficiency Office	Energy Consumption Guides, Good Practice Guides, New Practice Case Studies, Future Practice Projects.
U.K. Department of Trade and Industry Enterprise Initiative	Managing into the 90's scheme. The small firms merit award for Research and Technology.
Expert System Opportunities Programme	
The Materials Matter Programme	
Environmental Management schemes	
Demos (DTI Environmental Management Options Scheme	
Eureka Environ	
U.K. Dept. of Trade and Industry Innovation Advisory Board	Innovation Plans Handbook
U.K. Science and Education Research Council ACME Programme	Application of Computers to Manufacturing Engineering.
U.K. Science and Education Research Council Teaching Co Programme	Various co-operative research and development programmes between companies and Higher Education Institutions.

Fig. 2. A Selection of U.K. Government Initiatives

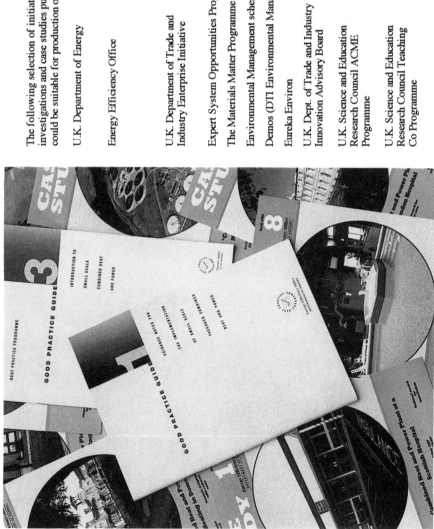

Fig. 1. A Selection of the Material used in the Pilot Study

The Study and Practice of Engineering Education in Industry Run Institutions of Higher Learning in China

Ma Changwei(*), Chen Kangmin(**)

Shanghai Institute of Mechanical Engineering (SIME)

Abstract

In present-day China, the distribution of talented people is brought in line with the plan of the state; therefore, the educational model for bringing up people of talent has to be more compatible with existing national requirements. Meanwhile, the rapid development of new technology is changing the choice for the type of talented people needed in national production and construction, that it puts to challenge the traditional teaching model which was designed mainly for the training of academic- and research-oriented intellects. Under such circumstances, a comprehensive study and practice aimed at the upbringing of people oriented to applied technology to cope with current needs have been carried out in the country; and the whole educational programs are set, or readjusted, to form a complete system operating towards this objective.

Keywords: Engineering education, Industry-run polytechnic, training model.

1. Introduction

SIME is an engineering-oriented institution of higher learning under the auspices of China's Ministry of Machinery and Electronics Industry committed to the training of senior engineers and technicians. Included in its curriculums, besides major courses in engineering, are also those of arts and sciences, management and commerce.

Since the adoption of reform and opening policy, there are marked fundamental changes taking place in China's society. This new situation, and the commodity economy thereby developed, impel us to restructure our educational mechanism, so as to make it fit in with the current needs of society. And, based on this understanding, and the inherent law of education that we, at SIME, engage in the aforesaid study and practice of upbringing people oriented to applied technology and embark upon the updating of our educational programmes given below.

---

* Deputy Director, Educational Administration Dept. (SIME)
** Executive Vice-President (SIME)

1. REVISION OF TEACHING PROGRAMS

In compliance with the characteristics of industry-run educational organs, the following changes have taken place in the guiding principle over the planning of our teaching programs these days.

Educational objective -- Besides the need for people of high-ranking professional knowledge, that for engineers and technicians to serve in the machine-building and electronics industry, as builders and successors to the trades, is also put forward.

Guiding thought -- In putting emphasis upon the need of appropriate handling of relationship between theory and practice, between basic education and specialized training, and between major discipline and its interrelated subjects, attention is also called to the need of widening the scope of major speciality, the building of sound basic education, and the boosting of working capacity as well as the enriching of service trades.

The planning of teaching period -- A three semester system of "two long and one short" is adopted. The purpose of this arrangement is to give students more opportunity for overall engineering-oriented training so as to enhance their capacity for making direct contribution to the machine-building and electronics industry.

Curriculum -- While giving good attention to sound basic education, a number of technical courses, as well as courses in economy and modern enterprise management geared to the need of machine-building and electronics industry, are also offered. To date, SIME has endorsed the building of 13 key courses; and, the work on curriculum set-up and its long-term objective and program have been drawn up in an endeavour to produce a number of good quality courses.

2. Reformative experiment on: enrollment by academic department, teaching according to category of specialities, and adoption of subsidiary (second) speciality.

These years, due to decreasing total demand for electromechanical products in the country, and because of the basically unsettled problems over the irrational structure of working personnel within the ministry-supported enterprises, the Ministry is facing a grim situation in this period of readjustment. It is to meet this challenge that SIME, as one sponsored by the Ministry, committed itself to undertake the following measures:

* Since 1989 -- students are recruited, grouped, and trained separately according to academic department and speciality; the range of common basic education for specialities of the same category are widened; the scope of speciality-related services enlarged; and its degree of specialization broadened so as to free specific speciality of its narrowness

Also, a requirement is made of a unified curriculum for the different departments and specialities of the same category for period from the 1st to 5th, or even the 6th semester. Only when coming to taking the specialized courses are they regrouped and taught according to existing needs of the electromechanical trades.

* Since 1987 -- Three subsidiary specialities (to be taken as 2nd major) are offered at SIME; they are, Scientific English, Systems Engineering, and Computer Engineering and Computer Utility. Students can apply for 2nd major under the assurance of their successful completion of major speciality within the stipulated period of study and with enough spare time to pursue a second simultaneously. The goal of this measure is to widen the range of their expertise where possible.

3. Establishing strong bond between school and enterprise so as to enhance the link for practical education.

Being educated at an industry-run university under the Ministry of Machinery and Electronics Industry, our college graduates are mainly assigned to work in the production forefront of enterprises under the ministry; therefore, SIME is all the more obligated to conducting teaching programs targeted at boosting students' working capacity in engineering and technological fields.

To date, SIME has established collaborative relationships with 25 enterprises, the nature of whose products are in line specialities offered at the institute. A 5-year reciprocal agreement has been signed with 16 of them on joint production and production practice (for students) in a bid to promote the integration of school education with actual production; and that the work on the upbringing of talented people and technological reform could be carried out simultaneously. This educator-manufacturer combination is an ideal and assured base for practice in cognizance and production, as well as for graduation fieldwork. Moreover, representative products are incorporated in our course design, whereby experiences gained are used for drawing inferences about other cases -- so as to fan out from point to area.

The result of this measure is gratifying as could be seen from the fact that there are above 80% of our graduation projects in these past academic years originated from the production forefront -- through tackling key research problems, participating in technological reform, and designing new products.

4. Optimization of educational management and upgrading of teaching quality.

In order to exercise effective supervision and control over teaching quality and the process of teaching, a set of regulations on regular checking of educational work, and data collection for education related information were established. Meanwhile, a committee of experts commissioned to making assessments of teaching quality is also set up, and their assessments are influencing factors in deciding the professional ranking and teaching bonus of individuals assessed. And, under the principle of appointment on one's merit and by mutual choice, a contract system is adopted for recruiting teaching staff. Moreover, SIME is ahead of its counterparts at home in the building of test paper bank, which has now a series of test papers for 14 courses stored to ensure the quality checking of students' academic work during their college years.

Also, in order to be oriented to world market economy, SIME has been putting continuous efforts in a bid to upgrade their English programme and raise the passing rate of its students taking the yearly English language proficiency tests conducted by state examination center. According to statistics issued by the center last year, the passing rate of students from SIME in the tests is above the average score of key universities in the country.

Investigation feedback of college graduates going through our comprehensive training system who are now assigned to society, manufacturing plants, and enterprises, indicated that they are well received by their emloyers. This fully testifies to the effectiveness of our undergraduate engineering education. On the other hand, the postgraduate programme for bringing up engineering-oriented graduate students at the institute is being patterned to chiefly relying on education taken in the school, and courses for adult education offered at the evening college for on-the-job training, are geared to the need of production, businesses and management -- to fulfill the goal of applying what we learn to practice.

5. An assumption on improving industry-run institutions of higher learning.

SIME's experience in running industry-run university gives proof to the vitality of such system in economic construction during current modernization drive in the country. The following is an assumption on improving engineering education sponsored by industry put forward by the authors who are taking part and involved in the leading and organizing of the reform in education at SIME.

a) The running of engineering education (in industry-supported institutions of higher learning) in China calls for the combined efforts and full initiative of related parties -- i.e., the sponsoring industry, sponsored institutions, and the enterprise involved.

From the sponsoring body, it is expected their macroscopic directive in personnel training, their initiative in giving support and care to the institution sponsored, and in matter of system and funding to ensure the development of educational career.

From the institutions sponsored, it is expected that their open-door attitude in course-building and the offering of special fields of study, as well as the nurturing distinguishing feature reflecting their image in running school. By no means are they to run their schools behind closed doors and indulge in self-improvement oblivious of what is going on outside. Furthermore, they are to take the initiative in adapting themselves with the needs of the enterprises, and offering their services so as to bring up qualified builders and successors to the machinery and electronics trade.

From enterprises, it is expected their initiative in accepting advanced education as well as their awareness of the significance of depending upon advanced education; they are to link their pursuit of profit and development with current quality of school education. Only through such measures could the industry-run educational organs prosper.

b) The state is required to loosen its control over engineering education in the industry-run universities and colleges, to enable the sponsoring industry to have more direct dealing with the educational institutions they sponsor; that is, in the offering and adjustment of speciality, and in the control over the scope of school's development, the sponsoring industry should correspondingly be vested with more authority; as the over-concentration of power and rigid control from above is liable to hamper the initiative in running educational institutions.

c) The system of industry-run institutions of higher learning provides a favorable condition for the integration of theory with practice. We oppose the closed-door policy and the break away of theory from practice type of education; but we would never repeat such practice as "school means factory" and "factory means school" pattern of education once practised in the past, letting school education be centered around productive labour, and productive work take the place of systematic regular specialized education.

What we're up to is to bring up qualified engineering-oriented personnel.

The Requirement for Integrated and Systems Engineers in a Complex and Flexible Future

D.A. Sanders, D.J. Harrison

School of Systems Engineering, University of Portsmouth

Abstract

Manufacturing and automated work places are becoming more complex as they strive to become productive and flexible. In the 21st Century, an engineer qualified and experienced in a specific area may only be capable of working at one level within a complex system hierarchy. If engineers are to be effective in the modern integrated factory, some education and experience will be required at all levels. This requirement is discussed and the implications for the future are considered with reference to a typical and future complex hierarchy.

Keywords: Integrated, systems, engineer, education

1. Introduction

Finniston *et al*(1989) reported a growing recognition of the need to increase the supply of professional engineers capable of working across traditionally specialist engineering disciplines. This need arises from the rapidly changing technologies and in the future, totally integrated engineering systems can be expected, Billingsley *et al*(1983), Sanders *et al*(1991.a).

Mechanization is changing to automation in western industries. During the 1920s and 1930s there was an upsurge in the design, manufacture and use of mechanical devices which replaced human muscle power with machines. These machines were independent of each other and required human operators. The situation changed with the invention of the transistor and then the computer. Electronic devices have allowed plants to be designed to reduce damage and down-time while working reliably at speed, Brady *et al*(1982). Changes must take place in engineering education to accommodate these changes.

In computer aided design CAD and computer aided manufacture CAM the computer has a central role, Brady *et al*(1989). As industry moves to computer aided engineering CAE, other changes will take place, Naghdy *et al*(1985), Jaques *et al*(1992), Sanders(1990). Mechanization is being replaced by automation, Finniston *et al*(1989). Much research in automation is attempting to achieve a

"Task" by partitioning the problem into stages, the input to each stage being the output of its predecessor, Sanders *et al*(1991.b). Three such stages may be considered as shown in figure 1. This suggests that in the future, flexible cells within fully automated manufacturing systems might be as shown in figure 2, reproduced from Sanders(1990). These cells will require automatic programming & reprogramming systems and the engineers designing and maintaining the systems will require knowledge of all levels.

2.   Changes to Engineering Education

Change is inevitable and the sub divisions of engineering are being eroded. The reasons stem from the ubiquity of the computer (Finniston *et al*.1989) and the increased complexity of engineering systems, Jaques *et al*(1992), Sanders(1990). Computing facilities are readily available and CAE can be seen as an integrating activity and Finniston *et al*(1989) report that most engineering courses now include CAE. The revolutions in complex automation, microprocessors and information technology are major contributory factors influencing the changing needs of engineering. This results in a change in the needs of engineering education and the structure of engineering education.

It is suggested by Amani(1989) as reported in Duggan(1989.a) that the educational systems in Europe and North America can be divided into two branches, one providing theoretical knowledge through taught courses to degree level, and the other emphasizing engineering technology or applied engineering.

Motion Planning

Given a Task and a geometric description of the environment, plan motions that avoid collision with obstacles. The motions are a function of space.

|

Trajectory Planning

Given a motion, the actuator constraints and a dynamic description of the machinery, find the positions and velocities for the actuators to achieve the motion. The trajectory locus describes trajectory curve in joint space and the trajectory specifies the machine configurations as a function of time and space.

|

Controller Trajectory Tracking

Given a trajectory locus and the dynamics of the machinery, track the given trajectory by servoing the movement of physical actuators

---

Figure 1:   Three typical stages of an automated system

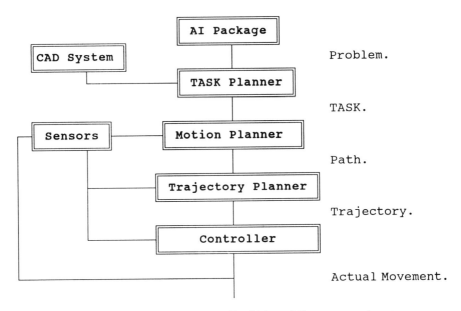

Figure 2:   A flexible cell within a fully automated system

The question of equivalency between courses can sometimes cause misunderstanding. In the future we may require some combination of the two.

Needs and cultural differences influence the system of teaching engineering in different countries.   Because of the rate of change of technology, it may not be appropriate to allow purely national and relatively short term needs to dictate the education of engineers for the 21st Century.

Expensive and modern laboratories and computing facilities are required. The bill for these facilities may have to be met in the future through collaboration with industrial partners.

In the UK, many Universities are extending their Engineering degrees from three years to four year "Enhanced" degrees. In other Higher Education establishments, the concept of a foundation year has become established, Duggan(1989.a). These courses could be used to broaden the knowledge base of our Engineers and the UK Institutions could require a more general knowledge of Engineering for the award of Chartered Engineer in the future.

Duggan(1989.b) and Finniston *et al*(1989) reported that integrated engineers are required that are educated across disciplines and capable of exercising a systems approach to planning and problem solving. This inter-disciplinary approach is reflected to some extent in the development of new engineering courses which are broad based but integrated engineering can only exist if the artificial boundaries between engineering disciplines are removed.

Developing a flexible and responsive system to provide relevant and up to date engineering education is difficult. Manufacturing commonly works to an assumed life cycle of five or ten years and the life cycle of engineering degree courses tends to be similar. This response time must be improved.

To achieve the changes required, the access to engineering education must be widened to include students with a variety of qualifications. The factors needing to be considered in major engineering projects were described by Duggan(1982). They are considerable, demanding creative talent and inventiveness, the ability to think logically, a good knowledge of mathematics and materials. The breadth of studies must be increased to include business studies and management and a full range of engineering disciplines. Stevens(1985) as reported by Finniston *et al*(1989) suggested that the majority of engineers become managers very early in their careers and spend many years in jobs which do not require the depth of engineering they have acquired. Greater emphasis can be placed on the understanding of engineering principles and their application. An inter-disciplinary and integrated attitude must be created, making full use of CAE. This was proposed by Levy(1988) but it has been suggested by Duggan(1989.b) that these courses may present accreditation problems with the specific engineering organisations and institutions.

To satisfy these requirements in an efficient and cost effective way requires a new approach. It is impossible to consider the education received in Higher Education establishments (18+) without considering the education received at the Further Education level (16+). In the UK a smaller and smaller number of students are leaving school with the traditional engineering qualifications. This is partly due to the perceived low status of engineers within the UK and partly due to a shortage of physics and mathematics teachers.

The Finniston report (Finniston 1980) recommended many changes to education in the UK. Engineering education has undergone substantial changes in recent years and the report led to the establishment of an Engineering Council.

3.   Conclusions

The continued advances in technology need to be rapidly incorporated in engineering education by moving research results into degree courses. This requires an even closer relationship between research and education institutions and an increased emphasis on research in education.

An integrated programme is required to halt the decline in graduates from first degree courses in the UK. Special initiatives and conversion courses have been developed, but they need to be recognised by the engineering institutions.

The decline of some industries has not been accompanied by an equal expansion in the new technologies. This must be a matter of concern as competitors make inroads into traditional markets. A major reason reported by Finniston *et al*(1989) has been the low investment in research and development as a proportion of Gross Domestic Product (GDP). This trend must be reversed and investment in education must be increased.

The development of an education and training system which consciously pursues the acquisition of knowledge and skills needed to cope with unfamiliar circumstances must involve both industry and schools. The system must be planned and integrated from secondary school (11+) through to Masters Degrees (21+).

Courses could initially concentrate on project work and methods rather than learning theory first. This can provide the opportunity for students to later specialise in a particular area and achieve a high academic standard, while extending their intellectual and theoretical activity.

The new approach to engineering education requires a broad base and must include other subjects more commonly associated with the social sciences, such as communications and economics. The degree level courses may require a common first year to create a common base line for the engineering profession as a whole. This could also encourage the transfer of students and staff between institutions.

Professional engineers of the future will be required to respond to continuing change and adapt to new and challenging situations. The emphasis will be on problem solving and thought. The move from mechanization to automation is a move of concepts and requires an equivalent move in education and training.

References

Amani L (1989). Engineering vs Engineering Technology in developing countries, **Int Conf on Engineering Technology**, Shangai, China.

Billingsley J et al. (1983) **The Craftsman Robot**, Electronics and Power, UK, December 1983.

Brady et al. (1982) **Robot Motion: Planning and Control**, MIT Press, ISBN 0-262-02182-x.

Brady et al. (1989) **Robotics Science**, MIT Press, ISBN 0-262-02284-2.

Duggan TV (1982). Engineering Integrity, **Inaugrial lecture**, Portsmouth Polytechnic.

Duggan TV (1989.a). How technology will change engineering education, **Int J Appl.Engng Ed**, Vol 5, No 6, pp 687-690.

Duggan TV (1989.b). How technology will change engineering education, **Int J Appl.Engng Ed**, Vol 5, No 6, pp 753-758.

Finniston (1980), **Report of the committee of enquiry into the engineering profession**, Cmd 7794, HMSO, London.

Jaques WS, Billingsley J and Harrison D (1992). Generative feature-based design-by-constraints as a means of integration within the manufacturing industry. **Computer Aided Eng Jnl**, pp 261-267.

Sir Monty Finniston, Duggan TV and Bement JM (1989). Integrated Engineering and its influence on the future of engineering education in the UK, **Int J Appl.Engng Ed**, Vol 5, No 2, pp 135-145.

Naghdy F et al. (1985) Craftsman Integrated Manufacture, **Quality Assurance UK**, Vol II June 85.

Levy JC (1988), **Restructuring of Engineering Higher Education**, (Discussion document), Engineering Council, London 1988.

Sanders DA. (1990) **Automatic Robot Path Planning With Constraints**, PhD Thesis, Portsmouth, UK.

Sanders DA, Billingsley J and Robinson DC. (1991.a) **Real Time Automatic Path Planning**, Proc of the dedicated conf on Mechatronics, (part of ISATA 91), Florence, Italy, pp 435-442.

Sanders DA, Moore A and Luk BL (1991.b), A Joint Space Technique for Real Time Robot Path Planning, Proc 5th **Int' Conference on Advanced Robotics**, Pisa, Italy.

Stevens JR (1985), Manufacturing engineering skills, education and training, (Discussion document), **National economic development office**, London, UK.

The University of British Columbia Engineering Physics Project Laboratory: A Partnership in Education

E.G. Auld

Engineering Physics, University of British Columbia

Abstract

The B.A.Sc. degree in Engineering Physics is considered to be one of, if not the most difficult first degree programs at the University of British Columbia. It is a five year degree which is essentially a triple honours program in Mathematics, Physics and Engineering. The program attracts, enthusiastic, entrepreneurial students, and produces approximately 35 graduates per year.

The degree requires that the students complete two separate project laboratory courses, one in each of the final two years of the degree, with a summer placement with industry a possibility between the two courses. These two courses provide the students with a unique opportunity to initiate advanced research and prototype development and learn basic entrepreneurial skills. Their projects can be initiated by their own interests, ideas from the faculty member in Engineering or Science, and from projects and ideas from local industry and research organizations. Some examples include, magnetic levitation, motion isolation mount for zero-gravity experiments, a computer mouse-emulator for the handicapped, the retrofitting of a golf cart with a Hydrogen fuel cell, and a high speed image processor for a scanning tunneling microscope. On average, at least one patentable device emerges from these projects every year, some of which have led to new commercial opportunities, and industrial innovations. Industry is an enthusiastic partner in the program, mainly because it allows them to get a close look at a bright group of students that would do any engineering research and development office proud.

1. Introduction and Historical background.

The Engineering Physics degree at UBC offers the student a broad base of core courses in Mathematics, Physics and Engineering. Over this core the student may choose one of six option disciplines, namely, Electrical Engineering,

Mechanical Engineering, Metals and Materials Engineering, Computer Science, Geophysics, or Oceanography. Half of the graduates follow their first degree with a graduate degree in Physics, or their option discipline. The other half find employment, in areas that tend to be related to research and development, and or management of development in companies, usually involved with new products. The extreme breadth of their first degree, gives them an excellent foundation for problem solving.

These skills are first put to the test in the two undergraduate project courses that they must complete before they are awarded their degree. These courses, named ApSc.459 and ApSc.479, provide challenging and relevant design and synthesis experience. The students are formed into teams of two, three or four, in order to see a project to completion in the limited time available. In each year, more than one of the reports leads to some significant commercial or scientific initiative.

The projects come from, other institutions, industries, and the research interests of the faculty members from Physics and from all six of the cooperating disciplines in Engineering Physics, as well as from other Faculties.

The organization of the Engineering Physics program as a five year degree within the Faculty of Applied Science allows the luxury of splitting the project laboratory into two separate years, with two courses, the first of which, ApSc.459 is a two-term course starting in the September of the students' fourth year and finishing in April. The second course, ApSc.479 starts in September of their fifth year and finishes in December. This sequence, shown in Table 1, allows the student the opportunity to sandwich between the '459' and '479' offering, a summer job that may have arisen from the project started in the '459' course; and provides an opportunity to plan longer term projects that will be of more interest to faculty or industry.

Table 1.   Student timetable for the Project Courses.

Month	Year IV	Year V
September	ApSc 459 Starts	ApSc 479 starts
October	Prepare Proposal	Work on project
November	"	~ 6 hrs per week
December	Proposal due	'479' Report due
January	Start '459' Proj.	ApSc 480
February	Work on Project	(elective course)
March	~ 6 hrs per week	"
	******Project Fair held for both classes*****	
April	'459' Report due	
May	Summer job	Graduation!

The combination of this arrangement with the broad mix of disciplines in the student population puts the Engineering Physics program in a unique position to invite local industries to become involved in educating our students in research and development. The mission of the Project Laboratory is to provide: the students with the most relevant design and synthesis projects possible, and a link between industry and the university, where our mutual interests in engineering education can be explored.

2. Choosing the Projects

The student, in choosing a project, must prepare a proposal, which is a contract with a schedule, list of equipment and a list of deliverables that he promises to provide by the deadline. A significant part of the grade for the course comes from how well the contract is adhered to. The proposal must be completed by the end of the first term. If it is accepted by the faculty, then the student team may start on their chosen project in January. If their proposal is not accepted, then the student(s) will be assigned a project chosen by the faculty member in charge. Usually the students submit their first attempt at a proposal early enough that any significant problems can be corrected before the end of the first term. We make every effort to give the student ample time to get the proposal contract correct and realistic.

The basic discipline of each project is matched as closely as possible to the students' Engineering Physics option. This means that faculty from many departments become closely involved with the project supervision; in fact the Project Laboratory program benefits a great deal from the assistance of faculty from all the supporting departments. Because of the nature of the Engineering Physics program, multidisciplinary teams can be formed to tackle the problems. It is our expectation that the laboratory would always have a mixture of projects from all three major sources.

It is expected that some or all of the commercially motivated projects will extend to both courses and thus possibly provide the student with a summer placement in between. In fact, the project might be continued into the following study year with a new group of students. As a specific example, a series of projects have been focused on developing a motion isolation mount to provide better control of the laboratory environment for zero-gravity experiments in space. The fundamental device, a magnetic bearing has been used to provide a freely floating mount that adjusts for minor deviations from g=0. The device was developed in the Laboratory, on behalf of the National Research Council Space Research Program and flown in the

space simulation flights out of Houston. Several students
have participated in the series of projects over that past
three years. Two of the students have flown in the
aircraft experiments. An interesting spinoff from this
project is that we now have developed a centre of
excellence in magnet levition which has resulted in several
other interesting applications and possible products.

3. The Laboratory Supervision.

There are several senior faculty and staff members involved
with the laboratory: the faculty members with academic
responsibility and the Coordinating Engineer. The workshop
and electronic shop staff become involved during the
planning, design and construction work for those needing
their services.

The faculty members are responsible for maintaining
the academic excellence of the two courses. This consists
of setting standards for the written and oral reports.

The grade for each course is based on an evaluation of
the following: (1) the content and presentation of the
final report: (2) the oral and informal reports presented
during the work: and (3) the technical competance of the
project work, with particular emphasis placed on the
comparison between what the student promised to produce in
his proposal and what he finally delivered. The overall
responsibility for the student grading is given to the
faculty member in charge of the specific course. He does,
of course delegate specific aspects of the grading to the
individual supervisors, but for the sake of consistency he
must provide an overview control.

The Coordinating Engineer has full time responsibility
for the Project Laboratory. He provides the continuity
from term to term. During the academic terms he manages
the discipline and organization of the Laboratory, and
provides the technical backup for the students. The
Engineer will be involved with helping all of the students
to some extent but he will participate in the detailed
supervision of some of the projects closest to his own
interests and experience.

During the whole year the Engineer will maintain close
links with industry in order to provide the students with a
source of realistic commercial and research engineering
projects. This duty requires that he communicate the
acivities of this laboratory to research engineers in local
firms who might be willing to farm out some of their
research and development activities.

The supervisors for each project are faculty members
from the various departments in the university or research
engineers from the participating companies. Their
responsibilities are to meet regularly with their student

team to ensure that the project schedule is being
maintained and to ensure that the necesssary support
facilities are available. The supervisor will also be
involved in the grading of projects under the guidance of
the faculty member responsible for the course.

4. The weekly activities

The students are expected to spend a minimum of 6 hours per
week on actual project work and attend a one-hour seminar.
     The seminar provides a weekly forum where progress
reports are presented, technical problems can be shared,
and invited speakers provide specific topical discussions.
At the time of the seminar, each group must submit a report
on their week's activities, comparing their progress
against the schedule they submitted at the beginning of the
term. The student's six hours of project work are carried
out at a time and place consistent with their timetable and
project activity. The students tend to spend too much time
on their projects; but the control of this is provided by
the schedule they submit, at the beginning of the term.
These schedules are checked carefully and the students are
asked to revise them if they are unrealistic. Each student
is expected to keep a log book record of their activities,
which can be inspected at any time.
     Each project can be supported with a few hundred
dollars for supplies and expenses. The students tend to
use the laboratory space of the supervisor, but there is
also a general resource centre laboratory, where the
Coordinating Engineer has his office and where there is
sufficient space to hold a small reference library, several
computer work stations, including large plotter for the CAD
system, the usual scopes and other diagnostic instruments,
assembly tables and small tools work area. All the
students have access to a fully supervised work shop with
the usual laithes, drills and milling machines.

5. The Project Fair

A technical fair is held once a year, to which all
students, faculty and industrial participants are invited.
New prospective participants are also invited. The format
follows that of a technical workshop symposium, where the
invited speakers and student speakers are mixed into the
program. A tour of the facilities and a luncheon round out
the day's activities.

6. The Benefits

6.1 Educational
These project activities expose senior engineering physics students to the type of "real-world" problems they will encounter after graduation. This Laboratory provides an opportunity for these students to experience the challenges, satisfaction and frustration of working on unsolved problems; problems that require them to investigate alternatives, exercise judgement and put into practice the theory they have learned. Time management skills and priority development in open ended problems becomes as important to them as the technical details of the problem. They learn a great deal about themselves during this exercise.
   With the participation of outside industry, a useful communication link has been established which will (a) give important feedback as to the relevance of the engineering education we are providing, and (b) allow us to react more quickly to the changing needs of industry.

6.2 Economic
To be realistic, the direct economic benefits of such a Laboratory are not likely to be high, especially at the outset. The real benefit comes from the better communication that will ensue between students, faculty and industry personnel. This must surely reap some benefits by: (a) improving the speed at which new ideas can be brought to commercial reality; (b) identifying problems and finding the experts to solve those problems; and (c) providing an opportunity for firms to observe the performance of students before they consider hiring them.
   Almost invariably during the initial steps of a research and development project serious underestimates of resources and time are made. By allowing the students the luxury of making such mistakes in the shelter of a university environment will mean that they are less likely to repeat such mistakes in an industrial environment where the implications are much more serious.

6.3 Public relations
Although possibly not as important as the educational and economic benefits, the public relations from the Engineering Physics Project Laboratory will help in breaking down the traditional barrier that tends to have been built between universities and industries. The new contacts obtained with industrial personnel can only help in fostering a better understanding towards post-secondary education, and the problems of modern industry trying to survive in a very competitive world.

An Integrated Formation for the Pulp and Paper Industry

J.J. Garceau (*), P. Lavoie (**), F. Carrasco (***)
(*) École de Technologie Supérieure, Université du Québec, Montréal
(**) Collège d'enseignement général et professionnel, Trois-Rivières
(***) Department of Chemical Engineering, Université du Québec, Trois-Rivières

Abstract

L'Université du Québec and the Collège d'enseignement général et professionnel de Trois-Rivières have developed, in cooperation with the Canadian Pulp and Paper Industry, an integrated training formation. The programmes offered at the College and University provide a vertical formation in pulp and paper: Technician in Pulp and Paper Technology, Bachelor in Chemical Engineering (with optional courses in Pulp and Paper Science), Master in Pulp and Paper Science and finally, Doctorate in Paper Engineering. These programmes respond to a precise need for qualified technicians and professionals destined for the pulp and paper industry. Moreover, these programmes contribute to the continuous education of technicians and engineers working in pulp and paper factories and also generate highly specialized professionals devoted to the advancement of knowledge and to the development of new technologies. This paper presents an overview of these programmes as well as the role played by both Pulp and Paper Research Centre and Specialized Centre in educational programmes.
Keywords: Pulp, Paper, Technician, Bachelor/Engineer, Master's, Doctorate, Education, Research.

1 Introduction

The forest industry is the most important industry in Canada. About one million Canadians depend on it, which is equivalent to 10% of the total manpower. Over $ 12 billion of forest products are exported each year. This corresponds to 17% of all Canadian exports. From 1980 to 1990, this industry invested more than $ 33 billion to operate modernized mills.

1991 was a traumatic year, companies experienced unprecedented losses in excess of $ 1 billion. Major contributing factors include: a severe recession, a strong Canadian dollar, the free trade agreement with the U.S.A. and an overproduction of major products.

Canadian producers will have invested about $ 1.2 billion to increase their recycling capacity and over $ 3 billion to meet new government effluent regulations (Hart 1992).

The industry has to meet a historical challenge. According to Enk (1992), new paradigm indicates a need for fundamental change. More educated and trained people have to be hired. The actual staff of workers require additional training and education. Lemaire (1989), President of the paper company Cascades Inc., also believes that the industry has a challenge to overcome by year 2000 in terms of the human being. Recently, Garceau and Leclerc (1991) presented a summary about a survey conducted to identify the training needs of the industry.

This paper presents the role of the two institutions (College and University) in the global structure of education in pulp and paper leading to the vertical formation from technician to doctorate degree, in order to prepare technologists and professionals able to perform efficiently in an industrial environment.

2   The integrated formation programme

The two institutions are offering vertical formation in pulp and paper by means of the following programmes: Pulp and Paper Technology (technician's degree), Chemical Engineering, Master's in Pulp and Paper Science and Ph.D. in Paper Engineering. Figure 1 illustrates the inter-relation between these programmes. The Pulp and Paper Specialized Centre (College) directly supports the programme destined towards the formation of technicians. Moreover, this Centre has up-to-date pilot plant equipments and offers technical services and special training programmes for industrial workers. The Pulp and Paper Research Centre (University) was created to conduct research and development works in pulp and paper and to support university programmes such as Bachelor's, Master's and Ph.D. by means of their human resources (professors, associate researchers, technicians and administrative employees), equipment facilities as well as part-time and summer works for students. Professors and researchers working in this Centre assume the supervision of both undergraduate and graduate students as well as post-doctoral fellows.

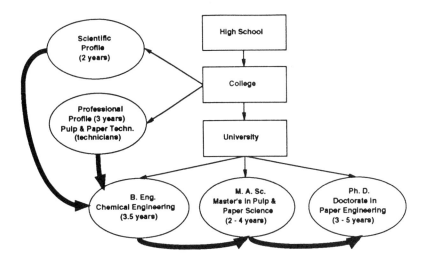

Fig. 1. Vertical formation in Pulp and Paper from technician to doctorate levels.

2.1 Pulp and Paper Technology

This programme has being offered for over 60 years. It requires three years of studies after the high school degree and leads to a technician's degree. The students have to take general courses as well as up-to-date courses dealing specifically with pulp and paper technology. In addition, they obtain very good training in both laboratory and pilot plant environment. About 800 technicians have graduated from this programme since 1958. Presently, 65% of them are mill workers. On another hand, 45% of the graduates have staff jobs and 55% are working on an hourly basis. Technicians are mainly (50%) working in either technical control or research and development tasks and only 20% are directly involved with production. Figure 2 indicates that the success for graduated technicians to find a job is higher than 80%, excluding the year 1976 and the recession period 1980-1983.

2.2 Chemical Engineering (B. Eng.)

Following a market survey (Garceau 1982), a classical programme in Chemical Engineering (B. Eng.) was started in 1985. Optional courses can be taken in the field of Pulp and Paper Science and Technology. This programme allows the students to learn and to understand the physical and chemical principles governing the transformation of matter. These principles are common to all processes involving physical changes and chemical reactions and, therefore, they are necessary to understand operations of the Pulp and Paper Industry. A part of the graduates in Chemical Engineering are working with or in connection to the paper industry.

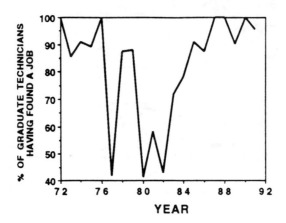

Fig. 2. Percent of graduate technicians having found a job at the end of the graduation year.

2.3 Master in Pulp and Paper Science (M.A.Sc.)

Already in 1975 a specially-designed master's programme was offered to satisfy the Pulp and Paper Industry needs. An academic calendar was adopted to satisfy the working staff and engineers. Lectures are given once a month on a week-end basis: Friday from 13h00 to 22h00 and Saturday from 8h30 to 16h30 during both fall and winter semesters. During summer time, there are two or three full-week courses. Free auditors, which have an acceptable background, can join the regular master's students.

Figures 3 to 4 illustrate some statistics about the 100 students having completed the Master's programme (87 men and 13 women). Most of them are working in the Pulp and Paper Industry. An annual average of 7 students graduated from 1978 to 1991. However, in the last three years, the annual average increased to 11 students per year. Full-time students (54%) took an average of 2.5 years to complete the programme whereas part-time students (46%) required 4.5 years.

The variation of the number of students according to age at admission is shown in Figure 3 for full and part-time students. On average, they are 28 years old. However, part-time students are two years older than full-time students. No significant relationship exists between student's age and the duration of studies.

From Figure 4 it can be seen that about three quarters of the students have an engineering background. Similar proportions are found in the Pulp and Paper Industry Staff (Branion and

Stevens, 1981). Furthermore, 78% have graduated from Canadian Universities and 22% from foreign Universities in equivalent proportions from either America, Europe, Africa and Asia.

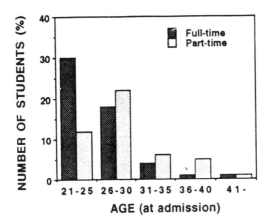

Fig. 3. Variation of the number of graduate students (Master in Pulp and Paper Science) as a function of their age at admission.

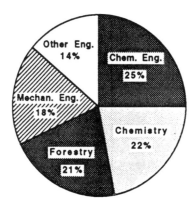

Fig. 4. Type of Bachelor's degree held by students admitted to the programme of Master in Pulp and Paper Science.

2.4 Doctorate in Paper Engineering (Ph.D.)

The vertical integration was completed in 1990 by offering a Ph.D. programme in Paper Engineering. Thus, students can now follow programmes from the technical to the doctoral level.

The objective of the Ph.D. programme is to form self-sufficient specialists dealing with the fundamentals of Pulp and Paper Science and Technology and having the ability to solve major problems related to the Pulp and Paper Industry.

3   Conclusion

The Canadian Pulp and Paper Industry is an a dramatic situation and has invested in R&D only 0.3% of its annual sales. The College and University at Trois-Rivières are well prepared to help this industry to become more competitive in an open world market.

4   References

Branion, R.M. and Stevens, F. (1981) Technically Trained People in Canadian Mills Surveyed, Pulp Paper Can., 82, 40-41.

Enk, G. (1992) New Paradigm Indicates a Need for Fundamental Change, Pulp Paper Can., 93, 27.

Garceau, J.J. (1982) Chemical Pulp and Paper Engineering: an Answer to a Mode Canadian Pulp and Paper Industry, Technical Section, CPPA, Montréal.

Garceau, J.J. and Leclerc, J. (1991) Canadian Paper Industry: A Tailored Education, East-West Congress on Engineering Education, Cracow, Poland.

Hart, H. (1992) Unconventional Wisdom Key to Seeing Us through 1992, Pulp Paper Can., 93, 23.

Lemaire, B. (1989) The Challenge of Managing for 2000, the People Resource, Technical Section, CPPA, Montréal, 8-10.

Engineering College and Industrial Enterprise Cooperation: Advantage, Problem and Strategy

Li Chengli, Zhang Gang
University of Petroleum, China

Abstract
In China, as the college-enterprise cooperation is a newly emerging thing, it is not yet perfectly recognized in theories, though mature experience is acquired through practice, there are still problems. Enterprises and colleges are, in general, state-run in China, it is advantageous to the development of the cooperation. To seriously analyze and summarize its advantages and problems to be solved, thus to put forward the strategy of the cooperation being developed, is no doubt of far-reaching significance for higher education and the economical, social development as well.
Key words: Engineering, College, Enterprise, Education, Cooperation, Benefit.

1 The Advantages of College-Enterprise Cooperation in China

The fundamental interests of enterprises and colleges are in accord with each other. In general, enterprises and colleges are public-owned though they have their own interests, each being a main body, under the guidance and the help of the government, their interests are fundamentally in accord. This, therefore, just serves as the basis of the union of both sides. The union, or rather, the cooperation can not only be mutually beneficial in common development, but also can be based on the all-national and long-term benefits, beyond their partial ones, to establish a much deeper relationship within the closer cooperation.

In China, the planning commodity economy is put into effect and the development of economy and education is adjusted, controlled or guided unitedly by the state. The background of the cooperated education abroad is of a market economy only, so the internal mechanism and motive force of the cooperation which is being carried on is built up on the basis of commodity market of productive labour under the condition of market economy, the development of both economy and education being restricted by the market. Enterprises and colleges look for a partner only according to the needs respectively. This kind of cooperation is often partial or local emerging of itself and perishing of itself, sometimes being blind. Some countries have understood by themselves the limitation of the market economy. However, in China, the labour force is deployed according to plans, and for enterprises, manpower is in exccess of it wanted. Therefore, enterprises have no imperative need to take students for the cheap manpower and at the same time students find no such social conditions to pay expenses for study by means of labour. Thus it can be seen that the internal motive force stimulated by college-enterprise cooperation in developed countries is not in existence in China where the development of economy and education both may be alive microscopically and controlled macroscopically. The cooperation between enterprises and colleges is not limited by the spontaneously mutual benefits, and more, it is a conscious behaviour adapting itself for the development of socialist commodity economy. The role of our government in the college-enterprise cooperation is much stronger than that in any of the developed countries. Its role is not only effected in the grasp of policies, but also in solving problems during the process of concretely carrying it out, so it is able to avoid the blindness and short-term behaviour in the cooperation.

In China, most of the engineering colleges are under the leadership of various government departments or local authorities, so it is easy for these colleges to find the joint point within the department or locality concerned. There are 286 colleges and unversities of science and engineering in China, except 14 which are under the direct leadership of the State Education Commission, the rest is all under the leadership of the department or locality concerned. This pattern of relationship concerning jurisdiction provides favourable conditions for the college-enterprise cooperation. Between the enterprises and colleges under the same department or locality their essential interests are in a good agreement, so are their departmental and local benefits; therefore, the joint point in the cooperation is easy to find. For example, there are several large enterprises and 6 colleges of petroleum under the Chinas General Company of Oil and Natural Gas, the graduates from these colleges are mainly assigned to these petroleum enterprises, and now , as we know, most of the backbone in technology are graduates from these colleges. In other words, the enterprises and colleges of this company have the common interests — for the development of petroleum industry in China, which is just their joint point. It is the common interests that make them connect themselves together consciously or unconsciously. The company' s enterprises function for oil, colleges carry on education for .oil; and the enterprises must replenish their technical personnel from these colleges,and make advances in technology; while the colleges know the needs for qualified personnel and find the chances and possibilities of worksites for practice from these enterprises. Recently, some of these enterprises and colleges have started their comprehensive cooperation, and for this the college-enterprise cooperation committee has been formed. For example, in March 1991, such a committee was formed between the Jianghan College of Petroleum and 6 petroleum enterprises in Jianghan and other oilfields; such a committee was also formed between the University of Petroleum and the Shengli oilfield in July 1991. The common purpose of these committees is to carry out comprehensively, the state policies in education, to make contributions to petroleum industry. As soon as these committees have been formed, concrete searches and testing points are begun in order to deepen and widen the extensive cooperation, and a good developing tendency has appeared. There are still many of cooperative forms like those mentioned above and they have appeared in enterprises and colleges of different departments or localities. For example, Capital Iron and Steel University (an affiliation of Beijing University of Technology) has been established unitedly by Capital Iron and Steel

Company and University of Science and Technology Beijing, which can serve as an example, too.

2 The Problems of College-enterprise Cooperation in China

Problems of thinking and understanding. There is still a lack of enough knowledge about the college-enterprise cooperation, which is the first unfavourable factor to the development of the cooperation. If viewed superficially, such a cooperation in China is active from one side but not so active from another side; that is, colleges display high enthusiasm while enterprises have a colder response. In fact, both sides have not paid enough attention to it, and the enterprises merely behave more obviously. As to our colleges, traditional education being overviewed vertically, it still remains old-patterned theoretical teaching as the main form, remains closed, scholastic, and such a viewpoint has been obstructing the unfolding of college-enterprise cooperation. *Education in combination with productive labour* is the main content of our policy in education. The college-enterprises cooperation just embodies this policy. However, for a long time the institutions of education have not thoroughly acted in the spirit of the given policy, appearing one or another deviation in its implementing. Sometimes more attention has been paid to theory than to practice, or on the contrary, thus making the knowledge of people confused to some extent. As far as the enterprises are concerned, some of them think that it is not yet the time when such a cooperation will bring them benefits, only thinking, from their own benefits, that the cooperation only asks them to offer money, offer students places for practice. Therefore, they often behave as if it would be better to avoid it. Some of these enterprises, pressed by the administrative means, deal with it reluctantly. And thus the cooperation at present lacks vitality, and advances come slowly. Sometimes the cooperation is relunctantly put together, formally only, having little real effect.

For graduates are assigned by the government gratis, enterprises take an unclear responsibility for the students training because of the lack of laws as the foundation. The government assigns graduates to enterprises gratis year by year, enterprises vie with each other in asking for manpower the more the better because they should pay nothing in any case. While talking about how to train technical personnel, they think that it is the colleges business, having nothing to do with themselves. Facing such a situation, the colleges are incapable of making it reasonable. The key problem lies in the system of graduates' gratuitous assignment. Since it is so, who will be willing to pay? Only those, to which graduates cannot be assigned, that is, enterprises of villages or towns, or individual, do not spare money for technical personnel. But the engineering colleges of which a rather complete series of branches in science, obviously, cannot turn to those small enterprises as their main objects of cooperation because they can only provide small ranges of cooperation, but to those state run large and medium-sized enterprises that occupy the leading position at market. According to statistics, in China, large and medium-sized enterprises account for 10% of the sum total, but their output value amounts to 60% of the total. The main direction of assignment of graduates, of course, is the large and medium-sized enterprises.

They should be the main objects, with which the engineering colleges deal to carry out the cooperation. However, as stated above, whether they participate in training technical personnel remains a question. Enterprises cooperate with colleges merely from their own interests respectively or under the administrative guidance, so they are at a quite passive position, which is rather unfavourable for the equal cooperation of both.

With the contracting out system being carried out, the enterprises would pay more attention to the short-term economic profit rather than invest in colleges. There really exists a problem of beneficial results between the training of qualified personnel and the production of enterprises; the former has a long cycle but the benefits appear slowly, while the latter has a short cycle and is imperative for interests; there are no enterprises which can be indifferent to their own current interests, so the problem is how to combine the present-day interests with those of long term. Owing to the fact that the system of responsibilities of managing and contracting is not so perfect, the contractors of the enterprises take into their account only short-term benefits within the period of contracts, while the personnel training is the cause of short-term investment but long-term benefits; therefore, some of their contractors merely think highly of the present-day interests, do not want to invest in education, and, of course, have no enthusiasm to cooperate with colleges. Apart from this, the enterprises now are wanting in motive force and pressure, they have no imperative needs for the achievements in science and technology, and the property rights of knowledge have not yet been well protected. All of this hinders the normal development of the cooperation.

There is still a lack of competitive mechanism among colleges, and a stronger idea of selfclosing remaining. They carry out the united and planned control from enrollment to assignment as a system, and all the outlay is given by the state. The educational institutions are not in need to take care of how many students are to be taken in, how the graduates to be assigned, —all will be arranged by the state. Whether the graduates are of high or low quality seem to be not so serious for they will all be assigned to new posts. From teachers to students — all rely on the state's equal share of provision, and thus colleges gave no enthusiam to cooperate with enterprises and a lack of necessary competition among colleges too. In colleges there is no such phenomenon as survival of the fittest and elimination of the inferior. The level of running education is high or low does not relate to other benefits, except for the influence on the reputation of the college concerned. In addition to this, some enterprises behave indifferently about the cooperation, colleges are even more unwilling to seek it actively. As to the colleges, there also exists a problem of their own short-term benefits in the cooperation with enterprises: whether to put education or benefit-bringing on the first position, which is not well handled by every college. As to the students, there is still a lack of competition, too. Entering a college means getting the iron rice bowl (ensured means of living) and the students pay little attention to seeking work after their graduation; the record of studies is good or bad, provided passing tests, their ability to handle different matters is high or low, etc. — all doesn't matter. Besides, at present all expenses for their study, except for some main spending on life, are undertaken by the state; in this way, problems about economics have not been the major difficulty for the students. Because of all this, the students and the colleges are difficult to form an open pattern, but to form a self-closed, which has serious influence on the cooperation.

3. The Strategy to Strengthen the Cooperation

As mentioned above, the urgent task we are facing is to overcome the unfavourable factors for the cooperation in China and find a way to develop the cooperation with the Chinese features, keeping abreast with the conditions and situations in China; this is the common responsibility of all cycles of higher education and enterprise.

I. Enhancing the knowledge and, correcting the idea about running education. The first to be made clear is as follows: to train qualified personnel, especially of high level, should be the task of not only higher educational institutions, but also that of the whole society. The enterprises as the direct gainers of benefits from qualified personnel training should have been responsible for it. Enterprises must dispel the idea of paying more attention merely to the short-term benefits but take in consciously the investment in education as a process, to stimulate advances in science and technology, to enhance the level of production will be the long-term benefits, and what is more important is to think personnel training as their own conscious behaviour that should be so. Colleges should break their self-closed ideas in order to raise the cooperation up to so high a level that is becomes the embodiment of the policy *Education must be combined with productive labour;* and it is required by the overall training qualified personnel. The second, the purpose of the cooperation should be such that it advances personnel training and stimulate the development of society and economics.

I . Deepening the reform of higher education system and correctly introducing the competitive mechanism. As to the cooperation, for which colleges must carry out a series of reforms in the managing system. First, the students' iron rice bowl must be broken to effect the two-way choice between the graduates and the employers, the state will no longer take over all the assignment. This will stimulate students to further efforts, adapting themselves to the society consciously; if not, they will be unable to find work. Second, with the going up of our economical level, the state should gradually cancel the students' study at public expense, changing to their study at their own or half of their own expense. Third, before concelling the united assignment of graduates, this work may be carried out with compensation, that is , the enterprises which receive graduates must pay the college or state in any way or in any form. This can stimulate enterprises to participate directly the training of qualified personnel. Fourth, the colleges should correctly introduce the competitive mechanism. They should take flexible measures about the policy of science and technology, personnel transfer and educational system, to make teachers and students have motive force to carry on the cooperation. Certainly, it would be impossible to complete all kinds of reform only on the efforts of educational institutions; it also needs the efforts of different departments or units of the whole society to play a supporting role in the coordination of a complete series of reforms.

I . Strengthening the formulation of laws and regulations can stimulate the cooperation. In China the social environment has not yet appeared for the overall cooperation between the enterprises and colleges, many of the concrete problems met with in the cooperation can not be all solved merely by the administrative means. Therefore, there is a need to establish a mechanism by means of laws and regulations to advance the cooperation. At present, though the legislation about education is advancing, the idea about the legal system is to be strengthened. In order to promote the cooperation, the legislation of education should be speeded up. In the process of legislating, the knotty and protruding problems about the cooperation must be considered in preference to others. To raise the enthusiam of enterprises in the cooperation, it should be stipulated whether or not the enterprises which undertake the education cooperated will be allowed to exempt some profits taxes, or to take them into the cost, or to have a preference to choosing graduates to be employed by them, etc. The legislation may start in some local laws and regulations. Different departments and regions may first complete some individual regulations according to their own features to accumulate experience and to pave the road for the state laws about higher education. For example, Shanghai is now carrying on investigations and researches to get ready for the establishment of *Shanghai regulation of promoting the college-enterprise cooperation*. This action should be taken into account and learned by other departments and localities. In a word, such a cooperation can be developed smoothly, healthily only under the protection and promotion by laws.

Technology Transfer from the University of British Columbia: continued growth on a strong foundation

E.G. Auld, H. Becker, A. Fowler, D. Gill, D. Jones, A. Livingston, J. Murray

University-Industry Liaison Office, University of British Columbia

Abstract

The University-Industry Liaison (UIL) Office of the University of British Columbia (UBC) is responsible for industrial contract research, university-industry-government collaborative projects, patenting and licensing and spin-off company formation for the third largest research university in Canada. UBC currently enrolls 24,000 undergraduate and 5,000 graduate students in some 12 different faculties including, Arts, Agriculture, Applied Science, Dentistry, Education, Medicine, Law, Forestry, Pharmacy, and Commerce, and had an operating budget and capital budget of $570 million in 1991/92. In 1991/92 the UBC faculty successfully competed for more than $110 million in sponsored research grants and contracts.

The University-Industry Liaison office receives approximately 90 patent disclosures per year, files 30 to 40 patent applications per year (13th overall in North America, and first in Canada), and has 96 commercial technology licenses which return approximately $.75 million per year in royalties and equities.

There are 87 spin-off companies (created by UBC technology or "know-how") which had sales in 1990 of more than $824 million and employed directly 4600 people.

Keywords: Technology transfer, patents and licenses.

1 Introduction

The University of British Columbia, founded in 1916, has grown rapidly since the Second World War and has become one of the top educational and research institutions in Canada. As it was the first in British Columbia it has always had special links with local commercial and industrial interests. Many faculty members maintain close personal contacts with industry and provide important consulting activities. The office that nurtures and encourages these links, in the process of managing and encouraging the technology transfer is the University-Industry Liaison office. The annual sponsored research budget has grown to exceed $110 million. A significant component of this research can have an important impact on the local industrial economy if the appropriate technology transfer functions are in place. It falls within the mandate of the University-Industry Liaison Office to ensure that these opportunities are found and exploited.

2 The industrial environment in B.C.

The industrial strength in B.C. has been associated with the traditional resource based industries of lumbering, pulp and paper, energy, fishing and mining. Much of the exploration of the Pacific Ocean was done with masts cut from the Douglas Fir and Sitka Spruce growing along the coast of British Columbia. Other world famous commodities that we have provided are: pacific salmon, copper, lead and zinc. As the world changes, so have we, in that we now have an emerging high tech industry that is focusing on biotechnology and information technology. Growth in these areas far outstrips that of the traditional resource industries. It is the intent of the UIL office to assist the emergence of new industries and strategic partnerships to create a more broadly based, diversified industrial infrastructure for the Province and Canada.

3 The government and agency environment

The support for funding R&D in new commercial developments comes from multiple sources in Canada. This is, in some cases, more of a problem than an asset because of the multitude of agencies and organizations one has to deal with in order to acquire the necessary critical level of funding to make a project viable.

The Federal Government has three major agencies for funding research and development; the National Science and Engineering Research Council (NSERC) and the Medical Research Council (MRC) program, for academic research in universities; and the National Research Council-Industrial Research Assistance Program (NRC-IRAP) program which supports mission oriented research in companies for the specific purpose of developing new products. In various parts of Canada there is also the resource of interest free loans for more extensive financing of manufacturing facilities to support the sale of new products. This is called the Western Economic Development Office, and was created to stimulate growth in the Western Provinces of Canada.

The Provincial Government provides through the Science Council of B.C. (SCBC) monies for doing targetted research and development for both university and local industry to explore applied research for possible new commercial enterprizes. The funds can be used for the traditional mission oriented applied research, reduction to practice prototypes for patent purposes, and more adventurously for market research analysis to help the inventor appreciate where the most likely application of the new idea may be pointed.

4 The operation of the UILO.

The activities of the UIL program are governed by the basic terms of reference as determined by our various sources of funding. The operation is funded from five different major sources that provide seven different operating contracts: UBC, the Provincial Ministry of Advanced Education and Technology Training, NRC, SCBC, and the National Centres of Excellence. The main points of our mandate and terms of reference from all these contracts are listed below:

1. To promote and commercialize research discoveries and inventions which have resulted from the research program at UBC.

2. To promote technology transfer and communication within the province and specifically to assist the faculty in developing collaborative projects with industry and provide B.C. industry with access to UBC's extensive faculty expertise, know-how and equipment. This includes both contract work from companies seeking specific research expertise on the campus and companies seeking to become strategic partners in the development of intellectual property emerging from the campus.

3. To protect the intellectual property through the patent process, which results as byproducts of both basic and applied research, and to use this property to provide a potential source of unrestricted income to the university, and to license University-generated technology to industry so as to optimize the benefit to B.C.

4. To enhance the rate of technology transfer from the University to industry, by exploring the possibilities of doing prototype development in a university atmosphere. This includes the preparation of marketing and business plans for the purpose of forming new companies, and the subsequent licenses to the emerging new company or strategic partner.

5. To improve access to patent literature at UBC, to increase the awareness among faculty, students and the public of the value of patent literature.

The staff in the UIL view the UIL program as working at the interface between university, industry and government. Each of these constituents has its own vision of how the program should operate and how success should be measured. The University community is diverse and, of course, wants different things. The President wishes UIL to generate revenue, and provide service to the community. The faculty, staff and students want prompt, efficient service, and information on how to access industrial grants, contracts and intellectual property issues. The industry on the other hand wishes to have relatively easy access to technology, equipment, and research expertise. Finally, the government wishes to have accelerated technology transfer, spin-off companies and economic diversification. The challenge, of course, for UIL is to find the middle-of-the-road that will satisfy the diverse constituents which we serve.

Because the office has the responsibility for both the research contracts from industry and for the marketing of the university technology to industry, it represents an important node in the essential networking that goes with these transactions. In many cases it offers a "one-stop-shopping" opportunity for individuals who want to enquire about any facit of industrial research and development in Canada or the Province. For this reason, faculty and students at the university find it a very useful resource.

5 Organization and division of responsibility

The structure of the operations has evolved to where we are initiating a "cradle-to-the-grave" division of responsibility so that one technology transfer person will be the principal contact for providing services, whether it be for research contracts, research collaborations, patenting and licensing or prototype development. Each staff person has a recognized group of disciplines that he/she would normally deal with. This system is not fully operational and can only evolve over a period of time as the personnel gain skills and experience in the different activities. In this manner, they will not only be able to provide one single point of contact for university, industrial and government clients, but also become more valuable employees with much broader skill sets.

6 Specific aspects of the operation

The office is very busy, handling approximately 90 invention disclosures, 65 research contracts from industry, 47 patents filed, 20 patents issued, 70 miscellaneous

agreements, and 25 prototype development projects per year.
It is imperative, when dealing with faculty and student
inventors to process their requests as quickly and as
efficiently as possible in order to get each project
evaluated and moving in the direction that all parties are
happy with. The patent policy of the university is that in
exchange for a faculty member assigning the patent rights
to the unversity, the university in turn provides the
inventors with 50% of the net revenue from the commercial
licensing agreement.

The description of each new invention is provided on a
standard invention disclosure form by the inventor. During
this early stage of the development, there is seldom
sufficient information available to make quantitative
assessments of the idea. A staff member of the office will
normally spend a few days, assessing the idea for
commercial merit. This will include extensive discussions
with the student and faculty inventors, as well as a first
order independent market analysis, and assessment of the
technology. Many things are considered in this analysis,
not the least of which is the level of enthusiasm and
commitment of the inventor to carry out their share of the
work. The quality of the idea is a necessary condition for
commercial success, but not sufficient; the personality
and enthusiasm of the inventor has more impact on the
success than the quality of the idea.

Many of the ideas are at too early a stage of
development to attract a commercial partner, but none-the-
less have sufficient commercial potential that further
development of a prototypal nature is encouraged. The
project individuals are given some limited financial
support to continue the development until, a commercial
partner is found, a new spin-off company is formed by the
principals, or further development has proven the idea to
be a poor business risk, or the lack of enthusiasm for the
project within the inventor groups proves that they did not
have the necessary interest. Regardless of the outcome,
the process has provided a group of highly technically
competent individuals a considerable insight into the
details of commercializing new technology. The impact of
that alone may be more important than the success of
failure of their first attempt at technology transfer. The
graduate students especially will have left the university
with much more experience than what they would normally get
from their academic degree.

Many other inventions lend themselves to more direct
licensing as soon as a strategy for the idea has been
formulated. The inventors play an important roll in this
process as providing the necessary technical "know=how" to
the appropriate individuals. Their response must be
timely, and they must show a genuine interest in the

company.   The possibility of many future successful
collaborations could be at stake.
   Faculty, research students and undergraduate students
(especially in engineering) all play important rolls in
this process at various times.   Therefore the UIL staff
provide am important educational service for the inventors.
Faculty members are usually brought up-to-date in patent
laws, research students are given a good insight into the
importance of intellectual property.   Undergraduate
students in Engineering, working on their senior project
laboratories are now dealing with the issues of
confidentiality and intellectual property as they seek
projects from local industry.   The UIL serves as an advisor
to the student and his/her supervisor as to the most
appropriate stance to take regarding the intellectual
property of specific projects and contracts.

7 The future

The University-Industry Liaison office at UBC is just that,
having strong roots both in industry and the academic
process of the university.   In developing a viable
technology transfer function, the office has recognized the
importance of maintaining close communication with the
faculty and students who provide the new inventions, and
who carry out the work of the research contracts developed
with industry.   In the long term we expect that the
knowledge these inventors have about the commercialization
process may be of more benefit to the community than the
specific technologies that they are developing at this
point in time.

Effective Technology Transfer Between Engineering Organisations: the User Agencies, and the Technological Institutions

J.K. Jain (*), R. Singhai (**)

(*) Department of Applied Mechanics, Maulana Azad College of Technology, Bhopal

(**) Department of Electronics, Govt. Engg. College, Bhopal

Abstract

The paper deals with the problem of interaction of future engineering education with user agencies; the various industries of public and private sectors. In the paper the focus is made on the future needs of nation and requirements of various other sectors, by 2000 A.M. The basic requirements of engineering education and the user agencies, in terms of future planning and national development are also discussed. Lastly various steps are suggested for the proper involvement of user agencies in the planning of future engineering education.

Keywords: Technology Transfer, Industries, Technological Institutions, Interaction, Future Needs, India.

1 Introduction

India is a developing country. The rate of development in India is faster compared to many other countries. The development of a nation mainly depends upon the successful utilization of available manpower and maximum extraction and utilization of natural resources. In the skilled manpower of a nation, the engineers and technologists are main links which convert the planning in to reality and natural resources in to usable form. For country like India, the planning of engineering education for future essentially involves development of technology which can meet the future national demands as well as can guarantee full employment to all available manpower. The nature of education should be such that it is fitted well within the frame work of satisfying the development requirements of nation; is able to accommodate research developments and able to attain the level of socio-economical requirements of the society. Since the engineers and scientists have to work within the constraints of specific requirements of the user agencies like various industries of public and private sectors, there is great interaction between the user agencies and the engineering education system. Hence a proper planning of future engineering education system is necessary.

2 Identification of Industries; The User Agencies

It is important that the industries which directly or indirectly employ skilled manpower are clearly identified with their requirements. The industries both in public and private sectors and government will have to think about the requirements of Food, Housing and Energy (Transportation and Fuel) for the projected population of India, approximately 950 millions by 2000 A.D. Therefore, the user agencies will have to spell out the future needs which may be used as "Feed-Back" in planning the engineering education of the future.

3 National Requirements

To avoid a gap between the production and utilization of skill, a equillibrium has to be maintained between the two. Any unbalance in this will lead to unemployment and loss of productivity. Therefore, there should be a perfect balance between the requirements and utilization of technical skilled manpower at all levels. The national requirements can be divided into following three main categories.

3.1 Rural Requirements
As our maximum population belongs to rural areas, the focus of planning should be around 'Rural Developments'. Most of the people in these areas depend upon agriculture as main source of their livelihood, and a larger percentage of these without agriculture land, are moving to industrialised big cities in search of job opportunities, causing not only housing problem, but also many other problems. Therefore, the rural development has to be done bifacially, covering the fields of 'Rural Technology' and development of 'small

Scale Industries' for farmers and other people of the villages. The rural technology must mean, decentralized, small and efficient production units in the rural areas to increase production and to create massive employment. This will require planning for imparting skill and utilizing the skills in their own environment without a violent disturbance to their value systems.

3.2 Urban Requirements
In the urban areas, the major fields of requirements are: housing, transportation and pollution free environment. The planning is to be done for the problem of faster growth in population. The requirement problem of houses is becoming a question mark to the planners. The transportation system has to be modified so that solar, wind and thermal energies can be used in place of petroleum energy. The pollution of environment is a challange to the scientists and technologists now a days, and the planning has to be done on massive scale for providing pollution free environment.

3.3 Industrial Requirements
There is certainly a gap between the requirements of industries and the skill producing institutions, due to the lack of involvement of user agencies in the education programmes. There is insufficient 'Built-in to' relation between the two. The programmes has to be charted out, about what the industries require and what the institutions produce. Therefore, the user agencies have to shed the present trend and embark upon the programmes of interaction and involvement with educational institutions to develop the required skill for future engineers.

4   Engineering Education

To make engineering education, a need oriented programme, the planners, technologists, industrialists and educationist should concentrate their attention on the future requirements of nation and the user agencies with special reference to the proper requirement, use and training of manpower. The engineering education should not only responsive to the needs of the development programmes of nation but also accomodate the faster changes in the field of research. In discussing engineering education system, following aspects should not be left untouched.

4.1 Future Needs
The education system has to workout the requirements of future, atleast by 2000 A.D., regarding food, housing and transportation and would have to develop and incorporate technologies of various levels and sizes.

4.2 Research and Development Units

The research and development units should provide the type, level and requirements of new technologies for the projected further needs. This should be achieved by having refresher and continuing education courses for not only teachers in engineering institutions but also for in-service engineers and representatives of user agencies. There should be seminars and symposiums time to time on the needs of user agencies. New research developments should be communicated to the user agencies through these medias.

4.3 Feed-Back System

Since the education is a continuing process, a gradual refinement to the desired target of future engineering needs can be achieved through feed-back process. An effective feed-back system could only exist when there is a contineous process of dialogue and interaction between the user agencies, and engineering educational institutions.

4.4 Education System Evaluation

The level of performance of a system has to be contineously evaluated. The success of engineering education programmes lies in the fact, as to how much level of skill is attained by a fresh engineer in comparison to the level required by the user agency. Therefore, the standard of education system has to be maintained according to the requirements of user agencies. The curriculum of education and syllabii have to be framed and changed accordingly time to time. The user agencies will also have to be kept informed regarding the level of expertise available and the quantum of skilled manpower to be employed to achieve a given objective. This may successfully eliminate manpower famine as well as unemployment.

5   Step for Successful Interaction between the Engineering Education and Industries; The user agencies

With the basic aspects enunciated in the preceding articles some distinct steps can be outlined for successful interaction between the engineering education and the user agenices. The steps are :

(i)   Estimate the projected population and available manpower which may suitably be trained by 2000 A.D.

(ii) Estimate the total rural and urban requirements regarding food, housing and transportation.

(iii) Estimate the future needs of user agencies regarding the recruitment of skilled manpower.

(iv) Establish a link between the educational institutions and the user agencies by suitable representation of user agencies on the academic bodies like Board of Studies, Academic Councils and such other statutory bodies.

(v) Organise refresher and continuing education courses for engineers, teachers and representatives of user agencies.

(vi) Organise seminars and symposiums on the topics related to the user agenices inviting the representatives of user agencies.

(vii) Modify the curriculum and syllabii time to time according to the requirements and feed-back received from user agencies. The education system should be such, as to accommodate the changes and long term requirements both in terms of breadth of diversity and depth of specilisation.

(viii) The research and development projects of the user agenices, national laboratories and engineering institutions should be discussed on a common plateform and a coordination should be achieved between the three. This will not only save the time but also save the money and manpower user, in unfruitful research projects.

(ix) The work should be motivated in the direction of rural technology. The engineering education should train the engineers not only in the direction of design and manufacture but also in the direction of proper implementation of knowledge in proper field.

(x) System analysis techniques are now well established and they could be employed to consider the involvement of user agencies in engineering education.

A multidimensional involvement of user agencies with the future engineering education is explained in the figure-1.

References

Khanna, S.K., (1978) Involvement of User Agencies in Planning Engineering Education of the Future, Pannel discussion on Educating Engineers of the future, Institution of Engineers (India), Roorkee.

Murthy, P.N., (1978) Educating the Engineers of the Future, Institution of Engineers (India), Bulletin, 27.

Newsletters (1981) Indian Society for Technical Education.

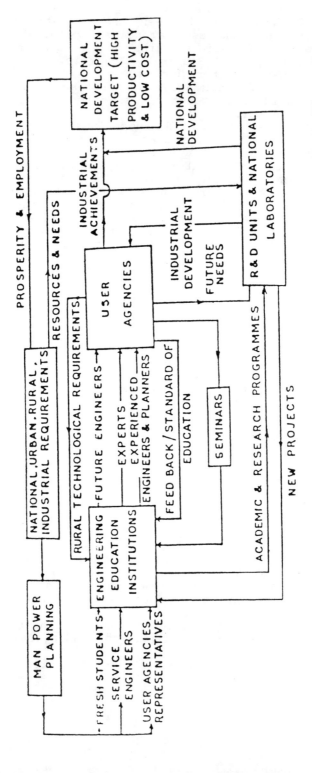

FIG.I. MULTIDIMENSIONAL INVOLVEMENT OF USER AGENCIES IN
FUTURE ENGINEERING EDUCATION

The Impossible Dream: Making Effective University-Industry Technology Transfer a Reality

B. Cunnington

Division of Commerce and Administration, Griffith University, Brisbane

Abstract

It is important that engineering students, particularly postgraduate, should understand the importance and nature of Technology Transfer. Yet many engineering faculty themselves do not understand the way in which it operates in their own University. This paper provides an overview of the process based on the experience of those involved in its day-to-day operation. It suggests that a certain critical mass of invention disclosure within an University is necessary in order for the process to be self sustaining. It shows how this may be achieved when the research budget of an individual University falls below critical mass.

Keywords: Technology Transfer, Engineering, Education, Universities.

1. Introduction

The process whereby ideas become translated into technology and ultimately into products can be thought about in a number of ways. One of the most common is that put forward by Booz, Allen and Hamilton in 1968. Adopting a new product development perspective they suggest a six stage process: exploration, screening, business analysis, development, testing and commercialization. One limitation of this model is that it assumes that the entire process is carried out within the same organization. By contrast the Technology Life Cycle model makes no such assumptions. It identifies seven stages through which a technology must pass in order to reach a commercial form suitable for use. They are concept, research, development, manufacture, distribution, sale and use. DAKIN AND LINDSEY (1984). This paper is especially concerned with the first four of these stages and in particular with the process whereby technology developed in a University setting is to be transferred to the private sector for commercialization.

The process of developing technology within the same organization is beset with problems arising from the different interests and associated perspectives of R & D, manufacturing and marketing functions. These problems became compounded when the developmental process involves a transfer of technology from a University to Industry or Commerce. They revolve about the claims of three parties to the ownership of Intellectual Property Rights and the dollar value that should be placed upon their claims. The three parties are the University, the Faculty and the Commercial/Industrial Sector. Although the conflict is motivated by self interest it is exacerbated by the differences in culture between the University and Commercial Sector. In addition the University itself is subject to a series of constraints and expectations arising from the state and federal legislatures. It is the responsibility of the Technology Transfer Function to ensure potential and overt conflict is limited through appropriate management strategies.

In this paper we shall explore the causes of conflict and methods of conflict resolution through the eyes of those charged with the responsibility for Technology Transfer. It is based upon research carried out while the author was a Visiting Fellow at the IC^2 Institute at the University of Texas at Austin. Although the interviews were carried out in the US the issues they encompass are of concern to all university engineering faculty.

Engineering faculty are charged with the responsibility of educating those assigned by the University to them; yet in the field of Technology Transfer the faculty themselves frequently need educating regarding Technology Transfer. It is hoped this paper will help to make faculty aware of some of the salient issues on which they must be informed.

2.   The Conflict Triangle

Figure 1 graphically illustrates the conflict situation in University-Industry Technology Transfer. The ownership and valuation of Intellectual Property Rights is the focal point of this conflict. These rights can be expressed in the form of (1) patents; (2) registered designs (3) plant variety rights; (4) copyright (5) trade marks and (6) know-how and trade secrets. HODKINSON (1987). It is the responsibility of the Technology Transfer Function in the University to minimise the causes of conflict through the provision of information upon which informed choices can be made and to resolve conflict situations through the process of negotiation.

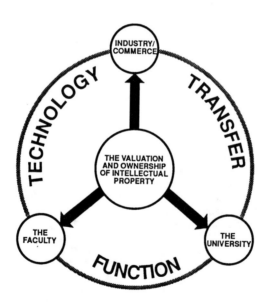

Fig 1: The Technology Transfer Conflict Triangle

2.1   University-Industry Conflict

The origins of conflict between these two parties is neatly summed up in the following extract from an interview with Dale Klein, Associate Dean of Research in the College of Engineering and Head of the Centre for Technology Development and Transfer at the University of Texas at Austin. Contrasting industry sponsored with government funded research he states, 'but when we are doing research that is industrially sponsored, the industry says "we're paying for it, therefore we should have a royalty free utilization", while the University policy is there will be no royalty free license except for education purposes. We have lost contracts with industrial sponsors because we could not come to terms on the Intellectual Property policy. The Industry on one hand says "you're a State Institution, we're paying this money, therefore we own all the Intellectual Property"; the University says, "we're not a job shop; the intellect is our property, that's what we do; therefore we own it .....

Even when the Industrial sponsor is content to assign rights to Intellectual Property to the University, it can still mistakenly believe that it should have the first right of refusal to a license; however this also conflicts with University culture.

'you get into these conflicts you know - the State cannot compete with private industry - and so when you start negotiating you have to negotiate with everyone. You can't pick a company - for example if T.I. sponsors some research and IBM wants to participate in the licensing of the Intellectual Property that comes out of it, you can't say "Gee, I can't talk to you; because T.I. sponsored the research we have to enter into an agreement with T.I." '.

One response of Industry to problems of ownership of Intellectual Property is defensive publishing. Glen Self is VP Research in EDS a subsidiary of G.M. He comments

'I will point out to you one of the things that I have done in dealing with Universities in order to get around this concept of "well you can't inhibit the publication of our Professors"; I have taken the other side which surprises them a lot of times and I say," that's absolutely right; in fact I insist on your publishing the results of this research we're funding and if you don't, then by contract I have the right to publish it"; of course that's defensive publishing.... see my point being I don't want to fund a Professor and some students and later on I have to buy my own technology from one of these students that worked on the project'.

2.2   Faculty-University Conflict

The major form of Faculty-University conflict is not concerning the ownership of Intellectual Property Rights. Most Universities have resolved this issue in terms of a policy which shares the proceeds equally between the University and the Faculty member after subtracting costs involved with the commercialization process. The real point of contention is whether a faculty member should choose to reap the benefits from publication in terms of academic promotion or the monetary benefits of commercialization.

Techcom is a for profit corporation jointly owned by the Texas Engineering Experiment Station (TEES) and the Texas A & M University. Its mission is to provide quality commercialization services to TEES. Dave Mueller is its CEO. His comments nicely summarise the above conflict and the role of the Technology Transfer Function in dealing with it.

'you've really got two different cultures here; they're different by design and I don't think its our job - certainly not our job - to try to change one into the other. The reward systems in the University and business are different you know .... what we talk about in Technology Transfer, we bridge between the two cultures rather than change one into the other. ..... so what that means is oftentimes we will say to the inventor, "You have the choice as to whether you want to publish or you want to commercialize"..... you can look on us as being on the periphery and (1) taking whatever we can to commercialize (2) educating them so they can make informed decisions. Shame on all of us, if their interest was in fact commercializing and they unknowingly lost commercial value by making an improper decision that wasn't based on information .....'

3.   The Achievement of Critical Mass

Despite many beliefs to the contrary the costs of running an effective Technology Transfer Function often outweigh the dollar returns - at least in the short run. This was a concern of many of those interviewed. It is clearly reflected in the following extracts from the interview with Dale Klein of the University of Texas at Austin.

'If you look at the royalty payments there is usually a 5-10 year lag; on this one technology (a new form of spark plug) that I think were going to do very well on; you know it ramps up; we still have to do some more development to get it really commercialized, and then what you get, the royalty payments sort of trickle in for a while and then they pick up, but it takes a while and by that time your patent's run out'.

'I spend a fair amount of time on Intellectual Property issues and it's frustrating when people dig in their heels on both sides; you know when the company says they own it all and the University by State Law says "we own it all" the truth ought to be somewhere in the middle - but the negotiations take so long ....'

'cause we spend a lot of time negotiating Intellectual Property policy issues on proposals that we know will not have Intellectual Property associated with it; but the legislature tells us that we have to do that and the companies sometimes have their own internal policies that say "we cannot fund unless we get a royalty free utilization"....

In addition once a patent exists there is still no guarantee a market exists for the potential innovation. HARC (Houston Applied Research Centre) is a consortium of 5 Universities established for the purpose of carrying out scientific research and wherever possible commercializing the results of this research.   David Norton is V.P. Research.   His comments upon their experience in attempting to commercialize a shielded magnet for a particular imaging technology are particularly pertinent.

'We had a technology, the technology I showed you, of the self shielded magnet .... then we spent 2 or 3 years trying to introduce this obviously better technology to the main players who make the imaging units; and we were told by one of the biggest, "If I think it's interesting we'll do it and you'll just have to sue me"; and by the small ones 'You know I don't have the money to invest and to change over because you know I've been making it this way and there's really not much of a market demand yet"; so we had to spend a lot of time educating the physicians going to expositions; and now you can't have a centre, a new one, that doesn't have a shielded magnet because everyone knows it's dangerous ... and so now all of a sudden we've had 3 or 4 opportunities .... but that gestation period was a full 4 years before there was a market pull for it ...'

Perhaps of even more significance than the decision as to whether to protect Intellectual Property or not, is the decision as to what extent protection should be enforced. This is evident in the preceding example; some companies flaunt Intellectual Property protection because of the extent of resources required for enforcement.

Because of the costs associated with extended negotiations regarding the protection and licensing of Intellectual Property; because of the costs of enforcement of Intellectual Property Rights and because of the time taken to transform Intellectual Property into products demanded by the market place there is a critical rate of invention disclosure within a University below which the Technology Transfer process can not break even.

This was frequently referred to by those interviewed in terms of a critical mass analogy.

'I think its this question of critical mass; you probably have a size, maybe size measured in terms of research dollars or dollars spent on research ... I would say there has to be (1) a research emphasis (2) probably some critical mass of research dollars to generate any kind of Intellectual Property worth dealing with' (DAVE MUELLER)

However even the existence of a critical mass research budget is not enough. As mentioned previously the returns from Intellectual Property protection will ramp up over the early years of a Technology Transfer program. A University must be prepared to commit the resources necessary to cover the costs of operation of any Technology Transfer Function over at least 5 years in order for the benefits of critical mass to be realised.

In the light of the previous section the question emerges as to what can be done in the situation where a University's research budget falls below the critical level or it does not have the resources to support Technology Transfer over an extended period before breaking even.

One obvious answer is collaboration and the shared use of a Technology Transfer Function. However, most Universities are extremely 'turf' conscious and unlikely to participate in any activity which threatens their own autonomy. It is therefore appropriate to review a method which allows participating institutions to maintain their autonomy yet still achieve effective Technology Transfer. This model has been termed 'The NASA Technology Transfer Network'.

4. The NASA Technology Transfer Network

The NASA Technology Transfer Program in the US has three major activities.
    (1)   Information publication;
    (2)   computerized scientific and technical database search;
    (3)   collaborative technology transfer.
It is with the third of these activities with which we shall deal at this time.

The first two sets of the above activities deal with the transfer of information. There are however projects which require a more complex Technology Transfer process. Doris Rouse is director of the NASA Technology Applications Team at the Research Triangle Institute in North Carolina. Commenting upon this situation she says:

'The second type of category that comes from both industry and the public sector - and that is: 'information is not all that I need; I need someone to help me adapt the technology out of this environment, the aerospace environment, and into the very different environment that I'm in; I can't do that by myself just with technical information .... I need your collaboration.'

The solution chosen by NASA to deal with this problem is the Application Team and a network of Technology Utilization Officers (TUO's) each located at one of 9 NASA regional centres eg Lyndon B Johnson Space Centre.

The TUO's basic responsibility is to stay abreast of R & D activities at his centre that have a significant potential for Technology Transfer.

'At one time there were 7 application teams around the country; in '83 NASA realised they didn't have enough money to continue to support that number and many of them at a low level wasn't as good as one at a larger level; and we won that competition and so we are the application team for NASA now '. (DORIS ROUSE)

Dean Glenn is TUO at the Johnson Space Centre at Houston. He describes the operation of the NASA network in these terms:

'It happens in a couple of ways; sometimes they call us directly and sometimes they call Research Triangle Institute. RTI is a NASA HQ contractor that matches the technology with the various field centres. What happens is, if a company calls here and I know the technology is here I'll refer them to that person ....; then if the technology isn't here I'll refer them to RTI.

What happens next is they (RTI) write a problem statement - what are you looking for, what is the problem - and that's circulated by RTI to all of the field centres; and we get those here and I circulate that at Johnson Space Centre to all the folks here; if we get it, someone that has the expertise will then carry on and determine what can be done as part of their project to re-engineer NASA's technology into their product'. (DEAN GLENN, TUO JSC.)

This model has a number of important features:-

(1)   Through collaboration it leverages the ability of any individual Technology Transfer agent (TUO).

(2)   The focus is upon the needs of users rather than pushing a particular technology;

(3)   It recognises that the development of technology for incorporation in commercial products can require an extended Technology Transfer process over a number of years;

(4)   No individual Technology Transfer agent has control of the day-to-day operations of the RTI centre although it is funded under contract to NASA;

(5)   Each transfer agent (TUO) is responsible for the transfer of technology from his own centre and where necessary collaborating with other TUO's to see the clients needs are met.

(6)   The objective of the process is to carry out effective Technology Transfer rather than making any particular centre wealthy.

5.   The Application of The NASA Network

For those Universities who have not achieved critical mass the model offers a way to effective technology transfer through regional collaboration.   In effect a number of Universities each below critical mass would jointly fund a Regional Technology Transfer Facility whose mission on a project by project basis would be to

(1)   provide advice as to whether a technology should receive some form of Intellectual Property protection, and if so what form;

(2)   find appropriate recipients for technology suitable for transfer;

(3)   to act as a first point of call for industrial and commercial organisations with problems capable of solution by Technology Transfer;

(4)   to enforce the protection of Intellectual Property Rights.

6.   References

1.   Booz, Allen & Hamilton 'The Management of New Products' (New York: Booz, Allen & Hamilton Inc 1968) pp 7-12.

2.   Dakin K.J. and Lindsey J 'Technology Transfer' (Chicago: Probus Pub. Co. 1991) pp 21-39.

3.   Hodkinson K 'Protecting and Exploiting New Technology and Designs' (London: E&FN Spon 1987) p 1.

University/Industry Technology Transfer - A Process That Really Works!

E. Rhodes (*), E.B. Cross (**)

(*) *Faculty of Engineering, University of Calgary*
(**) *Technology Licensing Office, University of Waterloo*

Abstract
The Waterloo Centre for Process Development was established in 1978 as an organization devoted to technology transfer between university and industry. Case studies of several individual projects such as the developments of

    (1)   a new animal feed single cell protein process,
    (2)   a computerized grain dryer controller,
    (3)   an ash fouling control system for utility boilers, and
    (4)   a new heat resistant rubber

will illustrate both the great risks and the golden opportunities for academics to engage in the transfer of technology. A University Centre initiated with a $1 million government grant has succeeded in protecting 25 technologies with 103 patents leading to 18 international licenses. Three Canada Awards for Business Excellence have been won by the Centre. The paper concludes that "strong market pull" is the most important ingredient of success in technology transfer. Universities should preferably invest technology transfer dollars in protection of intellectual property.
Keywords: Technology Transfer, Intellectual Property, Biotechnology, Polymer Technology. Grain Drying, Ash Monitoring.

1 Introduction

In 1977, the Department of Chemical Engineering at the University of Waterloo, Canada was just 20 years old, having been a cornerstone in the building of a brand new university strongly based on engineering, science and mathematics. Like many departments, it had grown very rapidly in the 1960s. In the following decade, this dynamic group of people had established an international reputation and had collectively published close to 1,500 research articles. Many of the faculty members had obtained patents on their inventions. One of the missing factors was technology transfer. Out of the research and the associated publications there appeared to have been very little industrial use made of the new technologies. A major barrier to technology transfer existed between the university and industry and this barrier was thought to be the lack of resources to enable demonstration-type projects to be undertaken.

Having discussed this problem with the Canadian Government's Department of Industry, Trade and Commerce, a grant of $1 million was provided to establish the Waterloo Centre for Process Development. This Centre had the mandate to find means of transferring technology from the university to industry. During its lifetime, the Centre has been extremely successful (see Abstract above). It has employed a very large number of full-time researchers, graduate students and Faculty supervisors.

This paper discusses four examples of projects which illustrate the experiences of the Centre. Conclusions are drawn as to the best way to transfer technology from the university to industry.

2   Four Case Studies

2.1   Single Cell Protein Process (1)

Following the Centre's incorporation, the technical committee surveyed the in-house technology of the Department and singled out a short list of potentially attractive technologies for further development and investment. A biotechnology process had been researched for many years and appeared to be extremely exciting. This process was one in which solid cellulose material could be converted into protein using anaerobic fermentation using an extremely active organism (chaetonium celluliticum) which had been isolated by Dr. M. Moo-Young in his biochemical engineering laboratory. Preliminary animal feeding trials had indicated that the protein produced by this process could be a very valuable animal feed and that it compared very favourably with commercially available products.

The Centre decided to build a pilot plant in the University laboratories which could be used to further develop the process and to demonstrate its industrial feasibility. Many attempts were made to commercialize the process and, much later, a company built a full-scale demonstration plant in British Columbia. Agreements were made to transfer the technology to protein poor/cellulose rich countries such as Yugoslavia. The financial performance of this project is shown in Table 1.

It can be seen that even though royalty fees of $380,000 have been received by the University for this process, the current University of Waterloo position is a negative $2.5 million. The Centre invested long before it had an industrial partner. The single cell protein project still continues, however, the right time and opportunity for a commercial breakthrough have still not occurred.

Table 1. Single Cell Protein.

Supporting Contract Research 4 Agreements at UW from 1981-1986 4 Separate Industrial Sponsors Provided	 $ 367K	$367K	
University Investment/Research Support 1979 - 1991 Direct Expense Interest	 $1,100K $1,800K		 $2,900K
Gross Royalties/Fees - 1982-1991			380K
Current UW Position			**-$2,500K**

2.2   Computerized Grain Dryer Controller (2)

In 1982 a local entrepreneur knocked on the door of the Waterloo Centre for Process Development seeking help. His business was selling electronic gadgets and microcomputers to Ontario farmers and he had identified an agricultural problem, namely, control of the moisture content of grains being dried in continuous processes. The problem was to produce corn at exactly 14.5% moisture content by processing feed stocks which would vary greatly in moisture content, grain variety, age, etc. The process control group, headed by G. R. Sullivan, identified this as a very interesting application for their expertise in the area of microcomputer-aided adaptive process control. Basic research was followed by on-site process control trials, equipment product development, marketing and selling. This has led to the installation of computerized grain drying technology in a large number of grain dryers in Canada and the U.S.A. These dryers process corn, beans, rice, animal feed and industrial products, etc. The financial details of the University's involvement in this project are given in Table 2, which shows that the University of Waterloo has a positive position of $186,000 from the project. Since the entrepreneurial company is now growing quite rapidly, and it is now a globally oriented company with an active R&D group developing new products in collaboration with the university, this project is regarded to be a great success and one which will continue to benefit the university in the future.

2.3   Ash Fouling Control System for Utility Boilers (3)

In 1982 the Canadian Electrical Association solicited proposals for research work to be done on the problem of monitoring and controlling ash fouling in large industrial coal-fired boilers. A team of researchers working through the Centre was successful in obtaining a research contract and subsequently

Table 2. Computerized Grain Dryer Controller.

Supporting Contract Research 8 Agreements at UW from 1982-1988 Paid by Licensee Paid by Ontario Government Total	 $351K 57K $408K	$408K	
University Support Investment for Patents/In-house Research			$290K
Gross Royalties and Fees 1985-91			476K
Current UW Position			**+$186K**

developed new instrumentation which could be attached to the walls and tubes of coal-fired boilers which, through the use of microcomputers, enabled operators to "see" on computer screens the extent and location of fouling. Subsequently process control routines were developed to assist the operators in reducing the effects of fouling on boiler efficiency. The down times due to catastrophic fouling in commercial boilers were reduced considerably. Demonstration installations were implemented in Alberta and Saskatchewan on full-scale boilers. The technology was subsequently licensed to Combustion Engineering Canada Limited and commercial installations have been made as far afield as Thailand.

Table 3. Ash Monitoring System.

Supporting Contract Research 4 Agreements at UW from 1981-1987 Funding from 2 Industrial Associates	 $642K	$642K	
University Support Investment for Patens/In-house Research			$341K
Gross Royalties/Fees from 1984-1991			323K
Current UW Position			**-$ 18K**

Table 3 shows that the University is still in a negative position. However, it is expected that future royalties will accrue for no further University expenses.

The figures show that the University had to invest its own money in order to take the research to the point where it could be commercialized.

2.4   Heat Resistant Rubber (4)

In 1981 the Polymer Research Institute of the University of Waterloo was providing a forum for discussion on its research activities which was attended by scientists from a major Canadian petrochemical company, Polysar Limited. Polysar indicated they had identified a potential market opportunity for a rubber material which would withstand high temperatures occurring around engines of modern high performance automobiles. It was felt that one of its existing nitrile rubber products could be modified by the addition of hydrogen to selective sites in the molecule, and that the end product would probably have the necessary temperature resistant properties. The question was how to add the hydrogen. Through the Waterloo Centre for Process Development, contracts were arranged between a Professor, G. L. Rempel, and the company and within a very short time that Professor had shown that by use of organo-metallic catalysts he could selectively add hydrogen to the nitrile rubber. Over a period of ten years the Centre has managed 12 research agreements and has worked with the company on pilot projects and the eventual building of a full-scale rubber manufacturing plant in Texas. This plant has subsequently been joint ventured with the major German company Bayer. The current financial status of this project is shown in Table 4, which shows that the University is now in a positive financial position and it expects to receive royalties for the technology in future years.

Table 4. Heat Resistant Rubber Catalyst.

Supporting Contract Research			
12 Agreements at UW from 1981-1991 Paid by Licensee Paid by Ontario Government	 $1,100K 400K	$1,500K	
Total	$1,500K		
University Support/Patent Expenses			$110K
Option Fees/Royalties Received 1988-91			120K
Current UW Position			**+$ 10K**

3   Observations and Conclusions

The four examples described above are quite typical of the projects which have been undertaken in the Centre for Process Development. Over the decade, the authors have come to appreciate the simple fact that one of the keys to success in University technology transfer is that an industrial joint venture partner must be involved early in the project. This provides the market pull which drives the research forward and focuses the researchers on real problem solving as opposed to curiosity driven research.

A second conclusion that can be drawn from Tables 1 to 4, which is confirmed by the authors' broad experience, is that early industrial involvement as joint venture partners is also very important so that University resources need only be spent or be confined to intellectual property protection rather than significant research/demonstration expenses as was evidenced in our first biochemical project.

The benefits to students and professors are many and often intangible. Many graduate students have moved out of the Centre into excellent industrial jobs and have at the same time enabled the successful transfer of technology. Research within the Chemical Engineering Department now encompasses a very potent blend of pure and applied research and industrial support of the Department of Chemical Engineering has been very significant. For example, complete computer laboratories have been donated to the Department. In conclusion, we believe that a formula has been developed for the effective transfer of technology from the University to industry.

4   References

Moo-Young, M. (1982) Bioconversion of cellulose materials to protein enriched product. Canadian Patent 11 24131.

Forbes, J.F., Jacobson, B.A., Sullivan, G.R. and Rhodes, E. (1984) Model-based control strategies for commercial grain drying systems, Canadian Society for Chemical Engineering Journal, 62, 773.

Wynnyckyj, J.R., Marr, R. and Rhodes, E. (1985) The Waterloo ash monitoring system at Alberta Power's Battle River generating station, Canadian Electrical Association Engineering and Operating Division Transactions, 24, 204-213.

Ling, S.S.M., Mohammodi, N.A. and Rempel, G.L. (1986) Hydrogenation of unsaturated nitriles with internal carbon-carbon double bonds catalyzed by the rhodium complex. Preprints Chemical Institute of Canada, Tenth Symposium on Catalysis, Kingston, Ontario, Canada, 244-247.

The Myth of Technology Transfer

W. Addis

*Department of Construction Management and
Engineering, University of Reading*

Abstract

The author challenges the popular idea that technology transfer between
academic establishments and industry is a valid and viable model for
the process by which engineering knowledge grows and by which engineering progresses. He argues that such a model is a curiously Anglo-Saxon
one, based upon various misconceptions about the nature of technology,
engineering design and progress, and supports this view by reference to
a variety of evidence.

Keywords: Technology, Transfer, Engineering, Progress.

1 Preface

In anticipation of possible misunderstandings, the author would first
like to state that he is aware that much excellent research is
undertaken in universities and that many academics have, usually acting
as private consultants, contributed a great deal to British industry.
He is also aware that many designers have imaginatively 'poached'
materials and techniques from outside their own industry - sometimes
from higher-tech industries. The argument which follows treats not of
individuals, but rather of a variety of cultural and institutionalised
matters which are to be found in Britain.

2 Introduction

The idea of technology transfer is a seductively simple one. It rests
upon the usually unstated principle that technology behaves according
to the physics of field theory - technology potential can be built up
(like charge or temperature) in certain places and the technology will
then tend to flow to areas of lower potential. Thus technology in a
high potential area such as universities, defence industries or
developed countries will naturally find its way to areas of low
potential, such as (respectively) industry, the construction industry
or third world countries. There are, however, several problems with
this model, especially concerning some assumptions upon which it is
based and which usually remain hidden.

The principal fallacy behind the technology transfer myth is that economic forces, which have a dominant influence on who learns which technology and from whom, are absent from the model. It is, however, not the author's wish to pursue this point here; rather to focus on a further fallacy of a more technological and philosophical nature.

The notion that it is both possible and desirable that technology be transferred from the academic environment to industry assumes that the knowledge and techniques which are the products of good academic research work are those which industry wants and is able to exploit. Usually this is not the case. British academics fiercely defend their right to investigate what interests them in the pursuit of science and understanding, irrespective of any practical and economically useful end. This gap between the products of the academic environment and the needs of industry is encountered in many contexts – the volumes of university research reports which sit on shelves gathering dust (along with yet more reports on why they sit gathering dust), the 'uselessness', as perceived by industry, of undergraduates which universities produce, and finally the well-known gap between theory and practice.

3 The Fallacy of the Gap between Theory and Practice

The gap between theory and practice has been written about in the English language with great frequency for at least the last 200 years. Yet, despite so much effort in debate, a viable bridge across this gap today seems as elusive as ever. It would, therefore, appear prudent to examine more carefully the question of how to bridge the gap in order to find out why an answer appears to be so elusive.

The author has argued elsewhere [Addis 1990] that the difficulties arise in the formation of the question itself. To pose the problem in terms of 'theory' and 'practice' is to ask a loaded question which already presumes a certain relationship between the two ideas, a relationship which, upon examination, can be shown to be invalid (in fact, meaningless). Thus, even to seek to bridge the gap is a fundamentally flawed quest.

The author is not alone in addressing this issue. Rankine (a Scot, not an Anglo-Saxon) discussed and virtually solved it in the 1850s, in conceiving a third kind of knowledge, in addition to the empirical and the scientific, which 'transcends' the concepts of theory and practice. More recently the difficulties have been dealt with by drawing upon the German concept of 'Technik' (from the Greek 'techne') which he renders into English as 'the design of artefacts' [Lewin 1981]. Most significantly, the issue was also raised in the highly influential Finneston Report on the engineering profession in Britain. Here, too, the difference between Anglo-Saxons and the rest of Europe was noted:

> It is significant and noteworthy that engineering education in [continental] countries is often provided in specialist institutions ... [which] claim a pedigree originating from the Technische Hochschule and the Grandes Écoles established in the early nineteenth century ... [and which are] based firmly upon the philosophy and concepts of 'Technik' – the synthesis and practical application of knowledge – rather than those of scientific

scholarship...
This [British] view of engineering science as an offshoot or application of science is held to have underlain many of the current criticisms of engineering formation in Britain today; in particular, engineering courses constructed on the basis of teaching first the underlying scientific analysis and theory and then the potential applications of it, build into engineering formation a dichotomy between 'theory' and 'practice'. This dichotomy does not arise in courses built upon the philosophy of 'Technik' which places everything taught firmly in the context of economic purpose. Theoretical teaching is from early on linked to its potential usefulness within the overall theme of an engineering system, be it mechanical, electrical or process... The debate which has continually dogged engineering teachers over the appropriate balance in engineering formation between theory and practice is a non-issue within the continental mode of engineering education. We would hope that our proposals ... will help render it a non-issue in [Britain] too.

[Finneston 1980 p89-90]

Although this report is now having an effect on some of our university engineering courses, it unfortunately did not address the closely-related activity of university-based research. Had it done so, it would surely have had some important recommendations to make.

In Britain, the challenge of bridging the gap is still treated as if it were the Holy Grail. This is so deeply embedded in our culture that hardly anyone now questions the assumption that practice (what happens in industry) has its roots in theory (what happens in universities). Based on the assumption that practice depends upon and follows from theory, it is naturally logical to aim to achieve improvements in industry (practice) by funding research in the theoretical world of the academic environment. This logic becomes suspect, however, when it is realised that there is no direct causal link between the activities of the two different communities of people. Those working in industry – design and production engineers – have fundamentally different aims to academics: the ones work to design and manufacture artefacts, the others to understand and explain the world, be it in the field of physics or engineering science [Bunge 1966, Addis 1990].

Such differences are illuminated by a typical and true example of a structural engineer who approached a university department for some help in analysing and designing a particularly complicated concrete slab floor. After a few quick and simple model tests and some analysis of the results, the designer was able to go away and justify the design of his slab with the necessary confidence. The designer later heard that the university researcher was still investigating the same problem (more thoroughly, no doubt) after the building containing the concrete slab had served many years of useful life and been demolished!

4   Progress in engineering

In addition to the above, there is further evidence that progress in engineering does not, in general, arise from academic research in science or 'applied' science[Ø] followed by some process of technology transfer from universities to industry.

4.1   Two examples from structural engineering

In structural engineering, which has been around for rather longer than many branches of engineering, it is often claimed that the use of engineering science has been prerequisite of all progress in the field. However, such claims are made without a knowledge of the way in which progress actually happened. It is, for instance, often implied (especially to student engineers) that the various branches of structural theory were developed first, and then different types of structure could be designed and built. In fact, there is only one example of a type of structure which was developed theoretically in advance of its use in practice (the hyperbolic paraboloid). All the other structural forms and actions were developed by practising engineers without the aid of academics. Even the most complex structural design, such as the Sydney Opera House, drew very little on academic establishments except for laboratory and computing facilities.

Two different types of progress in structural engineering need to be distinguished. One is the growth of engineering science, usually in the hands of academics. Experimentation in the idealised conditions of laboratories is essential to the development of theories of engineering science. These theories encapsulate (store) the knowledge gained from the experiments in a form which enables it to be retrieved easily. However, on their own, such theories are useless. It is, for instance, astonishing to our modern eyes to find out that the idea of resolving forces, suggested by both Leonardo (late-15th century) and Simon Stevin (late-16th century), was first used to help design a bridge only in the late 1840s. The same was true of much of our modern structural theory which had already been developed by the early 1800s.

It was Rankine, a practising engineer and, later, Professor, who first convincingly showed (in the 1850s) how engineers could use the theoretical products of the academic world. He did this by regarding the mathematical theories of engineering science as models of the real world which were known to be idealised and, therefore, inaccurate, but which could be used if account was taken of the inaccuracies. This he achieved by using an old idea – the 'factor of safety' – in a new way to take account of the possible lack of correspondence between the behaviour of the model and that of the real world. This step, which is arguably the most important step in the history of engineering design, was utterly independent of the work of the engineering scientists.

[Ø]   The term 'science' has gathered an inappropriate, indeed, almost magical power in English which is wholly absent in other languages. London's world famous museum of technology, engineering and science is always known as the Science Museum although its full name is Museum of Science and Industry. The author also tends to view that the very term 'applied science' was invented in order to suggest to grant-giving government bodies the potential usefulness of academic research much in the way as the 1960s saw so many attempts to justify the space race on the strength of the technological spin-off it generated such as non-stick frying pans (see also [Lewin 1981]).

A second example from the 1930s also illustrates how industry shunned the recommendations of the academic community. The Structural Steel Research Committee had been set up to try to introduce more rational methods into the design of steel frame structures. After several years the newly developed methods were tried by a number of designers but rejected because they were far too cumbersome for the required purpose, almost as irrational as the methods they were to replace and resulted in neither cheaper nor safer structures. The scientific research team, had, by and large, failed to understand the difference between the requirements of industry and their own aims as scientists. The impasse was only broken after the war by John Baker and his team who, like Rankine before him, developed a revolutionary way of looking at the problem from the designers' point of view which lead to the plastic or limit-state design methods which are so well-known today [Addis 1990].

4.2 Examples from other engineering disciplines

A host of studies undertaken in the last few decades have demonstrated conclusively that research work in universities does not, in general, lead to progress in industry. The following are a few examples:

- A study of 84 innovations which had helped British industry showed that only one had originated in a university environment (Baker's plastic design methods) [Langrish et al. 1972, Langrish 1974].
- The development of the transistor was not, as is often suggested, a science success story and exemplar of so-called technology transfer from university to industry. In fact, the contribution of the so-called inventor of the transistor was to propose a mathematical model of conduction and rectification which helped industry-based researchers to make new materials and to design experiments which might demonstrate semi-conduction [Gibbons, M. & Johnson, C. 1970].
- A large American study in the late 1960s showed that of all major developments in weapons systems, over 90% originated in industry as technological developments while only 9% originated in applied science departments of universities and 0.3% in pure science departments [Layton 1971]. The project was called Project Hindsight because it conclusively exposed the fallacy behind the tendency for 'science' to be credited retrospectively as the origin or source of engineering progress.

5 Conclusion

Despite the considerable evidence mentioned above, and the work of many other philosophers of technology [Gruber & Marquis 1969, Jobst 1974, Layton 1974, 1976, Price 1965, 1968, Vicenti 1990], our governments continue to accept without question the technology transfer model which is based on the fallacious belief that progress in engineering practice has its origins in engineering and other sciences.

This idea of technology transfer is founded upon a particularly Anglo-Saxon philosophy of knowledge. Many studies have shown the ineffective-ness with which ideas do find their way from British and American universities into industry. Similar problems seem to arise less often in the Continental European system of polytechnics and research institutes founded on the philosophical concept of 'Technik'. Just as engineering education in Britain is moving slowly towards continental models, so should the means by which engineering research is undertaken. This would be helped by choosing not to focus on the fallacious epistemological model which underlies the very idea of Technology Transfer.

References

Addis, W. (1990) **Structural Engineering: the Nature of Theory and Design**, Ellis Horwood, Chichester.

Bunge, M. (1966) Technology as Applied Science, **Technology & Culture, 7**, 329–347.

Finniston, M. (Chairman of Committee) (1980) **Engineering Our Future: Report of the Committee of Inquiry into the Engineering Profession** HMSO, London

Gibbons, M. and Johnson, C. (1970) Relationship between Science and Technology, **Nature, 227**, July 11th, 125–127.

Gruber, W. H., & Marquis, D. G. (Eds.) (1969) **Factors in the Transfer of Technology**, MIT Press, Cambridge (Mass.).

Jobst, E. (1974) Specific Features of Technology in its Interrelation with Natural Science, see [Rapp 1974:124–133].

Langrish, J. (1974) The Changing Relationship between Science and Technology, **Nature, 250**, 614–616.

Langrish, J., Gibbons, M., Evans, W. G. and Jevons, F. R. (1972) **Wealth from Knowledge**, MacMillan, London.

Layton, E. T. (1971) Mirror-Image Twins: The Communities of Science and Technology in 19th Century America, **Technology and Culture, 12**, 562–580.

Layton, E. T. (1974) Technology as Knowledge, **Technology and Culture, 15**, 31–41.

Layton, E. T. (1976) American Ideologies of Science and Engineering, **Technology and Culture, 17**, 688–701.

Lewin, D. (1981) Engineering Philosophy – the Third Culture? **Journal of the Royal Society of Arts, 129**, 653–666

Price, D. J. de S. (1965) Is technology historically independent of science? – A study in statistical historiography, **Technology & Culture, 6** No.4, 553–568.

Price, D. J. de S. (1968) **The difference between Science and Technology**, Thomas Alva Edison Foundation, Detroit.

Rapp, F. (Ed) (1974) **Contributions to a Philosophy of Technology**, Reidel, Dordrecht & Boston.

Vicenti, W. G. (1990) **What Engineers Know and How They Know it**, John Hopkins University Press.

Who Really Benefits From Technology Transfer?

J. Murray (*), A.R. Young (**)

(*) Napier Polytechnic of Edinburgh

(**) Department of Mechanical, Manufacturing and
Software Engineering, Napier Polytechnic of Edinburgh

Abstract

The Department of Mechanical, Manufacturing and Software Engineering at Napier Polytechnic in the last decade has committed a considerable part of its available resources to various aspects of technology transfer. This has included participation in the Teaching Company Scheme (twelve programmes), the establishment of four specialist technology centres, partly funded by the UK Government, and the offer to industry of a wide range of short courses and consultancy.

The paper describes the benefits to an engineering department of involvement in technology transfer, the opportunity costs of this work and the difficulties in formulating strategies which provide an appropriate balance between academic excellence, involvement in technology transfer and the need to generate funds from external sources.

1   Introduction

Academics in departments of engineering in universities and polytechnics in the UK are under pressure to increase the quality of their research and to raise additional funding for their institutions through activities which may be defined as technology transfer.

The UK Government has indicated that future funding to departments will depend on an assessment of the quality of their research and teaching and has also indicated that they see the majority of research funding being concentrated on a small number of prestigious institutions leaving the others to develop industrial or applied research.

The implications of these decisions will have significant effects on the policies to be followed by academic departments. The pressure on staff to publish, particularly in refereed journals, will increase and this could adversely affect the willingness of staff to participate in schemes for technology transfer such as the Teaching Company Scheme and consultancy.

2   Technology Transfer

Napier Polytechnic has had a long history of involvement in technology transfer dating from 1968 and the establishment of a Low Cost Automation Centre based on that of the TNO and the Technical University of Delft. The construction of this laboratory enabled the expertise of academic staff to be used to assist SME's to increase their productivity by automating their processes using pneumatic and electro-mechanical devices.

The Polytechnic further facilitated technology transfer by setting up four specialist technology centres, Computer Aided Engineering Centre, Computer Integrated Manufacturing Centre, Energy Centre and Advanced Materials Centre. These Centres were set up progressively over a five year period from 1980 and received funding from both central and local government This Centre structure has allowed technology transfer to continue and expand through the transmission of the expertise of staff in relevant topics to industry. The Centres also provided a useful vehicle for technology transfer to industry of the results of major SERC funded research projects in areas such as computer integrated manufacture, flexible manufacturing systems, flexible automated assembly systems, advanced materials and computer aided engineering. The Centres are a very successful means of developing formal links with industry particularly in the areas of consultancy and industrial funded research. This work also benefits the academics by providing relevant industrial experience for use in teaching and as a foundation for future research work. Students also benefit as the links develop lead to opportunities for undergraduate students to gain places in industry for periods of supervised work experience. A spin-off from the establishment of the Centres has been the development of a range of postgraduate Masters courses in areas of Advanced Technology, Quality Assurance and Engineering Design.

3   Teaching Company Scheme

Napier Polytechnic took the decision that one of the most effective methods of technology transfer was through the medium of the Teaching Company Scheme and has been an active supporter of the scheme since 1981. Napier Polytechnic's Department of Mechanical, Manufacturing and Software Engineering took the lead in this development. The principal criteria for the establishment of a Teaching Company was that this had to be of mutual advantage to both parties, academia and industry. The research expertise of Napier staff would assist the implementation of new technology and the experience gained by staff would be of direct benefit to teaching of postgraduate and undergraduate courses and provide a focus for future research. Companies with which Napier Polytechnic established Teaching Company Programmes are all engaged in advanced technology and include Marconi Instruments (computer aided production and design methods), Burroughs (computer integrated manufacturing), Cessna (flexible manufacturing systems),Andrew Antenna (advanced materials), Unisys (computer aided engineering), Motorola (computer intergrated manufacture), Motorola (materials management), NCR (computer aided engineering and systems modelling), Laidlaw Drew (computer aided design), Beckman Industrial (quality systems management), Ethicon, (computer integrated manufacture and flexible manufacture), Philips (quality assurance).

These programmes have been implemented by staff from the Department of Mechanical, Manufacturing and Software Engineering but have also involved staff from other disciplines, eg, Management and Mathematics. This has strengthened the interdisciplinary links within the institution and has led to collaboration in the establishment of the Napier Quality Centre and to Teaching Companies by the Departments of Electrical, Electronic and Computer Engineering and Civil and Transportation Engineering.

4   Napier Quality Centre

The Centre was set up to draw together into one coherent organisation the expertise of a large number of academic staff offering research, consultancy and training in all areas relating to quality.

The setting up of this Centre led to additional Teaching Companies and major interdisciplinary research projects, additional consultancy and promotion for a number of the staff involved. The results of the Centres' work has already been incorporated into the teaching of Master's degree courses in the Polytechnic and in particular in the Master's programme quality systems management.

5   Technology and Management Development Unit

Technology transfer also takes place through staff offering specialist short courses either in-company or using the facilities of the institution. The Technology and Management Development Unit has been set up to provide the facilities for short courses and Continuing Professional Education and Development (CPED). The formalising of the short course programme to meet the needs of individuals and the needs of industry has been a great success. The short course programme offered either as part of a general catalogue or as part of a bespoke programme to meet the needs of a company. Short course programmes can be credit rated so that successful completion of the course can make a contribution to an award under the CEPD programme. There are resource difficulties in mounting ambitious short course programmes both in terms of availability of high calibre specialist academic staff and facilities. Great care has to be taken to obtain an appropriate balance between the needs of full time undergraduate and postgraduate students and short course programmes and also to ensure that the workload of academic staff is not too high.

6   Conclusion

The benefits to be gained from a department participating in technology transfer are significant. However there are difficulties in formulating strategies which provide an appropriate balance between academic excellence, involvement in technology transfer and the need to generate funds from external sources. Napier Polytechnic has attempted to address this problem by setting up a Management Committee for its Centre and Teaching Company activities. This committee is chaired by senior industrialists and has a membership of academics and industrialists and is responsible for developing a business plan for the technology transfer work. The business plan carefully considers industry requirements, products or services that can be offered by the Polytechnic, the modes of operation, the management of the activities, the scheduling of the work and the financing of the projects. An important aspect of the business plan is the opportunity costs associated with undertaking particular activities in technology transfer.

However carefully a business plan has been developed there are often considerable hidden costs associated with technology transfer activities. For example, Teaching Company Schemes do not always run smoothly and industrial deadlines have to be met. Senior staff have to spend at least one day per week on the company premises and consequently the time for research is reduced. The Scheme allows for staff to be hired to compensate for the time devoted to the Teaching Company Programme. This invariably means that undergraduate and postgraduate students have less contact with the more experienced staff.

Napier Polytechnic has been successful to date in managing the many demands associated with a vigorous technology transfer programme. The Polytechnic would wish to maintain the balance it has achieved between research, technology transfer and teaching. However, in order for this satisfactory state of affairs to continue it is necessary that criteria used in determining academic funding gives due weighting to technology transfer.

References

Murray, J. & Young, A. R. (1985) Co-operation with industry over the introduction of new technologies, **First National Conference on Production Research**
Murray, Barron & Young (1985) University and college industrial collaboration in Scotland, **SEFI Conference, Madrid.**
Murray, J. (1987) Problems of applying research, **Proceedings of the European Symposium on the results of publicly funded research, Luxembourg.**
Fishwick, W. & Murray, J. (1988) Structures of technological education and contributing social factors, **UNESCO.**
Murray, J. (1988) The role of specialised centres in the development of continuing education, **SEFI Conference, Stuttgart.**
Murray J. (1989) Technology transfer to meet the needs of engineers in computer integrated manufacturing, **Proceedings of the 4th World Conference on Continuing Education, Beijing.**

A Means of Developing Students Managerial and Organisational Skills within the Engineering Curriculum

A. Halstead, J.A. Conlon

Department of Materials, Coventry Polytechnic

Abstract

Managerial, organisational and time management skills are very much an essential requirement for an engineering graduate, but within the confines of the curriculum it is not usually possible to incorporate them.

This paper examines the way in which final year engineering students have directed, supervised and appraised the project work of both individuals and groups of students in earlier years; an activity which can be described by the term proctoring.

The paper looks at the type of project that has been proctored and presents the methodology of the approach, the assessment strategy and beneficial modifications that have been made over the last two years. The enthusiasm and commitment created in this student supported activity seems far greater and more profitable to the individuals learning experience than a staff led excercise; whilst having the hidden benefit of reducing formal staff contact time.

It is clear that this sort of technique could be applied extensively within the curriculum.

Keywords: Proctoring, Groupwork, Student Centred, Materials Engineering, Curriculum Development.

1 Introduction

Proctoring is the helping of less advanced students by more senior students under the guidance of an academic. Experience at other institutions (Button (1987)) and (Button (1990)) has shown that proctoring is particularly suited to workshop, laboratory or project based activities. As the materials engineering component of the BEng Combined Engineering degree (Halstead (1991)) is predominantly project based (Conlon (1991)), this lends

itself to a proctoring activity.   Several schemes of this
nature are currently being run in higher education
intitutes, the two most similar being at Nottingham (Sims
(1990)), and Leicester Polytechnics (Buttery (1990)).
The main difference between the proctoring activities in
these institutes, is that proctors on the Coventry scheme
are not only in the role of a section leader but their
own project work depends on the students in their group
obtaining information for them.   In the other two
Institutions proctors supervise and direct the students
group projects independently.   In this paper the
structure and assessment of the Coventry scheme are
examined along with feedback from both the proctors and
the proctored students, as to the benefits of the
programme.

2 Structure of the Proctoring Scheme

The final year students work in pairs on a major
assignment which is based round a self selected
engineering assembly.   Typical examples are vehicle
bumper assembly, a bicycle wheel, helicopter rotor blades
or as shown in Figure 1, a piston and connecting-rod
assembly.

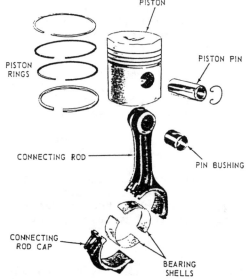

Fig. 1 Piston and Connecting-rod Assembly

After initial research on the assembly with regard to its
function and service requirements the proctors themselves
concentrate on the assembly and finishing processes,
quality control and problems in service whilst assigning
each of the individual parts, for example in Figure 1 the
piston, piston ring, connecting-rod and bearings to
individual second year students. The task for the second
years is to quantify the service requirements of the item
and select three materials from which the part can be
manufactured along with details of the specific
manufacturing routes. Each final year student assumes
responsibility for two second year students and meets
them every fortnight over the first term. The proctor
sets tasks and helps the students to go in the right
direction; effectively organising and managing the time
of the second year student. The proctor encourages the
student to think about the structure of their individual
report and completing the assignment within the pre-
determined time scale.

At the start of the second term the emphasis changes
to group supervision as the groups led by the proctor
discuss which of the materials to select for each item of
the assembly. Materials having been chosen, the second
year group widen their research to look at the structure
and structural changes that take place during
manufacture, to obtain the necessary properties to meet
the service requirements. The proctors know the students
well as individuals and the task in the second stage is
to encourage them to work together as a cohesive group.
A second and final report is due from the second years at
the end of the second term. This marks the end of the
proctoring exercise.

3 Assessment

Over the last two years the weighting of the proctoring
element has increased from 5% to 10% of the module. This
is a result of the scheme being expanded from one to two
terms to incorporate both an individual and group
proctoring activity. Proctors now take an active part in
the assessment and discussion of the performance of the
second year students, whereas initially the mark was
based simply on a final report and interview after a
group proctoring exercise.

The current assessment of the proctoring activity is based on

* assessment and discussion of the   20%
  second year students
* final report   50%
* final interview   30%

This strategy is similar although not as detailed as the scheme proposed by Metcalfe (1991).

During the two terms of the exercise staff meet the students monthly to discuss progress and problems, these meetings are based on a discussion of a proforma that is filled in on each second year student by the proctor after each meeting.

The final report is based round a record of the meetings, problems and progress drawn from the individual proforma's, an assessment of the proctored students individual and group reports, a discussion of how the aims of proctoring have been met and modifications that could be made to the scheme to benefit all students. These aspects are then discussed more fully at a final interview.

4 Observations

All feedback from the proctors to date has indicated that the scheme succeeds in its aim to simulate the role of an industrial section leader group proctor. Prior to meeting the second year students the proctors often feel apprehensive about the situation but seem to visibly grow into it as the students look to them for support and direction. The proctors rapidly come to appreciate how much they have learnt over the three years.

Certain groups run well because of the communication planning and organisation skills of the proctor, where these skills are not as well developed a greater amount of staff advice and direction is required. Some students have a natural ability to bring the best out of individuals and act as a catalyst for the group activity whilst others develop these skills more slowly. All participants gain a tremendous insight into the importance of personalities and how group dynamics influence project work. They see and begin to understand the difficulties of motivating certain students and develop a real appreciation of the difficult task that often faces lecturers.

Students being proctored gain invaluable support and guidance. Observation of the working of groups is much more that of colleagues, with the students asking and exchanging views freely with the proctors. As the proctor/student rapport develops, students take the opportunity to discuss many aspects of the course including both academic, personnal and career choices.

The presence of the proctor gives clear leadership and helps to strengthen the cohesion of the group. Tasks are set within the framework of definite project aims and objectives. The final product being the reports and the importance of the final report is made clear. There is driving force to work at a steady pace throughout rather than condensing work into the last few weeks. This develops the students abilities to organise, plan and manage their time successfully. Feedback on this activity from both years of students has to date been totally supportive.

A comparison between the Coventry scheme and the one running at Leicester Polytechnic shows that there is a significant benefit in organising the proctoring in such a way as to introduce a mutual need between proctored students, who want advice, direction, project management and guidance and the proctors who want the results of the students work as an input to their own project. This provides a sense of urgency and realism which puts a responsibility onto the second year students to turn up and participate which is occasionally lacking in the alternative model.

5 Conclusion

The scheme at Coventry which is now entering its third year is a highly successful example of the benefits of proctoring. As a large proportion of engineering courses have extensive amounts of project work associated with them, it is clear that this technique could be applied extensively within the curriculum benefiting students and staff at all levels.

6 References

Buttery T C (1991) Proctoring - its justification implementation. **Leicester Polytechnic, Department of Engineering. Private Communication.**
Button B L, Metcalfe R, White L (1987) Proctoring Engineering **Perigan 4-8.**
Button B L, Sims R (1990) Explotations in peer tutoring **Oxford Blackwell 110-119 Edited Goodland 5.**
Conlon J A, Halstead A The use of project work in the

assessment of engineering students 91-96 **Innoative teaching in engineering** edited R A Smith.

Halstead A, Conlon J A (1991) The teaching of materials selection and service failure to engineers 415-420 **Innovative teaching in engineering edited R A Smith.**

Metcalfe R (1991) The assessment of proctoring A E T T Conference **Polytechnic of Wales.**

Sims R (1990) Current developments in proctoring A student learning experience **Conference proctoring at Nottingham Polytechnic.**

Student Management of Systems Monitoring and Diagnosis Projects within the Industrial Enviroment

B.K.N. Rao, M. Ross, C. Tite

Technology School, Southampton Institute

Abstract
The involvement of total quality awareness, project management, JIT and communication skills are discussed in connection with a funded one year post-graduate course in Systems Monitoring and Diagnosis.
Key Words: Communication, Condition Monitoring, JIT, Prince, Project Management, Total Quality.

1 Introduction

The one year post graduate course in Systems Monitoring and Diagnosis, which is unique within the UK, was started in 1991, and has completed a successful cohort of students at Southampton Institute, Rao (1991, 1988a, 1988b, 1987). The funding of the course is from Hampshire TEC. It is required that students should have had formal education in one of the engineering disciplines, together with suitable industrial experience. The students were therefore mainly mature, and all male, in the first cohort. In order to receive grants, the students had to be unemployed. Additional students, either paying their own fees or receiving other grants, could also join the course. The aim, from the view of the sponsors, was for students to be employable by industry, either on completion of the course, or by the nature of the course, during the course. Some of the students left the course, to commence employment, in the field of condition monitoring. These students are able to complete the final modules and project at a later date, via part time study. The remaining students have now successfully completed the course and have been awarded the Post-graduate Diploma in Systems Monitoring and Diagnosis.

2 Course Structure and Content

The Post-graduate Diploma course is structured on a modular basis involving full time attendence over a 46 week period. The final module incorporates a supervised sixteen weeks industrial/Institute based project.
Each module is independently designed under the common theme 'Systems Monitoring and Diagnosis'. These modules offer the conceptual, critical, technical and managerial contents of a postgraduate education demanded by industrial sectors. The teaching and

learning strategies employed are designed to complement the multi-disciplinary nature of the course. These include lectures, some by invited speakers, tutorials, laboratory work, equipment and software demonstrations, simulation, role playing exercises, mini-projects, case studies and industrial visits.

A broad outline of the course structure is given below:-

Module 1 Balancing Studies and Introduction to Systems Studies.

The theme for this module is to revise and, where necessary, to introduce the fundamental concepts of engineering, management and manufacturing systems, together with the required mathematical knowledge, to enable the student to apply and expand on them in subsequent modules. The module is also used as a diagnostic tool to evaluate the suitability of the student for progression to the remainder of the course, and includes mini-projects and industrial visits. The philosophy of this six week module is to broaden the fundamental concepts of systems thinking, organisation and its behaviour dynamics and to enable the students to understand and appreciate the structure of engineering and manufacturing systems.

The outline syllabus includes revision of basic engineering and manufacturing concepts - Manufacturing organisation and systems - Computers in Engineering and Manufacturing - Systems modelling.

The assessment consists of two integrative assignments and a two hour written assessment ("open book" type). A similar assessment strategy is used for module 2, 3 and 4.

Module 2 Principles and Practices of Condition Monitoring Technology

Condition Monitoring is a concept which involves the routine acquisition of data which are related to the mechanical and operational condition of plant and machinery. Subsequent analysis and interpretation of these data can provide information as to current and future mechanical/operational 'health' of the machine. The theme of this six week module is to give the students an appreciation of the technologies available to effectively monitor, predict and control the undesirable conditions and the achievement of maximum cost benefits.

The outline syllabus includes cost-effective benefits - Instrumentation Technology - Vibration Condition Monitoring - Noise Monitoring - Corrosion Monitoring - Machine Tool Wear Monitoring.

Module 3 Principles and Practices of Diagnostic Technology

The philosophy of this six week module is to investigate why and how failures occur in engineering and manufacturing systems, and to apply the knowledge and skills necessary to diagnose the causes of various failures with a view to improving the overall performance and safety at an optimum cost.

The syllabus includes causes and effects of Engineering failures - Failure detection and Monitoring techniques - Metallurgical failures and their diagnosis - NDT techniques and case studies.

Module 4   Principles and Practices of Integrated Maintenance Management

This module provides an introduction to the importance of maintenance management in today's highly competitive industrial environment. Through an examination of the current maintenance management theories and the use of mini-projects and case studies, this module encourages the student to come to grips with managing the maintenance function effectively, efficiently and safely.

The philosophy of this six week module is to highlight the potential benefits of integrative maintenance management in today's engineering and manufacturing industries and to acquire the latest knowledge and the techniques and strategies employed to enhance the total quality of operating systems and to fully exploit the useful life of such systems to one's own advantages.

The outline syllabus includes Maintenance Planning and Organisation-Reliability Centered Maintenance - Maintenance Audit - Total Productive Maintenance - Maintenance Methods - Cost Effective Benefits.

Module 5   Principles and Practices of Total Quality

During this six week module, students learn to consider ways of improving effectiveness, flexibility and competitiveness of business activities through arrangement of resources with a Total Quality approach.

The syllabus includes managing in an Engineering Environment - Total Quality Management - Factors affecting the Business Environment - Project Management. The assessment for this module involves seminar presentations, simulation and role playing exercise, library assignments presentations and case study presentations.

Module 6   Industry Based Projects

In this sixteen week final module, the student carries out a carefully selected specialised project, generally based on engineering and manufacturing systems. The final project is a vehicle which enables integration of information covered in each of the taught modules. These projects are industry oriented and are supervised by both internal and industrial supervisors.

The following are some of the final projects:-

Solving problems with the manufacturing of carburetors; An investigation into the detection of rolling element bearing failure using envelope signal processing; Speculative failure mode and criticality analysis for a 4-stage, 50mm stroke, air gas compressor; Interceptor project; Implementation of an improved manufacturing cost system.

3   Total Quality

Total Quality is seen as a central theme of the course, and in addition to integrating the concept of quality into the modules, one of the modules (Module 5) is specifically dedicated to total quality. The

students are introduced to the need for and benefits of quality
assurance, including the BS 5750, ISO 9000, EN 29000 quality standards.
The concept of TQM is also viewed as an important aspect of this
module, as the skills and ideas that the students develop on the course
will be within the year, taken into industry. The majority of the
students are expected to attain managerial positions within their
future industries, and the training that they receive will have a
direct effect on their future performance, and those of their
employees.

4   Project Management

With the emphasis on mini and final projects the need to encourage a
structured approach to project management was required. The CCTA chose
the project management methodology, Prince, as the successor to Prompt,
as the preferred method for government projects,CCTA (1990). This
methodology is new widely used in the industrial sector. Prince was
identified as a suitable method for inclusion on this course,
particularly with its strong emphasis on total quality, Ross (1991).
   The method depends on the involvement, both at project board level,
and on the project assurance teams of representatives of the business,
the user department and the technical department.
   The project is divided into stages each led by a stage manager under
the overall guidance of a project manager. Within each stage
activities are identified, which are represented on a technical plan,
showing the relative dependences start and expected completion dates.
In addition to this Gantt like diagram, a resource plan is produced,
showing the costs in time and money of the different phases of a stage,
and of the overall stages, via a spreadsheet structure. These diagrams
provide a clear, visual understanding of the progression through a
project, for use both by the project manager and project board. The
requirement to ensure that a quality review is undertaken at the
completion of the various activities, by the project assurance team,
and to maintain a quality file, ensures that quality remains a major
consideration for the project.
   This project management methodology is used by the students, to
assist with their current mini and final projects. For experience, the
student is asked to provide a project plan for a completed mini
project, or actual industrial project, using the benefit of hind sight.
This is used as a basis for discussion on the advantages or otherwise,
of having a more structured approach to project management. Problems
that had occured with the actual project were discussed, and their
possible earlier identification using Prince was considered. The
formal approach for request for change procedures was seen as a major
advance of this method. Students were asked to use Prince plans for
their major project. The concept of formal stages, involving their
project and course supervisors, was seen as a major advantage, together
with the detailed identification of the activities, with the predicted
duration, required for each stage of the project. The need to identify
the methods of quality assurance, prior to the start of the project,
was also seen to be of benefit by the students, as a means of keeping
their project on the current track and on target for the official
completion date.

5   Just In Time

Since students are expected to attain managerial position in their
future employment, it is important to introduce management concepts
during the course, Macbeth (1989).

The JIT philosophy features as part of module 5. Explanation of the
JIT philosophy is covered in lectures and the information is assessed
by written assignment and a role play exercise. Students are placed in
a situation which is relevant to industry, and given roles within a
company structure, such as managers responsible for Production Control,
Sales and Marketing, Quality, Design Engineering, Personnel Finance,
Purchasing and Stores.

A scenario is outlined which involves the introduction of JIT into the
company. The students are given time to absorb the background
information which is given for the role play situation. A summary of
information on various areas of the company is given, which covers
Production, Production Control, Production Engineering (Planning Method
Sheets, Tooling and Methods), Purchasing and Stores, Sales and
Marketing, Quality, Personnel, Finance, Design Engineering, and list of
Standard Products with unit cost, together with total values profit of
each.

In addition, a synopsis of the trading year is given which outlines
the financial health of the company. The students are asked to
explain, in role, how the introduction of JIT will affect the company
from their viewpoint, and argue the case as to whether its introduction
will be beneficial for the company as a whole. If so, then they need
to persuade others how it can be implemented, and what effect it will
have on production and profit.

6   Communication

The need for communication skills is an essential requirement for a
student of condition monitoring. They are expected to present the
results of their mini-projects, throughout the course, and as their
final project is normally industry based, there is an additional
requirement for presentation and interviewing skills. These skills are
enhanced during the fifth module, when the students present their
project plans, for peer and self review. These presentations are
recorded by video, and a playback session is arranged, when suggestions
are made to improve their self presentation, use of visual aids, and
the structure and timing of their presentation.

7   Benefits of the Course

The new and novel PgD course in Systems Monitoring and Diagnosis is now
successfully running at the Southampton Insitute, since 1991. The aim
of this course is (a) to produce able, clear thinking and resourceful
post graduates who have undertaken a programme of advanced study in the
science, engineering, technology and management of Systems Monitoring
and Diagnosis, (b) to enable graduates from many backgrounds to further
a valuable and interesting career in industry and (c) to equip
graduates to make wider and more varied contribution to industry than
is normally possible with traditional engineering and/or management
courses. The initial reaction to this course from students,
industrialists and academic is very encouraging.

8 Conclusion

Condition monitoring and diagnostic engineering management is a fast emerging multi-discipline. The Engineering Council, see FEU/EC (1988), the House of Lords, Equipment manufacturers, the Technical Education Council and major professional institutions have recognised and stressed the importance of multi-disciplinary education and training in all technological disciplines, to meet the growing demands of the industry. A recent survey has shown that judicious implementation of this technology would bring significant cost-effective benefits to all sectors of industry.

Judging from the reaction of the students, invited lecturers and the industrialists, this course has great potential and has benefitted them all.

References

Rao BKN (1991) A new and Novel Postgraduate Diploma in Systems Monitoring and Diagnosis, in Proceedings of the third International Congress on Condition Monitoring and Diagnostic Engineering Management, (ed BKN Rao and AD Hope) Adam Hilger.

Rao BKN (1988) COMADEM - A Novel Education and Training Discipline, in Proceedings of the sixth British Conference on the Teaching of Vibration and Noise, Sheffield Polytechnic.

Rao BKN (1988) Design of a Continuing Education Development programme on Condition Monitoring and Diagnostic Engineering Mangement Discipline, in Proceedings of the International Symposium on Trends in Control and Measurement Education,University College Swansea.

Rao BKN (1987) Educational Needs in Condition Monitoring and Diagnostic Engineering management (COMADEM), Journal of Measurement and Control, Volume 19.

CCTA (1990) Prince Guides, NCC/Blackwell

Ross M (1991) Application of the PRINCE Methodology to Condition Monitoring in Proceedings of the third International Congress on Condition Monitoring and Diagnostic Engineering Management.

Macbeth, DK (1989) Advanced Manufacturing - Strategy of Management, IFS Publications.

FEU/EC (1988) The Further Education Unit and the Engineering Council. An occasional paper, 'The Key Technologies - Some Implementations for Education and Training'.

Innovative Solution to the Shortage of Manufacturing Engineers - the BIBS (Hons) Degree Approach to Manufacturing Systems Engineering

R. Rue, I. Christison

School of Engineering/Leicester Business School, Leicester Polytechnic (De Montfort University - Designate)

1   Introduction

Abstract
The paper describes the highly successful design, marketing and implementation of an innovative solution to the industry requirement for Engineers with Business acumen, significantly financial awareness. This response is in recognition of the shortfall in a new area of engineering, Manufacturing Systems Engineers, originally identified by industry and subsequently by government. This has been successfully answered at Leicester Polytechnic by the BSc (Hons) INDUSTRIAL AND BUSINESS SYSTEMS (BIBS) degree. (G.E.C. - Manufacturing Systems Prize 1990).

A brief history of the degree course, in which the strategy is used, is given together with the experience gained over 5 years of operation. Advantages and disadvantages of the techniques used are presented.

Keywords: M.S.E., Innovation, Integration, Case modules, Business acumen.

The paper describes the strategies adopted to develop multi-discipline abilities in a new type of engineer where traditionally engineers have not been receptive to business material. The strategies described have been highly successful in motivating students and producing graduates who are able to operate in both the technological and financial sectors of manufacturing industry.

In 1987 Leicester Polytechnic launched a new initiative in engineering undergraduate courses. The BSc (Hons) INDUSTRIAL & BUSINESS SYSTEMS degree (BIBS) was specifically designed to produce graduates who could interface between the technological and commercial activities within a manufacturing organisation. The degree was also structured so that a wider range of 'A' level applicants could be attracted.

Since the first intake of 60 students in 1987 over 400 students have enrolled onto the course with nearly 100 of these being female, the intake target for 1992 bringing the overall number of students to 500.

Industrial support has grown to a level such that the 100 or more third year students are now placed yearly with over 60 major companies who have offered sandwich placement both in the UK and on mainland Europe.

A key feature of the BIBS success is the innovation of a new 'teaching and learning' strategy, particularly adopted for the first year of the degree, where six theme targeted 'Case Modules' are used to produce a totally integrated overview of both engineering and commercial activities within a manufacturing company.   In this way students are stimulated to acquire engineering knowledge and Business/Accounting skills .

2   Teaching & Learning Strategy

A further success has come from the deliberate use of 'student centred' learning material to produce students with good communication and inter-personal skills, particularly relevant for professions not normally noted for these qualities.

Throughout the whole course a totally integrative and inter-active programme has only been brought about through team teaching with enthusiasm and flexibility between what were previously significant lines of demarcation.

3   Technology & Business Studies

The integration of multi-discipline studies has been approached in a number of different ways.   Traditionally the integration has been largely left to the student with the course curriculum being mainly composed of standard engineering subjects and standard business studies topics, usually in a 'bolt-on' structure.

The course team, composed of staff from both the Engineering School and the Business School, decided early on in the planning stages of BIBS that not only would a positive approach be taken to produce a genuinely integrated course but that a innovative approach would be needed to be taken with the teaching and learning strategy.

The strategy adopted was based on the well documented observation that students are better motivated and hence learn more if they are actively involved in the teaching process.   It was decided therefore that the first year of the course should be largely based on 'assignment-led' teaching modules.

Additionally it was recognised that because of the wider 'A' level spectrum and a wider range of student aspirations, the traditional method of presentation of material could demotivate many students.   Therefore the first year curriculum was designed to introduce the Technology/Business areas to the students on a 'need to know' basis.   This was achieved by focusing the studies in Year 1 of the course on the 'Business of Manufacturing in a consumer-led environment' in the form of a number of free standing Case Modules.   In this way it was anticipated that students would, and in the event, have to be seen to, develop Engineering knowledge and Business acumen.

3.1 Teaching Strategy - The Case Module Approach - (Year 1)
The Case Module is a free standing period of study in which a particular aspect of the 'Business of Manufacturing' is explored e.g. Business environment, Manufacturing environment. The Modules comprise of a mixture of case material lectures, industrial visits and uses a whole range of assignments/assessments methods.

The case modules provide a learning vehicle which enables general principles to be demonstrated together with an opportunity to expose students to the complexities involved in 'real' situations.

3.2 Teaching Methodology
The use of case material within a module, may on occasions illustrate principles but more often it is used as a means by which students can derive principles e.g. The Industrial Environment. The student is required to understand the facts of a case and then perform, individually or as a member of a team, the task of inducing from those facts one or more principles.

Essential to the Case Module approach is the parallel development of a pre-determined body of knowledge and skills.

The case module themes have been specifically chosen to ensure that this knowledge and skills base will be covered in a progressive and logical manner. Each Case Module systematically prepares the ground for successive studies in future years.

4   Case Modules (Year 1)

Aims

The aims of case modules are:
-    To provide the essential background knowledge and understanding of the opportunities for the use of technology/business principles.
-    To provide an awareness of sources of relevant information.
-    To develop skills in written and oral presentation.
-    To provide an insight into the interaction of individuals, organisations and the state in a manufacturing environment.

4.1 Philosophy of Case Modules
The primary aim of the Case Modules is to ensure that students are enabled to acquire appropriate knowledge and skills in a framework which emphasises the inter-disciplinary nature of industrial activity i.e. the first three Case Modules are presented sequentially, the Environment of Business, the Feasibility of Business, Operating a Business and are significantly based on the production of a Business Plan. The latter three modules are concerned with the Design, Manufacture and marketing of the product.

It will be obvious why the modules are presented in this specific order to take the student from a consideration of the business and industrial environment in which a business has to operate, to the skills and knowledge needed to actually operate a manufacturing company.   With each of the above modules material drawn from many and diverse disciplines are needed to introduce and develop sub themes of an inter-disciplinary nature.

5   Experience of Approach

At the time of initial validation, anxiety was expressed that the course might result in students acquiring 'bits' of knowledge from several disciplines rather than seeing the discipline as a coherent whole.   The course objective cannot be successfully achieved by presenting material in the traditional subject format and then allowing the students to do "their own integration".

The proposed method of delivery was also complementary in that it enables students from a broad range of 'A' level backgrounds to immediately demonstrate their individual experience and competence to contribute to group work.

The Case Modules are extremely student-centred in their approach to the learning process, indeed emphasis has been given to the process of learning as well as the content.

An emphasis has been placed on skills-development. Oral communication skill, analytical skills, report writing skill, problem solving skills, negotiating skills, quantitative skills, design and visual awareness.

The emphasis on skills has been clearly reflected in the nature of the assignments, which have been used not only as a means of testing but as an integral part of the total learning experience. Recognition has been given to the increasing importance within industry of team work and group decision-making.   Thus approximately 40%/50% of the time allocation in the modules has been allocated to creative group work.

Visits are organised to local industrial and commercial organisations.   Such visits are fully integrated into the teaching-learning strategy.   External speakers from the industrial sector have made various inputs into the delivery of the course. Case Studies have figured prominently within each of the Case Modules.   e.g. Organisational structure, market segmentation, wage negotiations, financial environment, manufacturing system, business planning, design methodology, industrial location. In all cases the case material has been complemented by a more formal input of knowledge, thus encouraging the student to perceive the relationship between, the "specific" and the "general".

Having been 'turned on' and stimulated to the need for a multi-discipline this interest and understanding has been observed to continue throughout the remaining two academic years of the course. These are taught in a more formal structure in this approach to manufacturing but still with the use of the Case Study approach.

5.1 Evaluation

There have been several approaches to the evaluation of the degree, eg. student questionnaires. Generally the feedback from the students has been both positive and encouraging. Notwithstanding this a minority of students in the first year of the course's operation did suggest that a little more coherence was necessary. In order to respond to this comment, while maintaining the integrity of the intergrative approach, the Case Module team strengthened the integrative links. More care has also been given to the method of introducing the Case Modules in order that students could themselves be even more clearly aware of the primary aims and objectives.

6   Conclusions

B.Sc.(HONS.) INDUSTRIAL AND BUSINESS SYSTEMS (BIBS) was specifically designed to encourage applications from students who had a wider range of 'A' level than for conventional engineering courses, especially women who traditionally are not attracted to engineering.

Five years experience of operating the scheme on classes of up to 150 students, has indicated that the strategy is highly successful. Students show increased motivation, broader understanding of manufacturing systems and a greater awareness of the role of finance/business in the manufacturing sector.

6.1 The Teaching & Learning Processes
The Learning Process

Advantages
- there is greater understanding of the role of the engineer in manufacturing industry.
- in general there is an increased rate of students' participation in the learning process.
- students become more familiar with sources of information, e.g. library, databases.
- there is a noticeable increase in the abilities of students in 'transferable skills'.

Disadvantages
- students are not in general, as well grounded in 'fundamental' material as on a conventional course.
- students dislike 'group work' where not all the individuals contribute and hence can become demotivated unless carefully monitored.

The Teaching Process

Advantages   - technique is particularly suitable for large
                  cohorts of students.
                - support can be given to tutorials/seminars as
                  and when required.
                - flexible curriculum encourages staff to
                  develop different teaching techniques.
                - good staff development through team teaching
                  across discipline areas.
Disadvantages   - overall organisation is more complex than for
                  a conventional course structure.
                - places more pressure on resources e.g.
                  library, computing facilities, tutorial rooms.
                - assignments require a great deal of pre-
                  preparation and support material.

6.2 Staff Development

The involvement of staff in interdiscipline teaching has required additional staff development.   Industrial consultancy, research and Teaching company projects have all been used to enhance the development process.

A Teaching Company Research Project with an Automotive Engineering Company which involved the transfer of 'Ownership' of the Accounting Information to the 'Engineer Users' has fully validated the principles inculcated in the BIBS degree.

It has shown that if a change of 'Ownership' from producers to users is to be fully achieved the information must be presented in a 'User friendly' fashion that Engineers are happy to accept. Significantly there must be a change in the traditional manner in which this has to be done.

To complement this and improve efficiency in Industry, that there has to be a new approach, as is being achieved in the BIBS degree, in the Teaching and Learning process, which fully confirms the innovations already in place in this degree.

Overall the strategies described have been highly successful in motivating students and producing graduates who are able to operate in both the technological and financial sectors of manufacturing industry.

References

Rue, R. Christison, I. (1991).   Innovative Teaching in Engineering,   Conference, Sheffield University.
Knight, J.A.G. (1991).   Engineers being taught Business, article in The Sunday Times (April 7).
Christison, I. Rue, R. (1992) Innovative teaching of Accounting to Engineers. - British Accounting Association National Conference, Warwick University.

FLEET: A New Approach to Training Professional Engineers

S.J.A. Curr

Rolls-Royce and Associates Limited, Derby

Abstract

This paper describes a novel approach to the development of young professional engineers in an industrial environment. It extends traditional industrial training practices in a way that stimulates rapid development of the full range of supplementary skills that are demanded of a rounded engineer in a modern engineering company.

Keywords: Training

1 Introduction

Rolls-Royce and Associates Limited have, for many years, operated a number of highly successful training schemes for young people. These involve not only graduate engineers, but all levels of staff from basic clerical support upwards. At any one time there are typically over 100 trainees at various stages of development. The bulk of these are undergraduate or graduate engineers, or technician engineer apprentices.

Until recently the training offered followed a traditional approach which blended off the job training into a core programme of line attachments. These involved a student spending 10 - 12 week stints working alongside experienced engineers in various departments, following a plan agreed between the training staff and the trainee's company mentor. This approach was fine for developing skills related to a particular aspect of our business, especially technical skills. It could give a good knowledge of, and experience in, the company's organisation, practical engineering skills, plant operation, modern methodologies and calculational techniques, etc. However, a major drawback was that many attachments inevitably had a narrow focus. Also, it ran a continuous risk that training could degenerate into 'sitting with Nellie'.

In the late 1980s we revisited the objectives of our trainee programmes in the light of changing signals from academia and the engineering institutions. Most important, however, was a growing realisation that this approach was becoming increasingly divorced from the role of the engineer within our business.

Our environment was changing. Industry was becoming leaner; organisations were having to become more flexible and responsive; management structures were being delayered and individual responsibilities increased. Engineers were increasingly having to work in dynamic multi-disciplinary teams, and were having to take on increased engineering and commercial responsibilities earlier. The old approach was weak in developing commercial, interpersonal and managerial skills that had become increasingly important for engineers within RRA. Also, it offered little scope for individuals to take responsibility and show initiative during training. A new approach was required that would address these issues whilst maintaining the level of technical skills and experience that the company needs.

2 The FLEET Scheme

In 1989 FLEET was born. FLEET stands for Flexible Local Engineering Enterprise Training. It is designed to be flexible, meeting the evolving needs of the company as well as the local needs of each individual. It is still very much to do with engineering but now also incorporates a strong element of business or enterprise training.

FLEET comprises two main elements (figure 1). The first extends the traditional approach of attachments, courses and external secondments. The benefits of this approach are still valid, and it still provides important Tailored Industrial Experience (TIE). The second element is new and involves training through Applied Business and Engineering Enterprise Teams (ABEET). ABEET provides an environment where trainees operate in small multi-disciplinary team where they are responsible, within a training framework, for marketing their skills and resources, tendering for contracts, planning, costing and executing projects for real customers against real time, cost and quality targets and with real resource constraints; they operate as a company within a company.

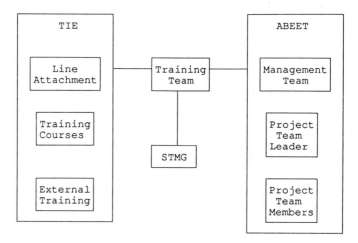

Figure 1 Flexible Local Engineering Enterprise Training

The project teams would comprise graduate and undergraduate engineers and scientists, plus clerical, technician and commercial trainees where appropriate, and have their own management hierarchy. Teams would be large enough to offer a mix of skills and personalities, but small enough for the impact of individuals to be directly visible on both the technical and financial results. All would be required to make judgements and take decisions that would influence the outcome of a project.

The benefits envisaged that FLEET would yield for both the individual trainees and the company are summarised in Figure 2.

```
For the Students                      For the Company
·  Engineering experience          ·   Commercial awareness
   alongside professional          ·   Broader, more mature young
   engineers                           engineers
·  Product awareness               ·   Increased teamwork across
·  Commercial environment              skill boundaries
·  Business awareness              ·   Complete projects undertaken
·  Management training             ·   Quality awareness
·  Interpersonal skills            ·   Increased trainee motivation
   development                     ·   Bottom-up influence on
·  Design and manufacture              company culture
·  Quality in engineering
·  Responsibility and job
   satisfaction
```

Figure 2 FLEET: Foreseen benefits

3 The Operation of FLEET

There are two bodies involved in the overall control of the training process within FLEET. The first is my training team, which administers the training process and ensures that it remains in-line with corporate objectives. The second is the Student Training Monitoring Group (STMG). There is, in fact, a separate STMG for each trainee comprising the student, his/her mentor and a professional trainer. It meets at the start of a trainee's career to set objectives and define a training plan, and again at key stages to review progress and revise the plan as necessary. This group will determine the balance between line and ABEET attachments and their relative timing, although typically a trainee will not join a project team until they have had at least one line attachment.

The structure of ABEET is shown in figure 3, and the main elements are discussed below.

At the heart of ABEET is the Management Team, made up of a Leader plus a team of up to three supporting trainees. It is responsible for marketing, costing and estimating, tendering, contract planning, resource management (manpower, finance, equipment and time), monitoring and quality assurance. It interfaces with the FLEET Board, customers, quality staff, consultants and the Project Team. Each project will be the specific responsibility of one management team member, and the whole team meets formally once a week with a member of the training staff.

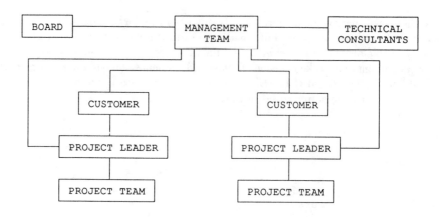

Figure 3: ABEET Structure

Four engineering managers chaired by the Training and Development Manager act in the role of a 'Board of Directors' for ABEET. They meet once a month with the Management Team Leader and are tasked to vet all proposed projects and contracts against the FLEET objectives and capabilities, approve budgets for contracts and oversee the monitoring of projects, set objectives for the Management Team, and generally play 'devils advocate'.

Some of the projects undertaken by ABEET have been of a highly technical nature and the availability of expert guidance has been crucial. This is provided by the group of mentors appointed for the trainee body as a whole acting as Technical Consultants.

A Project Leader is appointed to manage the day to day running of each project. He or she ensures that deadlines are met, and is the main point of contact with the customer while the project is live. The Project Leader is also an active member of the Project Team. Project Teams are typically 3 - 6 trainees of mixed discipline, type and experience. They are selected jointly by the Management Team and Training Staff, who match individual objectives with available Project Team roles. It can be seen that there is a natural progression that can be followed within FLEET, from Project Team Member through to Management Team Leader.

The role of the customer is vitally important, and is intended to mirror closely a true commercial relationship; it is not a supervisory role. It is the customer's responsibility to specify a suitable project, negotiate a contract with the Management Team, specifying milestones and deliverables. They must ultimately assess the success of the project in terms of the deliverables specified.

Customers are not expected to provide detailed technical supervision, but are expected to recognise that Project Teams are not just cheap labour. They must recognise that there are training objectives to be met as well as project deliverables, and these may at times be hard to reconcile. At the very least projects must require of the team good communications, teamwork, negotiation, problem analysis and solving, making and evaluating judgements, time management and resource control. They should be multidisciplinary and involve 20 - 50 man weeks of work.

Because the role of customer is a complex one, potential customers are given talked through detailed guidelines by a member of the Management Team when they first approach FLEET.

In addition to monitoring that occurs through the regular Management Team and Board Meetings (both of which involve training staff), there is routine contact between individual trainees and mentors, and periodic STMGs. Also, the teamwork and interpersonal aspects are reviewed in depth with the Project Team and relevant Management Team member by training staff at the end of each project, or earlier if judged necessary. These reviews have a contract of confidentiality, and frank, open and honest debate of individual and team performance is encouraged.

Overall there is a comprehensive framework of review by peers, mentors, training professionals and, through the Board, line management.

4 The Launch of FLEET

From the initial concept and a broad outline, a high level of responsibility for the design and development of FLEET has lain with the trainees themselves. This was tackled with vigour. Within six months detailed proposals had been worked up and consultation had taken place with nine engineering institutions, the main body of trainees, mentors, key managers and other staff. Initial marketing had been undertaken and pilot projects identified. Within twelve months two pilot projects had been completed and subjected to detailed evaluation by company training staff. Some problems were encountered, but these were not insurmountable, and the results led to the firm decision to implement the scheme fully in September 1990.

In its first eighteen months, FLEET has undertaken nineteen projects and rejected over forty. Many of those completed have involved innovative technologies and provided a high level of technical challenge for those involved. In most cases FLEET has exceeded our expectations in terms of the development of individual trainees. It has unquestionably allowed many to broaden both technical and other skills at a rate that was not possible before. It has also increased the involvement of mentors and line managers.

However, as indicated earlier, problems have been encountered. Those remaining fall into three broad categories. First, it has been difficult at times to ensure that proposed projects and available trainees are in line and that training objectives are correctly addressed. This requires constant attention from the training staff who oversee the scheme. Secondly, there have been times when the customer has attempted to act as close technical Supervisor and Project Manager.

This has tested the negotiating and interpersonal skills of trainees quite severely at times. Finally, exiting from a project team into a line attachment or final placement can be a difficult transition. Trainees have become accustomed to the responsibility and autonomy that ABEET gives them only to find that this is not immediately forthcoming when they move on. We encourage them to demand it.

For the future, there will undoubtedly be a continued refinement of the way in which FLEET operates, but the only major change planned is to extend its scope to staff who are not on a formal training scheme.

5 Conclusions

The introduction of FLEET has marked a significant change in the way in which RRA develops its young engineers, making it more relevant to the engineers role within our company. It has promoted the development of a whole range of supplementary skills required by rounded engineers, and has encouraged individual responsibility. From the outset there has been a strong sense of ownership towards the scheme amongst the trainee population, and a consequent high degree of motivation and commitment to both project and training aspects. The success of FLEET to date has already led to an increase in the motivation, flexibility, effectiveness and commercial awareness of new engineers. It has raised their expectations and enabled them to develop at a greater speed than has previously been possible.

IASI Project - A Technology Transfer Model for Industry-University Partnership

A. Adascalitei (*), P. Lindon (**), V. Belousov (***), M. Gafiteanu (***)

(*) International Centre for Engineering Education, Iasi
(**) Contract Education, University of Sussex, Brighton
(***) Iasi Polytechnic Institute, Iasi

Abstract
The objective of the Iasi Project is to restructure and extend the educational and training capacities of the Iasi Polytechnic Institute to facilitate economic regeneration within the Iasi Region (North-East Romania). The goals of the Iasi Project conform to the TEMPUS (Trans-European Mobility Scheme for Universities Studies) priorities.

Elements critical to university-industry partnership in Romania, in a European context start-up are discussed. These address especially: the composition of management, the planning process, and funding alternatives.

Keywords: University-Industry Partnership, Transfer of Technology and Training, Computer-Aided Learning, Distance Learning, Management and Environmental Education.

1 Introduction

The Iasi region of Romania is in the north-eastern part of the country bordering the Republic of Moldova, characterized by a mixed economy of agriculture and heavy industry. The town of Iasi has a population of half a million inhabitants and is situated six hundred kilometres from Bucharest. It is a cultural as well as an industrial centre and was, for a brief period in the recent history, the capital of the country.

The principal source of higher education and training is the Polytechnic Institute of Iasi (hereafter referred to as Iasi Polytechnic) which has fourteen thousand full-time students who study subjects in the traditional technology divisions. Two universities within the region, at Bacau and Suceava, are more recent additions to the higher education scene and were initiated from within Iasi Polytechnic. The region is therefore well served by an educational network which can act as an effective springboard for change.

The project has arisen from a local collaboration between Government, Higher Education and Industry, from which has emerged the "Iasi Consortium for Transfer of Technology and Training" (ICTTT). This body, with initial representation by Iasi Polytechnic, the Prefecture of the Iasi county, the Iasi Chamber of Commerce and Industry, and FORTUS S.A., a heavy enegineering company, has now been recognised by the Romanian government and exists as an organisation which may enter into partnerships with other national and international agencies. The Iasi Project will be the first example of such international collaboration, in this case with the University of Sussex at Brighton, UK.

2 Objectives

The Romanian economy requires a considerable development of its capacity to operate within a capital market environment. The Iasi Project intervenes by creating a platform of self-development, training and technology transfer, upon which investment and industrial development can be achieved, according to regional aspirations.

The Project is based on the fundamental principle that all developmental activities and outcomes will be Romanian owned except where joint ventures in the educational or business arenas can be created. The intention behind this policy is that confidence on the Romanian side in project developments may be secured and maintained, and that the process of development, because Romanian participate fully in design, has the continuing effect of maximising the effects of the creative process and securing commitment to the objectives. It is important therefore that those involved on the EC side are sensitive to cultural and historical differences, respect the basis from which change is being made and gain rewards from the process rather than anticipate preconceived outcomes. In short, the role of EC/EFTA collaborators in this project is to support a process of self-development by questioning, proposing and negotiating. Professor Belousov's work at Iasi Polytechnic on creativity and innovation will therefore be of important relevance to the project.

It is agreed that one or two key economic sectors requiring development and inward investment should be identified, and that activities within the project should be principally focussed upon those sectors. Although there is clearly a spectrum of development, from awareness raising through training to business decision making, it is convenient to regard the project as consisting of two principal elements, educational and business, which interact throughout the implementation period.

The objective, therefore, of the Iasi Project is to achieve, by facilitated self-development, improved industrial capacity through investment and joint ventures, based on a platform of improved training, high-level technological education and operational understanding of the market economy.

3 Regional Needs and Aspirations

ICTTT has identified the food and agriculture industries as being in prime need of assistance within the terms of this project and, in due time, resources permitting, this will be extended to include textiles.

It is intended that all industry, education and training that relates to the chosen sectors will be eligible for participation in the project. Without preempting the results of the planning processes (to be discussed later), it is evident that as in other parts of the former communist bloc, the Iasi economy has suffered from overly centralised control and the lack of a management culture which comprehends the market-based economy. The needs appear to be at least as urgent in relation to the development of human potential as they are for technological updating and investment.

With regard to environmental matters, it has been agreed with ICTTT that environmental education will be related specifically to technological development only; there is no generalised intention, within this project, to improve environmental conditions, however important that may be.

4 Project Processes

The preliminary phase of the project will be to install the necessary administrative infrastructure in Romania. Within the Iasi region, communications are poor and the Romanian co-ordinator will require assistance, space, office systems, communications and transport. The educational and industrial elements of the project will develop in overlapped sequences of four principal processes:

a) **Fact Finding.** A programme pf meeting and visiting, involving key participants in the project with the intention of fact finding, making professional acquaintances, developing mutual confidence, understanding cultural and historical implications for the project and improving the mutual understanding of the different contexts in which the partners work.

b) **Audit.** This phase will be conducted in Romania by joint teams with Romanian and EC membership. The intention is to ensure, consistent with project policy, that outcomes are owned on the Romanian side. This phase will identify the strengths, weaknesses and potential of elements identified by the management team to whom the teams report. The audits will be of both technology and management.

c) **Planning.** Using the results of each audit, the management team will evolve an action plan. The outcome of this process will be a series of subsidiary implementation projects.

d) **Implementation.** The results of audit and the brief

prepared by the management team will be used by
implementation teams to achieve change and steer resources.
e) **Reporting and evaluation**. Reports by implementation
teams on the outcomes of their work will be evaluated by
the management team.

5 The Generation of the Iasi Project

Initial meetings and visits supported by nondedicated
funding have created the basis for the project outline,
policy and principles stated above. Dedicated funding will
need to be obtained from a variety of sources to match the
scope of the project and to meet the requirements of
timing, planning logic and the objectives of the funding
organizations. The first application for funds was to
TEMPUS to support the university based elements of the
programme. Should that bid be successful, monies will not
become available until September 1992, but in the meantime
it is hoped that the results of a Know How Fund (UK,
Foreign and Commonwealth Office) application will allow the
creation of the necessary administrative infrastructure to
support the complete programme, overlapping that part of it
which is included within the TEMPUS bid. Other sources of
funding of which PHARE is a possibility.

As the project proceeds, and towards the end of Year
2000 when active industrial participation becomes more
important, further funding will be sought from European,
national and private sources. At that stage, it will be
timely to awaken the interested investors considering joint
ventures in Romania on the strength of the communications
network, training platform and collective know-how which
the project by then will have generated. It is considered
that an important element of the project will be the
production of a regular newsletter (journal), Iasi
Polytechnic Magazine (review essays about engineering,
business and management education) which will serve, in the
initial stages, to attract the interest of those whose
commitment and skills are relevant to the objectives of the
project and thus widen the project network, and later as a
marketing tool to secure the commitment of investors in
industry.

6 Iasi/TEMPUS Project

Objective

The objective of the Iasi/TEMPUS Project is, within the
context of the Iasi Project, to restructure and extend the
educational and training capacities of Iasi Polytechnic to
facilitate economic regeneration within the region, with
primary reference to the food and ancillary industry.

Aims

The Iasi/TEMPUS Project will function within the self-development methodology of the Iasi Project of which it forms part. The focusing of these developments on the food and ancillary sectors will prioritise resource allocation, but implementation projects will be of general application in other sectors.

The project will be carried out within a joint collaboration between EC/EFTA universities on the one hand and Iasi Polytechnic on the other, co-ordinated by the University of Sussex at Brighton, UK. Industrial collaboration is assisted through the mechanism of ICTTT on the Romanian side and the COMETT UETP network on the EC side. In the first year of the project, the project management and administrative will be set in place, and by a combination of visits, meetings and consultancy, the participants will become orientated to their tasks. Within the first year, three implementation teams will have been set up and some progress will have been made in organisational change, curriculum development and purchasing decision. Plans for the retraining of teachers and instructors will also have been completed. The second year of the project will continue with audit and implementation, but with higher levels of involvement with industry and with significant purchasing decisions being taken, with the intention of improving the education and training infrastructure of Iasi Polytechnic, specifically in the areas of learning technology and multi-media archives. Towards the end of the second year the benefits of the improved curricula and infrastructure should begin to be manifested in industrially relevant training and this will be assisted by the inauguration of a functioning technology transfer centre based at the Polytechnic. In year three, the principal thrust of the project will be to build up volumes of training in a structure that is sufficiently flexible to meet the needs of industrial developments. The training requirements will have been identified by ICTTT following a training needs audit of members and associated companies in the area.

The principal features of "Iasi/TEMPUS" are:

(a)   self-development methodology;
(b)   focus on specific developmental sectors;
(c)   programme based on "Project Iasi" model;
(d)   introduction of management and environmental education;
(e)   updated technological education and training.

Outcomes of the three-year programme

1   Updated curricula development and learning styles.
2   Teachers/instructors retrained.
3   Learning technology and distance learning capacity.

4   Computer-Aided Learning Laboratory and multi-media library.
5   Local availability of language training.
6   Industrially based Diploma projects.
7   Management and environmental education.
8   Retraining and continuing education programmes leading EUR.ING. (European Engineer) within the context of a postgraduate school.
9   Transnational (European) postgraduate education for Romanian engineers.
10   A technology transfer centre based at Iasi Polytechnic.
11   Education-initiated schemes to generate income.
12   Conferences, workshops and seminars for industry.

Management structure
     The project management team will be responsible for overseeing the general direction of the project, reviewing strategy and defining policy. In Romania and in the UK, there will be executive teams.

References
Adăscăliţei A. A.,Lindon P., Belousov V., Gafiteanu M., and Teodorescu H. N. "Continuing Engineering Education - A Romanian Case: The International Centre for Engineering Education, Iasi, Romania", in Proceedings of 5th World Conference on Continuing Engineering Education, Espoo, Finland, June 2-5, 1992, IACEE (to be published).
Adăscăliţei A. A. (1991) "Technology Transfer and Continuing Technological Education in Romania", Amsterdam, COMETT Conference, 13-15 November, 1991, ICEE Report, 1, 1-5.

Adăscăliţei A. A. and Teodorescu H. N. (1990) "Engineering Education in Romania: From Traditions to Possible Trends", in SEFI News, June 90, SN 35, 9-10.

Correspondence to be addressed to:
International Centre for Engineering Education, ICEE
c/o Iasi Polytechnic Institute
22 Copou Blvd.
P.O. Box 132
RO-6600 Iasi-1
ROMANIA
Tel.: +40-81-46577/40160
Fax: +40-81-47923
      and/or
      +40-0-415025 (CEPES/UNESCO, Bucharest)
Attn: Adrian A. Adăscăliţei, Director ICEE

Report on Second International Symposium for Engineering Deans and Industry Leaders

R.C. Jones

University of Delaware

Abstract

A successful International Symposium for Engineering Deans and Industry Leaders, held in 1989 with the sponsorship of UNESCO and the Ohio State University, focused on the strengthening of engineering colleges in third world countries as a key mechanism for economic development there. A second symposium was held in July 1991, with the primary objective of designing action oriented programs aimed at enhancing engineering education, technically oriented industry and thus economic development in such developing countries. The 1991 symposium was held at UNESCO Headquarters in Paris, with some 200 participants from some 50 countries, and many additional co-sponsoring organizations.

The program of the 1991 meeting was organized around action oriented projects, including:
- Development of sister university programs, pairing appropriate engineering schools in developing and developed countries for interchange programs.
- Development of mechanisms for industry-university interaction, particularly in developing countries.
- Development and maintenance of a comprehensive and accurate database on engineering education internationally (e.g. worldwide list of engineering schools, current leaders, enrollments, etc...).
- Development and maintenance of information clearing house in teaching equipment, courseware, etc... utilized in engineering education.
- Development of programs to promote completion of education (to doctorate in most countries) of faculty at engineering schools in developing countries.
- Promotion of educational equivalency recognition agreements, accreditation mechanisms, curricular standards, etc...
- Use of satellite information technology in delivering engineering education.
- Strengthening cooperation between engineering deans and industry leaders on a worldwide basis (e.g. Development of an ongoing worldwide organization of engineering deans).

Participants in the 1991 Symposium were leaders in engineering education, and industry leaders concerned about university interactions and about technology in developing countries.

This paper summarizes the discussions at the 1991 Symposium, and reports on actions recommended for ongoing programs.

Keywords: Engineering Education, Economic Development, University-Industry Relations, Developing Countries.

Introduction

The Second International Symposium for Engineering Deans and Industry Leaders was a successful forum for interchange of ideas and networking of those concerned with the improvement of engineering education worldwide. Engineering and technology are fundamental to meeting major human needs--including sustainable development and environmental protection. High quality engineering education is essential for the effectiveness of the practice of engineering. New mechanisms must be found to enhance engineering education programs, particularly in developing countries, in order to allow all peoples to benefit from advanced engineering and technology.

UNESCO, a key intergovernmental organization for the enhancement of engineering education, sponsored the Second International Symposium for Engineering Deans and Industry Leaders in Paris in July 1991. As the second in a series of meetings focused on engineering education worldwide, the 1991 symposium concentrated on designing action oriented programs aimed at enhancing engineering education, technically oriented industry, and thus economic development in developing countries.

One of the major ways in which Third World countries can be assisted in necessary and desirable economic development is through the formation or enhancement of an effective technical personnel base, upon which technically oriented industry can be established and grow. Key to such development is the strengthening of colleges of engineering in Third World countries, and the resulting flow of qualified engineering graduates into the technical manpower pool. With such a manpower base, technically based industry--both locally initiated and that stimulated as a portion of multinational corporation activity--can be effectively sustained, with resulting economic gain for Third World countries.

Recognizing the potential of such an approach, UNESCO and a group of co-sponsors organized the Second International Symposium for Engineering Deans and Industry Leaders around a series of action oriented projects in the areas of: Sister University Programs, Industry-University Interaction, Database on Engineering Education Internationally, Information Clearinghouse on Equipment and Courseware, Programs to Promote Completion of Education of Faculty From Developing Countries, Promotion of Curricular Standards and Equivalency Agreements, Use of Satellite Information Technology, and Development of an Ongoing Worldwide Organization of Engineering Deans. Following is a summary of each of these areas as they evolved during the July 1991 meeting.

Sister University Programs

The working group on "Development of Sister University Programs, Pairing Appropriate Engineering Schools in Developing and Developed Countries for Interchange Programs" was chaired by Dean Ke-Yang Li of National Cheng Kung University in Taiwan. The group began its deliberations by recognizing the value and need for the establishment of Sister University arrangements between engineering schools in developing and developed countries, but pointed out that such arrangements should be on an equal basis, with mutual interests and benefits for both partners.

In addition to specific sister relationships between individual universities, the working group suggested consideration of regional programs where groups of schools in the developing and developed world might collaborate with one another. It was pointed out that the individual needs of each institution would still have to be met, but that synergy might occur in such regional or even global sister university consortia.

This working group suggested that UNESCO might serve as a stimulus and clearinghouse for the development of sister university relationships. It was felt that UNESCO could serve as a catalyst for pairing appropriate engineering schools in developed and developing countries, and also as a reference point for connecting such academic institutions with other appropriate entities including government groups, development banks, and other intergovernmental agencies.

University-Industry Cooperation

The working groups sessions on "Development of Mechanisms for Industry-University Interaction, Particularly in Developing Countries" where chaired by Rector Hans Peter Jensen of the Technical University of Denmark. This group began with the observation that future symposia in this series should be rotated between different geographical locations, with some of the meetings held in developing countries so that participants might gain first-hand experience with problems and opportunities in engineering education there.

The working group also pointed out that basic needs in university-industry cooperation are different in various developing countries, and need to be carefully analyzed and defined before action is taken. A partial listing of categories which might be considered in such an analysis would include, lack of human resources, lack of appropriate learning materials, lack of laboratory facilities, lack of technical assistance, and lack of financial support.

The working group suggested that a follow-up effort be conducted under the auspices of UNESCO, on the basis of identified needs and generally accepted benefits from having university-industry cooperation. It was suggested that such an effort might concentrate on a feasibility study to be conducted in three or four specific settings in the developing world (e. g. Africa, Latin America, the Arab region, East Asia).

It was suggested that the concept of "Developing Centers" could be valuable in creating interfaces between universities and industry in developing countries. It was observed that in developed countries this is done through research parks or science centers. In developing countries, however, it was suggested that a less structured approach be taken. The "Developing Center" approach might have the following dimensions:

With respect to universities, stimulate academic units to market themselves and make cooperation rewarding for departments and professors. Also, stimulate universities to understand the culture of and the working conditions in local industry. Further, help universities in developing business plans, providing mechanisms for graduates to initiate new companies based on their academic or research work, and promote consultantcy by university professors.

From the company point of view, a "Developing Center" should set up networks between the university and industry, contact appropriate organizations to bring together appropriate members from universities and companies, and in the long term persuade companies to provide financial assistance for appropriate activities at universities. In addition, companies might promote cooperative education opportunities where students spend time and earn both academic credit and salaries by working at companies during a portion of their educational experience.

The working group pointed out that multinational companies should be urged to extend relationships to appropriate universities in developing countries like they currently have in place in developed countries. The group also pointed out that curricula and university-industry relationships in developing countries should not simply be copies of those in developed countries, but should reflect the needs and environmental conditions of the particular countries in which they are developed.

Database on Engineering Education

The working group on "Development and Maintenance of a Comprehensive and Accurate Database on Engineering Education Internationally" was chaired by President Miguel Angel Yadarola of the WFEO Committee on Education and Training. The group concluded that it was necessary to establish paths for cooperation between engineering schools in Third World countries and those in currently developed countries, as well as to provide ways for cooperation between engineering schools and technically based industries.

As a necessary precursor to illuminating such paths for cooperation, the group recommended that it is necessary to have substantial information available on engineering schools throughout the world. It particularly recommended the creation of a permanent international database on engineering education, and the periodic updating of that database. Such a database would include a worldwide list of engineering schools, current leadership at those schools, enrollment information, degree levels, staff information, descriptions of activities, data on placement of graduates, etc.

This working group recommended that an advisory committee be established, perhaps under the sponsorship of UNESCO, WFEO, and UATI, to determine what information should be collected for a database, and how both an initial and ongoing effort at gathering such information and making it available might be organized and funded. The group recommended that currently existing international bodies such as FEANI, SEFI, ABET, and ASEE would provide an appropriate source of information for institutions in Europe and North America. The group also recommended possible funding sources for such an effort, and described the characteristics and tasks of the Secretariat which might carry out the work. It further recommended that the database be developed in English, although it might be translated into other languages at a later time as appropriate. The data should also be stored in the native language of each country to allow for future correlations of information.

Clearinghouse on Equipment and Courseware

The working group on "Development and Maintenance of Information Clearinghouse on Teaching Equipment, Courseware, etc., Utilized in Engineering Education" was chaired by Executive Director Zenon J. Pudlowski of the Australasian Association for Engineering Education. The group focused on creation of a framework for the support of transfer of engineering courseware, software, equipment, and teaching methodologies between nations.

Specific action proposals were recommended. One was a pilot project concerning investigation of the applicability of existing materials from developed countries for possible transfer to developing countries--particularly in the areas of context dependent and problem oriented education of engineers. After such a pilot project, a more broadly based project concerning the implementation of problem oriented education methods suitable for developing countries would be highly desirable and beneficial.

As a matter of urgency, the working group recommended that a clearinghouse on teaching equipment, courseware, software, and methodology of training utilized in engineering education should be established to carry out and supervise the suggested projects. Such a clearinghouse or center would facilitate the collection, description, and storage of information, and also develop suitable methods for the subsequent dissemination of the collected and digested information. The working group recommended that the clearinghouse be established at an institution of higher education, with external funding (e.g. from development banks and intergovernmental agencies) to carry out the recommended clearinghouse functions.

Completion of Degrees

The working group session on "Development of Programs to Promote Completion of Education (to doctorate) of Faculty at Engineering Schools in Developing Countries" was chaired by Director Jacques Levy of the Ecole des Mines des Paris. This groups discussions started with the general question of how to train faculty members in developing countries, then moved on to the secondary question of how to promote research programs in engineering in a developing country.

The working group pointed out that the situation with regard to preparation of faculty members is very specific to each developing country or region of the world, and that it may change considerably over a period of time. It was observed that in many effective institutions, research activities by faculty members must be promoted in addition to teaching activities. The question of appropriate research projects relevant to the country of origin of students needs to be addressed in the preparation of faculty members who travel to developed countries for their educations. It was pointed out that when relevant research projects are defined, they should be funded for sustained effort over a period of several years, including the period after the faculty member returns to the country of origin.

This working group also recognized the importance of the relation of faculty members in engineering schools in developing countries to local industry. It was strongly recommended that returned faculty members be stimulated to pursue areas of mutual interest with industry, including research and development interests and the placement of appropriate graduates.

It was recommended that UNESCO stimulate activity in this area, for example in designing mechanisms for the support of relevant cooperative research programs, promoting interchange mechanisms between engineering faculty members in developed and developing countries, and promoting local cooperation between industry, engineering colleges and their faculty members.

Educational Standards/Equivalency

The working group on "Promotion of Educational Equivalency Agreements, Accreditation Mechanisms, Curricular Standards, etc." was chaired by Executive Director David R. Reyes-Guerra of the Accreditation Board for Engineering and Technology in the United States. The group reviewed accreditation mechanisms for engineering programs which are currently in place, reviewed proposed accreditation systems currently under development, discussed the need for evaluation systems for education and their desirable characteristics, then made a series of recommendations.

One recommendation was that a base general criterion for engineering studies be prepared, and submitted for worldwide discussion and possible adoption. A committee to develop such a general criterion for a first professional engineering degree might consist of representatives of organizations currently concerned with accreditation, engineering education, and engineering practice. It was recommended that the basic criterion should be kept general, but allow provisions to introduce special disciplinary criteria beyond the basic common areas. It was also pointed out that secondary school preparation should be held responsible for proper backgrounds in mathematics and science of their university-bound graduates.

It was suggested that a coordinating body such as UNESCO should establish a project office to bring together the organizations to develop and promulgate these general criteria, and also to provide assistance in carrying out experiments on accreditation and evaluation in countries which currently do not have such mechanisms in place. Finally it was pointed out that engineering technology and engineering technician programs might also profit from such an activity, and that a parallel effort geared toward their needs may be desirable at some point in time.

After a mechanism to develop base criteria and seek acceptance of those criteria on a broad worldwide basis has been established, UNESCO might also serve as a meeting place for those developing educational equivalency recognition agreements.

Use of Satellite Technology

The working group on "Use of Satellite Information Technology in Engineering Education" was chaired by President Lionel Baldwin of the National Technological University, in the United States. The group observed that instructional television effectively links students with exceptional teachers for distance learning, and pointed out that current applications in developed countries include enriching programs of study for campus students, and providing career-long education to engineers currently working. It was observed that the evolution of technology, such as new digital video transmission which will significantly enhance the use of today's geo-stationary satellites, provides even greater opportunity for the use of satellite information technology in engineering education.

The working group also observed that electronic networking provides opportunities for communication worldwide which can underpin collaboration and resource sharing in engineering education. Such technologies as low orbit satellite information systems may readily meet the needs of developing countries. The group noted that early demonstration projects in this area are encouraging, and that UNESCO might be effective in developing an action plan for extension of such systems.

The group recommended that an appropriate mechanism under the umbrella of UNESCO be developed to coordinate efforts in educational technology, such as satellite information systems, to provide access and enhance engineering education worldwide.

Worldwide Organization

The session on "Strengthening Cooperation Between Engineering Deans and Industry Leaders on a Worldwide Basis, Including the Possible Development of an Ongoing Worldwide Organization of Engineering Deans," was chaired by Vice President Donald Glower of the Ohio State University in the United States. As a capstone group, this action plan sub-unit reiterated the fundamental goal of strengthening cooperation among appropriate groups to improve the prosperity of peoples in all countries, through 1) improvement of each country's technical infrastructure, 2) enhancing relevant engineering education, and 3) industry's use of the graduates and other products from the educational system.

The working group recommended that a steering committee composed of individuals who are champions of this goal be established immediately by UNESCO. The activities of the steering committee would include establishment of an international network of engineering deans/rectors and industry leaders to bring engineering education worldwide to a uniformly high level of usefulness to industry, to organize local, national and international meetings to carry out the work of this network, to seek appropriate funding for its activities, and to pursue the other action plans developed by the seven working groups detailed above.

Summary and Conclusions

At the final plenary session of the Second International Symposium for Engineering Deans and Industry Leaders, the assembled participants unanimously adopted a resolution summarizing the impact of that Symposium, and setting directions for future action.

It was resolved that the organizers of the two Symposia continue the efforts at effective networking of Engineering Deans and Industry Leaders between developing and developed countries; and that such networking build upon the strengths and activities of current organizations concerned with the enhancement of engineering education, particularly in developing countries, and with university-industry interactions; and that the action program of this network include, but not necessarily be limited to, the following efforts: Sister University Programs, University-Industry Cooperation, Database on Engineering Education, Clearinghouse on Equipment and Courseware, Completion of Degrees, Educational Standards/Equivalency, Use of Satellite Technology.

It was further resolved that a steering committee be established to pursue the development of this network and its activities, and to continue this series of Symposia as appropriate.

An Enhanced First-Degree Course with Integrated Industrial Projects

A. Henham, D.J. Pollard

Department of Mechanical Engineering, University of Surrey

Abstract

The University of Surrey has 25 years' experience in the provision of first-degree courses in which professional training forms an integrated part. Based upon this the Department of Mechanical Engineering has developed recently a Master of Engineering course in Industrial Engineering. Industrial Engineering in this context is intended to indicate that the graduates are provided with the combination of academic and professional background which equips them best for a position in industry rather than for research in academic institutions. The paper describes the general departmental philosophy, the selection of MEng candidates, the structure of the course and its relationship with existing BEng courses, the particular features of the syllabus and the nature of industrial involvement in the course - training, sponsorship and projects.

Keywords: Engineering education, industrial projects.

1   Introduction

Many new courses in Engineering were established in the UK following the Finniston Report (1980) on the future of engineering formation. Some involved changes in title, typically from BSc to BEng, some real changes of attitude, others were concerned with establishing closer ties with industry and with the professional societies. One of the outcomes was the so-called *enhanced* course. The Surrey example of this genre, as are other courses in the department, is fully compatible with the SARTOR philosophy and includes in the early stages engineering science and applications including laboratory, design and an initial experience of workshop practice. The wider implications of engineering in society and communication skills are also included. There had been, for many years, two basic Bachelor of Engineering courses - Mechanical Engineering and Engineering with Business Management - in the department. Within these there is a choice of options at final year level and, from 1992, there will be specific provision for the study of a European language alongside these. Until now this has been available as an informal addition to the standard courses.

2   The Department of Mechanical Engineering

The Mission of the University of Surrey has as one of its main features the provision of courses in which academic study is integrated with periods of professional training in industry, commerce and public service. The Department of Mechanical subscribes to that mission and has provided first-degree courses of this nature throughout its existence in the University and for many years in its former guise as part of Battersea College of Technology. At all times it has been a prime requirement for course design that it should receive full accreditation from appropriate Engineering Institutions and that the training content should be recognised fully as part of their training requirements. That this requirement must be met has not in any way reduced the normal academic requirements for a university department to conduct research and scholarship which, in the case of the University of Surrey, essentially also provide direct benefit to industry and society. The Department is, therefore, one in which the whole ambience of its operations is that of a high academic standard together with an open and flexible approach to industry in which the academic and industrial members are regarded as equal partners in their endeavours.

The general structure of the degree courses in the Department is that of a first year in which the basic engineering science is provided and the Engineering Applications (Finniston 1980) are emphasised through a design-make-evaluate project undertaken by the students in groups and conducted with the cooperation of Guildford College of Technology. Through these projects the students practice the application of their knowledge of both engineering science and manufacturing gained during the year both at the University and the College. The second year follows a conventional academic year and it is during this year that the industrial placements for the third year are negotiated and possible transfer to the MEng course is decided. Students on the BEng courses return to the University for the fourth and final year after a full year on placement..

There are two BEng courses in the department which are essentially a degree in Mechanical Engineering and a degree in Engineering with Business Management. All students enrol on one of these courses and the first year of both is a common one which allows transfer between the two courses at any time before the commencement of the second year. The Mechanical Engineering courses are designed for students with known preferences for mechanical engineering science and with ambitions to practice their technology at a high level and possibly undertake engineering research in industry or academia. The Engineering with Business Management course is designed with a broader base to include more manufacturing and production systems as well as a greater content of business management than the mechanical engineering courses. Graduates from this latter course might be expected to proceed to industry where their roles will be much more related to implementing current technology rather than design, development and research. In each course there are options provided in the final year which allow students to follow a more limited range of courses in subjects related more closely to their future careers. Professional training placements in each of the courses as the third year take place in industry and the public services through the United Kingdom, on Continental Europe and sometimes further afield. All students are visited during these placements by specially chosen members of the academic staff on at least three occasions as well as meeting during the study return-period to the University at Easter.

The approval and involvement of the Professional Institutions is an essential part of the courses. All of the course options are accredited by the Institution of Mechanical Engineers and the Offshore & Maritime Option of the Mechanical Engineering course is also accredited by the Institute of Marine Engineers and the Royal Institution of Naval Architects. Further to that the Department was the first academic establishment to receive approval to operate the Monitored Professional Development Scheme of the IMechE which is the premier route to corporate membership of that Institution. Similarly students wishing to enter the Institute of Marine Engineers may now enrol on the equivalent route in that Institute. It is a mark of the partnership between the University and those institutions that the award given by the University for its professional training, the Associateship of the University of Surrey, is in the case of the Department of Mechanical Engineering awarded jointly with those professional institutions. It is natural that an integrated MEng course should be developed with a total commitment to producing high quality engineers wishing to practise in industry to complement the existing high standard BEng graduates.

Members of the staff of the Department contribute regularly to the development of the profession and serve on many of the committees considering all its aspects (e.g. education, training, research, national and international standards). The Department is, therefore, true to its mission to be a professionally involved department with high academic standards and a commitment to industry.

3   MEng Course Objectives and Methods

The aim of the course is to produce, in collaboration with industry, graduates of very high calibre with a broader and deeper competence in engineering and associated business attributes than is possible in the more limited timescale of the BEng course.   The graduates from this course are expected to be primarily motivated to follow a career as a Chartered Engineer in the manufacturing or process industries or consultancies rather than in research and academic establishments.

Selection methods for MEng courses vary - some departments attempt to recruit high-flyers from the outset while others select after one or two years of study. In this pattern selection takes place from within the two main BEng courses. A preliminary list is drawn up at the end of the first year. The results of academic examinations, tutorials, communications skills, laboratories and the Design, Make & Evaluate group project are all available at this stage. The combination of these many assessments provides much more of a student profile than the limited information available from A-level or Btec results at entry to the first year. Academically the standard required should show the promise of a good honours degree. A general introduction to the implications of transfer is given to this group of students. In the early days of the second year the students on the preliminary list are interviewed and any questions about the advantages or perceived disadvantages answered. Final selection depends upon satisfactory achievement of the expected high level in the second year assignments and examinations and on the successful arrangement of an industrial sponsor for the remaining period of the course. Some BEng students in the Department are sponsored but there is no requirement for this. After the interviews companies are approached about sponsorship, based upon the student's preference for type of industry as far as possible. Some of the companies linked with the Department are known to appreciate the special benefits brought by an MEng student and these will be approached first. Where a student is studying a European language alongside the engineering course then at least one of the placements will be in a country where that language is used. The department has a continuing relationship with companies in France, Germany and Switzerland and sometimes a UK company with a sister company abroad is available. There is a range of sizes and types of organisations involved so far and this is indicated in Table 1.

Table 1   Organisations sponsoring MEng students

Multinational Oil Company
Shipping Register
Large Engineering Consultancy
Steel Company
Large Electrical Manufacturer
Aero Engine Manufacturer
Foundry and Domestic Equipment Manufacturer
Manufacturers of Combustion Equipment and Compressors
National Gas Supplier
Offshore Engineering Consultancy
Specialist Precision Engineering Company
Diesel Injection Equipment Manufacturer
Defence Consultancy
Large Telecommunications Company
International Consumer Electronics Company

For business reasons some students have had to transfer companies during the course and so have carried out industrial periods with more than one employer.

From the end of the second year students selected for the MEng course follow a different pattern, increased in both breadth and depth by comparison with the BEng courses on both of which it draws for course modules. This is shown in the block diagram of the whole course structure in figure 1. The increased breadth derives from a wider range of engineering science and management subjects and the depth from a special design course, 'Design for Manufacturability' and from the demanding final industry-based project. The Design project is undertaken by the students acting as an industrial design office, making decisions and allocation functions at regular progress meetings at which the students act as chairman in rotation. This takes place in two parts in the third and fourth years.

The final industrial project is in addition to the individual, university-based, project undertaken by all undergraduates and takes place after all the examinations are completed. It comprises a real graduate-level problem tackled during a six-month period in industry and jointly supervised and assessed by one academic and one industrial supervisor. Projects cover a very wide range of topics, requiring both engineering science and management skills in various proportions according to a genuine need in the industrial placement for the project to be undertaken. The terms of the project brief are always the result of a three-cornered discussion between University supervisor, company supervisor and student. There are various general criteria concerning the amount of time required, supervision, visit and contact arrangements etc but the most significant is that the project topic: "shall be related to the requirements of the sponsoring company and shall be one in which the company has a particular interest". Table 2 shows a number of project titles.

Table 2   Some Industrial Project Titles

* Totally Enclosed Motor Propelled Survival Craft -
  Launch and Sailaway Parametric Study and Program Verification
* Competitive Advantage through Effective Supply Chain Management
* Validation of the Mott MacDonald Tunnel Thermodynamics Computer Program
* Low Pressure Gas Holder Station Safety Monitoring Systems
* Effect of CAD Systems on Conceptual Design

Fig 1   Block diagram of course structure

Master of Engineering in Industrial Engineering

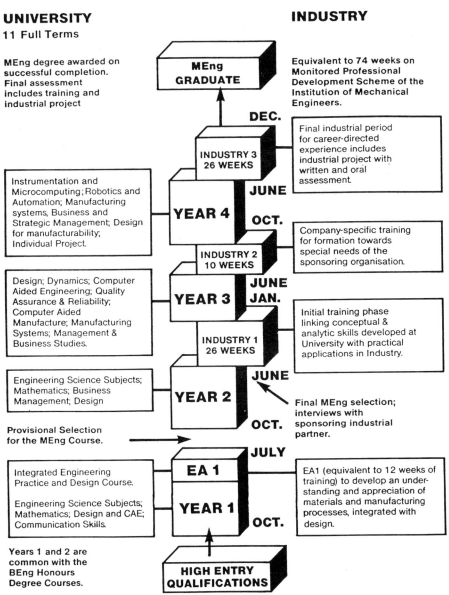

UNIVERSITY
11 Full Terms

MEng degree awarded on
successful completion.
Final assessment
includes training and
industrial project

MEng GRADUATE

INDUSTRY

Equivalent to 74 weeks on
Monitored Professional
Development Scheme of the
Institution of Mechanical
Engineers.

DEC.

**INDUSTRY 3
26 WEEKS**

Final industrial period
for career-directed
experience includes
industrial project with
written and oral
assessment.

Instrumentation and
Microcomputing; Robotics and
Automation; Manufacturing
systems, Business and
Strategic Management; Design
for manufacturability;
Individual Project.

JUNE

YEAR 4

OCT.

Company-specific training
for formation towards
special needs of the
sponsoring organisation.

**INDUSTRY 2
10 WEEKS**

Design; Dynamics; Computer
Aided Engineering; Quality
Assurance & Reliability;
Computer Aided
Manufacture; Manufacturing
Systems; Management &
Business Studies.

JUNE

YEAR 3   JAN.

**INDUSTRY 1
26 WEEKS**

Initial training phase
linking conceptual &
analytic skills developed at
University with practical
applications in Industry.

Engineering Science Subjects;
Mathematics; Business
Management; Design

JUNE

YEAR 2

Final MEng selection;
interviews with
sponsoring industrial
partner.

**Provisional Selection
for the MEng Course.**

OCT.

JULY

Integrated Engineering
Practice and Design Course.

EA 1

EA1 (equivalent to 12 weeks of
training) to develop an understanding and appreciation of
materials and manufacturing
processes, integrated with
design.

Engineering Science Subjects;
Mathematics; Design and CAE;
Communication Skills.

YEAR 1

OCT.

Years 1 and 2 are
common with the
BEng Honours
Degree Courses.

**HIGH ENTRY
QUALIFICATIONS**

4   Conclusions

The four and a half years of the course are designed to produce high calibre graduates destined to make rapid progress in a wide variety of industrial careers.   Early results suggest that this process is beginning and employers and graduates are finding the advantage of the completion of the University course while the student is within a company.   The continuity of education, training and employment, and the much more intimate involvement of the employer in this process, is seen as a considerable benefit.

5   References

Finniston, Sir Montague, (1980), 'Engineering Our Future", Report of the Committee of Inquiry into the Engineering Profession, HMSO Cmnd 7794.

University of Surrey, (1989), "University of Surrey 2000 AD, The Strategic Vision of the University into the 1990s and Beyond".

Industry and Academia - Blurring the Boundaries

A.A. Collie (*), J. Billingsley (**), J.P. Stuart (***)
(*) Department of Systems Engineering, University of Portsmouth
(**) University of South Queensland
(***) Transtech Engineering, University of Portsmouth

Abstract

The paper narrates the development of a relationship between the University and a Portsmouth company.

The initial contact was through consultancy, where the company approached a member of the University, (then Polytechnic) under the Mapcon Scheme to develop mirocomputer technology applications for consumer products. After some years of successful cooperation, the New Products manager of the company applied successfully for a Royal Society Fellowship to spend two years researching in the University on the development of mobile walking robots.

The industrial collaborator has formed a sister company, Portech Ltd, now devolved into complete independence, which has an impressive turnover based substantially on mobile robots. The company works very closely with Transtech Engineering, a division of Portsmouth Polytechnic Enterprise Ltd (University of Portsmouth Enterprise Ltd), with commercial benefit to the University, to the commmercial company and to Nuclear Electric plc, which is able to enhance its reactor safety through employment of the robots.

Keywords: Industrial Collaboration, Teaching Company, Royal Society, Consultancy.

1. Industry and Academia

Industry has, in the UK, traditionally regarded Academia with some suspicion. It is difficult to rationalize this attitude since many senior industrialists have benefitted from higher education but, particularly in the engineering profession, academics are seen to be impractical, theoretical and given to analysis instead of getting down to the job. Only when all internal resources are failing and the cost of ignorance is plain to be seen does an industrialist start to get involved with an academic!

It was against this sort of background that the Royal Society, through the Science and Engineering Research Council, set up a scheme whereby academics could temporarily take up positions in industry and industrialist positions in Academia. The idea was that by exposure to each other's problems and working environments both would benefit.

The authors' experience relates to the case of an industrialist in an academic environment. Of the two possibilities, hearsay evidence indicates that this is the more satisfactory arrangement.

In industry there is the problem of commercial and product responsibility which is not easily delegated to temporary staff however senior and capable they may be. Such considerations do not pertain in academic institutions and the newly recruited industrialist can contribute fully almost from the start, either as a researcher, lecturer or both.

2. Consultancy

The relationship between the authors started with a consultancy. A local company, Turnright Controls Ltd, had recruited a new Development Manager to introduce a line of microprocessor based domestic appliance controls. As is the way with such endeavours, after a few specialist low volume products had been produced a sudden upsurge in interest by Turnright customers required two potentially high volume products to be developed simultaneously with resources for only one. At that time consultants capable of writing assembly language programmes for the rather primitive four bit processors appropriate for the industry were difficult to find and very expensive.

Fortunately it had been a custom of the company to recruit students from the Portsmouth Polytechnic, as it then was, to help out during the summer months. It was one of those, working in the development department, who said his professor was exactly the man we needed. At the same time a Department of Industry initiative was launched to help with microprocessor applications in industry. This scheme, MAPCON, offered to pay for feasibility studies by an approved microprocessor consultant. It was then only a matter of negotiation to persuade the DTI that the newly found colleague was a suitable consultant and then to persuade him to write software for the fee available.

It is a curious coincidence that Professor Stuart was in fact the man responsible for setting up this scheme on behalf of the DTI and, although we did not meet at the time, we now find ourselves writing a joint paper!

The collaboration which followed resulted in a line of products which has continued in production for more than ten years. Both parties benefitted, a number of papers were written, the concepts were realized in products and a mutual respect between the University and the company developed.

3. Royal Society Fellowship

The success of the enterprise led to the Development Manager taking a serious interest in what could be accomplished in an academic environment and, with the polytechnic's help, was successful in obtaining Royal Society/SERC funding to carry out research of his choice. For most development engineers there is little or no opportunity to investigate anything outside the direct commercial activities of their employer and if they develop an interest in any other activity they may never be able to pursue it. The Royal Society's scheme pays the basic salary back to the institution releasing the grantee and, at the same time, through the Science and Engineering Research Council, project funding may be obtained. The attractiveness of this scheme to a frustrated development engineer is very considerable!

The research started with an investigation into compressssed air/ microprocessor powered walking mechanisms in the robotics group led by Professor Billingsley. The research was novel and has important implications. It is believed that mobility led to the development of intelligence in animals. The design of a walking robot gives some practical insight into autonomous behaviour which is the precursor of intelligence.

After two years work and at the end of the fellowship a robot was produced which, although not completely successful, demonstrated that the techniques discovered had application. Mr Collie returned to industry for almost a year while work continued privately on an idea for an improved robot and while further funds were sought. Careful analysis of the market had indicated that a climbing machine had application for the inspection of structures in hazardous situations. A DTI sponsored feasibility study had also come to the same conclusion.

The NAB scheme provided this new funding and Mr Collie was able to negotiate an arrangement with his employer to continue his research. During the fellowship period, Mr Collie's company had been the subject of a management buy out, so that it became possible to set up a new specialist subsidiary company in the hope that a profitable product would eventually ensue.

4. Climbing Vehicles

The second robot successfully climbed buildings and demonstrations of the device received considerable publicity in the press and on TV. This publicity resulted in the group being approached by Nuclear Electric plc to design a device to assist with their safety review of a Magnox nuclear reactor. The University set up a research laboratory as a cooperative venture through their engineering commercial division Transtech and a formal commercial arrangement was made with the University. The first of the Nero range of robots was produced by the company and the University in only nine months using the technology derived from the earlier research. One of the great advantages of close cooperation between industry and institutions like the University of Portsmouth is not only that experts are on hand to give advice but equipment which no small company could afford is available when not required for teaching purposes. The availability of this expertise and equipment greatly facilitates work when time is at a premium.

NERO was successful and Nuclear Electric subsequently ordered two more machines, each embodying more sophisticated features. The software, electronic and mechanical design is carried out at the University and the manufacture at the company, Portech Ltd.

The team now regularly visit the nuclear power station where they operate the robots, thus gaining practical experience of the actual working conditions. The experience of working on site and operating the vehicles originally designed in a research establishment is of great benefit to the team. Hands on experience in the real world changes the emphasis and provides a focus for their efforts.

5. Teaching Company Scheme

The new NERO devices have allowed the inspection of the reactor containment vessel to take place on schedule and at the same time allowed the polytechnic to be considered a centre of excellence in this field. Nuclear Electric have placed a long term contract and Teaching Company Scheme so that this expertise can be maintained. The Teaching Company Scheme is a UK Government initiative with the objective of strengthening the competitiveness of UK industry by facilitating technology transfer and increasing industrial investment in research and development. It provides academic supervision for graduates intending to pursue a career in industry.

The scheme started in 1975 with the intention that the Training Company Scheme would become to industry what Teaching Hospitals are to the work of the Health Service. Suitable staff can be recruited and industry contributes about 40% of the cost of the funding. The scheme has proved of great benefit to small enterprises which can acquire first class recruits at a reduced cost provided that they are prepared to train them.

At the current time, the research team at the University of Portsmouth is wholly supported by research grants and industrial funding. Portech Ltd is particularly interesting in that a concept which many people considered eccentric in the extreme has developed into what is hoped will be a major growth industry using revolutionary technology in the decontamination of nuclear plant in Europe and the United States of America.

6. Conclusions

This paper has described a real example of the interaction between industry and an educational establishment. It is a good example as it includes a wide variety of methods. The benefits are very great to both parties and many of these can be achieved even if the interaction is limited to a single method.

Transtech, the Engineering division of the University's commercial enterprise is flourishing by undertaking research, consultancy, designing, testing, prototype manufacture and the provision of short courses to industry. Transtech's consultants are mainly the academic staff of the University. Most of the work is a straightforward commercial venture, based on standard business procedures. Transtech gains the income from industry in return for the work done, but there are substantial intangible gains as well. Industry gains from interaction with the academic work which is frequently at the cutting edge of new technology, without needing to directly employ new staff. The University gains by providing a mechanism to gain by having lectures presented by professional engineers who are regularly undertaking real commercial projects against real business constraints and timescales.

The paper has also mentioned various UK government initiatives. There are also European and worldwide initiatives by various organizations that assist with the costs of bringing industry and academia closer together to work on real and substantial projects. These initiatives exist because many governments realize the vast gains to be made by encouraging the industry and academic interaction and thus further blurring the boundaries between education and commerce.

Bringing Realism to Business Awareness in Engineering Undergraduate Courses

G.M. Chapman (*), D.A. Snow (*), P. Willmot (**)
A. Stephenson (***)
(*) School of Engineering and Manufacture, De Montfort University, Leicester
(**) Department of Mechanical Engineering, Loughborough University of Technology
(***) Land Rover Power Train Group, Rover Group Ltd

Abstract
This paper describes a scheme based upon training programmes used by industrial companies to introduce the concepts behind business skills using competitive games over a short, highly intensive time period. By reducing formal lectures in Management Science and releasing time at the end of the second year of study, an intensive one week course entitled 'Business Management for Engineers' is currently operated annually immediately after the second year examinations at a time when no other commitment is expected of the students. The scheme has been run over the last four years and is now an established permanent feature in the education of undergraduates studying courses leading to careers in a variety of engineering disciplines. The programme has been devised along with the co-operation of industry and makes use of industrial involvement to ensure a sense of reality.

A major theme for the week is to pressurise the student body to the point that team working becomes essential and to allow individuals to investigate their own abilities to perform in such an environment.
Keywords: Business Education, Engineering Courses, Business Management Training.

1 Introduction

The education of engineers at the Higher Education level has traditionally concentrated on a thorough understanding of fundamental technologies based upon knowledge in Mathematics and Physics. As technologies develop, more emphasis has to be placed upon a more general understanding of applicable knowledge so that graduates can enter industry with awareness of modern practice.

Many engineering courses include studies in Business Management and use formal lectures aimed at introducing an awareness of business practices followed by experience gained during sponsored industrial training placements.

However in attempting to ensure a full coverage to meet the skills demanded of todays Professional Engineers considerable increases in lecture material places pressure upon the time available for course delivery. This increased demand takes up more and more of the available timetable and very often is neither stimulating or seen to be relevant by the students whose primary interests lie in the hard core engineering studies.

2   Course Pre-Preparation

By planning a series of preparatory lectures aimed at heightening awareness of business skills and concentrating on motivating students towards an acceptance of the intense week course, it was possible to maximise the benefits to be obtained for both undergraduate and industrial participators.

Lectures are timetabled throughout the year on Company Law, general Management, business structure, basic Business Finance together with courses on presentation and communication skills.

3   Course Operation

In order to ensure a successful and meaningful course a senior Engineer is invited to act as the course Director and industrial companies are asked to provide senior personnel to act as full-time tutors.

The course caters for over eighty students supported by twenty two invited 'Young Managers' from industry. It runs for four days, typically using a 14 hour day with every hour occupied by a timetabled activity. Meal breaks are also timetabled to reinforce the team approach. The intensity of the course together with tutor controlled pressure applied to the student groups, forces the students to develop integrating team skills to meet the demands put upon them. The techniques learnt are presented in a variety of ways during the course exercises and are continually brought to the attention of the students at regular briefing meetings. Throughout the exercise the students are guided towards improving their understanding of effective management in a real-time situation.

4   The Main Theme

The main theme of the 'Business Management for Engineers' course is centred on a business game requiring students to set up a company to manufacture domestic central heating boilers for the wholesale distributor market. Each Company has to control raw materials ordered, set up and maintain a production system, survey markets, arrange advertising campaigns, select a target customer base and organise a sales force. Each student group (the Company) is required to make strategic decisions on company policy based upon currently available data which may not always be complete but very often is too detailed for a full understanding in the limited time allowed for decision making.

The game is controlled through a computer which ensures competitive interaction between companies within a simulated market. All decisions are collected and delivered through a central office. Strict enforcement of deadlines for decision submission is maintained with lateness being penalised by fines on the company.

Each company is assigned a Young Manager whose prime responsibility is to offer assistance to groups and to pass on his\her experience as to how problems that arise are dealt with in industry. The Young Managers are drawn from graduates having at least two years post graduation experience in industry or commerce. Their personal business experience adds realism to the simulated environment of the exercises. In selecting the Young Managers care is taken to draw them from a wide range of companies offering different industrial activities and from widely differing employment functions. The broader the spread of business knowledge among the Young Managers, the greater the opportunity for the undergraduates to question the multiplicity of functions required to operate modern business.

There are twelve Business Game decisions throughout the course, each restricted to a half hour planning period. To create pressure and a sense of realism the tutors who operate each Industry (a collection of Companies) are encouraged to generate problems which require additional response from the Companies. Strikes, resigning salesmen, aggrieved customers threatening to sue the Company and many other highly original problems are interjected into the game which causes each Company to deploy some of its man power to deal with the immediate problem whilst the remainder of the team concentrate on meeting the decision deadline. The ability of each Company to meet the extra demands placed upon them by such problems is evaluated and weighted into the computer programme to reflect the response.

Reinforcement of concepts learnt is continually introduced by the principal tutors and mid-way through the course 'training sessions' are offered to provide support to meet group requirements. All Companies are encouraged to send delegates to courses on business finance, strategic planning, team motivation, exhibition techniques and presentation skills. To emphasise the relevance of training to business there is a charge levied against each company for use of the courses.

Because the nature of the course puts students under constant pressure it is necessary to inject activities specifically to raise motivation and morale at intervals throughout the four days. One such highlight is the introduction of a Trade Exhibition to assist company sales. This is held on the penultimate evening of the course where all Companies first acquire exhibition space by attending an auction and then have to build an exhibition stand with limited resources. The time available is limited to spare moments that the group can generate from within the highly timetabled days activities. Each company has to develop a sales theme for an open market to entice invited visitors who act as potential buyers. Many buyers will have been primed to buy against a predetermined plan i.e. the cheapest on offer, the best perceived value for money, the most persuasive salesman and even in some cases to deliberately absorb the salesman's time with no intention to purchase. As a reward for their efforts the Companies benefit from inclusion of their sales in the next decision period in the Business Game.

5   Supporting Games

To highlight specific business awareness the course is supported by six
three hour games with specific themes. The students are organised into
larger groups and are presented with tasks based upon different
business scenarios. All the exercises follow a common pattern, with an
initial briefing followed by a period to familiarise themselves with
the problem. A second briefing session is then used to assist the group
with organising the solution approach to be taken before the students
allocate responsibilities and set about the problem. At the end of each
session each group will present its solution in front of the other
competing groups. Finally the tutor will comment on the merits of each
groups activity and give a typical method of approach often based upon
knowledge from the actual case study on which the exercise was
modelled.
   Senior industrialists are invited to supervise these training
exercises and they can add considerable realism to the problems under
study by drawing upon their own managerial experiences.
   It is important to plan these exercises to cover different
activities, so that the complete course package illustrates a wide
experience of the application of team working in different functions of
business practice.
   Among exercises used todate are:-

5.1 **Negotiating skills** based upon a dispute between Management and
Unions attempting to achieve conflicting goals. Each group is divided
into two factions with briefing papers for a variety of specific
activities. An overall time is set for a decision to be reached and
both groups are advised that they must report their negotiated
settlement within the allotted time period.

5.2 **Marketing** based upon a company aiming to introduce a new product
into an overseas country where the culture of the population needs
considerable sympathetic consideration. Details such as infrastructure,
legal requirements, distribution networks, advertising campaigns all
have to be planned and approved by the local Minister for Development.
Considerable role play can be introduced to this game and students are
directed towards having their publicity vetted by local censorship etc.

5.3 **Personnel management** based upon a major retail outlet wishing to
close two medium sized stores and to combine the trading activities
into one site in a larger retail outlet. The business plan is presented
to the student group along with detailed information on the personnel
involved. The group have to make decisions affecting the work
environment and lifestyle of employees whilst being cognizant of the
constraints of the business plan. They are subjected to additional
pressures by persons taking the roles of some of the employees who
reveal extra factors which handicap the decision process.

5.4 **Business organisation and financial control** is covered by an
exercise modelled on an inefficient process plant with poor quality
control techniques. The data provided to the students is extensive and

requires the group to sub-divide the analysis by business activity.
Financial records, production control, quality control systems and
personnel records are all areas that have to be investigated and from
the incomplete data available they have to advise the financial backers
what level of funding should be injected and what alterations to
company procedures should be imposed.

5.5 Production control is highlighted dramatically in an exercise in
which groups compete to produce exercise books for customer orders. The
groups have sufficient materials to meet initial orders which if
completed on time to the satisfaction of the customer are purchased
with cash which allows the group to restock their raw material supply.
Any defaults in quality or meeting target times results in non payment
and the need to raise loans to purchase materials for further
production. The purchaser has exacting demands, the supplier of raw
materials has irregular trading times and the bank providing loans is
very vigilant in repayment periods. All these constraints build up
extreme pressure on the groups and reinforce the theme for team
working.

5.6 Operating a small business is highlighted by building a case study
around a real example. The success of this exercise hinges around
revealing incomplete information about such a business at a crucial
point in its development. The students are instructed to analyse the
data presented, to prepare questions to be asked of the representative
of the business and to make recommendations for the route that should
be taken. They are then given the opportunity to present their solution
to the 'small business' and after hearing comment on their solution
they are told what decisions the company actually made.

6   Assessment of Student Learning

There is a conscious decision not to assess students whilst the course
is running as it is felt that such an arrangement would be inhibiting
to enthusiasm and entrepreneurship. However students deserve credit for
their efforts and so an overall assessment is made based upon an essay
task set after the course has been completed. The theme for the essay
is modelled on their experiences gained whilst on the course.

7   Organisation of Programme

The whole course which lasts for the four day period requires
considerable enthusiasm from the University staff as its success
depends very much on their willingness to take on role play activities
to keep the motivation high even though students start to wilt under
the pressure. The University Careers Service is a major contributor to
the course both with advice on contacts and also in their willingness
to be involved in the scheme as tutors.
    Pre-planning of the course takes up majority of the ten weeks prior
to the event as contacts with industry must be developed and

maintained. Equipment has to be organised, support resources for games have to be purchased and the considerable co-ordination of the masses of paper work instructions for each game have to be packaged up for each student.

The course cannot operate without full participation of industry to give it the credibility that students respect. The whole exercise is a credit to the collaboration enjoyed between the University and Industry.

8   Assessment of Success of Scheme

The course runs in the last week of the Summer term at a time when most students are enjoying the pleasure of relaxation after their examinations. It is a tribute to the course that the students who participate are prepared to complete the course and with very few exceptions they all remain to the last session when a 'mock' prize ceremony is held.

All students acquire an insight into how business operates and are able to apply their knowledge in their next training assignments and also to their projects in the final year. They will have developed an elementary understanding of the relationships required between groups of people working towards common goals and the benefits of team working. Their awareness of the many activities of business and how they relate to one another is gained in a simulated environment and provides a stimulus for an enquiring mind when faced with their first appointment.

The industrial collaborators gain useful insight into potential recruits and value the commercial awareness that the students acquire. The Young Managers have the opportunity to experience group dynamics in an environment remote from their workplace and this acts as a catalyst in their assessment of their usual working environment.

The major benefit of this scheme is to open the eyes of young engineers to the demands of modern business practice.

9   Acknowledgements

The authors wish to thank both De Montfort University, Leicester and Loughborough University of Technology for the support in preparation of this paper. They are indebted to the many Companies who released staff to participate on the courses and in particular to the Careers Service at Loughborough University, CRAC, Land Rover Ltd and Ford Motor Company who have been the main supporters of the scheme from the first exploratory meetings and have continually sustained their interest.

Practical Industrial Training of Chemical Engineering Students and Technology Transfer in Germany

G. Fischer

Department of Mechanical and Chemical Engineering, Fachhochschule Hamburg

Abstract
This paper introduces a model of industrial training for chemical engineering students that has been introduced at the Fachhochschule Hamburg 14 years ago and has since developed very successfully. The training in industry is part of the curriculum and takes place in the 5th semester, after having finished most of the basic chemical and engineering topics. During their industrial training the students are supervised by professors of the Department of Mechanical and Chemical Engineering. The second part of the paper deals with the technology transfer between the chemical engineering department and the local chemical industry. In the recent years an increasing number of final graduation work of our students has been performed in chemical companies and supervised by the academic staff of the Fachhochschule. By this way the professors of the department stay in close contact with industrial research and development. Several projects of applied research for companies have been carried out in the laboratories of the Fachhochschule initiated by chemical or chemical engineering problems in industry. The technology transfer in the Fachhochschule Hamburg is part of a larger concept of technology promotion that includes several research institutions and institutions of higher education.
Keywords: Applied Research, Curriculum, Graduation Work, Industrial Training, Practical Semester, Supervising, Technology Promotion, Technology Transfer.

1 Introduction

Upon the first view practical training of students and technology transfer do not seem to have much in common. But going into more detail many similarities can be seen. The reason for this is the active involvement of members of the academic staff of the Fachhochschule in supervising the students during their practical industrial training and their final graduation work in industry and in technology transfer by doing consultation or research work for the chemical industry.

In this paper the situation in the Department of Mechanical and Chemical Engineering of the Fachhochschule Hamburg, Germany is described. It deals with the activities of the chemical engineering students and the faculty staff of this department. Due to the limitation of the

length of this paper a comparison of the practical industrial training and
technology transfer of our institution with other German Fachhochschulen
(they equal the British Polytechnics) is not intended, but as I know from
my work in the DECHEMA Board of Education in Technical Chemistry the
situation in other German Fachhochschulen is very similar.

The common link between the two parts of this paper, the practical
industrial training and the technology transfer, are the professors who
act on both sides. They are supervising the students in industry and by
this way stay in close contact to chemical companies. So they will
receive information about developments and research activities in
industry that can be brought to the knowledge of the students in
chemical lectures. On the other hand ideas and experience of the same
professors are often used to help smaller companies solve their problems.
By this way the technology transfer is not done in a one-way matter,
but it works in both directions to the mutual benefit of industry and the
Fachhochschule.

In the first part of this paper a model for industrial training of
chemical engineering students is introduced that has worked very
successfully during the last 14 years. The second part deals with the
technology transfer and shows several possibilities of our department in
doing research or consulting work for the chemical industry. It also
shows which structures of cooperation already exist between industry and
universities/Fachhochschulen in Europe, in Germany and in Hamburg.
Some examples of technology transfer from academic members of our
department to chemical industry in and around Hamburg are presented.

2 Practical industrial training

Since the foundation of the Fachhochschule Hamburg in 1970 there was a
broad consent about a practical training in industry for students in
technical departments. For a chemical engineering student it had always
been necessary to absolve a basic practical training in the chemical
industry before he could take up his studies. Exceptions were made only
for students who had finished an apprenticeship as laboratory technician
or had finished a technical college with chemical practical coursework.
But the main problem was to introduce an advanced practical training in
industry that is actually part of the curriculum and is referred to as the
Practical Semester in Industry. After the senate of the Fachhochschule
had agreed to the model of the practical semester in 1976 it took about
two years of hard work to convince both industry and students of the
advantages of this model. It was Prof. E. Wiebe, Head of the Department
of Mechanical and Chemical Engineering of the Fachhochschule Hamburg,
who was able to persuade with high personal engagement several local
industrial companies to support the idea and offer the necessary number
of jobs for our students. In the summer semester 1978 the first group of
54 students started their Practical Semester in Industry. As Prof. Wiebe
(1979) mentioned in an review article, 80 percent of the industrial
places for the first group of students could be offered by the Fachhochschule. The Practical Industrial Training is now fully integrated in the
curriculum and since 1978 has developed very successfully to both the
benefit of our students and the companies.

The intention of the practical semester in industry that takes place in the 5th semester (out of 8) and includes a period of 20 weeks is to introduce to the students the practice orientated field of activity of an engineer in the chemical industry. The student gets the possibility of applying the theoretical knowledge gained in his studies at the Fachhochschule to the complex problems in industry. He learns the different aspects of economic decision and gains a deeper understanding of technical, economic and social context of industrial operation. The practical semester in industry shall enhance the ability of the student to transfer the scientific findings and methods of his studies to the given corporate situations. This will lead to a more intensive interconnection between theory and practice, and the experience and knowledge gained during his practical semester will stimulate the student during his last semesters at the Fachhochschule. This is actually the case. Most of our students are practically converted when they come back from their practical semester in industry and are much keener and mature in doing their final studies. The companies get the possibility to have a close look at prospective employees without any obligation. Many students who were not the most brilliant during their studies and courses take up their industrial jobs with high motivation and show a performance and ability for team work that would have never been expected of them. As a side-effect of the Practical Semester in Industry many chemical companies offer our students the possibility of performing their final graduation work (in German Diplomarbeit) in the same company and in several cases there follows a permanent affiliation with the company due to the students good performance in his work.

The students themselves are responsible for a job application to do their Practical Semester in Industry. We have in our department two staff members in charge of the practical industrial training of the students. They offer any kind of help and have a list of companies who offer jobs for the practical semester. They know most of the companies personally and prepare for our students introductory seminars before they start their Practical Semester in Industry. The introductory seminars mostly consist of three block seminars of 18 hours total duration and are obligatory for the students. In these seminars the students learn how to write a correct job application and are prepared with possible questions in the industrial application interview. They even practice some situations between employer and employee by role-playing in small groups. They are informed about legal questions concerning their role as a future employee and will discuss their expectations about their work and career possibilities in industry.

During the Practical Semester in Industry every student is assigned to a professor of the department who is supervising him. The professor visits the company and especially the working place of the student and has interviews with the industrial supervisor and the student. In many cases the student will be asked to give a written report after finishing his industrial semester. While working in the practical semester the students remain full members of the Fachhochschule with all rights and duties. The students normally get a payment from industry that varies in amount according to the branch of industry and the students performance but is roughly orientated to a last year apprentice salary. After finishing the Practical Semester in Industry the students attend an assessment seminar where they will reflect their experiences and compare them with their expectations and give interviews to younger students who are about to start their practical semester. The introductory seminars and the assessment seminar are organized and attended by faculty members and are part of the curriculum.

3   Technology transfer

Technology transfer between institutions of higher technical education and industry is organized in Hamburg at different levels. Under the roof of the European COMETT programme (Community Action Programme in Education and Training for Technology) different University–Enterprise Training Partnerships (UETPs) have been founded. Prof. M. S. Wald of the Department of Mechanical and Chemical Engineering of the Fachhochschule Hamburg is the initiator of the Hamburger Ausbildungspartnerschaft (HAP, Hamburg Educational Partnership). As mentioned in the journal **ndv news** (1991) the HAP is involved in organizing international educational workshops, technology transfer and developing multimedia educational software. The activities have been extended over the European community members to the EFTA countries and are now expanded to Eastern Europe. Six North German states have coordinated their activities in technology transfer, training and education in the NDV (Norddeutscher Verbund, North German Network). The North German Network of technology transfer now has his own journal, the **ndv news** that informs about the contribution of industry and science in Northern Germany towards European technology training and education.

The Fachhochschule Hamburg is now deeper involved in local and European technology transfer and student and staff exchange between industry and academic scientific institutions by founding the Institut Hochschule–Wirtschaft (Institute for Science and Enterprise) at the initiative and hard and persevering work of Prof. M. S. Wald of our department.

A second level of technology transfer in Hamburg is the permanent Study Group for Technology Promotion. Members of the study group are the Fachhochschule Hamburg, the University of Hamburg, the Technical University Hamburg–Harburg, DESY (German Electron Synchrotron), GKSS research center in Geesthacht near Hamburg, NATEC institute for scientific technical services. These institutions work together with several communical organizations and professional associations and offer in 13 scientific and technical disciplines over 300 technical procedures or analytical methods to solve problems especially in smaller enterprises who are not able to finance a research department of its own. All these offers are listed in a book entitled **Technology Offers of Scientific Institutions in Hamburg** (Technologieangebote wissenschaftlicher Einrichtungen Hamburgs, 1989). The areas of knowledge offered in the above mentioned book include mathematics, information and data processing, physics and physical technic, geological science, chemistry and chemical engineering, biology and biotechnology, medicine and medical technique, material science, mechanical engineering and manufacturing, naval architecture and marine technology, electrical engineering, process control and microelectronics, architecture, energy science, environmental science.

In the field of chemistry and chemical engineering there are more than 40 different technical or analytical procedures offered. In the Department of Mechanical and Chemical Engineering of the Fachhochschule analytical methods including methods of physical instrumental analysis and membrane techniques and dialysis are offered.

A third level of technology transfer are the many contacts of members of the Department of Mechanical and Chemical Engineering with local chemical companies. These contacts have been intensified in the recent years by supervising students in their Practical Semester in Industry and during their final graduation work (Diplomarbeit) in industry. In many cases smaller enterprises directly asked the Fachhochschule for help with chemical or technical problems. Same companies are afraid of the possible costs of a consultation. Help was provided by the **Technischer Beratungsdienst** (Technical Consultation Service), an institution established by a German commerce and industry organization (Rationalisierungs-Kuratorium der Deutschen Wirtschaft). Up to 5 hours of technical consultation was paid by the technical consultation service to smaller companies in Hamburg upon request. Many applications arrived in our department, and in most cases the professors of our department were able to give technical advice or consultation. And if not they nearly always knew of a colleague who was an expert in this special field of interest and could help. After these 5 hours of consultation it could be said what further measures had to be taken on the side of the company to solve the problem. With more complex problems detailed investigations had to be done. Our department could offer many research facilities, and smaller companies without laboratories of their own gladly took the opportunity to have a chemical or technical problem solved by applied research in our laboratories. For this research the companies will pay the professors and assistants directly according to the actual time required for the work. This procedure of external applied research in a laboratory of a department of the Fachhochschule is in most cases much cheaper for the companies than to set up own research facilities or hire technical assistants. All the results of the consultation and applied research carried out in the order of a company are handled strictly confidential and in some cases secured by a contract.

Another aspect of research and consultation of faculty members of the Fachhochschule for the local chemical enterprises is the close contact to latest technical developments in chemical industry. This is further enhanced by the frequent visits of companies in connection with supervising students in their Practical Semester in Industry and their final graduation work in industry. So the professors become familiar with new methods in laboratory techniques and with new technical developments. This knowledge can influence the lectures and course work in the Fachhochschule and bring to the students more information about the current situation in their future work-place. So an intensive exchange of necessary theoretical background and modern industrial technology is achieved. This could be referred to as technology transfer back and forth.

In the following I would like to give some examples of technology transfer in the form of consultation and applied research that has been carried out by colleagues of our department.

A producer of organs had problems with his pipes. After being played a while the mouth pieces would be blocked by an unknown substance. In our organic laboratory a professor of our department was able to analyze the blocking substance with Infrared Spectroscopy and Gas Chromatography and found out that it was the plasticizers from the plastic air hose being washed out by the air current. Advising the producer to use another type of air hose solved the problem.

A large German producer of compasses that are sold worldwide for the marine industry had trouble with the liquid that fills the compass case. The liquid was not light stable but discolorated after some time. All the components of a compass that could get in contact with the liquid were tested with the liquid separately under stress conditions, but with no result. Finally it was found out using Derivative UV-Spectroscopy that the liquid contained unsaturated contaminants causing the discoloration by polymerisation.

A local company for plant technology with no chemical laboratory of its own got an order from abroad to plan and construct a plant for producing sodium hyposulfite. A professor of our department was able to give the necessary information about the chemical processes and calculated the mass and volume flows. A flow diagram of the plant was discussed with the company, and safety hazards and questions of environmental protection were emphasized.

A large German subsidiary of an American company produces all kinds of plastic bottles, mostly for the detergents and cosmetics industry. They used a new method of attaching the labels to the bottles, called the in-mould-labelling. This technique can cause problems with the correct positioning of the labels. Bottle with even slightly wrong positioned labels cannot be sold and have to be regarded as rejects. Recycling of these plastic bottle was not possible because the residues of the paper labels damaged the newly produced bottles. In our department the problem could be solved with a long series of laboratory experiments with many variations of chemical and technical conditions. At the end of this applied research a method could be developed to completely separate the chopped up reject bottles from the paper label impurities and so recycle the production waste.

I am now at the end of my paper and hope to have given you an overview and some interesting details about Practical Industrial Training and Technology Transfer in the Department of Mechanical and Chemical Engineering of the Fachhochschule Hamburg.

4   References

Wiebe, E. (1979) Praktisches Studiensemester als integraler Bestandteil des Studiums an der Fachhochschule Hamburg, in Praxisorientierung des Studiums, Campus-Verlag, Frankfurt/New York.
Wald, M.S. (1991) The European Community Action Programme, ndv-news 1, 6-7, 10.

Academic and Industrial Research - A Case Study

C.A. Brebbia

Wessex Institute of Technology of the University of Portsmouth

Abstract

This paper discusses the important issue of how academic type institutions carry out research of relevance to industry. The solution proposed and carried out by the author has been the creation in 1986 of a new type of Centre independent but federated to an academic institution. This type of organization needs to be highly specialized in a particular field in order to be a centre of excellence not only in the UK but internationally.

The importance of developing strong industrial and academic international links cannot be overemphasized as it is the best way to ensure the quality of the research and to help industry to become more competitive in the international market place.

Research at the Centre is carried out by several teams consisting of Research Fellows and students under the leadership of full time members of staff. This structure ensures continuity in the work and is analogous to the type of teamwork which is typical of industrial establishments. It has proved to be as well a very efficient way of carrying out research and promoting industrial awareness in engineering education.

The existing Centre (Wessex Institute of Technology) has achieved most of the objectives set up in its Charter and is now in the process of growing at an accelerating rate.

Keywords   engineering research, computational engineering, engineering training, centre of excellence, industrial research

1. Introduction

The Wessex Institute of Technology was created in 1986 dedicated to the "advance and development of engineering and its applications to industry" and with the primary objective of providing "the link between research engineers and practice". The Institute focused on the transfer of advances in engineering sciences to industry, in particular in the field of computer applications.

The decision to create the Institute originated in Dr Carlos Brebbia supported by a group of well known academics and industrialists from Europe and the USA. It was felt that while industrial research organizations could provide the developmental research required on a day to day basis, there was a need to carry out longer term industrially oriented research to create new processes and technologies. In other words while many industrial research facilities work on problems of immediate concern, The Institute would concentrate on more strategic industrial research. This implies a longer perspective and consequently, an important element in the structure of the new Institute is the presence of PhD students who develop their research while working as part of a specialist team. These teams or divisions are problem oriented and allow for the easy flow of information between different researchers as well as with the industry supporting the work.

Another characteristic of the Wessex Institute of Technology is its emphasis on international contacts and the frequent visits to the Institute made by members of its Advisory Committee as well as many other researchers from academia and industry. A key element in fostering such visits is a very active programme of international conferences, seminars and courses organized by the Institute. All staff and researchers are actively encouraged to participate in these as well as external meetings. Through these activities the researchers are fully aware of the latest developments in their field throughout the world.

The establishment of WIT was originally possible due to the financial support of several organizations, including two companies which are now associated with the Institute. These two companies now provide important ancillary functions in the development of the Institute. One of them specializes in advanced software for engineers and has produced a number of research projects for WIT through its wide range of industrial customers. The company also benefits by applying research originated at the Institute in their advanced engineering software which is used by the major engineering companies around the world.

The other company publishes advanced engineering material which is also sold throughout the world. The company produces the publications of the Institute as well as those of other research, industrial and academic institutions. The association of the Institute with this imprint has publicised its work internationally, enhanced the reputation of its research and helped to strengthen research and industrial links. Through these two important companies the Institute has a unique and powerful international information network. A very active office in Boston, USA, has been set up by the companies to benefit from a presence in the all important USA market.

The Institute's researchers were recognized by the CNAA for postgraduate degrees until the beginning of 1992, when a special agreement was signed between the then Wessex Institute and the future University of Portsmouth. As a consequence the Institute is now federated to the University of Portsmouth. The agreement enhances the importance of the Institute without losing in any way its independence, which has been the cornerstone of its dynamic and original approach to engineering research.

2. The Concept

The Institute has been created to act as a link between academia and industry. Extensive experience in different academic environments convinced its founder that there was a need to establish a different type of Centre in order to communicate effectively with industry. Existing academic institutions were not sufficiently flexible to accommodate the requirements of industry. In particular, the type of response afforded by academic departments or institutes was not efficient. Academia with its emphasis on teaching and administrative duties usually can only afford a low priority even to long term

industrial research.
The Wessex Institute was created to fulfill the following functions.
i. Undertake two to three years projects on behalf of industry.
ii. Set up a PhD programme which allows for the participation of mature
students with industrial experience.
iii. Offer a training and update programme oriented towards industrial
needs.
At the same time its aim was to become an international centre of excellence in computational engineering attracting the best researchers in the world. This has been achieved by a series of link agreements with different institutions and a lively programme of international conferences and seminars.
At present the Wessex Institute has three main divisions which are centres of excellence in their own right. They are:

a. Computational Mechanics Division - This is renowned for being the birth place of a technique (The Boundary Element Method) which is now widely used throughout the world for engineering analysis. The method is much better suited than existing ones to computer aided engineering applications and because of this is becoming popular with industrial users. Research on advanced applications of the technique continues in fields such as stress analysis, fluid dynamics, vibrations, heat transfer, electrical conduction, conduction and many others. The problems being solved originate in industry.
b. Damage Tolerance Division - This Division is involved in the development of advanced computational methods for fracture mechanics. It works with problems such as three dimensional cracks, fatigue, crack tracking and others affecting the integrity of structural components. It works in close contact with many industrial partners and has been very successful in raising funds.
c. Advanced Computing Division - It specializes in applications of supercomputers in engineering and new areas of engineering computing as well as environmental engineering problems. Although it is the most recent division it has grown considerably in the last few months.
Each Division is headed by a Reader who is a well known researcher. The quality of the Senior Staff at the Institute has been the main reason for the rapid growth of the Wessex Institute and its excellent international reputation.
Each Division consists of a series of (post doctoral) Senior Research Fellows and Research Students under the supervision of the Reader. The students are registered with the University of Portsmouth and the Institute is federated to the University, with the Director being a Professor at the School of Engineering.
Two members of the University sit in the Institute Advisory Board while the Director of the Institute is a member of the Faculty of Engineering Board of the University. Major decisions regarding policy matters are taken by agreement between the President of the University and the Director of the Institute and referred to the Advisory Board in due course for approval.

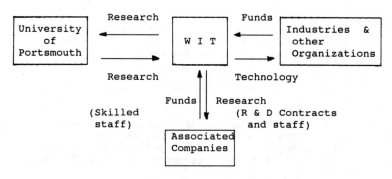

Figure 1   The Concept

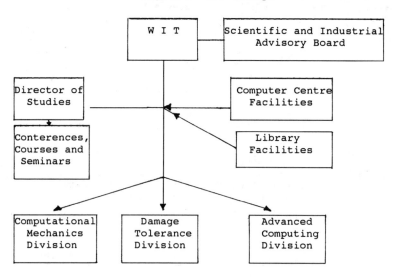

Figure 2   Internal Organization

3. Organization of the Institute

The Institute is organized in the manner described in Figure 2. In addition to the main three research divisions already described there is a Department headed by the Director of Studies who is responsible for

i. The day to day administration of the Centre.
ii. The registration and administration of all PhD students.
iii. The organization of a Training Programme consisting of Conferences, Seminars and Courses.

The training programme of the Wessex Institute of Technology is particularly important as it involves a series of courses and seminars for the researchers plus a set of 20 or so international conferences, half of them organized in the UK and half abroad, with most of them taking place within the EEC. The programme is well known throughout the industrial and scientific communities and has added to the prestige of the Institute. Of particular interest is the fact that the vast majority of the Proceedings are published at a very high standard and distributed throughout the world through one of the Associated Companies. This helps to increase the visibility of the Institute.

The Institute's strategy is decided by the Scientific and Industrial Advisory Board, which meets twice a year to shape its policy. Members of the Board come from different European countries and the USA and have all been actively involved in the development of the Centre to whom they have committed considerable amounts of time and effort.

Wessex Institute has a wide range of in-house computer facilities, mainly through a series of workstations networked together. In addition, it uses several major computing centres, including the SERC Rutherford Laboratory supercomputing facilities near Oxford through dedicated lines. Library facilities are provided by the local University as well as the interlibrary loan service. The Institute has its own small library specializing in Computational methods in Engineering and receives a number of international Journals.

Associated Companies

The Institute initially supported by its two associated companies is now self-supporting but its links with these two companies are still highly beneficial.

The first is a software company which markets a computer code based on the same boundary element technology by which the Wessex Institute of Technology is famous throughout the world. This technique is gaining rapid acceptance in industry and the company has sold more than 300 copies of the code to major industries in USA, Europe and Japan. This has opened a large number of contacts to the Institute and resulted in many research projects. In general lines the BEASY company is dedicated to development, support, marketing and sales of the particular code, while it seeks the support of the Centre for long term research activities.

The second associated company is CML Publications, which is dedicated to publishing advanced engineering material. The Institute's researchers are keen in publishing with the company but in addition CML produces the proceedings of the conferences and seminars held at the Centre. This ensures that the work at the Wessex Institute of Technology is not lost to the industrial and academic community, at the same time that it publicizes its name throughout the world. The relationship is beneficial for the Institute as well as for the Publishing Company.

External Links and Contracts

Over the years the Institute has set up a series of agreements with different organizations and institutions. These provide a steady flow of Research Students. Applications for contracts to government, including the EEC are an important part of its income.

One of the most productive links has been the training of industrial people to complete PhD degrees on a Full time or Part time basis. These frequently mature students are able to complete projects of interest to their supporting organization at the same time that they receive a degree. These agreements ensure flow of staff between the Institute and industry.

The main sources of income for the Institute are from industry and come in three ways, i.e. through its training programme support, tuition fees paid for students carrying out PhD and research projects.

The Institute's income is as follows.

Training	40%
Tuition fees	20%
Contracts	40%

The current tendency is towards obtaining a larger share of the income through contract research.

Potential for Future Growth

The Institute is now set for further growth in the near future. The importance of the technologies developed at the Centre are fully appreciated by industry. These new developments ensure faster and more efficient solutions to engineering design and analysis. Further integration of computer codes and better visualization techniques imply that in the future, manufacturing industries will rely more heavily on computer integrated systems. The Centre provides a unique centre of excellence for this type of work with emphasis on the design and analysis.

4.   Conclusions

The model developed at the Wessex Institute of Technology has achieved some of the objectives set up by the Fraunhofer Institutes in Germany and the proposed Faraday Centres in the UK. In particular:
i)   The Institute has served as a bridge between the academic community and industry to effect technology transfer.
ii)   It has achieved a more effective exploitation of science and technology through its many industrial contacts and its associated software company.
iii)   It has given graduate students the opportunity to gain a PhD degree while involved on work of industrial relevance.
iv)   It has served as a centre of excellence for technology transfer and information at the national as well as international level.
The importance of the Wessex Institute of Technology is also that it has demonstrated that the idea of intermediate organizations engaged in technology transfer and development is not only feasible but very much welcomed by industry.

Bibliography

1.   Whelan, R.C.   "The Technology Transfer and Fraunhofer Institutes", CEST (Centre for Exploitation of Science and Technology), UK, 1991.

2.   Whelan, R.C.   "The Faraday Programme" Working Paper 1, CEST (Centre for Exploitation of Science and Technology), UK, 1992.

3.   Interim Report. The Working Group in Innovation, CEST (Centre for Exploitation of Science and Technology), UK, 1992.

Interaction Between the Practice of Engineering and the Academic Education of Engineers

A.N.S. Beaty

Department of Civil Engineering, Royal Military College of Canada

Abstract
University engineering serves as a preparation for engineering practice, thus teaching and practice are closely inter–related. The current publish or perish policies of North American universities have resulted in a divorce of teaching and practice. Steps to redress the balance are proposed.
Keywords: Engineering, Universities, Teaching, Practice, Integration.

1. Introduction

Engineering is not an abstract discipline studied for its own sake. Although the engineering training provided by universities should teach students how to think and should educate them in the broadest sense, it is generally pursed with the intent of becoming a professional engineer. To achieve this status it will be necessary, through apprenticeship or on–the–job training to complement the knowledge of basic theory and techniques acquired at the university by a period of guided experience in practical application. Engineering is an essentially practical discipline and is aimed at the design, construction and operation of structures, machines, or systems in the service of mankind. In its Royal Charter granted in 1828, the Institution of Civil Engineers defines civil engineering as *"The art of directing the great sources of power in nature for the use and convenience of man."*

If the aim of students of engineering is to become practising engineers, then the teaching of engineering should not be divorced from the practice of engineering. This implies, in particular, that engineering design courses must be relevant to design as it is currently practised and also that teachers of engineering design should either be practising engineers or should at least have had recent experience in engineering practice. Schaffner (1982) has argued that:

> *"Engineering education should be restructured to resemble other professions such as medicine, law, and architecture where a substantial part of the teaching is done by practitioners and where a substantial portion of the full–time faculty have been in practice and are currently active to some degree."*

It can be observed that many university engineering courses develop students' analytical skills far more than their ability to synthesize or design. This is closely related to the fact that far too many university teachers of engineering have had little or no experience of the practice of engineering.

2. Academic Engineers

The reasons for the lack of integration of the teaching and practice of engineering are to be found in the criteria for the appointment and advancement of university teachers in North America. It can be seen that the quickest way to become a senior, tenured, professor is to obtain a junior academic appointment as soon as possible after obtaining a master's degree and then to obtain a Ph.D. degree, which has become mandatory for career academic staff. The statement:

> *"Many engineering faculty members have not had an opportunity to round out their career development with actual experience in the practice of the profession for which they are preparing their students."*

by Bradley (1977), in the journal of the American Society for Engineering Education, is to me an indictment of the basis on which university teachers of engineering are recruited. He goes on to describe a scheme which aims to give these young engineering educators a period of twelve to fifteen months of engineering experience. While this acknowledges the problem, the short period of experience offered does not constitute a complete solution.

3. Publish or Perish

Having obtained a Ph.D., the next hurdle, for the aspiring career professor, is to obtain tenure which, in the words of Professor X (1986), requires five to ten refereed publications over the next four to six years. As virtually the only criterion for obtaining a permanent (tenured) university appointment and for promotion and salary increases, is the number of refereed publications produced, it is not surprising that academic staff ambitious for security and promotion, put their best efforts into producing publications. This has a number of undesirable consequences: first, in order to attain higher academic rank as quickly as possible, no time is spent gaining experience of engineering practice, secondly, as teaching quality appears to be irrelevant to advancement, teaching is disposed of as quickly as possible and thirdly, the need to have as many publications as possible leads to the salami approach— slice it as thin as possible, Goulter (1981) has indicated that material, which might justify one reasonable paper is often spread over three or more papers which are mediocre at best and which are submitted to different journals under different titles, fourthly, as "publish or perish" has become the law of the North American academic community, the number of publications has escalated, making the task of keeping abreast in a given field enormously more difficult, if not impossible.

As most university research is now done simply because it must be done to produce papers, most of it adds little or nothing useful to the sum of knowledge. Sykes (1988) believes that fewer than one university professor in ten ever makes a significant contribution to his field, that the great majority of academic research is *"utterly without redeeming social value"*, and that *"much of what passes for research is trivial and inane."* In the same vein, Smith (1990) says that *"the vast majority of the so–called research turned out in the modern university is essentially worthless."* I would hazard a personal view that most university research would not be missed if it were not done. The great majority of papers published go unread and deservedly so. Unfortunately it has become difficult to find the few worthwhile contributions to knowledge amongst the mass of worthless prose emanating from the "publish or perish" factories which the universities have become. It may be that this situation is marginally better in engineering where some applied research is carried out under contract to find solutions to particular problems.

Those in favour of the current situation often say that the purpose of what they mistakenly call "scholarship" is to enhance the quality of a professor's teaching. However, several studies have reported that there is no significant correlation between teaching effectiveness and research productivity, for example Neill (1989) and Turns (1991). Smith (1990) quotes a study from which Finkelstein (1984) concluded that *"research involvement detracts from good teaching."* Rushton et al (1983) concluded that the characteristics which define a good teacher and those defining a good researcher are largely mutually exclusive. Furthermore, it is clear that, if research and publication are the primary objectives of a university teacher, then teaching will be given a lower priority, will suffer and may even become regarded as an obstacle in the way of the "real work" of the teachers. If research is really at the cutting edge of new knowledge it may enhance teaching of the doctoral level courses which are given in North America, but it is unlikely to have any immediate relevance to what is being taught to undergraduates.

In this context "scholarship" has been interpreted narrowly to mean publication in a journal for which the referees are other professors. Neill (1991) has raised the question *"are articles in professional journals really worth less than those in scholarly journals?"* My own view from an engineering perspective is that articles in professional engineering journals and major conference proceedings are likely to be of more value as they will have been reviewed by practising engineers not simply by academic engineers. In Canada recently there have been several calls for the word scholarship to be interpreted less narrowly; perhaps the most significant of these was by Smith (1991) in his report on the educational mission of Canada's universities.

4. Teaching Assistants

As a university teacher advances in rank he will try to acquire students at the master's and doctoral levels so they can produce material for publication to which he can add his name. In addition these post–graduate students are paid small sums to be teaching assistants; in many cases however they don't assist but actually give the lectures so that the professor can devote his time to what he believes really matters— publishing. To make matters worse the majority of these teaching assistants are often not native English speakers and are not sufficiently fluent to be properly understood, Sykes (1988).

5. Separation of Practice and Teaching

If an engineer, having gained some years of professional experience decides he would like to teach, he is unlikely to be able to obtain an academic appointment unless he has a Ph.D. Even if he has a Ph.D., his years of practical experience will be considered to have been "unproductive", that is, they did not produce published papers. The very quality which would be of value in undergraduate teaching — experience in the practice of engineering — will be what loses him the post to less experienced candidates who have applied themselves to the rat race of "publish or perish". As Sykes (1988) has pointed out, in his searing condemnation of American higher education, if Shakespeare were to apply to teach English in a North American university he would be turned down, because although his plays had been published, it was not in a scholarly journal and he had not earned a Ph.D. I suppose we could say the same if Stephenson, Telford or Brunel were to apply to teach engineering in a North American university. The academic career structure is based on remaining within the university system on completion of a bachelor's degree and progressing up through the rank structure. An experienced engineer seeking to become a professor in the North American system finds it biased against him because of the structure of the salary and pension plans and because it has no way to reward engineering experience.

Sykes (1988) has also pointed out that a reputation as a good teacher in a university is the kiss of death where tenure and promotion are concerned. In 1987 three of the four previous recipients of Harvard's teaching award had been denied tenure. He quotes Douglas Kankel, a tenured associate professor at Yale as saying *"it's extremely unlikely that if you are a professor with an exceptional teaching background, you will survive the tenure process."*

6. Teaching versus Research

There are signs that the pendulum has reached the limit of its travel between teaching and research. The "publish or perish" dictum is being increasingly questioned and voices are being raised in support of the importance of good teaching and away from equating scholarship with narrowly based research publications. Last year in Canada this debate raged through the pages of University Affairs (the monthly newspaper of the Association of Universities and Colleges of Canada) and the report of the Commission of Inquiry on University Education, Smith (1991) made the following statements *"Teaching is seriously undervalued at Canadian Universities"*, *"too much emphasis is being put on research and too little on teaching and learning"*, and *"I was astonished at the degree to which research and publications have become the royal road to success at universities and the degree to which teaching excellence has become unimportant."*

Articles such as "Our obsession with publication is killing us" Neill (1991), "Publish or perish: game in which education is the loser", Kennedy (1991), and "Universities" too much emphasis on research, too little on education", Goulter (1981) indicate a ground swell of concern in the academic community.

The words scholarship and research have become debased. The essence of university teaching is surely that the teacher, through wide reading, is extremely knowledgeable about his field of specialism and is able to interpret and organize the knowledge so as to be able to convey it to his students. This idea is embodied in the following quotation from Smith (1990): —

"It is my contention that the best research and the only research that should be expected of university professors is wide and informed reading in their fields and in related fields. The best teachers are almost invariably the most widely informed, those with the greatest range of interests and the most cultivated minds. That is real research, and that alone enhances teaching."

7. Engineer in Residence

Chapman (1977), looking for ways to compensate for the lack of industrial experience among university teachers of aerospace engineering, proposed that about one in ten of the teaching posts should be filled by an experienced practising engineer seconded to the university for an academic year. He also pointed out that as the engineer in residence would have no vested interest in the department, he could be a useful critic of the curriculum and of teaching methods. Furthermore this would ensure that students were exposed to someone practising the profession of engineering rather than that of engineering education.

8. Towards Integration

The problems arising from the current separation of engineering practice and engineering education are unlikely to be solved either quickly or simply. However, I believe that a solution is necessary and suggest that consideration of some of the following points may help in its formulation:

- the aims of the university education of engineers need to be carefully re-thought and redefined
- the means to achieve these aims need to be examined, including a redefinition of the qualities and experience required of university teachers of engineering and a change in the criteria determining their remuneration and promotion
- university teachers should not all be expected to contribute equally to both teaching and research; effective teaching should be clearly valued and rewarded
- to re-integrate the teaching and practice of engineering, engineers must be able to move more easily between the university and the engineering firm; the latter must demand and provide more professional input to engineering education
- before becoming a university teacher, an engineer should be required to have a prescribed, minimum period of approved engineering practice and exchanges should be established to enable (or require) engineering teachers to spend regular periods in professional practice while their teaching role is assumed by practising engineers
- experienced practising engineers should be closely involved in all engineering design courses
- external moderation or auditing of engineering courses, examinations, and marking should be introduced; accreditation of engineering programmes (judgement of how they meet the academic component of licensing regulations) should attempt to assess more than the written descriptions of courses and professors' qualifications, to consider how well the programme is actually taught and how good are its graduates
- the effectiveness of a university engineering department should be judged by the competence of its graduates and not by the number of papers published by the academic staff
- feedback should be sought from employers of engineering graduates and from the graduates themselves after about three years of employment

9. Conclusions

1. It has been argued that, in North America, engineering education has become divorced from engineering practice, due, in large part to the publish or perish syndrome currently governing academic careers.
2. There is increasing recognition of the negative impact of this problem on the quality of engineering graduates.
3. Considerable resistance will have to be overcome to achieve the necessary changes to the undergraduate education of engineers.
4. The principal agents of change will be engineering employers, through the kind of graduates they recruit. They will be assisted by accreditation boards, by professional engineering bodies, and by those university engineering professors who believe that a true measure of the value of a university engineering department is the quality of its graduates rather than the quantity of papers published by its professors.

References

Schaffner C.E., 1982 Working engineers belong in front of classes, Professional Engineer, 52,1, 17–19

Bradley F.X., 1977, Faculty residencies in engineering practice, Engineering Education, 68, 1, 31

Professor X, 1986, So you came here to teach?, ASCE, Civil Engineering, August, 40–41

Goulter I.C., 1981, Universities: too much emphasis on research, too little on education, ASCE, Civil Engineering, February, 77

Sykes C.J., 1988, Profscam: professors and the demise of higher education, St. Martin's Press, New York

Smith P., 1990, Killing the spirit: higher education in America, Penguin Books, New York

Neill S.D., 1989, No significant relationship between research and teaching, research reveals, AUCC, University Affairs, April, 18

Turns S.R., 1991, Faculty research and teaching– a view from the trenches, Engineering Education, 81, 1, 23–25

Finkelstein M., 1984, in Smith P., 1990 opus cit., 178

Rushton J.P. et al, 1983, Personality, research creativity, and teaching effectiveness in university professors, Scientometrics, 5, 2, March, 93–116

Neill S.D., 1991, Our obsession with publication is killing us, AUCC, University Affairs, January, 15

Smith S., 1991, Report of the commission of enquiry on university education, AUCC, Ottawa

Kennedy M.P.J., 1991, Publish or perish: game in which education is the loser, AUCC, University Affairs, March 16

Chapman, G.T. 1977, The resident engineer, Engineering Education, 68, 2, 192–194

Teaming Up Engineering Undergraduates with Industry

E. Allison, J.J. Collins

Engineering Division, University of Humberside,
Kingston upon Hull, North Humberside

Abstract

This paper describes a novel means, developed by staff at the University of Humberside, to expose final year engineering undergraduate students to the design process, under real life industrial circumstances.

Groups of three or four students are allocated a problem which has been identified by an industrial company but for which they have not yet obtained or been unable to obtain a solution.

Students have to identify and define the design problem, then devise several possible solutions and select the best from these. They then seek financial backing from the industrial firm to pay for any necessary build and test work to enable them to demonstrate the effectiveness of the best solution.

A description is given of the implementation of this approach, together with reflections on its effectiveness during the past two years of operation.

Keywords: Engineering Design, Industrial Problems, Group Working, Industrial Funding, Build and Test Group Projects.

1 Introduction

The authors are final year Engineering Design Tutors for the B.Eng.(Hons.) in Engineering course and have, between them, over fifty years industrial experience in engineering design related activities. They have developed a means that enables engineering undergraduates to work with industrialists, as part of their final year course of studies in Engineering Design, to solve design problems to overcome particular company operational difficulties.

The aims of these final year design studies are:

(a)   to expose students to industrial circumstances within which they have to apply their understanding of mechanical and electrical engineering;

(b)   to enable students to examine engineering issues together with broader economic considerations to devise design solutions to industrial operational problems, within time and financial constraints;

(c)   to work effectively, within a group, in a competent professional manner.

2   Design studies and Engineering Applications

Within the B.Eng.(Hons.) course at the University of Humberside, design is the integrating theme. Exposure to the design process is given to students during each of the three terms for each of the three stages in the degree programme. Written examinations for each stage of the course are held during the first two weeks of the third term. The remainder of the third term at each stage is allocated wholly to design related engineering applications activities.

Students are first exposed to the demands of the design process during the early part of their first term studies, when they are expected to design their own experiments in the first year subject entitled Experimentation, more details of which are outlined elsewhere in these proceedings.

Later that year, during the second and third terms, students, working in groups of four or five, apply their understanding of engineering drawing and their grasp of mechanical and electrical fundamentals to design, build and test a simple artefact e.g. electrically-powered fatigue-testing devices.

In the second stage, during the first two terms, the students' understanding of engineering design is further developed, culminating in a major case study involving the optimisation of materials and manufacturing considerations for a particular artefact. Later, in the third term of Stage 2, students working in groups of two or three undertake a major design related industrial problem solving assignment. They work at least one day each week in the company which has specified the problem. Second year students give an oral presentation at the University on their findings and recommendations to staff from the company where they worked. The presentation is also given during an Open Day for Humberside Industrialists. This event is staged by the students during the final week of each academic year.

The described student work gives a foundation of understanding and skills to enable them to cope with the major industrially based design assignment that they have to undertake in the third stage of the course, the details of which immediately follow.

3   Implementation of Stage Three Design Studies

An important element of the strategy of the University of Humberside Engineering Division is to work closely with industry. Accordingly, academic staff have developed the necessary range of industrial contact to identify sufficient numbers of suitable design projects for the students.

The search for these projects commences in the second term of each session, to ensure that by the start of the following academic session, a sufficient number of design projects are available for allocating to the student groups, (see sample brief at the end of this section).

Each problem is assigned to a group of either three or four final year students attending the B.Eng. (Hons.) in Engineering course at the University. The group is then acquainted with the relevant industrial procedures and briefed on effective team working. Students are reminded of the crucial need to meet deadlines and keep comprehensive records of their design work. Throughout their final academic year, the student groups hold weekly, one hour formal meetings with their tutors, to report on their progress and to seek help or advice when necessary. The students take it in turns to write the minutes of these meetings; these and other student records, are included in a group design file.

In the second week of the academic year, the student groups visit the companies, whose problems they are due to address, to be introduced to the relevant staff who provide additional background information and who show the students any necessary procedures or equipment. Companies usually nominate one of their staff to act as a contact for students should they require any further company advice or information.

The first phase of these design projects involves the students in identifying the industrial need, defining the design problem and devising several possible solutions, before selecting, using declared criteria, the most promising solution. This phase culminates in the preparation by the students of a formal written Interim Report, a copy of which is given to the company, before they make an oral presentation of their findings and recommendations to the company staff. This exciting and crucial stage is reached before the end of the first term, when normally the company will choose one possible solution and agree to provide funding for the production of any necessary hardware to demonstrate the effectiveness of the chosen solution. In one instance, funding in excess of £55 000 has been committed, as a result of the recommendations of a particular student group.

During the second phase, students work within company defined budgetary constraints, to prepare the necessary manufacturing instructions or purchasing requests. This information is included in a second formal written report, a copy of which is submitted by the students to the company before the end of the second term. The company then undertakes to arrange for the necessary manufacture or purchase of equipment.

The final phase occurs immediately following the final written examinations, which are held during the first two weeks of the third term. Meanwhile, the company has arranged for the delivery to the University of the requisite hardware for the students to assemble and test for the remainder of the term. The students then write a Final Design Test Report, which is sent to the firm before company staff visit the University. They receive a final Oral Report from the student group, during which students usually demonstrate the operation of the assembled design.

Sample Design Problem Brief

Existing Situation

Lidless paint tins are manufactured by joining together three steel parts:

(a)   a seam welded cylindrical tube, the ends of which are bell shaped;

(b)   an upper ring, which may be coated on one face;

(c)   a lower end, which also may be coated on one face.

During the manufacture of the upper rings a circular hole is pierced out and the circular blanks produced are re-used to make lower ends for smaller sized tins. The pierced blanks fall from the press and are collected in a rectangular bin which is manually hauled to the press used for making smaller sized lower ends. Individual blanks are then correctly orientated manually and fed by hand into the press. The correct feed is not always achieved, due to human error.

The Problem

The Manufacturing Manager has been asked to pursue alternative arrangements that will eliminate the reliance on the operator; in particular by:

(a)   improving the means by which multiple blanks are separated prior to their being fed into the press;

(b)   sensing whether multiple blanks are fed into the press and rejecting them before they reach the press dies;

(c)   sensing whether wrongly orientated blanks are fed into the press and rejecting them before they reach the press dies;

(d)   releasing by automatic means correctly orientated, single blanks to ensure that these reach the required position on making contact with the pair of dies.

Prepare a design proposal for consideration by the Manufacturing Manager.

4   Reflections on Design Studies at the University of Humberside

4.1   Students' viewpoint

On completing this course, students have commented very positively on the benefits which they have obtained during these reported design studies. A number have remarked that design was the highlight of the final B.Eng. year. Particular features that students felt were of value were:

(a)   the opportunity to develop the skills needed for effective group working;

(b)   the practice the course provided in conducting formal meetings including the preparation of minutes, chairing meetings, persuading others of the value of design solutions;

(c)   the design, build and test features of these studies, particularly the need to demonstrate to industrialists that the hardware manufactured to their own design drawings meets the identified industrial need.

4.2   Participating industrialists' viewpoint

Major manufacturing companies employing Chartered Engineers within Humberside have participated in this work. All have commented favourably on the value to their firm of this involvement with final year engineering design studies at the University and have expressed the wish to maintain this working partnership in future years.

Typical remarks made by engineers, who have been involved in the reported final year engineering design studies include:

" I am pleased to tell you that the design recommendations made by the University final year students earlier this year to improve the reliability of our mechanical handling equipment have now been fully implemented. I am sure that you will be pleased to learn that I am now very satisfied with the improved reliability resulting in improved operations as a direct consequence of your students' design work".

R. Skinner, Chief Building Services Engineer.

" I am pleased to inform you that my Company has decided to install the leak detection equipment that was designed by your final year engineering undergraduates this year. We look forward to continuing this working relationship with the University's Engineering Division in future years".

J. Maher, Manufacturing Manager.

4.3   The authors' viewpoint

The described final year engineering design activities enrich the formation of final year B.Eng. undergraduates in a number of ways including:

(a)   giving students a valuable exposure to industrial circumstances, within which they have to learn how to work as a team member to collectively address and solve a real life design problem to improve industrial operations;

(b)   affording students the opportunity to make a more informed choice of the sector of industry, especially for those seeking their first industrial employment.

This partnership provides industry, without professional charges, the opportunity of additional graduate level assistance. It also enables its staff to meet and become more acquainted with students and staff at the University, who could be of further assistance in future years.

5   Pointers for future operation

In order to further develop this approach to teaching engineering design at final year undergraduate level, the authors are exploring the following changes:

(a)   giving even more emphasis on Health and Safety at Work issues, by inviting a Safety Officer from industry to address the students on this topic, at present the authors deal with this aspect of design;

(b)   increasing the amount of contact that students have with practising engineers in industry during the initial problem definition phase of the design assignment.

(c)   introducing means for broadening the students' awareness of interdisciplinary group working demands of future professional roles.

Engineering Education Through Industrial, Artifact Study: A Comprehensive Engineering Applications Approach

G.T. Taylor

School of Engineering, Glasgow Polytechnic

Abstract

The integration of Engineering Applications (EA) as a pervading element in undergraduate engineering education requires substantial development. Ever since Finniston, engineering educators have, in general, striven to transform entrenched traditional courses to courses with an applications character. Any approach taken depends very much on staff perceptions of EA. Essentially, the basic concept is to relate course content to the "real world" of industry and engineering, which means either the student is taken to the "real world" or the "real world" is brought to the student. In either case, industry is required to play a vital role.

This paper addresses the latter approach as a way forward and presents the results of ongoing research at Glasgow Polytechnic directed at the development of engineering utilities centred on "real world" artifacts used to support the EA requirement and the methods of delivering the EA requirement.

The paper describes the generation of EA utilities considering the rationalisation and relevant laboratory development. Methods of delivering EA using the utilities are described.

The Role of Industry in underpinning the EA educational strategy is examined. The appropriate interaction of Industry and Academia is discussed, in particular the required industrial committment.

Full consideration is then given to the merits of adopting the proposed EA educational approach. This includes the ease of implementation, cost factors, the educational value and response of students.

Keywords: Engineering, Artifact Study, Engineering Applications, Laboratory Development.

1 Introduction

The terms Engineering Applications EAI and EAII were first introduced by the Finniston Report 'Engineering Our Future" in January 1986 where EAII was defined as:

"Application of engineering principles to the solution of practical problems based on engineering systems and processes."

The overall aim of EAII is essentially to create in the student an appreciation of the solution of real problems in engineering. Real problems suggests association with engineering systems/assemblies and components designed and manufactured in industry and not problems created purely within an academic framework.   It is then logical that some form of engineering 'hardware' drawn from industry should become a focus for EAII as it perhaps should for EAI. Undergraduate students, who have very little experience of real engineering hardware (nomenclature, function, scale etc) are then exposed to engineering 'reality'; a useful contribution to the establishment of engineering intuition.
Ongoing research at Glasgow Polytechnic has been directed at the development of:
a) engineering utilities centred on "real world" artifacts used to support the EA requirement:
b) the means of delivering the EA requirement considering two modes:
   i) concentrated EA project work
   ii) "illustrative" EA work supporting subject content.

1.1   Engineering Application Utilities and Concentrated Project Work

A compact system of assemblies (mechanical and electrical) and components inter-relating many subject areas and affording a broad diversification of engineering problems and case studies is desirable. The automobile lends itself ideally; the inherant engineering generality is obvious. A variety of sub-systems is easily identified each becoming a focus for individual student groups who may consider not only WHAT is before them and not only HOW it works/functions but more importantly, to meet the EAII aim, WHY their sub-system and its components are as they are. This would include for example design, material selection, manufacturer, cost and maintenance considerations. The automobile, also enables the student to appreciate how sub-systems are brought together to interact as a complete system. The motorcycle is another ideal artifact.
The restricted time envelope, within which EAII may be required to be met, can be regarded as advantageous . It offers the opportunity to consider as an important aspect of project rationale WHEN. With a given objective to be achieved in a limited time a major project can be developed to illustrate elements of planning, organisation and management with an emphasis on the importance of teamwork. A deadline and a challenge can be set. Project financing and budgeting can also be considered in the same way.
The initial research in EA concentrated on project work extending over a 10-11 week period full time. This was developed for BTech(Bsc) and HND students.

2 Automotive Project - The Proposal

In compliance with the foregoing ideas the following was proposed:

i That EAII activity, constrained in a 10-11 week period (350 hrs), centre on an automotive project wherein a variety of automobile sub-systems are identified as focii for EAII studies. These studies are to consider primarily the design, material selection, manufacture, cost and maintenance of each sub-system. The scope of the activity is thus enormous and the achievement of EAII aims will be dependent on staff perception of EAII activity and how they utilise the project to apply engineering principles and practice to problem solution.

ii That a road vehicle be a focus of study. A Land Rover or motorcycle is identified as the 'best', most convenient project vehicle principally due to its construction - it bolts down and up very easily. The vehicle should be restored to good working order. This sets a secondary project objective and serves to capture the imagination and interest of students with the result that the knowledge gained will be greater.

iii The project should be organised as if it were subject to the constraints normally encountered in industry namely cost and time constraints. This requires invokation of planning, organisation and management principles which will be presented to students and discussed.

iv That the already established contact with Land Rover Ltd be developed with a view to seeking an industrial input to the project.

3 Automotive Project - Outline of Scheme
This section outlines briefly the general structure of the EAII project covering a 10-11 week period and catering for around 36 students. Throughout the development of the project particular attention must be paid to safety regulations.

3.1 The Phases of the Project
PHASE 1 Vehicle strip down to its sub-systems; a record kept of all identifiable faults and service requirements. All sub-systems to be cleaned. Each sub-system to be located in EAII work cells. Required tool up/cleaning materials/safety shoes and overalls.
    Phase 1 to be carried out by technical staff. All activity, findings etc., to be reported to students as part of the introduction to the project.
    Phase 1 to be completed before the start of the EAII period.
Subsystems: No of Students

a	Engine/cooling system	8
b	Gear box/Transfer box/clutch	6
c	Axle Front/wheels/suspension	6
d	Axle Back/wheels/suspension	6
e	Braking system/fuel system/steering	6
f	Electrical system and components	5
g	Chassis and body components	4

PHASE 2   Student project work begins with comprehensive introduction to set the scene.
i Sub-system description (<u>WHAT</u> and <u>HOW</u>) by stripping down; identify all parts and their assembly; assess the wear and tear; data recording. To consider function of sub-system and its interaction with other sub-systems. Workshop and spare parts manuals used extensively. Extended use of tools etc.

ii Engineering Applications. To consider the design, material selection, manufacture, cost, maintenance etc of the sub-system and its components. This will form the heart of the project and considers <u>WHY</u>. Biggest proportion of time will be spent on this activity. Illustration: chassis consideration. How designed by manufacturer. Check calculations. Use of CAD as a tool to aid the chassis design. State of existing chassis. How to strengthen for prolonged service. Engineering drawings/design spec/design method/all procured from manufacturer if possible. Perhaps a chassis load test. All staff supervised. All data logged.

iii Renovation and Rebuild of Sub-system. Path of work/organisation/team tasks/availability of parts, where and when, communication with suppliers/buy or make/expedite parts and work schedule/assembly/testing of sub-systems and checking. All supervised and progressive inspection by staff. All data logged.

iv Assembly of subsystems as one system. Critical planning/sub-system interaction (WHAT, HOW, WHY)/interaction of student groups/road testing.
PHASE 3   Student Reporting (written and oral)
Individual reports. Log book appraisal. Oral presentation organised by each sub-system group. Assessment by Staff Supervisors.

3.2 Project Management

External Assessors

Project Coordinator

Chief Supervisor/Group

Student Sub-system Group

With the advent of the new EAll philosophy, it is important that where possible all departmental staff be involved in a supervisory capacity. Staff, have then the opportunity to:
i)   create a fresh dynamic,
ii)display their perceptions of EAII,
iii) use their initiative,
iv) learn from each other.

To cater for such, the project was defined in relatively general terms with the specific activity being defined by the sub-system team from Chief Supervisor to Student. The Project Coordinator and Chief Supervisors were to meet each week to discuss the problems and progress. Each group had to keep a Group-Log Book of all EAII activity. A Spare Parts register was to be kept by Coordinator; parts orders were to pass through this channel only. A photographic record of the project work was to be kept.

4 Automotive Project – Implementation

A Land Rover Series IIA, Safari top, seven seats was obtained. While in running order was 16 years old with plenty of wear and tear. Complete sets of workshop and spare parts manuals were obtained. The technical staff completed Phase I of the project successfully and staff/student teams set about their sub-system with great enthusiasm.

Over the project period a series of films and video programmes were organised. These dealt mainly with design and manufacturing processes.

A number of audio-visual packages on particular sub-systems were obtained from Land Rover Ltd. These were slide/tape presentations for axles, gear box and engine. Visits to the Rolls Royce factories at Hillington and East Kilbride were organised as were visits to the Hoover factory at Cambuslang and in later years to Land Rover Ltd. Computer Aided Design activities were also arranged. All of the activities were expected to be logged by each group and reference/discussion to be included in each student report. Student Study centres away from the workshop were arranged on a weekly basis. The assessment procedure required the supervisory team within each sub-system group to examine each report submitted and to assess it on the basis of a pro-forma assessment form.

5 Automotive Project – General Appraisal

It will prove rather difficult to assess the educational value of any EAII activity. Means of quantifying what 'registers' with the student or measuring the learning outcome and development of engineering intuition or 'feel' will require much thought. It may transpire that no method of truly assessing the student gain may be found. However, it is likely that exposure to the proper EAII activity, namely a presentation of real engineering objects in association with real engineering processes will awaken in the student an awareness and appreciation of the function of the engineer and the demands in knowledge and skill required of the practitioner. The students engineering vocabulary will be significantly enlarged.

The project described in this paper should achieve EAII objectives and as designed provide significant educational benefits at a very low cost. Once the utility is established there is virtually no cost.

In the operation of the project no problem was encountered such
as to invalidate the project. However, certain difficulties became
obvious. Of these the principal problems were:-
i) acquisition of replacement parts - this proved very difficult
and contributed to an undermining, in some sub-system groups, of an
initially high enthusiasm. The secondary project objective of
complete vehicle rebuild was not achieved until the following years
project;
ii) acquisition of design, manufacturing data for the particular
vehicle from Land Rover was not forthcoming at this stage in the
development of the project and groups had to fall back on the
'in-house' know-how. A strong liaison with an industrial company
signficantly enriches the project.

6 Illustrative Engineering Applications

Since EAII is meant to pervade undergraduate courses the EA
utilities established have been exploited extensively for Design and
Analysis subjects in the BEng(Hons) programme. First year students
are exposed to the artifacts as examples of engineering systems,
subsystems assemblies and parts. More detailed studies of these to
varying degrees, are conducted in subsequent years. Students much
prefer to have 'hands-on' engineering hardware as a focus to support
any material delivered in class. The perception of scale/weight,
names of parts, shape etc are confirmed. Case studies targeted at
specific subjects and topics are easily drawn from the utilities and
the established project work but in general need further development.

7 Conclusions

The following conclusions can be made:
a Students enjoy the 'concentrated' EAII type project; excellent
for technician engineers. Restoration work captures the imagination
inculcates a sense of purpose and instills enthusiasm.
b Such project work creates utilities to be used as laboratory
equipment.
c A lot is gained educationally for very little cost.
d Students enjoy 'illustrative' EA which is made easier with
availibility of utilities. Illustrative EA enriches all areas of a
course hence can be pervasive. The student learning experience is
enriched.
e Artifact study is an excellent vehicle for student centred
learning. Development of case study material can minimise staff
involvement.
f Project type is transferrable across the engineering spectrum and
further.
g Artifact study is an excellent mechanism for links to industry.
Committment by industry enriches project significantly.
h There is no limit to educational exploitation within this type of
project. Only the imagination is the limiting factor.

Building Services Engineering Design and Management Undergraduate Course

D.J. Croome, G.K. Cook

Department of Construction Management and Engineering, University of Reading

Abstract
The role of building services engineering is to ensure that optimum standards are met within a building so that it is always both pleasant and healthy for those who live and work there. Building services engineering covers all the environmental services (airconditioning, ventilation, heating, lighting, sound) and the utility services (electrical power, communications, fire protection, water, lifts) which make a building function. As technology advances and the needs of building clients become more discerning and exacting, the costs and professional responsibilities of designing, installing, controlling and operating building services are increasing. Depending on the type of building they cost 30% to 60% of the total building cost.
  The new course in building services engineering design and management is about systems which produce healthy environments for people to work and live in; are economic in the use of energy; meet the challenge of reducing atmospheric pollution and devising ways to reduce the impact of buildings on the biosphere. The inter-relationship between climate, people and buildings is an integral part of the course.
Keywords: Building Services Engineering, Engineering Design, Management.

1   Course Philosophy

The essence of Building Services Engineering is the design and management of energy resources and environment for people. It is this fundamental belief that led a group of international electrical and mechanical contractors to sponsor a new Building Services Engineering Design and Management (BSEDM) degree course at Reading University. In the words of a world famous German firm of design contractors and more recently by the Design Council:

  'People are the focal point of our thoughts and actions. Plants   are designed, planned and constructed for people. Ecologically compatible systems are constructed to the latest, most advanced technical standards to comply fully with customer requirements. At the base of all our activities stands the principle: Technology for People & Environment.'
Rudolf Otto Meyer, 1990

'Engineering is more than applied science. It has a demanding intellectual, creative, philosophical, and human content, the serious study of which has frequently been neglected. It also has essentially pragmatic aspects, since its ultimate measure of success is the satisfaction of practical human needs. In this Report, engineering should be taken to include those design activities described above where functional safety, reliability, quality, efficiency, and economy must be assured, no matter how they are realized.

Attaining Competence in Engineering Design, 1991
The Design Council and The Engineering Council.

It is important that graduates acquire not only advanced engineering skills, but expertise in management and business operation. As technology advances, and the needs of clients become more discerning, the cost and professional responsibilities of designing, installing, controlling and operating building services are increasing. Buildings are no longer designed by one person. They are designed and constructed by teams of people. This new course in building services engineering emphasises the balance needed between design and management skills. Students learn about the importance of meeting the needs of clients and users; the development and implications of using advanced technology in buildings; the use of alternative energy resources; and the management of the design and construction processes. In addition, students study a modern European language, thus recognising the expanding market potential for the construction industry in mainland Europe and other countries.

2   The Interdisciplinary View

The home of the course is the Department of Construction Management & Engineering, which, since its inception in 1972, has provided the education in technology and management needed by the construction industry of the future, Croome (1991a, 1991b). It has a interdisciplinary view of construction and engineering and is contributing to the debate concerning the education of both professions, Cook (1991). Its staff are from many construction professions and relevant academic disciplines. The Department, including within it the Centre for Strategic Studies in Construction, has an international reputation in research and teaching in the design and management of the built environment.

The course is taught in other Departments as well as Construction Management and Engineering. Those other Departments are: Engineering, Meteorology, Cybernetics, Psychology, Economics and Languages. The course, which has been planned using the experience and insight of professional engineers and academics from several of the university's departments, represents a significant development in course design in the UK. Equally, the highly collaborative Industry-University approach to project work represents a major milestone. Building on the enthusiasm and commitment from industry, graduates of the course will be able to make a major contribution to meeting the increasing challenge of international competition and advancing technology with respect to the design, construction and management of healthy buildings.

The course is a full-time one of three years duration which includes an equivalent of one term in each of the second and third years spent on project work jointly monitored and assessed by the University and industry.

3   Experiential Learning

Each student has an industrial mentor, as well as a tutor in the University. The course thus exploits the advantages of experiential learning, Kolb (1984), by using the industrial and academic work places. There is also an Advisory Committee for the course which meets approximately three times per year and includes two Consultants as well as six Contractors. In planning the course a wide interpretation of design has been adopted to cover concept design, installation and construction, commissioning, maintenance and facilities management. Thus, the course aims to familiarize students with analytical, synthesis and evaluative skills. Students completing the course are being educated to cope with the increasing rate of change in technology.

4   Economic and Social Blend

Most major decisions in the building industry require a blend of economic and social as well as technical understanding and it is appreciated that however brilliant the original design this will not be successfully achieved unless management processes are equally as good. Thus, the spirit of the course reflects the view expressed by the Engineering Council in its publication entitled, Raising the Standard:

'Engineers of tomorrow must be technically competent, market conscious, commercially adept, environmentally sensitive and responsive to human needs.'

This is nowhere more true than in the building services engineering sector where the services costs of a building can be as much as 60% of the total building cost. The impact of modern technology is having a profound affect on building services, not only with regard to electronics, microprocessors and communication systems, but also with respect to materials, energy and the environment. In the next decade it can be expected that the architect will need to rely increasingly on the skills of the building services engineer. In turn, the engineer will have to develop a wider understanding of building design including passive as well as active solutions. Climate changes are now directing a new impetus to saving energy so that equipment has to be designed to operate with very high efficiencies over the heating and cooling seasons. Even more fundamentally, engineers and architects have to rationalise with the client the need for effective energy use. Health in buildings is another aspect that emphasises the need to understand the holistic nature of environmental design.

5   Effective Communication

However good the base of knowledge, it is less effective unless there is good communication. Throughout the course the need for good communication is emphasised. For example, in the final year the students have to present their major project work to a review panel which includes practitioners as well as academics. Such project work also provides the principal way in which the subjects are integrated.

6   Breadth and Depth: A Framework

It is sometimes alleged that a broader course cannot impart a depth of engineering knowledge. Building services engineering, is by its very nature, a wide discipline and one course cannot possibly cover all of the basic knowledge in every area. Increasingly it is being recognised that many traditional engineering courses have become over-stocked in factual knowledge, particularly with regard to analytical techniques. This course aims to provide a substantial framework to which the student can develop further understanding by self-learning and experience. The Engineering Council has suggested that the overloaded nature of some single subject syllabuses derives partly from an insistence on cramming students with excessive amounts of material in every subject. Such an approach is neither satisfactory for intended research workers nor for those entering the industrial and commercial worlds. Rather, it is the ability to solve problems and for self-learning which is very important.

7   Course Aims

The general aim of this course is to provide an educational foundation for a Chartered Building Services Engineer to pursue a career in the design and management of building services and environmental systems.
The specific aims of the course are:

(a)   To provide a knowledge and an understanding of the engineering and management skills required in the building services industry.

(b)   To provide a substantial framework to which the student can develop further knowledge by self-learning, continuing professional education and work experience.

(c)   To enable the graduate of this course to undertake decisions in industry which are based on sound engineering, management, economic and social knowledge using analysis, synthesis and evaluative skills.

(d)   To foster communication skills and the ability to be an effective member of a design and management team.

(e)   The ability to communicate with other professionals in a second European language.

The structure of the BSEDM course is shown on Diagram 1 and the syllabus for the course is shown on Table 1. The course has received accreditation by the Chartered Institution of Building Services Engineers.

References
Cook, G.K. (1991) Foundations Built on Science, **Chartered Builder**, 3   (9) 14-15.

Croome, D.J. (1991a) Educational Futures for the Construction Industry, **Industry and Higher Education**, 5, (1), 35-46.

Croome, D.J. (1991b) Education for the Built Environment, **Proceedings of Ove Arup Conference on Education for the Built Environment**, Cambridge.

Kolb, D.A. (1984) **Experiential Learning**, Prentice-Hall.

BSEDM Course

Year	Autumn Term	Lent Term	Summer Term	Vacation
Number / Week	1 2 3 4 5 6 7 8 9 10	1 2 3 4 5 6 7 8 9 10	0 1 2 3 4 5 6 7 8 9 10	1 2 3 4 5 6 7 8 9 10 11 12
1	Lectures (10 Weeks)	Lectures (10 Weeks)	Exams; Fieldwork; Lectures (9 Weeks)	EA 1; Industrial Placement (10 Weeks)
2	Lectures (10 Weeks)	Lectures (10 Weeks)	Exams; AROUSAL; Options + Integrated Project (8 weeks); Proj Assesment	Industry/ Europe (6 weeks); Industrial Placement (6 weeks); Integrated Design Project
3	Lectures (10 Weeks) + Integrated Design Project & Diss (1.5 day/week)	Lectures (10 Weeks) + Integrated Design Project & Diss (1.5 day/week)	Proj Assesment; Lectures; Exams; Examiners Meeting; Graduation	
Number / Week	1 2 3 4 5 6 7 8 9 10	1 2 3 4 5 6 7 8 9 10	0 1 2 3 4 5 6 7 8 9 10	1 2 3 4 5 6 7 8 9 10 11 12

Diagram 1

Table 1   Building Services Engineering Design and Management Course
Syllabus

Part	Subjects
I (two terms)	The Construction Industry Building Construction Building Engineering Science Economics for Managers Electrical and Mechanical Engineering Science Management I Management and Engineering Applications $ Engineering Mathematics I Atmosphere and Climate
II (three terms)	Environmental Engineering Systems § Electrical Engineering Systems and Control I § Lighting Acoustics and Noise Control § Management II Construction Economics Human Factors Engineering Applications (EA1) $ Modern European Language Computer Aided Design $ Atmosphere and Climate Engineering Mathematics II
III (four terms)	Environmental Engineering Systems and Architecture § Utility and Space Engineering Services § Electrical Engineering Systems and Control II § Modern European Language Business Management Exercise (Arousal) $ Integrated Projects * Integrated Design Project and Dissertation * Management Options (choice of two from: Innovative Technology, International Construction, Site Management and Practice, Construction Project Management, Facilities Management, Business Organisation and Planning, Finance for Managers).

Note:
$ 100% weighting on coursework and/or laboratory work.
§ 70% weighting on examination 30%, weighting on coursework/laboratory work.
* 85% weighting on project 15%, weighting on project presentation.
All other subjects have 100% weighting on the examination.

Industry and Higher Education Working Together

I.T. Hornett (*), I.M. Cox (*), M.J. Hopkins (*), T.J. Oliver (**)

(*) Teaching Company Associate
(**) School of Systems Engineering, Portsmouth Polytechnic

Abstract
This Paper presents the advantages of creating co-operative links between Academia and Manufacturing Industry. The specific benefits to both parties are illustrated with practical examples. Proposals are made for the development of this mutually beneficial rapport into relevant commercial applications.
Keywords: Teaching Company, Academic Links, Undergraduate Development, Industrial Projects, Credit Accumulation and Transfer, Continuing Education,

1   Introduction

The goals and objectives of Manufacturing Industry and Academia are fundamentally different.

Overall, Academia strives to extend the boundaries of knowledge to give a greater understanding of the universe. The enormity of this task means that research is largely conducted without a fixed time scale. Dissemination of information to others such as students and other researchers is conducted via formal lectures and conferences and backed up with an information database held for the use of all interested parties. The academic institutions equip students with the necessary skills to be successful in their chosen career, the major "consumers" being manufacturing industry and commerce.

In contrast the primary goal of manufacturing industry is to delivery a financial gain by satisfying a carefully targeted customer requirement within a tight time scale. To meet these requirements manufacturing industry requires constant improvement to products, services and production processes. This is achieved by directed research with problems particular to the objective being overcome. Having solved the prescribed problem the research information is usually of a high commercial value and its release is suppressed to hold the marketing advantage for as long as possible.

Both academia and industry have expectations of each other. Industry relies on Academia to educate and train potential employees to suit its needs. Academia requests funding for research relevant to the requirements of Industry.

Although there is a great divide between the goals of the two bodies, both are often engaged in similar research with common interests. The potential for information exchange is immense but often is limited by communication constraints.

2   Current Links Between Academia and Industry

On Engineering Degrees, a traditional link between academia and manufacturing industry has been the student final year project. Involvement varies, but in essence industry provides a problem and sometimes logistic and financial support. Often the level of support is directly dependant on the strength of the previous commercial success of such links.

Final year projects are intended primarily to develop the student's theoretical skills in a real situation to solve an industrially relevant problem. The support offered by industry can in some cases result in tangible hands on experience which might not otherwise have been available. No less important, but rather more difficult to quantify, is the effect practical experience can have on learning motivation. In addition the student gains an appreciation of the industrial environment in preparation for employment.

Employment opportunities may often develop from projects, particularly where students can add to the sponsoring company's experience base. In such cases, continued links with academia can be more readily promoted.

The sponsoring companies may themselves benefit in a number of ways. Solutions to long-standing problems can often be solved from a fresh and unbiased standpoint. Such an approach can be provided by the student, who is frequently able to overcome "tradition blindness" and provide a small but vital break-through.

An important aspect of this contact, is the academic database available to the student. This can take the form of papers, reference works, or professional monitoring by the academic supervisors. The fund of knowledge held in both formal and informal sources can be difficult for industry to exploit and by using the project student as a guide accessibility can be enhanced for the sponsor.

Academia can gain vital research funding through the promotion of such student links. In the short-term, through funds for student projects and in the long-term through specific research projects and consultancy.

Current links reach only a proportion of what could be gained by full cooperation. The potential for mutual gain and development is tremendous and must be pursued if economic growth and technological progress is to be enhanced.

3   A Structure for Successful Links

An increasingly popular form of the linking of academia and industry within the United Kingdom is the Teaching Company Scheme. This programme was initiated in 1975 and derives its identity from the concept of Teaching Hospitals where theoretical knowledge is enhanced by practical application.

The methodology of the Teaching Company is straight forward. A proposal for a project is developed over a fixed time scale, usually three years. The proposal contains the objectives of the project, the academic and commercial partner's previous history of successful joint ventures, details of the commercial benefits and a specific project plan demonstrating the targets to be achieved.

One such scheme is the TRW-United Carr Ltd/University of Portsmouth Teaching Company Scheme administered and supported by the School of Systems Engineering.

This proposal which began in December 1990 and which currently employs three postgraduate Teaching Company Associates has three main objectives. These are:-

1   To investigate and improve the design methodology, processes and tooling involved in the manufacture of metal stamping and moulding components.

2   To implement a policy of tool standardisation of the large scale manufacture of automotive components, initially at Aylesbury, then on a European basis.

3   To investigate and then develop the concept of flexible manufacturing cells in moulding, metal stamping and assembled components.

The Commercial successes so far of the proposal are:-

1   A capital injection from TRW Inc, the American parent company to develop manufacturing methods.

2   Identification of the Aylesbury facility of TRW-United Carr Ltd as the centre for metal parts manufacture in Europe with transfer of equipment to the UK from Europe.

3   The development and initiation of an information collection system required for the manufacture of fasteners throughout Europe from April 1992.

4   The development of new methodologies for fastener design to be implemented in January 1993.

The success of the Teaching Company Scheme obviously depends entirely upon the working relationship of the academic and industrial partners which can be enhanced or invalidated by the Associates employed to develop solutions to the original proposals.

High qualified, motivated and energetic Associates can assist the academic partner in many ways. Some specific examples are:-

1   The enhancement of knowledge at the academic partner. Experience gained from the development of this teaching Company proposal enabled three lecturers, to tender successfully for a major consultancy.

2   The development of fresh final year undergraduate projects. For the Academic Year 1992/93, eight projects have been identified to which the Associates will make a major contribution.

3   The enhancement of links between European institutions. Two, three month, projects have been developed for these co-operative ventures.

4   The generation of case studies. Case studies have been developed in Materials Engineering, Manufacture, Design and in Management Studies.

5   The formation of new Teaching Company proposals through the Associates raising the level of awareness amongst Academic staff.

4   Credit Accumulation and Transfer

Additionally the Teaching Company Directorate, through the Council for National Academic Awards has established the award of Master of Science by Credit Accumulation and Transfer.

The registration for the Associates for this award was a major event for the academic responsible for this Teaching Company Proposal.

The production of an individual Learning Contract, arrangements for assessed work, developing links with external examiners can only serve to enhance the development of new courses at the University of Portsmouth.

The MSc by CATS overcomes many of the disadvantages of full and part time Masters programmes and is yet another method of enabling graduates to achieve their potential.

The CATS scheme enables the intellectual ability of the Associates to be assessed in developing solutions to the real problems associated with resolving the commercial objectives of the Teaching Company proposal.

The enhancement of the Associates competence by external influences such as training courses, conferences, production of papers, the development of their personal and social skills through vertical as well as lateral access in the company and the academic institution. Continuing improvement in presentation skills and confidence levels may also be assessed.

5   Conclusion

The School of Systems Engineering has since 1986 developed six Teaching Company Proposals. Of these four have current existence.

Projects have included the design of manufacturing systems, development of lower limb prostheses, environmentally friendly combustion processes, electrical and electronic design and robotics.

Associates have gained higher qualifications and enhanced career prospects. Industry has gained new products and processes with the associated increased commercial success. Academia has gained from relevant industrial experience with recognisable improvements in both teaching, research and consultancy.

To conclude the effect of the Teaching Company Scheme has been totally successful in enhancing methods by which Industry and Higher Education work together.

The Development of a Learning Contract Postgraduate Diploma/MSc in Business and Manufacturing Practice Between Academe and Industry

C.U. Chisholm

School of Engineering, Glasgow Polytechnic

Abstract

The paper reviews the development of a Post Graduate diploma and/or an MSc where all the learning is completed within the work place. Most qualifications developed with industry to date involve a course being completed partly in the academic institution and partly in the work place with conventional lectures, tutorials and laboratory work forming part of the course. The model developed is based on learning goals, learning objectives and assessment criteria being identified from a work programme agreed between the employee, the company and the academic institution. It incorporates as part of the assessment agreed business growth objectives to be achieved by the end of the contract.

The basis of the Learning Contract is the establishment of a programme of up to 2 years which incorporates the award of SCOTCATS credit points to each goal and makes use of open and distance learning materials in conjunction with coaching, counselling and mentoring. The model invokes the philosophy of business growth training where delivery of business growth objectives decided by the company are correlated to the learning and the outcomes identified for the employee within the Contract.

The project is controlled and monitored by academic supervisors, lead consultants and external examiners working closely with industrial supervisors in the form of a learning contract team.

The paper outlines the transferability of the Framework and illustrates how it could be extended within an academic institution and to institutions in Europe and Worldwide.

Keywords: Work Based Learning, Postgraduate Study, Business, Manufacture, Europe.

1 Introduction

The increase in challenges facing higher education through the 1990's and into the 21st century demand by increasingly flexible patterns of learning to be developed. The conventional model of higher education is being challenged and it is conceivable, particularly with relevance to post graduate learning that graduate entry to full-time courses will become less appropriate as a means whereby such learning is achieved. It is to be expected that flexible patterns involving learning integrated with work will increasingly have a vitally important role to play in the delivery of opportunities to a large range of employees within industry and commerce. This could simultaneously address the demands of the economy for a better educated labour force, the demands of employees for professional and career development and demands of industry and commerce for learning within the work place directly correlated to objectives within the company. Such a model would require to be designed in the context of the rapidly changing environment in which higher education must operate where partnerships with industry and commerce can maximise flexible learning systems and ensure client satisfaction.

It could be used for the unemployed and as a vehicle through which the unemployed person could return to full employment. This could be accomplished if appropriate grants were made available to industry and commerce. In this way highly flexible but individualised awards could be obtained at the post graduate level in business and manufacturing practice.

In terms of correlating the business objectives of a company to the learning objectives of a Learning Contract this could be achieved through the establishment of a Business Growth Training approach where growth of the company is synchronised with growth of the people. Thus in establishing the model, particular consideration was given to the government based scheme named Business Growth Training (option 3) for industry and commerce. [1] It is based on the use of an initial strategic analysis of the company to establish and identify areas for growth. From the identified areas and in agreement with the company, work programmes would be evolved and from these work programmes the Learning Contract relating to the employee would be developed.

To ensure accurate measurement of the learning it is proposed to use the SCOTCATS Scheme at post graduate level where the learning would be measured using credit points and assessed using the grade points scale. To assist the learning it is proposed to establish a database of open learning materials which would then be used to allow the individual to underpin the learning taking place in the work place.

It is anticipated that many individuals within industry may only qualify for entry to the Framework through assessment of their prior learning and therefore it is essential that the model accommodates entry of the individuals through formal assessment of prior learning and experiential learning either singly or in association with formal qualifications.

2   The Business Growth Training Aspect

The basis of the Framework is a work programme agreed by the company where the objectives required by the company are firmly linked to the Learning Contract for each individual. The areas for growth form the basis of the determined work programme for the individuals within the company. To ensure delivery of the growth outcomes agreed with the company, a lead consultant or consultants will operate within the organisation throughout the duration of the project and will coordinate the development of the individuals chosen to take part. Thus company growth is matched by people growth. Once a project is complete the individuals who have been trained through the Framework should be able to promote further growth in the absence of a lead consultant. Thus the Framework is primarily supported by consultants leading and delivering the required objectives agreed with the company while at the same time ensuring that there is growth of a number of individuals associated with delivery of these objectives and where the learning and the implementation outcomes are measured for each individual with a view to the award of a post graduate qualification.

3   The Learning Contract Framework

The Contract for each individual is based on the learning which can be achieved from the agreed work programme set up by the company to achieve required growth objectives. Fundamental to the Contract is that emphasis must be placed on the learning that the individual has acquired and not the experience itself.

Normally the work programme would be produced in the form of a Gantt Chart indicating the amount of time required to achieve each part of the work programme. For an MSc degree this would probably involve a 2 year period. Each part of the work programme would then be examined for the learning which could be achieved and a set of learning objectives established. Sets of learning objectives coherent to the programme would then be developed as a learning goal. Once sets of learning objectives have been identified a number of learning goals would thus be built up from the work programme. Thereafter the activities required to achieve the learning objectives would be established and appropriate assessment criteria evolved. On the basis of the assessment criteria a number of assessment methods would then be allocated against each learning goal. In setting up the assessment procedures due account would be taken of the fact that the basis of the Framework is to ensure that not only is the learning achieved but the learning is converted in practice.

Once the learning goals have been established, the SCOTCATS scheme would be used to allocate each learning goal credit points correlated to the amount of effort required by the individual to complete that learning goal.

In deriving the Contract from the work programme, it is essential the identified learning should be designed as a coherent, integrated and progressive programme of learning and in this sense it can be regarded as equating with a conventional taught postgraduate programme.

For each learning goal established within the Contract, credit points allocated will be on the basis of the notional effort required by the individual as a proportion of the total credit points required to complete the Contract. This will include the effort required to complete the activities associated with the learning goal, directed/structured studies and associated private study. The total Contract will identify a number of learning goals each of which will be different in terms of the learning process required and the knowledge and skills expected.

As the Framework is intended to operate within a company, it is recognised that programmes may change during the course of the Contract. Learning goals may require to be altered to reflect changes in the company's work programme. It is proposed that where marginal amendments to the Learning Contract are required these will be made as they arise but where substantive changes are required it will require re-approval by the appropriate committee in the academic institution. Where a change is required the opinion of the external examiner will also be sought. If the external examiner judges that a substantive change has taken place then re-approval of the modified learning goals will be sought.

Each learning objective will be assessed by an appropriate method of assessment which takes into account the learning and its subsequent implementation. The modes of assessment employed to measure the assessment criteria will accurately reflect the learning achieved by the individual in close integration with practice. For example, an individual may be assessed on the design of a piece of equipment, the implementation of a hardware/software system within the company, the completion of a market survey, the establishment of new methods of manufacture, or the establishment of a control system. Oral assessments will be combined with these methods to examine each learning goal. After each goal has been assessed, grade points will be awarded from the SCOTCATS scheme for satisfactory performance during assessment and the individual will accumulate credit points at each stage assessment. Failure to demonstrate satisfactory fulfilment of the learning objectives will result in no credit points being awarded.

4   Progressive Learning Contract

In the majority of cases it is expected that a Learning Contract will be able to be developed on the basis of a projected work programme for the company. In some instances, due to the nature of the work within an organisation, a Learning Contract may not be able to be derived and established as the programme cannot be determined sufficiently far ahead. In this case, a Progressive Learning Contract would be used, first defining the strategic objectives required by the organisation and as the work programme is established, it is proposed that learning objectives and learning goals could be established progressively. A partial derivative of the total Learning Contract would be submitted for approval to the academic institution. In this way a number of partial parts of the total Contract would be developed at appropriate intervals. It is proposed to operate a set of partial Learning Contracts in organisations where the work programme can only be developed progressively within the organisation.

5   Articulated Learning Contract

Where individuals wish to enter a Learning Contract without an Honours degree or its equivalent as determined by assessed prior learning it is proposed to make available an Articulated Contract where the individual will be required to complete a greater number of learning goals than the minimum specified where entry is via an Honours degree or its equivalent.

Where a person enters the Learning Contract with either an Honours degree or its equivalent, they will be required to complete 120 credit points for the MSc, a minimum of 70 for the post graduate diploma and a minimum of 35 for the certificate.

With an articulated programme, where a person enters with an appropriate degree or its equivalent, the individual will be required to first complete a postgraduate diploma of 90 credit points prior to continuing for the MSc. Where an individual enters with an appropriate diploma or its equivalent in terms of assessed prior learning, the individual requires to obtain 65 credit points for the postgraduate certificate prior to entry to the remainder of the programme leading to Diploma or Master's level. The candidates will be counselled as to whether the average grade points achieved indicate that further progression is advisable. The Articulated Contract is designed to widen access for individuals who do not have an appropriate Honours degree or who cannot establish its equivalent through the use of an assessed prior learning portfolio.

6   Progression and Assessment

The grade points allocated to the learning goals will be decided by the internal examiners who would normally be the academic supervisors of the Contract. The external examiner will be kept informed of each assessment and will be present at the assessment of the first learning goal and the final learning goal and overview of the total Contract. At the final overview the external examiner(s), in consultation with the internal examiners will agree a recommendation for an award. The individual will require to complete all learning goals described in the Contract and achieve an average of five grade points for each learning goal. Where entry to the Framework is by appropriate Honours degree or its equivalent, the candidate will be awarded an MSc on the completion of 120 credit points, a postgraduate diploma on completion of 70, a postgraduate certificate on completion of 35. Where entry is through an Articulated Learning Contract at degree level or its equivalent the candidate will be awarded a postgraduate diploma on completion of 90 credit points and the MSc on completion of 140. Where entry is by a higher diploma or equivalent, a postgraduate certificate will be awarded for completion of 65 credit points, the postgraduate diploma for completion of 100 and the MSc for completion of 150.

Individuals will be considered for distinction where an average of at least 14 grade points is maintained over the Contract.

The nature of the Framework is such that it will not be possible for an individual to repeat parts of the Contract which forms part of the company's development programme. Individuals who fail in their first assessment of a learning goal will be allowed one reassessment. It would not be permitted to substitute learning goals to replace a learning goal which a candidate has failed.

7   Transferability Within The Academic Institution

The Learning Contract Framework could be developed as a general Framework mechanism, available to the Institution to be used for a number of disciplines where it can be demonstrated that Learning Contracts can be developed with the Industry and Commerce associated with that discipline. The only limitation in terms of transferability to other fields would be the need to provide the professional consultancy backup in the discipline area.

8   Development Of The Framework In Europe And Worldwide

The Framework could be implemented in Europe and worldwide on a similar basis to that described. Again the problem associated with transferability into Europe and worldwide would be the requirement for the professional consultancy being completed. Where the foreign Institution has no experience with a consultancy company then the host Institution in the UK operating the Framework could provide through a joint venture the lead consultancy. It would be possible through joint supervision of the Framework for joint awards of the two Institutions to be made. This would provide an ideal way for an Institution in the UK to collaborate with Institutions in Europe and worldwide.

9   Summary And Conclusions

Over the past eighteen months the model for the Learning Contract Framework has been developed and recently formally validated. The Polytechnic is in negotiation with companies to establish the first Contracts as a pilot study over the next two years. A progressive Learning Contract will be tested in Budapest, Hungary, to assess the difficulties of operating at a distance from the Polytechnic.

The establishment of the Framework for Postgraduate awards in Business and Manufacturing Practice provides a creative and innovative development where learning is achieved within the work place integrated to a work programme with specific company objectives where success in achieving an award is a function of completing the learning and demonstrating its successful implementation.

10   References

1. Business Growth Training/1 Training Agency, United Kingdom, 1989.

The GEC Professional Development Consortium

G.R. Jordan

GEC Professional Development Consortium, Dunchurch

Abstract

The development of the managerial and technical expertise of the professional staff within a Company is essential to its continued success and future, particularly if it is to respond to the many changes taking place in the business world. GEC have always recognised the need to develop and maintain its staff at the highest level but considered around 2 years ago that something further needed to be done and established a major new initiative, the Professional Development Consortium. The scheme is targeted at all levels of the professional staff in the Company, whether these are graduates of a few years standing or established engineers and managers who require knowledge and understanding of the latest management techniques coupled with the most up-to-date technical expertise.

This paper describes the main features of the scheme which is an association of Universities and Polytechnics in partnership with the Companies to produce modular, high quality education and training at postgraduate level in subjects ranging from business studies, such as finance and marketing, to specialised technologies. The overall objective is to present flexible PERSONAL DEVELOPMENT PROGRAMMES to suit the needs of an individual and the Company. The manner in which this has been achieved is discussed together with the question of cross-accreditation of courses between the academic partners which is a major feature of the Consortium. The scheme continues to develop with the need to include an increasing element of in-house Company developed courses.

Keywords: Engineering, Continuing Education, Universities, Polytechnics.

1 Introduction

The challenges presently facing industrial Companies in the UK are probably the most complex and far reaching that have been seen in modern times. The doubling of knowledge every two and a half to three years, particularly in the electronic and related areas of engineering, means that engineers are practising in a world where the constant up-dating of skills is required. A market oriented economy with a reduced commitment to Defence requires that engineers and technical staff must possess a deep understanding of the business in which they operate and that this knowledge must be complemented by technical skills of a high order.

The recognition that a new and radically different approach to management development and the education and training of its professional staff led GEC to search for a scheme which could address these important issues. Such a scheme needed to be flexible, satisfy the needs of the Companies and their employees, cost effective and integrated with the many other training schemes already in operation. It was clear that the Company alone could not provide the comprehensive scheme that was required and that the expertise and knowledge within the University and Polytechnic sectors should be utilised in partnership with the Company. The concept of the Professional Development Consortium (PDC) was born.

This paper describes the scheme and presents the principles and philosophy under which it operates. The experiences to date and the difficulties encountered in integrating the scheme into a highly decentralised Company where each business unit operates under the demands of its particular market sector is discussed.

2 Underlying Principles

The principles upon which the PDC is based may be summarised in the broad statement of its objective;

"To improve the current performance and secure the longer term earning capacity of the technology based Companies comprising GEC through raising the technical and managerial competences of its professional staff".

In practical terms, the scheme must satisfy a number of requirements. These were determined in the many discussions and debates that took place in the formative period, and are:-

- the training must be modular, consisting of short intensive courses.
- quality controlled in some way.
- relevant to the needs of the Company and the individual.
- absence from work should be limited, 5 days maximum at any one time.
- flexible delivery, principally residential but with distance learning and part-time study where required.
- training should be at post graduate level and allow the award, where appropriate, of a Post graduate Diploma or Masters degree,
- training should be available to all professional staff; senior managers, middle managers, engineers and technologists at all stages of their careers.
- no barriers should be presented to study in terms of prior academic qualifications.
- the modular courses should cover the whole range of management and technical subjects relevant to GEC.

The above required a fundamental change to the way training and management development schemes currently operated. In particular it required a change in approach both from the Company's point of view and within Higher Education.

3 The Scheme

The only way that was considered feasible to produce a scheme which satisfied the above criteria was to form a Consortium with selected Universities and Polytechnics which would provide and deliver the comprehensive range of courses required. The key element was the establishment of PARTNERSHIPS between the academic Institutions and the Companies which would together develop programmes tailored to the needs of the Companies. A number of Institutions were approached which had existing links with the various individual business Units and possessed relevant expertise and knowledge. Most importantly the Institutions either had existing courses which fitted the basic criteria, viz modular, post graduate, quality assured etc, or could provide from their present portfolio, material which could be easily adapted.

The academic partners are either Full or Associate Members of the scheme depending upon whether a complete modular Masters programme is offered or a group of modules at post graduate level, validated by an appropriate body but not comprising in themselves a full programme leading to an award. 9 Institutions are presently Full Members and these reflect the geographical spread of GEC Companies from Scotland to the South Coast. 2 Institutions are associate members at the present time and these are likely to increase in due course.

A complete list of the Institutions is given below:-

Brunel University
The Brighton Partnership (Brighton Polytechnic and the University of Sussex)
Coventry Polytechnic
Cranfield Institute of Science and Technology (Royal Military College of Science, Shrivenham)
Henley, The Management College
UMIST
The Open University
The University of Strathclyde
The University of Warwick (Warwick Manufacturing Group, Warwick Business School)
and the Associate Members, the Universities of Birmingham and Essex.

Around 200 modules are available and these have been grouped into six categories.

- Personnel and Group Skills
- Managing Business, viz finance, marketing etc.
- Managing Logistics, viz project management, control etc.
- Design and Manufacturing Operations
- Information Technology
- Technology for Products and Systems, viz specialist technical modules

Each of the 200 or so modules have been validated by the Institution concerned either through its own internal processes or through a delegated authority, i.e. the Council for National Academic Awards. In all cases, a credit rating has been assigned which means that some form of assessment is involved, generally a post-module study or assignment; for the distance learning courses, a written examination is usually required.

The credit system used is the U.K., CNAA Credit Accumulation and Transfer Scheme (CATS) which at post graduate level (level M) requires a total of 120 points for the award of a Masters degree with typically 60 or 70 points for the taught element and the remainder given for a major project dissertation of between 10 to 15,000 words. A typical module is a 5 day residential course plus pre-reading and a post-module task or case study requiring a further 15-20 hours of study to be submitted within 6 weeks of the completion of the course. This would attract 6 credit points.

No attempt was made to obtain complete uniformity between the credit ratings of the various modules. The CNAA CATS scheme is used as it was intended, that is, to provide a framework for the interchange and cross-linking of modular courses between Institutions. Cross-accreditation is extremely important as the extensive and varying needs of the Companies requires flexible arrangements in terms of the mix of management and technical courses with the added constraints of time, cost and availability.

It is possible with the scheme to produce PERSONAL DEVELOPMENT PROGRAMMES for employees consisting of combinations of management and technical courses arranged to suit the individual's and Company's needs.

In order to ensure that the highest standards are maintained and that coherent programmes of study are arranged and the degree regulations at each Institution are satisfied, the following guide-line was drawn up, viz each academic Institution will have the control over the content of its degree programme and while agreeing to accept material from another institution it will have the final say in its relevance to the proposed programme.

In practice, this means that the Institution supervising the project would also present around half of the taught element, the other half (typically 5 modules) would be from elsewhere. An employee has therefore to decide at some stage in his programme the direction in which he wishes to proceed and then to register with the lead Institution.

Such an approach means that the employee pursues a coherent programme of study and not a random mixture of courses from a range of Institutions. Such an approach has proved to be acceptable to the Institutions involved in the scheme and cross-accreditation achieved in this way has not proved to be a problem. Close adherence to the guidelines that were established in the formative days of the scheme is important however and the constant re-assurance needs to be given that the lead Institution controls the programme of study for an individual and can, if need be, exercise a veto on what is proposed.

For those employees who are attending STAND ALONE modules only, the decision to proceed towards a degree or post graduate diploma would be taken only if and when appropriate, normally after 12-18 months from attending the first module. The majority of employees will follow this route and attend courses tailored to their particular needs; the framework of a Masters programme providing the means of ensuring quality.

4 Present Position

There has been acceptance throughout the many individual Companies constituting GEC, that the concept of the scheme, the principles on which it is based and the many features that it provides is the way forward. This does not mean that the scheme can be easily integrated into the extensive training and management development initiatives that already exist. The decentralised nature of the Company and the varied mechanisms and hierarchical structures that exist means that each business operating in its own market sector must be treated in its own individual way. The difficulties can be clearly seen when one considers the extensive range of GEC's interests in defence, telecommunications, power engineering, consumer products etc. with operations throughout the UK and Europe.

Crucial to success is the requirement to present the training needs of the Companies in a structured and planned way. These may be short term to respond to an immediate requirement for skills to fulfil a particular contract and the changing demands of a major project. In these cases the portfolio of courses can provide an immediate solution.

The main purpose however is to provide for the medium to long term and to develop the managerial and technical skills of the professional work force. This requires the structure and mechanism to prepare the PERSONAL DEVELOPMENT PROGRAMMES for individuals. Such an approach requires in many Companies a more ordered and systematic method to personal development than is presently in force. While there are many excellent schemes aimed at new or recent graduates which fulfil their training and development needs in their formative years, there is considerably less attention given to an engineer established in his/her career. Particularly important is the lack of training to provide for mid-career changes, job or Company re-structuring, technical updating and for interchanges between managerial and technical positions. Critically important for a technically based Company is the ability to develop managers who have maintained their technical expertise and engineers who have developed business acumen.

5 The Way Ahead

The scheme provides the means to develop the managerial and technical expertise of the professional staff in the Company in a structured, coherent and extremely flexible way.

As it develops the balance of courses between residential, distance learning and part time attendance will change with an increasing element of distance learning material. At the same time, a greater number of company developed courses will be included; these "in-house" courses, while of a high standard, do not usually include any assessment procedures and therefore will have to undergo a validation process before acceptance into the scheme. This will clearly take some time and involve a learning exercise both on the part of the Company and the validating Institution.

Cross-accreditation of modules between Institutions is also likely to increase and while this has not caused any serious problems to date, difficulties are likely to be encountered as the need increases to balance management modules with more and varied specialised technical subjects. Provided however that true partnerships have been established between the Company and the academic Institution and that the present flexible approach is maintained, insurmountable problems are not likely to arise with each case treated individually.

The introduction and development of methods to produce Personal Development Programmes is essential if Companies are to utilise the Professional Development Consortium to its fullest extent. This will be difficult in many cases and will take considerable effort and determination on the part of all concerned, the personnel and training managers and engineering and technical staff.

The ultimate success of the scheme however will depend upon the number of employees who attend and satisfactorily complete courses, either as a single unit, in a group comprising a programme of integrated study or a full degree programme. While the take-up is increasing, this is a slow process and there is some way to go before the scheme is firmly established. While it is principally for GEC Companies the scheme is not exclusive and could be used as the basis of a National Scheme in Continuing Education. It is particularly relevant for companies which share a common technological base such as customers or suppliers to GEC.

There are many difficulties and problems to be overcome before the scheme becomes an integral part of the management development and training operations of the Company. There is confidence however that its objectives will be fully met, viz "to develop partnerships between academia and industry to provide high quality, relevant training and education tailored to the needs of the Companies in order that they will prosper in the 1990's".

The Management of Academic Research

J.Mavor
Faculty of Science and Engineering, University of Edinburgh

Abstract
This contribution to the debate on the organisation of university research, from a Dean's perspective, confirms the timely need to explore novel management structures. Competing teaching pressure requires the merits of graduate schools and other models to be examined and adopted, where appropriate, to maintain research momentum.
Keywords: Research, Graduate Schools, Universities, Management.

1 Background

The funding climate for university research in the UK is now in rapid transition. All observers predict that this will lead inevitably to a division of universities into a hierarchy led by an elite of 'research dominated' higher education institutions (HEIs). For all universities therefore the objective will be to attract and manage research funding even more effectively than hitherto, and provide encouragement and support for staff who are high achievers in research. This changing climate (HMSO, 1991), which is certain to continue unabated to the 21st century and beyond, is placing unprecedented demands on the organisation of research as well as on financial control. For many universities the management burden of these increased responsibilities will fall upon deaneries, rather than upon their constituent departments as was often the case in the past.

Traditionally, a dean's role in furthering research has been relatively passive with low-profile intervention. Principal investigators have been primarily responsible for initiating and prosecuting research projects and operated virtually independently of heads of departments, let alone a deanery. Committees which debated faculty research strategies were fairly uncommon; and the research profile of a faculty was an *ad hoc* aggregate of academic staff participating in primarily curiosity-led activity. Accountability was predominantly at individual level, and the ready availability of research money enabled a degree of compensation to counter the inevitable overspends. Deans have had, of course, important roles to play in allocating resources, notably expensive equipment money to departments. Gradually, however, deans have been drawn into a debate on priorities; involving strategic decisions on finance and the organising and structuring of research. Many research frontiers demand an interdisciplinary approach which must be underpinned by effective management. Such key issues will not disappear: there is a positive correlation between quality departments in research and their corresponding funding levels.

Providing an appropriate management structure to support interdisciplinary research is not, of course, a new consideration. Deaneries have been drawn into research management in a major way with the advent of interdisciplinary research centres (IRCs), funded by the Research Councils and other ancillary sources. With this organisational model for research, pursued in a university environment, the prime role is research although with attendant postgraduate student supervision. Such IRCs, having either a broad or specialised remit, are rather removed from academic departments being distinct, fully-funded entities.

What is of future importance is the efficacy of organisational processes under the pressures referred to above. The aim of this paper is to highlight the vital need for appropriate organisation which might require radical solution.

2 Competing Pressures

Academics in the UK have always had to set priorities to satisfy the dual demands of teaching and research, specified in their employment contracts. What has become more apparent of late is that there is an emphasis towards teaching efficiency to satisfy high undergraduate student throughput demands. Many able academics are now questioning their ability to amply satisfy the dual demands on their time and are now feeling the strain. Deans are naturally fully aware of such pressures and are examining ways in which to counter these, that will provide lasting solutions and not just be stop-gap. Two such approaches are of topical interest in the UK and their merits are being widely debated. Both could perhaps maintain postgraduate research levels which in some HEIs may well be under threat. One relates to the status of the individual academic and the future form of their contracts; and, the other, relates to research structures based on graduate or research schools which are not prevalent here. The merits of these will be briefly discussed as part of the continuing debate.

3 Contractual Aspects

Traditionally, UK academics have engaged in both teaching and research on a broadly equal basis. Indeed, their contracts of appointment require them to participate in both aspects to a greater or lesser extent, according to their latent abilities. Heads of department naturally perceive the particular strengths of colleagues and deploy these attributes to best effect to satisfy the overall teaching burden. This approach has the added advantage of matching to the aspirations of academics in their charge, and enabling ambitions to be fulfilled to some extent. Carried to its logical conclusion, some staff could solely assume the role of teacher, whilst others could be solely researchers. The current debate is whether individual contracts should specify a separation of the two duties and whether this outcome would be good for individuals and/or the profession.

The disadvantage in separating the two normal roles, contractually, in the author's view, outweighs any advantage gained. On initial appointment the future career path of a young academic cannot be foreseen. Individual careers develop according to inherent ability and are strong functions of the changing external influences. In engineering particularly, research activity depends largely upon success in achieving major research income both from national and international sources. True, different contracts could be issued periodically to reflect changing duties but a liberal interpretation of a more general one preserves flexibility. Having said this; it must be ensured that promotional exercises are responsive to the range of possible career profiles and are not polarised. This aspect remains a perennial problem.

4 Graduate/Research Schools

Graduate schools are common in some countries, particularly the USA, but are less often found in the UK. Perhaps one reason is that American students seem more likely to progress through a masters course often wholly or largely taught, rather than research based, before embarking upon postgraduate research leading to a doctorate. In the UK such a progression is less common, and those students wishing to move towards a a higher degree are more likely to enter a postgraduate research studentship directly following the award of their batchelors degree. Therefore here, there has been little apparent need for a 'separate' graduate organisation, because both undergraduate and postgraduate education goes hand in hand. Moreover, academics, with their flexible contracts, span the 'divide' naturally with no perceived difficulty. This having been said, a debate on the need for and merits of graduate schools has been opened by Sir Mark Richmond, Chairman of the UK Science & Engineering Research Council (SERC), Richmond (1992). The feeling is that for financial exigence's sake, scarce research funding can only be harboured in the university sector if new structures are adopted, unencumbered by undergraduate teaching. Without such channelling of research income the quality of research could be undermined. Furthermore, such structures could be wide in formation and span faculties, if not be inter-institutional in remit. The attendant advantages of graduate or research schools, provide:

- a focus for postgraduates and their work, particularly fostering common interests, needs and problems

- an additional 'marketing' focus for recruitment and research funding, by demonstrating a special care for and interest in postgraduate affairs

- an administrative focus for postgraduate activities generally

- a focus for the introduction of new taught postgraduate courses and continuing education programmes
- a co-ordination point for seminars, lectures, workshops and conferences
for postgraduate students.

Such a list of advantages, which could be expanded further, is persuasive and
almost certainly outweigh any disadvantages.

One critical factor relating to accountability is that a graduate school can
provide a financial 'ring fence' within which postgraduate education and
research can be clearly accounted for and value for money easily assessed.
There is no question that research-based advanced teaching is a vital objective,
the question for an HEI is whether a graduate school is the correct way forward
to achieve this goal?

The prime concern about graduate schools is whether the existing beneficial
interaction between undergraduate and postgraduate education would be
reduced or even eliminated. Most academics acknowledge that undergraduates
benefit in their honours-level projects if they are conducted in a research-
orientated environment. Also research staff careers can benefit from (limited)
exposure to undergraduate tutorials and laboratory demonstration. These benefits should not disappear with the formation of a graduate school, provided that
the interface is carefully managed in time and cash terms.

5 Conclusions

Universities in the UK have a key role to play in fundamental research (Hilsum,
1992) although, in future, research activity levels may vary more widely across
all HEIs. Because of teaching pressures and the dearth of funding in some
fields, universities will be obliged to investigate and adopt new structures in support of research. Suitable features of the American graduate schools can be
considered for adoption, and we can learn from the Fraunhofer Institutes in
Germany which incorporate a vital industrial dimension. The search for a suitable model appropriate to each HEI must proceed apace, so that a suitable focus
for quality postgraduate education can maintain momentum.

References

Hilsum, C. (1992) Regaining the path to British prosperity, Physics World,
February, 26-33.
HMSO (1991) Higher Education: A new Framework, HMSO, London.
Richmond, M. (1992) Brain cells with a Nobel mission, The Higher, February
28, 18.

Engineering and the PhD - Standards and Relevance

J. Butcher

Faculty of Engineering, Science and Mathematics, Middlesex University

Abstract

For many years, the PhD has been understood in the UK and many other countries as an academic qualification for research into a fairly tightly specified scientific or technological subject. PhD graduates sometimes continue to follow research careers in academia or industry, but many transfer to other activities, such as teaching, production, marketing etc. It is often not obvious that their training relates to the requirements of their employment, especially in the various fields of engineering, where the constraints of the job differ widely from those of the PhD project.

In the UK, the Science and Engineering Research Council has recently taken an initiative towards a distinctive doctoral award in engineering, different from, but complementary to, the traditional PhD. SERC is funding a pilot program by which a small number of Institutions will offer innovatory programs leading to such an award. These programs incorporate features deemed particularly relevant to engineering, and also involve close cooperation with industry which is expected to contribute significant additional funding.

The paper presents the author's view of the current situation in the UK, including an assessment of the relative merits of the 'traditional' PhD and the 'Engineering doctorate'. The questions of international comparability and the differing perceptions of postgraduate study and qualifications will also be addressed.

Keywords: Engineering, education, doctorate, PhD

1 What is a PhD?

Although there are many pages of academic regulations governing the award of a PhD degree, it is not easy to define precisely its value and relevance to the student, to his present or future employer, to his Institution or to mankind in general. It has been said that "I can't define it, but I know one when I see one". Unfortunately, even this is not true, because PhD's are awarded in a huge range of disciplines, from Philosophy itself to Pure Science, Engineering and, more recently, to Performance and Visual Arts. Anyone who has sat on a Research Degrees Committee will be aware that a PhD rewards very different skills and intellectual qualities in the various fields of activity.

A possible, though cynical, rationale for this diversity may take the view that a PhD is a key to some kind of material or psychological advancement - a career booster perhaps. Thus if one discipline has one, why not all? Certainly it is often a sine qua non for a career in Higher Education. What particular recommendation it constitutes, other than for self-replication, is not always clear.

Perhaps the most common and uncontentious definition of a PhD program is that (a) it must make an original contribution to knowledge, and (b) it must encompass training in research methods. The latter criterion, of course, begs the question: "what is research?", a debate which, fortunately, is outside the scope of this paper.

In the context of Engineering PhD's, we are left with the historical prescription that a program of study must involve research together with 'appropriate' training. So how does a 'traditional' PhD project satisfy these criteria and simultaneously meet the requirements of a future career in an Engineering environment, which almost certainly will make quite different demands from those asked of a career academic, a research physicist or indeed a philosopher?

2 What is Engineering?

Here is another awkward definition to be circumvented if possible. It will suffice for now to take a broad view that engineering is about products, and thus puts emphasis on the **application** of knowledge rather than on its acquisition. This is, of course, rather simplistic, but it provides plenty of scope for exploring how an Engineering PhD might differ from doctorates of other flavours.

There is a school of thought that the introduction of such considerations as product viability, cost, marketing, quality control, production and other such pragmatic manifestations of the real world somehow degrades the academic worth of research. Whether or not this is tenable, these constraints certainly make life difficult for the practising engineer. He or she certainly needs the advanced training implied by a doctoral program, providing that it is relevant to the engineering ethos. The word 'ethos' invites mention of another word from Greek, albeit with a German connotation. This is the term, "techne"; yet another indefinable! Again, it is a quality which many of us would claim to recognise in a subliminal way, being an expression of the very essence of engineering awareness, flair and competence. "Techne" is a word which perhaps could elevate a slightly suspect engineering PhD to a position unequivocally alongside the safer and more esoteric 'pure' science awards. All we need to do is define it, or at least show how its acquisition may be attempted in the context of a doctoral program.

3 Deficiencies of the Engineering PhD

Many feel that there is nothing wrong with the framework of a conventional PhD, in the sense that it can be interpreted so as to permit the application of engineering criteria. However, others believe that there is a need for a redefinition in order positively to prescribe these criteria and to distinguish clearly the engineering-oriented award from the traditional one.

Engineers, and particularly employers, tend to believe that most PhD's are too remote from the real world of industry, and suited only for the few graduates who continue to follow a career in fundamental research. Some employers, indeed, positively discriminate against PhD's.

Generally, it is felt that postgraduate training for subsequent employment in engineering (or for any career) should have a broader base. While there is general agreement that a major 'research' project should continue to be central to the program, the environment in which this is carried out and the inclusion of a significant proportion of additional studies is often recommended.

The project itself can legitimately be organised as a group collaboration. This approach, rare in conventional studies and presenting problems of defining individual contributions, is positively encouraged, being seen as an opportunity to gain experience in planning, group organisation and commercial awareness. The 'original contribution to knowledge' and the 'intellectual challenge' criteria can be satisfied no less rigorously than in a conventional PhD, even though the nature of the contribution or the challenge may need to be defined in a different way.

Formal coursework and assessed taught elements of the program are seen as important. This is not new, though relatively rare in the UK. However, for engineering, the nature of such studies is seen as broader and less focused on the specialism of the research investigation than would be the case in many other disciplines. Development of the individual's personal skills and task-related abilities are deemed equal in importance to his/her subject knowledge.

The project itself can perhaps be defined within a broader spectrum than before. Design techniques, product development and production methodologies are legitimate areas for research, provided that the objectives can be defined and the student's performance measured with a rigour and a level of academic validity comparable with that previously required for more conventional phenomenological and knowledge-based studies. 'Commercial' criteria such as cost, marketability, competitiveness, etc become almost mandatory considerations instead of being seen as a dilution of academic standards.

4 The SERC "Parnaby" initiative

In 1990, the Education and Training Committee of the UK Science and Engineering Research Council published a report on the relevance of the PhD to Engineering. This report, arising out of a working party chaired by Professor John Parnaby of Lucas Industries plc, was circulated widely to academia, industry, professional Institutions and other interested parties. Reactions were mixed, but there was widespread confirmation of the value of designing an engineering doctorate program substantially different from the conventional PhD. On the strength of this response, SERC decided to fund a pilot scheme, and set up an implementation group to select three HEI's or consortia to take part in the experiment.

4.1 The SERC criteria
Certain assumptions and conditions were decided in advance. The most significant of these were as follows.
- Each participating group would receive funding for 40 students, designated "Research Engineers", over four intakes, ie 10 students per year.
- The selected groups would need to demonstrate not only strength in a normal academic sense, but would need to guarantee substantial industrial support. This would need to include real participation in planning and operating the scheme, and also significant financial commitment.
- The proposals would have to show an innovatory approach to the doctorate program, along the lines of the Parnaby report. Studies could take up to four years, would include up to a 25% weighting on assessed coursework, together with an emphasis on teamwork and technology transfer.
- A considerable proportion of the project time was expected to be spent in a collaborating company.
- The award was intended to be of equivalent standard to the PhD, but distinctive. A designation such as EngD was favoured.
- The chosen groups could be multidisciplinary but the 'RE's' would need to form a coherent group. Recruits were expected to be high flyers, carefully selected for aptitude as well as academic achievement.

4.2 Funding
In order to attract high quality applicants, SERC set the basic stipend at £7000pa, which a participating company would have to increase by at least £2000pa. In recognition of the centres' costs in running the scheme, a grant of £50000pa would be made for each group of 10 students.

4.3 Parnaby Outcomes

Thirty-three outline applications were received, of which nine were from consortia. The working party selected eight for further development. These Institutions then submitted expanded proposals, and were visited by members of the working party. In the end, three schemes were recommended to be funded from October 1992.

The selections were made on the published criteria, with a deliberate intent to achieve a mix of groups in terms of the type of scheme proposed.

4.4 The nature of the EngD

The majority of proposed schemes followed the general philosophy of the guidelines (not surprisingly). The major differences were in the details of administration, the type of industrial participation and the degree of commitment demonstrated by the department(s) and collaborators.

It seems that a 'typical' EngD program will have the following features.
- It will take four years, although there may be provision for partial exemptions, based on previous experience.
- It will involve close collaboration with, and supervision by, an industrial collaborator, with significant periods spent in the company.
- There will be a requirement for at least 20% of the time to be spent on assessed coursework, including taught courses which will cover a wider field than the special research topic(s).
- Industrial relevance will be ensured, in part, by the inclusion of group work, project management and similar activities, all contributing to the final assessment.

5 After "Parnaby" - The Future of the EngD

In assessing the likely outcomes of the pilot scheme, it is important to remember two facts.
- The SERC is a funding body with no direct control over degree awarding Institutions or the regulations covering such awards.
- If the experiment is seen to succeed, it will be taken as a model for the future. SERC itself has speculated that 25-30% of all Engineering doctorates might then be on the "Parnaby" model.

Two conclusions can be drawn. First, that if the EngD becomes a widely offered qualification, many students and Institutions will not receive the same high level of funding as enjoyed by the participants in the pilot groups. Even if industrial support on a sufficient scale is forthcoming, it is improbable that the SERC will be in a position to maintain their support at the level of the pilot scheme. It follows that many EngD programs will be undertaken under conditions determined solely by the HEI's and with a highly variable level of funding.

It is certainly not suggested that any particular EngD award would be devalued. Indeed, it has been said that many PhD's already meet most or all of the Parnaby criteria. Probably many more could do so by relatively minor changes to regulations and program specification. It is not yet clear to what extent the success of an EngD program depends on the scale of the operation and the level of funding in the host Institution.

Unfortunately, the SERC experiment will probably not answer this question. A high level of funding in large and prestigious centres might be thought to guarantee success, or at least make failure the only meaningful result. After all, if the results are not unequivocally acclaimed under these 'ideal' conditions, it might be doubted whether the concept could ever be successfully implemented?

Seen at this time, perhaps the most likely outcome is a qualified success or a valuable indicator for the future. There is little doubt that the public and private scrutiny of engineering PhD programs will result in some re-thinking and probably considerable changes in practice. Not all the Parnaby-style features of a doctorate program depend on having top quality students or massive funding in the supporting departments.

Whether we will see a wholesale change towards the EngD designation is a moot point. To some extent this debate has obscured more important issues. Although the benefits are obvious, especially in marketing terms, so are the dangers. It could be seen as divisive, unnecessary and as an added confusion in a scene already complicated by too many award designations and at a time when there is an increasing need to seek comparability and uniformity on the international stage. Perhaps, in the end, it doesn't matter very much. If the EngD experiment results in a significant increase in the number and quality of relevant postgraduates working in the various engineering disciplines, whether in industry or academe, then the investment will have been worthwhile.

6 Bibliography

Edwards, Prof Sir Sam (1975) Report on Postgraduate Training, SERC

Technical Change Centre (1986) Report on the Careers of Postgraduate Scientists and Engineers, SERC

Ford, Sir Hugh (1987) Report on Postgraduate Engineering Research, SERC

Prais S J (1988) "Qualified Manpower in Engineering", National Institute of Economic Research

"Education and Employment of Engineers" (1989) Report to the US National Academy of Engineering

Engineering Education and Career Development as a Continuum

J. Byrne

Department of Education Affairs, The Royal Academy of Engineering

Abstract

The Royal Academy of Engineering has for some years operated a programme known as the 'Engineering Education Continuum' which provides a continuity of engineering education and training from the lower sixth at school to graduation and possibly to post-graduate studies. The Continuum is extended by a series of other industry linked programmes. These include a mime theatre which presents engineering topics in a visually exciting way to children from the age of five to twelve; a number of further schemes which assist undergraduate and post-graduate students to travel abroad; support for exchanges of staff between industry and universities; provision of the opportunity for qualified engineers to update their engineering expertise by way of further education courses; supplementing the salaries of young academics while in the early stages of their teaching careers; sending of experienced young engineers to work for a period in Japan, and the funding of senior, industry-based engineers as Visiting Professors of Design at a number of universities. Access to this extended continuum enables a student to form an appreciation of the full potential of an engineering career, including the various forms which post graduate development might take, and in addition offer him or her help and guidance in achieving it. The extent to which these various activities can be linked to form a coherent education-industrial progression, and so ultimately a total career development plan, is discussed.

Keywords: Engineering, Education, Career Development, Continuum Pre-university, Undergraduate, MBA.

1 Introduction

In September 1991 a paper was presented at Sheffield University describing the continuity of engineering education experience provided by what was then The Fellowship of Engineering, but is now The Royal Academy of Engineering, with generous support from Mr David Sainsbury's Gatsby Charitable Foundation. The education experience provided then by the Continuum ran from pupils in their lower sixth at school to graduate engineers in their first job and to one particular piece of post-graduate training, the intensive one year MBA course taken at one of certain designated European business schools.

The Academy's involvement in engineering education however, extends beyond that described at the Sheffield meeting. It starts with children as young as five years old and carries formal training well beyond that associated with undergraduate or immediate postgraduate procedures.

2   Education and Career Development

It is commonplace in current thinking to accept that even a qualified individual must requalify from time to time. The logic of that is partly that his or her role may change and partly that the rate of change of technology itself makes it necessary continually to update individual knowledge and competence. That leads to the concept of an education and professional development continuum which is shown graphically in Fig 1.

2.1   The Schools Programme
The circle labelled "School" in Fig.1 covers three levels of activity. The first is a mime theatre working with children aged from 5 to 12, the second working from 12 to 16 and the third is concerned with students in their lower sixth form year - that is to say the year before 'A' levels.

2.2   The Year in Industry Programme
The Year in Industry Programme is one in which students who have obtained a deferred place to read engineering at a university spend a year with an industrial company in a well defined job - as opposed to pursuing a learning programme - for which they are paid and which they write up as a project at the end of their time.

2.3   The Undergraduate Programme
The Undergraduate Programme does not concern itself with the details of the university course itself but enhances the period at university by a number of devices including the award of bursaries which can be used for specific purposes such as travel or language learning or can take the form of a two or three week tour of industry. In the second year of the course this tour will be overseas and will embrace the cultural and social aspect of the countries involved as well as the industrial interest.

2.4   The MBA Programme
The MBA course is self explanatory except to say that it is the one year

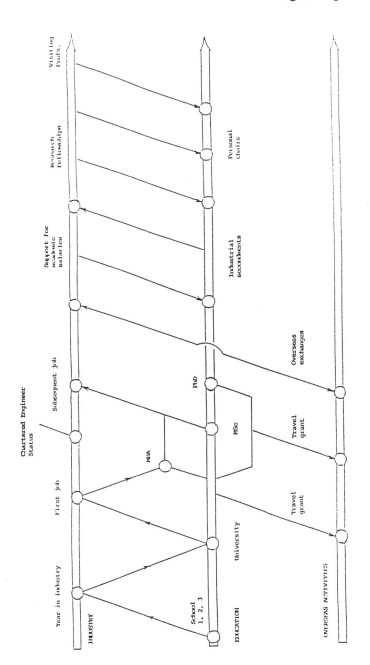

THE EDUCATION AND CAREER DEVELOPMENT CONTINUUM – FIG.1

intensive course taken, at the moment, at certain specified business schools in France and Switzerland. They are IMD in Lausanne; INSEAD, EAP, the Ecole Nationale des Ponts et Chaussees, and Theseus, in France. This specification of the continental European schools is not a comment on, or a criticism of, the capability or value of the United Kingdom schools or those in the United States but has the particular purpose of using the limited resources available to ensure that the students involved form an appreciation of attitudes and practices in Europe in preparation for working within the Single Market.

2.5   Further Undergraduate and Post Graduate Activities

Other support programmes are available and are shown, not necessarily in strictly chronological order, from the university element onwards.

2.5.1 For example, there is an undergraduate travel programme which enables undergraduates to travel abroad to take engineering courses or work in industry. There is a similar arrangement for graduates to travel abroad, particularly those staying on at university in teaching roles or to do higher degrees to enable them to attend or to read papers at conferences overseas.

2.5.2 There is also a programme, funded by Esso which provides money to top up the salaries of young academics during their early years. A similar scheme is funded by ICI and support is given also to specific PhD students.

2.5.3 There is a programme of Senior Research Fellowships which enable individual lines of research to be pursued in collaboration with industry and a university and there are personal chairs for specific topics. The Chair in the Principles of Engineering Design at Loughborough University is an example.

2.5.4 Other programmes enable academics to spend periods in industry of up to a year at a time by reimbursing the institutions for the replacement cost of releasing the staff concerned.

2.5.5 Finally, there is a particularly satisfying reverse flow provided by a visiting professor scheme which is currently sending 50 industrialists to some 21 higher education institutions as Visiting Professors of Design.

2.5.6 Reverting to the industrial line, Panasonic funding provides the opportunity for qualified engineers to take modular MSc courses in various aspects of new technology to add to, or to update, their initial qualifications.

2.5.7 The way in which an engineer must extend himself or herself is of course not purely technical. The MBA is an example of a totally new sort of qualification, but less dramatic kinds of development are needed closer to the technical function as, for example, the acquisition of experience in engineering practice in different countries and against different cultural and political backgrounds. To this end there is a programme, which sends young engineers to Japan for periods of up to a year and there is an exchange arrangement with Canada which is privately funded.

3   Eligibility

The minimum conditions for eligibility vary with the nature of the award and the age range for which it is intended. For example, the mime theatre sets no conditions of eligibility for its audiences other than that the children be school pupils and that the performance be at the school and by arrangement with the school authority. At the other extreme the MBA Award is highly competitive and made after fairly exhaustive selection procedure against a background of conditions which include a good first degree and Chartered Engineering status or being close to achieving Chartered Engineering status. Generally speaking, for all the other programmes, very precise conditions are set down for applicants and an assessment of the merit of the applications made, often using assessors drawn from the Members of the Royal Academy of Engineering. The existence of the awards is publicised by a series of devices ranging from advertisements in the national press and in such periodicals as the 'Economist', to articles and notices in professional journals and academic publications. A good deal of passing of information is, however, by word of mouth with successful applicants talking to fellow students or University Department talking to University Department. Most of the programmes depend on industrial co-operation and involve "triangular" liaison amongst academic departments, industrial companies and The Royal Academy of Engineering.

4   Summary

The programme overall is a mechanism for exciting interest in engineering at school level, for enabling a student embarking on a engineering career to progress in an orderly way to the status of Chartered Engineer and to obtain coherent professional development from there on. It provides also a link between three strands of engineering, those of commerce, technology and academia.

The main objectives of this integrated programme are:-

(a)   To excite in children, as early as·possible, an interest in engineering and to sustain that interest throughout their pre-university schooling.

(b)   To persuade students of suitable calibre to elect to read engineering at university level and to go on to become Chartered Engineers.

(c)   To provide for those who develop an interest in the managerial and commercial aspects of engineering the opportunity to undertake first class business training at an appropriate point in their careers.

(d)   To provide for those who elect to pursue a technical career the opportunity of revising and updating their technical qualifications or enlarging their technical development in other ways as they progress.

(e)   To assist those who opt for an academic life with financial support and other encouragement through such post graduate development as doctoral research; to provide also the opportunity of refreshing their awareness of industrial practice by periods of secondment to industry.

(f)   To provide a reverse flow of industrial experience and industrial practice through such devices as the Visiting Professor of Design programme.

(g)   To assist in financing overseas visits for the purposes of attending or presenting papers.

(h)   To give the opportunity of experiencing engineering practice in other countries by such schemes as visiting engineers to Japan and the Canadian exchange programme.

4   References

Byrne, J.   An Engineering Education Continuum, Conference on innovative teaching in engineering, Sheffield University, September 1973

The Industrial Centre Approach to Applied Engineering Education in Developing Countries

P.B.U. Achi

Federal University of Technology, Owerri

Abstract
For the teaching of engineering in developing countries appropriate practically oriented textbooks are lacking just as the number of local industries are too few. Therefore the use of "students industrial work experience scheme" (SIWES) provides only a limited and inadequate solution to the problem of low practical skills possessed by new engineering graduates. This paper presents the practical approaches to the inclusion of industrial practice in the curriculum for engineering education in tertiary institutions using industrial centre (IDC) with optimised multidisplinary engineering operations. This way the cost of sound applied engineering education, is brought within the reach of tertiary institutions in developing countries.
Keywords: Engineering Education, Industrial Centre, Industrial Training, SIWES, Academic, Skill.

1. Introduction

In 1985, the "International Conference on Science and Technology Education For Future Human Needs" at Bangalore in India strongly recommended the integration of existing local industrial operations into the teaching of technology at all levels of education nationally. In developing countries the teaching of engineering in particular had been based on textbooks written by industrial nations who cite practical examples based on experiences often foreign to the developing countries.

From developments spanning two centuries western industry of today is rather too sophisticated for the engineering understanding of many developing countries by way of cursory references made in engineering textbooks in these countries. Although indigenous authors in developing countries are beginning to write engineering textbooks, the progress in this direction has been too slow to make an impression. Until recently the practical ability of the Nigerian engineering graduate, for example, had been too low on first entry into a job that job finding had been too difficult for fresh graduates in engineering.

To improve the situation, the Federal Government in Nigeria had made the attachment of engineering undergraduates to industries for some periods during their studies compulsory.

2. Limitations In The Use of Off-Campus Industrial Attachments

The "students industrial work experience scheme" (SIWES) attachments prescribed for engineering undergraduates last between 6 and 12 months (for 4 and 5 years of study) before the students enter for final year. The SIWES attachments are expected to be made to industries considered related to the students discipline of study The majority of engineering schools in Nigeria schedule the SIWES exercise for three long vacations and engineering schools in Federal Universities of Technology do one semester (4 months) of SIWES in addition.

The engineering institutions (at University level), establish liaisons with industries through the university SIWES liaison officer and the university SIWES coordinator both of whom are senior administrative and academic staff respectively. Usually, it is the industry that decides on what number of students and disciplines of study it is competent to train. Often this decision goes contrary to the plans of the schools which are beset with a large number of students usually in the conventional engineering areas of agricultural, civil, chemical, electrical/ electronics, materials and mechanical engineering.

The industries usually consider the SIWES student a little nuisance who at best is unproductive and occasionally destructive and a burden to quality management!

2.1 Few Industries and their Limited Range of Operations

Developing countries are so classified because they lack adequate developmental industrial base. In Nigeria, for example, the number of industries suitable for SIWES is so few compared with the population of engineering students requiring SIWES (over 20,000 each year) that many of the institutions fail to attach a good percentage of their students each year. Since SIWES is included in the engineering curriculum as two, three, or four courses (in the 2nd, 3rd and 4th year) the students graduation is delayed if he misses some attachments. When such students spill over to the future years the problem is compounded and the engineering school sees no alternative but to arrange some makeshift and grossly inadequate SIWES to clear a backlog of incomplete attachments using simple maintenance workshops.

The situation is also not helped by the frequent closure of industries due to lack of adequate foreign exchange to purchase raw materials and spare parts following the wake of severe economic recession. Even when in operation the industries suffer severe limitations in the range, variety and engineering content of the operations they engage in. In a lot of cases the industries are "turn-key" systems which do not design or formulate their products and tools in - house. They are mainly factories imported from abroad with so many "black boxes", mysterious chambers, enclosed mechanisms and processes. It is a well known fact in developing countries today that turn-key factories do not train people and cannot bring about regenerative development. Even the supply of spare parts is by way of sealed sub-assemblies which have to be completely replaced whenever a minor component within it malfunctions; that is maintenance by use of "turn - key" spare parts!

Also because of the limitations on training resources the industries are unable to follow the training programmes drawn up by schools for different disciplines.

Therefore the SIWES undertaken with such industries is inadequate and does not meet the objectives, so it became necessary to devise other training strategies for students of engineering.

3. Industrial Centres In Engineering Education

As the operation of SIWES continues to be pursued in Nigeria, the involvement of industrial centres and estates in the attachments is helping to ameliorate the perennial problems encountered with purely profit-oriented industries. The first three industrial centres (IDC) started in Nigeria by the sixties and more are being established in each state of the federation. From their inception the function of the industrial centres has been to provide consultancy services and engineering training to small scale industrial owners and their operatives at minimal charges. The IDC'S are organised in departments along the lines of the engineering disciplines: mechanical (machine shops), electrical/electronics, chemical, structural and carpentry departments. Meanwhile the departments are equipped to produce simple spare parts, repair and maintain general industrial appliances and equipment, dye cotton and textile fabrics. They also produce castings in concrete and provide engineering training in these areas. Since the 1980's on - campus "centres for industrial studies" have been in operation in some tertiary institutions in Nigeria as described in Achi

(1987).
These on - campus industrial centres are owned and
financed by their parent institutions and are also used for
teaching engineering skills, developing new products and
processes, and the other functions performed by the state
owned industrial centres. The provision of support services
to local artisans and tradesmen enables some of the skills
possessed by the local small scale industries to be
conveyed to the students of the engineering schools using
these centres.

3.1 The Functional Educational Objectives of the Industrial
Centres.

The industrial centres are designed to achieve the
following educational purposes:
(a) functional skill training in engineering and technology
(practice).
(b) development of new products and processes through
research in engineering and technology involving the
students of the tertiary institutions.
(c) engineering management skills required for generating
cash revernue.
The limited facilities in the centres serve to train the
participants in the need for very prudent management of
resources (time, machine, equipment and materials). The
zonal sharing of industrial centres between educational
institutions and small scale industries facilitates the
tailoring of engineering curriculum to the industrial
processes and technology available in the shared centres
and local small industries.

4. Designing Engineering Curriculum with Industrial Centres
in Mind

The principal educational role of the IDC'S is the
imparting of practical engineering skills required by local
industries in relation to the theoretical knowledge
previously acquired or to be acquired by the participant.
As described by Otieno (1987) the requirements of
education for industry in developing countries are centred
around:
(a) General academic but socially relevant education
(carried out in tertiary academic departments with
industrial centre) - based academic curriculum as
illustrated in Achi (1988).
(b) Laboratory training (in academic departments and
industrial centre).
(c) Specialised sectoral (skill) training in the IDC and
industrial estates.

4.1 Industrial Centre- Supported Academic engineering
education

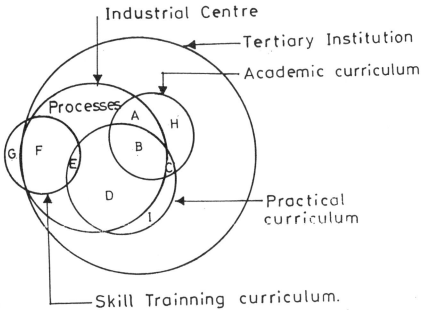

Fig. 1. Industrial centre-based curriculum.

For each engineering discipline the academic curriculum
is tailored considerably to the interfaces in the
industrial centre processes (fig 1); namely:
$$A + B + D + E + F$$
The portions of the academic and practical curriculum
outside the industrial centre (fig.1),namely;
$$H + C + I$$
represent the relationship of the academic/laboratory
education with the society within (and outside) the
tertiary institution.

In the (H + C + I) experiences, the future graduate is
trained to relate the economic and engineering processes in
(A + B + D + E + F) to other disciplines of engineering and
the society. The "practical" and "academic" trainings are
interwoven and evolve mainly from the industrial centre and
the needs of the society within and outside the campus. The
industrial centre-based academic curriculum solves the
problem of studying engineering as mere book work removed
from local industrial realities. The students understanding
of the theories which are practically introduced by
industrial processes enhances the possibility of future
original contributions to the area of engineering. This

approach narrows the students theoretical knowledge but
deepens his understanding of chosen theories and exposes
him to a multi-disciplinary study of engineering.

4.2 Specified Skill Training

The final phase of the industrial centre based
curriculum is at E +(F)+(G), (Fig. 1) where the student is
involved in skill training specialising at E in the
commercial processes at (E+F) to provide the skill needed
by local industry at (G). During the final year the student
concentrates at (E) which is related to his area of
engineering. The students final year project falls within E
while availing himself of opportunities at (F) and (G).
Appropriate staff are identified at the engineering
departments (academic) and periodically seconded to the
industrial centre to enable the engineering students
benefit from the engineering skills possessed by such
staff.

5. Conclusions

With industrial centres in place the SIWES attachment to
external commercial industry is planned to fit into the
penultimate year of the undergraduate engineering
curriculum only. In the other years at the IDC the student
now learns the rudiments of his discipline of engineering
and engineering practice. With the needs of industry
changing with economic fortunes and technical innovations,
especially in computer involvements in industry the subject
matter of the industrial centre-based curriculum possesses
in - built flexibility.

6. References

Achi P.B.U. (1987) "How best the Universities of
Technology can help industrialise Nigeria", Education,
Industry and Development, (ed. D. Waddington, et al),
Pergamon Press Ltd, Oxford.
Achi P.B.U (1987) "Developing local industry through
'centres for industrial studies' in tertiary institutions
in developing countries", Industry and Development, UNIDO
JOURNAL, 21
Achi P.B.U. (1988) "Approaching tertiary curriculum
design from industrial training perspective", International
Journal of Applied Engineering Education, 6/4.
Otieno F. O. (1987) "Needs of Industry in a developing
country", Education, Industry and Technology (ed. D.
Waddington et al), Pergamon Press Ltd, Oxford.

An Analysis and Some Suggestions on the Cooperative Education Between Enterprises and Institutions in China

B. Chen, Y. Wang

Shenyang Institute of Aeronautical Engineering

Abstract
The significance and functions of the cooperative education between enterprises and institutions (CEEI) are analyzed in this paper. It introduces several concrete practices of CEEI in China. Finally, some suggestions based on the actual situation of our country are also presented here.
Keywords: Cooperative Education, Practice, Higher Engineering Institutions, Enterprise.

1 Introduction

In recent years, various forms of ''Coopeerative Education between Enterprises and Institutions'' (CEEI) are constantly emerging in the process of higher engineering education reform in China. A number of universities have achieved great success after their concrete practice of implementing the cooperative education with some enterprises. The result shows that the education of this kind has great vitality.

2 The Significance and Function of CEEI in China

For more than ten years, the economic construction, especially that of high technological industries, has been developed at high speed in China. However, there are much more difficulties encountered in a number of enterprises during the development. One of the most important reasons is the shortage of experts. Therefore, how to train highquality engineering and technological experts in practical form effectively is now a key problem which is in need of immediate solution within the engineering education circle.

With the increasing development of science and technology, the old education system is far from meeting the sampling by question-and-answer investigation of the training-quality of graduates, the result shows (see Table 1) that 20 factories and institutions in our country consider the present graduates lacking in spirit of reform, keeping forging ahead and getting right on the job, no good in ability of practice and operation, especially short of creative ability when solving the engineering technological problems about production.

Table 1. Investigation Table on the Quality of Graduates of Higher
Engineering Institutions

Items of Investigation	Percent of Qualification
Suit the needs of new post	59.03%
The ability of practice and operation	38.19%
Theoretical knowledge	68.06%
Computing ability	64.58%
Creative ability	11.81%
Organization ability	29.73%
Sense of responsibility	60.42%
Devotion to one's work	63.89%
The spirit of reform and keeping forging ahead	36.01%
The spirit of getting right on job and bearing hardship	49.31%
The spirit of solidarity and cooperation	52.78%
Average value	48.94%

The main functions of CEEI are:

(1) For higher engineering institutions, they can obtain new technology, and the information feedback about personnel quality, enlarge enrollment quality, improve teaching quality and train various personnel for enterprises and society. At the same time, universities and colleges may utilize the productive or experimental base in enterprises to improve the condition for running a school.

(2) For students, they can themselves speed the engineering practice and master the practical skills needed for production, management and administration, and expand employment opportunity after graduation.

(3) For teachers, they can make full use of practical and experimental conditions in enterprises to take part in scientific research, tackling technical problems and developing new products so as to broaden their outlook, combine theory with practice, apply scientific achievements to classroom teaching and then to raising the teaching ability.

(4) For enterprises, they can use rich scientific and technological resources of higher engineering institutions and receive a great deal of cheap intelligent labour, besides, they can carry out technical reform and innovation on backward conditions of equipment and production, develop new products and other productive fields, thereby, increase their economic benefits.

As a result, CEEI not only has immediate significance and a positive role,but also a vastly bright prospect.

3. The Concrete Practice of CEEI in China

Many universities or institutions and enterprises have tried in various aspects of cooperation and have achieved good results through joint efforts and through organizing with the best of care. The different forms of CEEI being adopted are as follows:

(1) Higher institutions and enterprises run cooperatively a school to

train high level engineering personnel required by the enterprises for urgent needs. Both sides make joint efforts to investigate, study, determine program and draw up a teaching plan. There are different forms of CEEI being adopted. One is to provide the practice base and instructors for higher institutions by the enterprises. Another is that teachers in universities or colleges go among the enterprises to run a few specialitics with ''directional''enrolment and distribution. Such cooperative education carries out a bold reform, increases the teaching hours of practice and strengthens the training of basic quality being engaged in engineering and technological work for students. (See Table 2)

Table 2. Some Types of Cooperative Education of Practical
Enterprises and Institutions in Shanghai.

Higher engineering institution	teaching molded	Time of practice	percent of practice
Shanghai Polytechnic University	four-term per year system	one term per year	25%
Shanghai Mercantile Marine Institute	graduates pre-distributed system	the eighth term (half a year)	33%
Shanghai Textile Institute	three-term per year system	ten weeks per year	33%
Shanghai Machinery Technical School	three plus one system (Sandwich form)	the second and forth school year	48%

(2) A few universities have established boards of directors, such as China's Mining University and Changzhou Institute of Engineering. They invite many concerned enterprises and institutions to join them. The board of directors can give some advice to the development scheme, the set up of specialities. They also can examine some major issues under discussion and supervise the sitution of carrying out the agreement by individual director's unit.
(3) Both sides jointly form a research entity, sign bilateral cooperation agreements, establish long-term stable relations, and, make joint efforts to develop new products, new processes and new technologies. As examples, North-South Polytechnical University and Si'an Aircraft Manufacturing Company have signed an ''Agreement of Comprehensive Cooperation'', both sides are mutually benefited by making up each other's deficiency and by mutually providing favourable terms for education and technological cooperations.

4. Some Suggestions on CEEI

4.1 We don't hold identical views on this point that CEEI is an effective form of higher engineering education and an important way to train engineering technical personnel in application form, so it is necessary to unfold a wide-ranging discussion to analyze the advantages and disadvantages in the education circle of engineering. In practice, it is not suitable to take the conventional methods of treating equally without discrimination. At first, it can be done by a small number of higher engineering institutions making experiments. Summing up their experiences and lessons, and lastly spreading their course of action progressively.

4.2 Our country is a big country. There are more than one thousand higher schools, among them about three hundred units are higher engineering institutions. The training levels, historical background and conditions for running the schools, for all institutions are quite different, and their development are in disequilibruim as well. So it is not proper for them to adopt the same measures. They should take a different form of CEEI according to their own conditions.

4.3 The goal for enterprise and institution is both consistent and different. So we should develop the superiority of both institutions and enterprises respectively in carrying out CEEI, and respect rights of the opposite side to develop their own way. Neglecting the interests of any sides will obtain no satisfactory results.

4.4 On the basis of the condition of our country, the guidance and support from government of different levels are necessary for the reform of higher engineering institutions. If governments attach great importance to CEEI, it will be going on smoothly and obtaining reliable guarantee to train high-quality specialized personnel.

4.5 The higher authorities assign some factories as practice base for universities or colleges according to their corresponding specialities, and ask enterprises to take the CEEI into one of the important tasks, and order both sides of cooperative education to appoint some competent persons to form a leading group of CEEI to work out together the cooperative plan and to put it into effect.

5. Conclusion

On the whole, CEEI is a very good way to train the higher quality personnel of engineering for society and economic construction. So long as various relations between enterprises and institutions can be properly handled, it will be beneficial to both of them. Therefore, we should persist in implementing the CEEI till achievement is assured.

References

Jiahua Wang. (1989) Cross Alliance: An Important Means in the Higher
   Education Reform.   Researches in Higher Education of Engineering

   1989, 1, 66.
Rong Chen, Weiquian Yu, (1990)   Expansion of Cooperative Education
   between Enterprise and University.   Proceedings of International
   Symposium on Higher Engineering Education 1990, 20 -- 24.

Academia-Industry Interaction - An IIT Bombay Experience

M.S. Agarwal

Department of Electrical Engineering, Indian Institute of Technology, Bombay

Abstract

The Indian Institute of Technology, Bombay, established in 1958, has evolved over the last three decades as a premier institution in India for higher education, research and training in various fields of engineering and technology. The strategic location of the Institute in the region with a high concentration of engineering industry, is ideal for interaction with industry and it has, since its inception, been interacting through its highly-qualified and strong research-oriented faculty and young and bright-minded students. The effort is reflected in its excellent academic programmes and a strong commitment to research.

Keywords: Engineering, Education, Universities, Industry, Interaction.

1   Introduction

1.1 Establishment and Role of IITs

The availability of highly-qualified technical manpower is a vital resource for speedy industrial growth of a country. Recognizing this, the Indian Government had, by an act of Parliament, set up in 1950s and 1960s five Indian Institutes of Technology, one each in the eastern, western, northern, southern and central regions of the country. These institutes, recognised as institutes of national importance with the status of universities, play a key role in giving the direction to the country in terms of top-quality higher education, research and training in various fields of engineering and technology. The standard and quality of education at both the undergraduate and postgraduate levels at these institutes are on par with the best in the world.

1.2 The I.I.T. Bombay

The Indian Institute of Technology, Bombay was established in 1958. Because of its strategic location in Bombay, which has a high concentration of engineering industries, the institute is ideally suited to effectively interact with industry. The Institute has, since its inception, been playing a decisive role in the development of technical manpower with leadership qualities in their profession, in the creation of new knowledge leading to new processes and products, in the adaptation of available technical know-how to Indian conditions and in the development of products and processes to meet the specific needs of the industry.

The Institute has well-equipped Departments of Engineering (Aero-nautical, Chemical, Civil, Computer, Electrical, Mechanical and Metal-lurgical), Departments of Sciences (Chemistry, Earth, Mathematics and Physics) and the Department of Humanities and Social Sciences. It has a Computer Centre with large scale computing facilities inclu-ding a fourth generation Cyber 180/840 mainframe computer system.

The Institute has several Schools of Studies, viz. Materials Science, Environmental Science and Engineering, Cryogenics Engineering, Laser Systems, Bio Medical Engineering, Bio Science and Engineering, Energy Systems Engineering, Industrial Engineering and Operations Research, and Industrial Management. Besides these Schools of Studies, the Institute also has several specialised centres, such as Advanced Centre for Research in Electronics (ACRE), Centre of Studies in Resources Engineering (CSRE), Industrial Design Centre (IDC), Regional Sophisticated Instrumentation Centre (RSIC), Computer-Aided Design Centre (CAD Centre), and the Centre for Technology Alternatives for Rural Areas (CTARA).

The ACRE was established in 1971 as a part of the research and training programme of the Ministry of Defence, Govt. of India. Under this programme, research and development on advanced topics in the fields of Radar and Communications is carried out at the Centre. During the past twenty years, the centre has offered degree programmes and organised short-term courses for defence personnel and has trained more than 700 persons.

The CSRE was established at the Institute in 1976 with the objec-tive to develop techniques of visual and computer-oriented capabili-ties in the area of remote sensing pertaining to resource identifica-tion, exploitation and management.

An IDC exists at the Institute, which aims to develop the design culture in our industries for enhancing the marketability of their products, both in the country and abroad (with particular emphasis on export promotion) by making their appearance aesthetically appea-ling and humanly functional to the customers.

The RSIC, established in 1975, has an array of very modern sophis-ticated instruments for use in frontline research programmes. It also caters to the research needs of industry and other institutions in the western region of the country.

The CAD Centre has been established with an aim to inculcate CAD culture in the Indian industries.

The CTARA is concerned with the development of technologies accor-ding to perceived needs of a specific rural region.

With the extensive facilities available, the Central Workshop helps in fabrications from small prototypes to full-scale models, from small machines and devices to large instruments. The Central Workshop is strengthened by a machine tools laboratory equipped with a range of heavy-duty, special purpose and precision machine tools.

The Institute has the support of a large library providing immense amount of reference material for its faculty and students. It subs-cribes to about 1300 current journals and periodicals and has back volumes of most of the journals of the past more than 40 years. There are more than 160,000 books and other volumes in the Library.

During the past 25 years, the Institute has made all efforts to achieve the distinction of its being called a Centre of Excellence.

2   The Institute-Industry Interaction

During the past two decades the Institute has been making sustained efforts to have a closer interaction with industry through:
 i) industry involvement in academic programmes, and
ii) sponsored research.
   This interaction has led to :
a) the development of technical manpower with potential to be leaders in their profession, be it teaching, research and development, design, production, planning or management;
b) the enrichment of academic programmes by restructuring them taking into account the contemporary and developing technology, initiation of interdisciplinary programmes where such inputs are required, ensuring a judicious blend of theory and practice, and laying adequate provision for industry-oriented projects; and
c) the research and development leading to generation of new ideas, concepts, methodologies, products and processes comparable to the current state of art and consistent with the national needs.
   Let us now discuss the above-mentioned points (i) and (ii).

3   Industry Involvement in Academic Programmes

The various possible components of academic programmes that can have industry involvement have been identified and are discussed below:

3.1 Practical Training
All the undergraduate students spend about 2 months, during the summer vacation following third year course programme, in industry in an effort to see the application of scientific principles and engineering techniques they have learnt in classrooms, have a hands-on experience of the industrial processes and inculcate in themselves an industrial culture. This experience of industrial environment helps them better understand the classroom teaching in the later years of their education in the Institutes and better execute the research projects in the final year.

3.2 Five-year Integrated M.Tech. Degree Programme
The Five year Integrated M.Tech. Degree Programme, introduced five years ago, is an innovation aimed at providing incentive to both the student and the sponsoring industry. Here, the student takes only five years to earn an M.Tech. degree instead of the usual five and a half years, i.e. four years for B.Tech. degree and a further one and a half year for the M.Tech. degree.
   A student and a sponsoring industry are matched together in the fourth year of this programme. The industry provides the financial support to the student during his last two years of the programme and the student takes the courses and the research project (of one year duration) on a topic of direct interest to the industry. There is no obligation or commitment on either side at the end of the

programme, i.e. neither the student has to execute a bond to serve
the sponsoring industry on completion of the course nor the industry
has an obligation to provide him with a job. Of course, having worked
in co-operation with each other, the close contact may often result
in the industry offering a job to the student. Thus, the programme
is designed to develop technical manpower closer to the needs of the
Industry. This programme, currently on in Chemical, Mechanical and
Electrical Engineering Departments, is running with adequate success
and recognizes the students' existence in the R & D activity of the
industry.

3.3 Sponsored Research Projects

The Institute has, about ten years ago, instituted the scheme of sponsored research projects at the B.Tech., M.Tech. and Ph.D. degree
levels on a suggestion from the Industry and with a great deal of
optimism on both the sides. These projects from the industry help
in orienting the student to time-bound, goal-oriented, and live industrial projects. Currently, the sponsored projects offered by the
industry constitute about 8% of all the projects undertaken by the
students at various levels. A representative sample of the industry
-sponsored projects recently undertaken is given below:
   Indian language word processor for IBM PC
   Laser printer controller card for IBM PC
   Language card for IBM PC
   Design and development of an algorithm to recognize printed or
      typed Devnagri script
   Shading and rendering of 3-D display
   Electronic weighing machine
   Design of suitable work system of PCB assembly
   Microprocessor based instrumentation system for measuring circuit-
      breaker parameters
   HRC fuse design

3.4 Sponsored Engineers from Industry for M.Tech. & Ph.D. Degrees

The Institute has been, for the past 10-15 years, offering its
M.Tech. and Ph.D. degree programmes to the engineers working in industry. This arrangement has been very popular with the industries having
strong research and development activities. Here, an industry can
sponsor its engineers for M.Tech. and Ph.D. degree programmes, to
be carried out either fully at the Institute or partly (i.e. theory
courses and seminars) at the Institute and partly (the research
project) at the industry. This programme helps the industry in strengthening the theoretical base of its engineers, in their acquiring
new knowledge, and obtaining the guidance and expertise of a faculty
in executing a research and developmental project in the field of
its interest.

3.5 Experts from Industry as Examiners

The Institute has, on its panel of examiners for B.Tech., M.Tech.
and Ph.D. theses, names of reputed practising engineers from the
industry and invites them for refereeing the theses and for conducting
the viva-voce examinations of the students. These engineers are also

often invited to deliver expert lectures in their field of specialisation and talk to the students about various aspects of industrial
environment and for bringing about the industrial orientation among
the students. The Institute has also appointed renowned industrialists
on its governing bodies to enhance the interaction.

4 Sponsored Industrial Research

4.1 Sponsored Research as a Mechanism for Forging Interaction
The sponsored research plays a vital role in creating a suitable environment for interaction with industry. Research promotes creativity,
sharpens technical skills and demands a long-term commitment from
faculty and students. The push towards research has caused a spurt
in sponsored research activities leading to nucleation of active
research groups in various key areas, e.g. biomedical engineering,
robotics, resources engineering, HVDC,Switchgear and rural technology.
The intensification of sponsored research for forging interaction
has been achieved through various measures taken by the Institute,
such as setting up of mechanisms for removing psychological and administrative barriers between the Institute and industry.

4.2 Industrial Research and Consultancy Centre
A major problem in effective institute-industry interaction is the
isolation of faculty and industry. As a significant step in that
direction, the Industrial Research and Consultancy Centre (IRCC) was
set up to provide the link between the industry and the institute.
The IRCC lends a helping hand to industry for identification of faculty
expertise and the institute facilities and assists the faculty in
identification of industry problems. The R & D newsletter provides
to the industry an up-to-date information about R and D activities
in progress. Thus IRCC has been playing a key role in promoting the
industrial consultancy activity of the faculty. A large number of
consultancy projects have been carried out involving design and development of processes, preparation of feasibility reports and development of software packages.

4.3 Avenues for Sponsored Research
The Institute has created several avenues for interacting with
industry in sponsored research and the projects undertaken usually are
of the following types:
  i) The problem connected with a project which is within the purview
     of the normal scope of research interest of a faculty member.
     These are short-term projects aimed at solving immediate problems
     of the industry, related to design, product and process develop-
     ment, trouble-shooting, failure analysis etc.
 ii) A long range research and development project coinciding with
     the interest of a group of faculty members drawn from the Insti-
     tute and requiring the Institute facilities available to this
     composite group. It may also require additional facilities not
     provided through regular Institute resources. In such cases
     the sponsor is expected to provide additional funds for carrying
     out investigations on projects which are of mutual interest.

iii) Engineering development and design problems undertaken by a team
of faculty members along with research and postgraduate students.

  iv) A sponsor may engage an individual faculty member in consultation
work with the proprietory rights of the sponsor protected. He can
also engage himself for a longer consultation work during vacations
and may work at the sponsor's facility location for an extended
period.

  v) Advanced undergraduate and postgraduate students are in many cases
desirous of engaging themselves in summer jobs in industry.

  vi) Industry can also sponsor their engineering personnel for working at
the Institute with the faculty having mutual interest in a project.

5   Continuing Education Programme, Get-togethers and Feedback

As part of the Continuing Education Programme, the Institute organises,
besides seminars, conferences & workshops, a large number of week-end,
1-week and 2-week industry-oriented courses on specialised topics for
the benefit of practising engineers. A CEP cell has been set up at
the Institute to make the Continuing Education Programme more effective.
The cell has evolved plans for offering a variety of short-term courses
of relevance to industry engaged in modernisation and expansion to
high-technology areas. The Institute also organises I.I.T. industry
get-togethers at regular intervals.

The alumini of the Institute have formed an IIT Bombay Alumini Association and regularly hold meetings/get-togethers and arrange lecture
programmes at the Institute to maintain contact with the Institute
faculty and discuss topics of mutual interest. Many Institute graduates
and post-graduates who have become entrepreneurs share in these meetings,
their experiences in the Industry with the faculty and students of the
Institute which exercise benefits all the three parties.

The Institute also conducts periodic surveys to monitor the quality
of its education. The system includes the feedback obtained directly
from the alumini and also from the management of the industries about
the quality of students and their performance in industries.

6   Conclusions

This paper highlights the role and objectives of the Indian Institute
of Technology, Bombay in setting the direction for development of engineering education, training and research in India. The paper also
projects the various ways in which the Institute interacts with the
engineering industry in its academic and research programmes. A close
look at the activities shows that the main focus is on bridging the
two gaps, viz. between knowledge and application, and that of adjustment
with industrial environment and commitment.

References

Agarwal, M.S. (1989) I.I.T. / Industry Co-operation in India, in Procee-
dings of 1st Annual Convention and Conference on Engineering Educa-
tion, Australasian Association for Engg. Education, Sydney,
Australia, 202 207.
IIT Bombay (1991-92) Courses of Study Bulletin.
Handouts at various I.I.T. - Industry Get-togethers.

Evolution of a Continuing Education Programme on Maintenance Engineering and Management for Practising Engineers from Developing Nations - An Indian Experience

P.N. Ramachandran

Indian Institute for Foremen Training, Orissa

Abstract
The Indian Institute for Foremen Training (IIFT), a pioneering centre for the training and development of supervisory management personnel from industries, has been conducting programmes on various aspects of plant maintenance since its inception in 1983. By combining various modules on Mechanical Maintenance, Electrical Maintenance, Maintenance Management and Man Management Techniques an integrated programme on Maintenance Engineering & Management has been developed and offered to practising engineers from developing nations. The salient features of this programme are described in this paper. The programme gives a comprehensive exposure not only on various maintenance methods, but also on modern management techniques with emphasis on human relations aspects. A systems approach to the solution of problems relating to the maintenance of plant and equipment is emphasised. The 10-week programme imparts in-depth knowledge, develops necessary skills and inculcates appropriate attitudes for successfully carrying out maintenance activities. The increasing demand for this programme from several countries in South East Asia, Africa, the Middle East and the Carribeans has confirmed its suitability for the development of their human resources in this vital area.
<u>Keywords</u>: Continuing Education, Plant Maintenance, Developing Nations.

1 Introduction

It is an accepted fact that effective maintenance management contributes substantially to the achievement of higher productivity & profitability and increased capacity utilisation of plant and equipment. The entire philosophy of maintenance has changed considerably over the past few years. It is no more considered simply as a process of repairing faulty components or equipment, but as a system of keeping the machinery operating at rated capacity without failure over extended periods of time at minimal cost. In this context the need for the systematic training of shopfloor personnel engaged in the maintenance function cannot be overemphasised. This is more so in the case

of developing nations, where considerable amount of money is being
spent on procuring capital equipment, but infrastructural facilities
for the training and development of their maintenance engineers/
technicians do not exist. The Indian Institute for Foremen Training
(IIFT), an autonomous institute set up for the training and development of shopfloor supervisors, has since its inception in 1983
identified plant maintenance as a major field in its training activities. From 1985 onwards these specific modules on Mechanical Maintenance (2 weeks), Electrical Maintenance (1 week), Maintenance
Management (2 weeks) and Man Management Techniques (1 week) have been
combinedly offered as a package on Maintenance Engineering & Management (6 weeks) for foreign nationals sponsored under various schemes,
alongwith Indian participants, who generally attend the individual
modules. Since 1987 the duration of this package has been increased
to 10 weeks. Encouraged by the good response from lesser developed
nations in this programme and considering the special requirement of
candidates from such countries, the institute has redesigned this
programme and has been offering it exclusively for them from 1989
onwards. This paper highlights the salient features of this programme.

2 The Programme - Its Objectives, Coverage and Philosophy

As mentioned in Section 1, the 10-week programme on Maintenance
Engineering & Management is an integration of four separate modules
viz. Mechanical Maintenance, Electrical Maintenance, Maintenance
Management and Man Management Techniques. The target participants
are degree/diploma holders in Mechanical/Electrical Engineering, who
are engaged in maintenance activities in industries. The broad aim
of the programme is to give a comprehensive exposure in various
maintenance methods and management techniques with special emphasis
on human relations aspects.(for details please see APPENDIX).
    The programme takes a holistic approach to the solution of problems
in maintenance. Emphasis is placed on underlying principles and their
application to practical situations. Thus a thorough grounding on the
principles of Industrial Tribology is given before dealing with lubrication management and selection & maintenance of bearings. Similarly
the characteristics, special features and the method of selection of
electrical drives are covered in depth before going into the effective
maintenance and trouble-shooting of such equipment. Likewise Network
Analysis and Value Engineering are covered in such detail that the
participants develop the capability to gainfully employ these techniques
back at their work.
    Since in many industies maintenance personnel are called upon to
take care of mechanical as well as electrical systems, equal importance
is placed on both these topics. Moreover as in many cases the failure
of electrical equipment is due to mechanical reasons and as many
mechanical equipment are operated by electric power, the two areas
cannot be compartmentalised. Thus to give a broader perspective, equal
weightage is given to both mechanical and electrical maintenance
aspects in this programme.

As predictive maintenance is going to be increasingly used in the coming years for increased plant availability, considerable importance is placed on condition monitoring techniques. Even though most of the developing countries are still in the realm of 'Breakdown Maintenance', a change in approach is visualised with the increasing investments that are being made on costly equipment. Exposure to various aspects of Condition Based Maintenance prepares the participants to face the challenges of the future.

As the maintenance supervisor has to get his job done through various people, his skill in managing people is of paramount importance to the success of his activities. Hence special importance is given to interpersonnel skills covering communication, team building & team leading and motivating self & others. Thus in essence the programme looks at maintenance as a system encompassing technical, managerial and behavioural aspects.

3 Salient Features

3.1. Faculty
Apart from institute's core faculty, experts from successful industries, teachers from academic institutes, specialist manufactureres and management consultants are called upon to handle various sessions in the programme. Thus engineering professionals from steel plants & engineering industries, manufactures of bearings, diesel sets, fluid power devices etc; Industrial Engineering consultants and behavioural scientists form part of the external faculty sharing their expertise and experience with the participants. This makes the entire programme a good blend of the best in theory as also in modern industrial practices.

3.2. Methodology
Class-room lectures in the programme are amply supported by audiovisual presentations, demonstrations and hands-on exercises in the workshops/ laboratories at the institute, use of computer based training material, group discussions, case studies etc. Extensive practical work on Industrial Hydraulics & Pneumatics, Repair Welding and Condition Monitoring form a special feature of the programme. Participants are encouraged to bring live problems for discussion during the programme and to find possible solutions. Since the participants are from several countries, the programme provides a rare opportunity for a special kind of learning i.e. by discussion among colleagues hailing from totally different environments.

3.3. Pre and Post Tests
The knowledge level of participants before and after the training are assessed by pre and post tests conducted at the start and end of the programme respectively. A set of objective type questions is used for this purpose. Each question is in the form of a true/false statement.

The questions cover the entire range of topics covered in the programme. Participants are specially told that these tests are not
really examinations, but a means of assessing their knowledge levels.
They are also advised not to make guesswork in answering the questions
and given the option to mark 'Don't know' for questions from areas
not known to them. The test scores are revealed to the participants
at the end of the programme. These tests have not only been a good
method for giving feedback to the participants on their performance,
but also have helped the institute to identify the topics to be
emphasised in the programme and to pinpoint areas of weakness in a
realistic manner, thus enabling it to bring about improvements. The
sense of achievement, confidence and satisfaction generated in the
participants on seeing their pre and post test scores has been a
valuable plus point of this type of evaluation. This will work as
a great motivator for many of them in their future learning activities.

3.4. Action Plans

On the last day of the programme, participants are asked to make a
short presentation highlighting the new ideas/techniques learnt from
the course and how they propose to put these ideas into practice back
at their workplace. This has helped the institute in evaluating to
some extent the training effectiveness and learning outcomes in
addition to identifying the topics of general interest to the trainees,
allowing these to be expanded further in future programmes. Some such
action plans put forward by the trainees are given below.
- Proper care in handling, storing and applying lubricants
- Selection of right types of bearings and avoiding wrong practices
  of their mounting and dismounting
- Reclamation of worn-out parts by welding techniques
- Systematic selection of electrical drives for various applications
- Use of PERT/CPM for the planning & controlling of various activities
- Value analysis in evaluating alternatives
- Procurement and use of condition monitoring instruments
- Effective spare parts planning
- Formulating maintenance budgets & controlling costs
- Following safe practices in maintenance activities
- Achieving tasks through cohesive teams of motivated individuals
- Conducting training programmes to disseminate knowledge gained
  from the programme.

The last mentioned action plan i.e. conducting training programmes
is of great value since its produces a multiplier effect.

Some participants have written to the institute that they have
successfully put into practice some of these ideas.

3.5. Industrial Visits

Visits to reputed industries for study by observation is an essential
component of the programme. The last week of the course is devoted
for such visits. The institute has access to large integrated steel
plants, modern heavy/light engineering industries, large cement plants,
power generating/distributing stations etc. for this purpose. These

also happen to be some of the places from where external faculty is drawn for the programme. Thus this arrangement helps in directly relating what they see, to what has been told in the class, thus reinforcing knowledge.

4   Results

The first group of 5 participants from 2 developing nations in South East Asia was admitted to this programme in 1985, when they attended it along with their counterparts from India. The demand for this programme from overseas has been so continually increasing since then, that it is being offered exclusively for them from 1989 onwards. Further the frequency of this course has been increased from once to twice a year since 1990. By the end of 1991, this continuing education programme has been attended by 127 participants from 36 developing nations spread all over the globe. This amply illustrates how from its remote location in a small country town in India, IIFT has been successful in catering to the human resource development needs of developing nations in the all-important field of maintenance management.

5   Conclusions

In the developing world there is a growing need for updating the knowledge of front-line supervisors from industries in modern maintenance management techniques. Comprehensive programmes of the type described in this paper are quite suitable for this purpose as evidenced by the increasing popularity of this particular programme among developing countries all over the world.

APPENDIX

MAINTENANCE ENGINEERING & MANAGEMENT PROGRAMME (10 Weeks)

1   Objectives

At the end of the programme participants will be able to
- Prepare lubrication schedules for plant & equipment
- Write down operation & maintenance procedures for diesel sets
- Do trouble-shooting of fluid power systems
- Perform repair welding operations
- Select electrical drives for various applications
- List systematic procedures for the maintenance of electrical equipment
- Properly plan, schedule and control maintenance activities
- Perform condition monitoring on operating equipment
- Apply modern management concepts to maintenance operations
- Improve upon their interpersonal skills for shopfloor management.

2   Coverage

2.1. Mechanical Maintenance (Weeks 1-3)
Overview of Maintenance Practices
Selection and Application of Materials for Maintenance
Principles of Lubrication
Lubrication Management
Selection & Maintenance of Bearings
Operation & Maintenance of Diesel Sets
Repair & Reclamation by Welding Techniques
Machine-tool Maintenance

2.2. Electrical Maintenance (weeks 4 & 5)
Selection & Application of Electrical Drives for Industries
Solid State Motor Control
Protection of Electric Drives
Installation, Commissioning & Testing of Electric Drives
Operation & Maintenance of HT/LT Transformers & Switchgear
Power System Protection
Maintenance of Motor Control Centres
Installation, Commissioning & Testing of Industrial Power
Distribution Systems.

2.3. Maintenance Management (weeks 6-8)
Objectives and Techniques of Maintenance
Maintenance Organisation
Preparation of Maintenance Schedules
Maintenance Planning & Control
Condition Monitoring Techniques
Spare Parts Planning
Value Analysis in Maintenance
Maintenance Budgeting & Cost Control
Computer Based Maintenance
HRD in Maintenance
Safety Management
Industrial Relations

2.4. Man Management Techniques (week 9)
Effective Communication
Interpersonal Skills
Team Building & Team Leading
Motivating Self & Others

2.5. Industrial Visits (week 10)

Engineering Education in India - Provision for the Needs of Industry

A. Janaki Rao

Department of Civil Engineering, Andhra University

Abstract

The demands of Indian industry are so diverse that Engineering curriculum cannot be designed completely by Engineering Institutions alone. In this paper a review of the present status along with suggestions for improvement is attempted.

Keywords : Industry, Engineering curriculum, Engineering Institutions.

1 Introduction

Among the major changes that the latter part of 20th century has realised is the emergence of Technical Education as a major human resource of any nation. The role, the content and the importance of Technical Education in society is undergoing constant major changes since the last two decades. Technical Education became the tool for economic development in the industrial civilisation. The western nations developed the type of Technical Education, which is suitable to their socio-economic and cultural needs. The third world countries, realising that the standard of living in a nation depends on the strength of Technical Education, are trying to improve in this direction. The Engineering Education today faces more challenges than education in any other discipline. In Engineering, the demands from the employer are varied and diverse. The Engineers of today have to meet the challenges of phenomenal growth, rapid changes, fast obsolescence and multidisciplinary complexity. The rapid emergence of innovations and discoveries is creating obsolescence malady not only for machines and material but also for skills and knowledge. Unfortunately the user (the employer) is not consulted at any stage in the design and development of technical education.

2 Technical Education In India

India is a vast country with a population of 843.9 millions (1991 census) with a literacy rate of 52.11%. India is a nation having 25 States with 15 constitutionally recognised languages and different socio-economic structures representing unity in diversity. Majority of the people live in rural areas. Caste system which is hereditary is a pecularity of the Indian Society. The upper caste and urban elite still dominate all fields including education. Inspite of all the efforts by Government, the disparity among the castes could not be wiped out successfully. The education system (Including Technical Education), developed during the colonial rule to cater to the needs of the then rulers, is yet to be geared to the needs of the present socio-economic needs. The needs of Indian Industry and society are so varied and diverse that Engineering curriculum cannot be designed completely by Engineering Institutions to suit their demands.

The first intake in the Engineering Colleges/Schools in the country are directly due to need to train Technical manpower for the newly established Engineering Industries. (Training School at Poona 1865; Survey School, Sibpoor;Engineering College, Calcutta 1880; Victoria Jublee Institute, 1857).

During 1947-48 (just after independence) there were 38 Engineering Colleges and 53 Polytechnics turning out 1270 graduates and 14410 diploma holders. There are 333 (1990) Engineering Colleges, 750 Polytechnics, 79 Women's Polytechnics and a number of Industrial Training Institutes in addition to 6 Institutes of Technology of higher learning, turning out 39,000 graduates, 6000 post graduates and about 1,00,000 diploma holders every year.

There is a three tier Educational system in Engineering Education in India namely technical/craftsman, Diploma and Degree level. The Indian Education is not terminal at any stage and Indians are often interested in reaching upto the dead end than confining to a need based education.

	1981	1990
Total number of Engineers	3,24,699	11,89,200
Graduates and higher level of qualification	1,56,620	4,54,400
Diploma holders	1,68,079	7,34,800

Women Engineers constitute 1.4% (Based on Report of Department of Science and Technology, Govt. of India)

3 Present Status

The major crisis in Professional Education in India is the poor quality on face of the best student input, and relatively high cost. The curriculum planner, teacher, administrators, students and industry point their fingers to each other. Emphasis is given on modernisation of Technology and not on the modernisation of organisation and transfer of knowledge.

In Engineering the demands from the Industry is diverse. The small industries want immediate employable engineers which means narrow preparation. The big industries stress an engineer with strong base in sciences, analysis and design. The requirements of Government Departments are hardly spelt out.

The All India Council of Technical Education (AICTE) regulates, controls and governs all the activities of Educational Institutes of all categories of Engineering. The curriculum suggested by AICTE for undergraduate curriculum is as follows :

i)   Languages, Humanities and Social Sceinces   : 5-10%

ii) General Basic Sciences   : 15-25%

iii) Engineering subjects & Technical Arts   : 15-25%

iv) Professional subjects   : 45-65%

Many of the Engineering institutions compare their curriculum with the institutions of advanced countries. Hence the best students feel their education and training is more useful in advanced countries but not relevant to the Indian job situations.

Inspite of stressing the need on University - Industry interaction Academics, Administrators and Industry, they are still moving on parallel lines. Engineering consists of basic sciences, Analysis and Design, construction, operation and maintenance. The first three are general, the last three are regional in character and they cannot be fully controlled and taught by institutions alone and participation of industries is very much essential.

4 Suggestions For Improvement

i)   The Technology Developments should be watched and trends should be identified earlier to minimise the lead time for the responding system of the changing curriculum.

ii) Projecting possible connections between presently distant Technologies and identifying the need of the emergence of new fields.

iii) Professional bodies like Institutions of Engineers (India) should be more closely associated with the Technical Educational Planning.

iv) The curriculum of all Institutions can be varied and diversified to suit the regional needs and for developing appropriate Technology.

v)   Starting of Science and Technology Entrepreneur Park (STEP)
     for effective interaction between University and Industry
     (Example, Birla Institute of Technology, Pilani, India).

vi) At present the industry is getting a ready made Engineer for
     which their contribution is almost zero and this situation is
     to be changed. The industry should share cost of Engineering
     Education by providing funds for R & D, Industrial Training,
     consultancy etc.

vii) Industry should not be a silent spectator and critic on
     Engineering Education but it should take a positive role in
     solving present problems.

viii) The industry should spell out their requirements for the next
     five years in terms of quantity and quality of Engineering
     Graduates and involve the Institutions to plan to match the
     above requirements.

Conclusion

The academics alone cannot develop Comprehensive Educational
Programmes that would reflect the fast growing needs of industry and
academics, administrators and industrialists should work out viable
system of education.
      Dr. Swaminathan's model of University - Industry symbiosis is
one of the best models to be adopted in the Indian Context.

SWAMINADHAN MODEL
FOR
UNIVERSITY _ INDUSTRY SYMBIOSIS

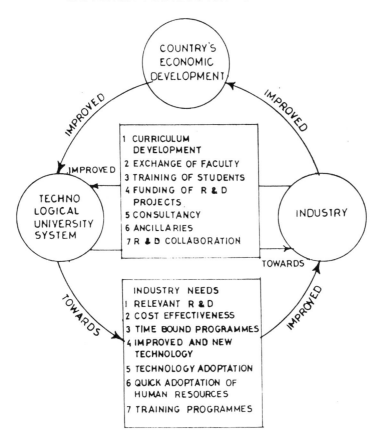

Acknowledgement

I thank Prof. V.C. Kulundaiswamy, Vice Chancellor, Indira Gandhi Open University and Dr. Swaminadhan, Member, Planning Commission, Government of India for using some of their data.

Experiential Learning via Projects planned by University and Industry

D.J. Croome, G.K. Cook, M. Curtis

Department of Construction Management and Engineering, University of Reading

Abstract

There is a need for an integrated approach to the planning and running of undergraduate engineering projects if the objectives of self learning and engineering application are to be met. This paper explains an innovative approach to the formulation and application of integrated engineering projects for undergraduate Building Services Engineering Design and Management (BSEDM) students at The University of Reading. The role of thorough curriculum planning and the commitment of industrial tutors from sponsoring companies is identified as crucial for their success.

Keywords: Experiential Learning, Projects, Industry.

1   Introduction

The role of projects in engineering education pre-dates the requirements of the Finniston Report of 1980, since its contribution to theoretical courses was seen as providing the link with engineering practice and its contribution to practical courses was to provide academic depth and test communication and research skills. The formation of an engineering person was attempted by placing the student into an environment where problems demanded engineering solutions. Projects of an essentially practical type (EA1) and those demanding theoretical and research skills (EA2) were seen as ways of achieving lower and higher order educational objectives as well as producing better engineers.

The Reading BSEDM students carry out a design and make project (EA1) involving mechanical and electrical components during the first year of their course.

Projects which are carried out by individual students give a sharp focus on their ability but make significant resource demands on supervision and do not test the students ability to work in a team.

The industry sponsored BSEDM course at the University of Reading is innovative for a number of reasons including its use of integrated projects which involve experiential learning, Croome (1992). From its conception the course has been strongly linked with the building services industry and in this way it brings together the qualities of academic leadership and industrial expertise. This co-ordinated approach is particularly well demonstrated in the integrated project work. The overall plan for the course in shown in Diagram 1. The integrated project work has been timed to arrive at a point where students have foundation engineering knowledge of sufficient breadth and depth to permit the synthesis, analysis and evaluation of new knowledge.

2   Experiential Learning

Experiential Learning theory offers a different view of the learning process from that which underlies traditional educational methods. The term 'experiential' is used for two reasons. The first is to refer to its intellectual origins in the works of Dewey, Lewin and Piaget. The second and the principal one as far as we are concerned is to emphasise the central role that experience plays in the learning process. Traditional learning theories give emphasis to acquisition, manipulation and recall of information, whereas the behavioural learning attempts to introduce some experience into the process by project work, for example. Experiential learning combines experience, perception, cognition and behavior.

"Here and now" concrete experience is used to validate and test abstract concepts. Immediate personal experience is the focal point for learning giving life, texture and subjective personal meaning to theoretical concepts and at the same time providing a concrete publicly shared reference point for testing the implications of the validity of ideas. By a feedback process learning transforms initial ideas, feelings and concrete experience into higher order purposeful action. This involves observation of surrounding conditions, knowledge of what has happened in similar situations in the past, and judgement which puts together what is observed and what is recalled to see what pathway to take next. Piaget describes the dimensions of experience and concept, reflection and action as forming the basic continua for the development of adult thought. Ideas are not seen as fixed and immutable elements of thought, but rather as things that are formed and reformed through experience.

Kolb (1984) suggests that learning is by its very nature a tension and conflict filled process. New knowledge, skills, or attitudes are achieved by four principal modes of experiential learning which involve concrete experience, reflective observation, abstract conceptualisation and active experimentation abilities. So people should be able to involve themselves fully, openly and without bias in the new experience, and be able to reflect and observe their experiences from many perspectives. They need to be able to create concepts that integrate their observations into logically sound theories and they must be able to use these theories to make decisions and solve problems. Thus experiential learning is a holistic concept describing the central process of human adaptation to the social and physical environment, whereby knowledge is created through the transformation of experience.

3   Existing Project Work in the Construction Courses

The new Building Services Design & Management course is part of a Departmental portfolio of construction courses. The established Construction Management (CM) courses produce undergraduate chartered quantity and building surveyors and chartered builders. These students pass through a matrix of common course subjects during the first two years of their three year full-time study and in the third year take specialist subjects and a number of broad based options. The overall plan for these courses is shown on Diagram 1. Project work is an integral part of these CM courses. In the second year this work is group based and in the third year is single student based.

Typically, during the second year, a group of five or six second year students work on a single student project for five weeks. In the last week the students give an oral and visual presentation of their work to an assessment panel and then submit a report. A particular feature of this group project work is that although it carries no mark forward to the year assessment it has consistently motivated students to produce work of the highest quality. Groups are awarded grades and no attempt is currently being made to assess individual contributions, although other patterns, Conlon and Halstead (1991), are being considered.

Although the requirements of the Engineering Council, through the SARTOR guidelines, are not directly applicable to these CM courses there is some commonality.

4   The New Building Services Engineering Design and Management Project Model

Although there is a continuing debate (Cook 1991, Croome 1991a and b, Harris 1991) there appears to be a need for a different approach to the education of engineers compared to surveyors and construction managers. Engineers must be able to apply principles to the solution of engineering problems within a management framework. Constructors and Surveyors must be capable of managing a process involving considerable technical detail without necessarily understanding and applying its scientific and engineering content.

The new BSEDM project model has been designed to meet the requirements of systems engineers who require design and management skills. It is single student based and integrative in approach through a binary tutoring system. The use of industrial tutors from the sponsoring companies gives the course a unique dimension. They bring with them engineering expertise and provide realistic project material. This departure from the fictional documentation normally provided is another significant difference between the BSEDM projects and the CM projects undertaken in the department.

There are many good educational reasons for considering the integration of the CM projects and the new building services engineering projects. These include the present climate of higher education funding, and the need for commonality and modularity. Unfortunately due to the significant differences between course content and programme (see Diagram 1) this has not yet been achieved. CM group projects take place throughout year two with individual coursework in year three and the BSEDM engineering projects take place in one term of year two and throughout year three. The BSEDM students work on four projects during term six (Integrated Projects) and these are the subject of this paper. They then concentrate on an integrated building design project (Integrated Design Project) which continues through terms seven and eight with assessment in term nine. This final project is subject to regular review panels which include external as well as internal assessors in a similar way as in Schools of Architecture.

The aims of the Integrated Projects are:
§ To allow the student to integrate the different bodies of knowledge which are
   important to practicing engineers and are essential for rigorous decision making.
§ To expose the student to the practice of building services engineering through
   projects with an academic breadth and depth using real engineering problems.
§ To improve the students skills in visual, written and oral communication.
§ To improve the decision-making skills of the student.

The design of buildings is a process involving synthesis (the traditional strength of the architect), analysis (the traditional strength of the engineer) and evaluation. The integrated projects, although of relatively short duration, place the aspiring engineer in a model of the design process similar to those of Gregory and Hamilton (1991). The projects are jointly planned by university and industrial tutors in a way which enables each student to integrate their theoretical engineering knowledge with vocational and industrial experience. In this way they realise the objectives of (EA2) in a real world context. This form of experiential learning offers the student an insight into engineering, with additional resources, and insights beyond those offered in a purely academic setting. The subject matter and content of all of the projects is developed as the result of the stimulus of ideas generated by a series of meetings of a joint committee of university and industrial tutors. In this way content is considered against the background of the overall course structure and its objectives. This is not a straightforward exercise for the industrial tutors who are not experienced in the educational process.

Due to the rich array of practical engineering experience of the joint committee a wide range of project titles is developed.The joint committee each year establishes a range of topics which will test and extend the students knowledge. The content of the integrated projects is considered in relation to the content of the total course. It is weighted to give 75% engineering and 25% management of engineering content.

The apportionment of projects to students is carried out by the university tutors and is generally based on the projects supplied by the sponsoring company. However in order to offer a challenging range of projects to each student the university tutor may choose from the complete range of projects.

5   Project Logistics, Assessment and Presentation

Following the apportionment of projects to each student the background information is issued to the students and their industrial tutors. This occurs towards the end of the Lent term and is followed by a joint project meeting between university tutors, industrial tutors and students. The objectives of this meeting are to discuss the aims of each project, to formulate a programme of work for the 8 week period and to select which project to offer on the presentation day. The programming is seen as a critical factor in the success of the projects. It is important that information is provided and the dialogue between industrial tutor and student is started before the project period begins. This enables initial thought processes to begin and information to be gathered. The Easter vacation provides a suitable time for this gestation to happen.

The quantity of student effort involved in each project is about 48 hours. Although the timetable for the summer term had been planned to allow a maximum time for integrated project work it is recognised that some final year subjects will have to be taken concurrently and foreign language tuition will also continue. BSEDM students are encouraged to take one of their optional subjects in the summer term. This provides two contact days with the university tutors. Each of the projects is to be completed in two weeks (6 working days). This gives a complete terms work with one week for the presentation.

Projects are marked by university tutors who request comments from industrial tutors. This process strengthens the links between the industrial and university tutors and gives a new dimension to student assessment.

An oral presentation of one of the projects is deemed essential since it reinforces communication skills and builds upon Departmental strengths in the field of presentation. All projects are also presented as written reports. The presentation day adopts a traditional architectural school approach and is also built on the communication skills learnt in the first year. Students take 15 minutes to present the project of their choice using any audio visual aids they deem necessary for an audience of academic and industrial staff. A further 10 minutes are allocated for questions. A pin-board display is required from each student. The presentation carries 15% of the total projects mark.

6   Conclusions

This innovative approach to engineering projects places a considerable burden upon the tutoring system. The link with industrial tutors has obvious benefits but brings into direct conflict commercial and educational demands on time. A sensible compromise can only occur when there is real commitment from the engineering companies. In the Reading approach this commitment is linked to sponsorship which brings with it a company view on education and training.

The apportionment of at least 60% of one university term to student centered project learning requires strong motivation by the students.

The content of the projects is kept under review by the joint university and industrial tutor committee.

This innovative integrated project programme was run for the first time in the summer of 1991 and was received well by students, tutors and invited guests from industry on presentation day.

Clearly the use of the workplace in industry, as well as the University, enriches the experiential learning process. There is a compound effect of using industrial, as well as academic mentors, to plan, to review and to assess projects.

References

Conlon , J.A., Halstead, A. (1991), The Use of Project Work in the Assessment of Engineering Students, **Proceedings of a National Conference on Innovative Teaching in Engineering**, (ed R.A. Smith), Ellis Horwood, London, 91-96.

Cook, G.K. (1991) Foundations Built on Science, **Chartered Builder**, 3, (9), 14-15.

Croome, D.J., Cook, G.K. (1992), Building Services Engineering Design and Management Course, **World Conference on Engineering Education.**

Croome, D.J. (1991a) Educational Futures for the Construction Industry, **Industry and Higher Education**, 5, (1), 35-46.

Croome, D.J. (1991b) Education for the Built Environment, **Proceedings of Ove Arup Conference on Education for the Built Environment**, Cambridge.

Gregory, R.D., Hamilton, P.H. (1991), Interdisciplinary Design Project, **Proceedings of a National Conference on Innovative Teaching in Engineering**, (ed R.A. Smith), Ellis Horwood, London, 409-414.

Harris, F.C. (1991) Some Views on Education and Training in the Construction Industry, **Chartered Institute of Building Technical Information Service**, No.140.

Kolb, D.A. (1984) **Experiential Learning**, Prentice-Hall, London, 1984

BSEDM Course

Year / Number	Autumn Term (Week 1–10)	Lent Term (Week 1–10)	Summer Term (Week 1–10)	Vacation (Week 1–12)
1	Lectures (10 Weeks)	Lectures (10 Weeks)	Lectures (9 Weeks) / Exams / Proj Assessment / Graduation	EA 1 / Industrial Placement (10 Weeks)
2	Lectures (10 Weeks)	Lectures (10 Weeks)	Options + Integrated Project (8 weeks) / Exams / Examination Meeting	Industry/Europe (6 weeks) / Industrial Placement (6 weeks)
3	Lectures (10 Weeks) + Integrated Design Project & Diss (1.5 day/week)	Lectures (10 Weeks) + Integrated Design Project & Diss (1.5 day/week)	Lectures	Integrated Design Project

Fieldwork / AROUSAL / Exams / Proj Assessment (Summer Term week 0 column)

CM Courses

Year / Number	Autumn Term (Week 1–10)	Lent Term (Week 1–10)	Summer Term (Week 1–10)	Vacation (Week 1–12)
1	Lectures (10 Weeks)	Lectures (10 Weeks)	Lectures (9 Weeks) / Exams / Graduation	
2	Lectures (10 Weeks)	Lectures (10 Weeks)	Lectures (9 Weeks) Options / Exams / Examination Meeting	
3	Lectures (10 Weeks) Options	Lectures (10 Weeks) Options	Exams	

Fieldwork / AROUSAL / Exams (Summer Term week 0 column)

Diagram 1

Promoting Engineering Insight in Secondary Schools

J.J. Collins, M.A. O'Donnell

Engineering Division, Humberside Polytechnic, Kingston upon Hull, North Humberside

Abstract

This paper describes a novel initiative in Humberside, England, to raise the awareness of sixth form pupils, particularly females, of the career opportunities available across the whole spectrum of engineering.

Female engineering undergraduates visit sixth formers in schools and colleges to talk about engineering whilst facilitating problem-solving activities undertaken by the pupils. The pupils are thus exposed to the excitement and interest of doing things successfully in an engineering way.

Reflections on this initiative are given from four viewpoints, the sixth form pupils, their teachers, the undergraduates and the authors who helped them to develop the initiative.

Keywords: Engineering Insight, Sixthform Pupils, Problem-solving Challenge, Female Undergraduate Facilitators.

1 Introduction

Anyone who dispassionately assesses the requirements for the role of a professional engineer will conclude that women should be regarded as "engineering equals" in the predominantly male engineering profession. In Britain, in the past, prejudice and discrimination against women have needlessly almost halved the supply of professional engineers, the demand for which is certain to grow in the future.

The percentage of females in the engineering profession in the United Kingdom is less than 10% ; this is significantly less than in other parts of Europe. In recent years however, the percentage of female students admitted to engineering degree courses has been increasing; in 1990 the proportion of first year engineering undergraduates who were female was 15%. There are regions of the United Kingdom where the number of school leavers who opt for engineering studies has a proportion of females which is substantially less than the national average. In Humberside, for example, this proportion is only 7%.

In an attempt to redress this regional disadvantage, the authors have launched a novel initiative, in which female engineering undergraduates introduce engineering ideas to 16-18 year old pupils in Humberside.

2 The Humberside schools engineering initiative

2.1 Background.

Staff within the Engineering Division at Humberside Polytechnic have, for many years, been actively involved in schools liaison events on behalf of both the Polytechnic and the professional engineering institutions, such as The Institution of Mechanical Engineers. They have come to question the value of "engineering events", during which pupils play a passive role.

Engineering staff have assisted in careers events at secondary schools in the region and have consequently formed strong links with these schools and Advisers within the Humberside Careers Service. This Egg Race Challenge initiative, which exposes pupils to active learning activities, was devised in partnership with teachers of 16-18 year old 'A' level pupils and Careers Advisers in Humberside.

2.2 Aims of Humberside Egg Race Challenge.

The aims of this initiative are listed below.

For 'A' level pupils:

(a) to stimulate a greater awareness of and interest in engineering;

(b) to expose female and male pupils to the demands of engineering problem solving whilst working as part of a team;

(c) to involve the pupils in conversation with female engineering undergraduate students.

For engineering undergraduates:

(a) to broaden their awareness of the demands of group working, whilst facilitating problem-solving activities given to teams of school pupils;

(b) to develop their oral communication skills;

(c) to expose them to the demands of designing and appraising problem-solving type learning activities.

3   Staging the Humberside event

3.1   Participating Schools and Colleges.

The following described activities were staged for the benefit of sixth form pupils at a number of schools including:

(a) Wilberforce Sixthform College, Kingston upon Hull, North Humberside;
(b) Wyke Sixthform College, Kingston upon Hull, North Humberside; and,
(c) Immingham School, Immingham, South Humberside.

3.2.   Programme of Insight Activities:

1. Introductions .... 5 min.

2. Problem Solving Activities .... 85 min.

3. Model Testing and Summing-up .... 15 min.

3.3   Details given to sixth form pupils

Humberside Polytechnic Egg Race Challenge.

This afternoon let's pretend we are engineers!
Our afternoon's task is to position the structure of an offshore rig onto a prepared location.

The first job we have is to carefully describe the part of the sea bed, onto which the rig is to be positioned.

TASK 1   SPECIFYING FEATURES OF SEA BED.

(TIME ALLOWED 15 MINUTES)

Describe and sketch the important features that will enable the assembled platform support structure to be suitably positioned on the provided model section of the sea bed.

TASK 2   BUILD & TEST PLATFORM SUPPORT.

(TIME ALLOWED 70 MINUTES)

Build and cost a stable structure that will be easily   located   on the provided sea bed in a suitable position. The structure must support horizontally a model of a North Sea Gas Platform positioned at least 150 mm vertically above the sea bed.

The structure will be tested as follows:

(i)   to ensure it can be suitably positioned;
(ii) to note the "cost" of resources used in building the structure;
(iii) to ensure that the Model Platform is at least 150 mm above the section of the sea bed;
(iv) to determine which structure can support the heaviest weight.

The "best" structure is the one that supports the heaviest load. For structures supporting equal load, the one of lowest cost is judged the "best".

Available Resources for Structure

(a) Drinking straws, the purchase cost for each = £ 350
(b) Mapping Pins, the purchase cost for each = £ 750
(c) A rule, no hire charge for first 50 minutes, £15 000 for hire thereafter;
(d) A pair of scissors, hire charges equal to those given for a rule.

(Thimbles are available if required.)

3.4 Pupils' Questionnaire

Following the event, pupils are asked to answer the following questions.

(a)   Did you enjoy the event?
(b)   Did you have enough time?
(c)   Were the tasks too difficult?
(d)   What did you dislike most?
(e)   How could the event be improved?

4   **Reflections on staging past events**

4.1 From the viewpoint of sixthform pupils

The responses, by those completing and returning the questionnaire, were forceful and positive and, in particular, they indicated that:
(a) most pupils highly valued the event as a alternative to passively listening to a careers talk by an "expert";
(b) all pupils found participating in the event an enjoyable experience;
(c) the vast majority found the tasks they were given were not too difficult and that the time allowed to complete them was sufficient;
(d) most of the dislikes referred to administrative details that had also been identified by the facilitators and therefore were remedied at an early stage.

Useful pointers were also given to improve the event.

4.2 From the viewpoint of teachers

This event was viewed by staff at participating schools and colleges as both worthwhile and enjoyable for their pupils. Accordingly, the Polytechnic have been requested to stage an event of this type each year in the future.

At one college, the teachers were very impressed by the interaction of their pupils whilst working in groups of four or five. They have subsequently reviewed their arrangements for practical work and intend to move away from the normal practice of pupils working in pairs, towards allowing their pupils to work independently, or in pairs, or in groups of up to five, depending on the task to be undertaken. There will be a corresponding increase in the variety of practical work, with more open ended experiments being introduced.

4.3 From the viewpoint of undergraduates

The reaction of the undergraduates was also very positive, as evidenced by their willingness to participate in more than one school or college visit.

The undergraduates also assisted in the development of the activities by attending meetings with the authors to review the effectiveness of past school and college events. These discussions revealed that they had become more aware of the nature of group working, which they felt would be beneficial to them both as students and later, when they practice as professional engineers within a team.

4.4 From the authors' viewpoint

These reported events were most enjoyable and proved to be well received by both pupils and staff at each school and college where the event was staged.

It was also pleasing to see the undergraduates becoming more competent in interpersonal skills, whilst playing a facilitating role, by helping a number of pupils who did not have the maturity or experience to exploit the potential of group working.

Another source of encouragement was the amount of support received from industry in the Humberside area. In particular, British Gas PLC, whose staff at the Easington Shore Terminal kindly invited the winning group from each participating school or college, together with the undergraduate facilitators, to visit the Terminal at Easington.

The visitors were able talk with practising professional engineers, who explained to them how gas, that had been piped ashore from North Sea Gas Platforms, was processed to raise its quality to meet the supply requirements of domestic and industrial gas users.

5. Acknowledgements

The authors wish to acknowledge the support given to them by:

(a) the staff and pupils at each participating college or school;

(b) the staff at British Gas PLC Easington Shore Terminal;

Finally, the authors wish to record their thanks to their undergraduate students, without whose enthusiastic assistance the reported activities would not have been so effective; indeed, these would never have been staged!

An Interactive Learning Approach Towards the Development of Manufacturing Managers

N.M. Grant, R.H. McKeown

Department of Mechanical and Industrial Engineering, University of Ulster

Abstract

Northern Ireland has recently experienced a sizeable growth in the small manufacturing business sector comparable to that of other regions within the United Kingdom. This developing small-business environment requires the management skills of a multi-disciplined manager rather than those of a conventional departmental manager. This paper outlines a systems learning approach to develop managers to fulfil these requirements.

Keywords: Manufacturing, Management, Education, Systems Approach, Iterative Process.

1 Introduction

The development of an effective industrial development policy for Northern Ireland has been a key task for Government over the years, and, as economic conditions have changed, the emphasis of industrial policy has shifted accordingly. The recession in the mid-1970s redirected the focus of government away from large multi-national companies towards smaller indigenous enterprises. In the mid-1970s the growth of the small business sector world-wide was fairly rapid. Research has indicated that the bulk of job creation in the United States between 1969 and 1976 took place in companies with less than 200 employees and was highlighted in the Birch Report (1979). Over the same period the rate of job loss in the United Kingdom was significantly higher in large manufacturing plants compared to those employing 200 or less people. A census of employment for Northern Ireland between 1984 and 1989, as shown in Fig.1, indicates that the employment trend of the mid-1970s was still being reflected in the 1980s. The most rapid growth was in companies with less than 25 employees. The current economic climate suggests that this trend is going to continue through the 1990s. It is not envisaged that the single market of 1992 will have a significant effect on this.

The rate of formation of small manufacturing businesses is lower in Northern Ireland than in any other United Kingdom region. This can be attributed to a past dependency on branch plant development coupled with the demoralising effects of high and lengthy unemployment. Many Northern Ireland firms serve narrow geographical areas and in some cases very small markets. This may be attributed to lack of confidence in products, poor innovation, inadequate marketing skills, lower productivity and under-utilisation of modern equipment.   Therefore the success of the manufacturing sector in Northern Ireland is dependent on the education, or re-education, of many of its managers to address these problems.

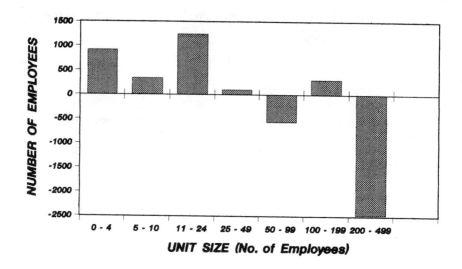

Fig.1   Census of Employee Growth for Northern Ireland (1984-89)

The systems learning programme outlined below offers both prospective and practising manufacturing managers the opportunity to develop a strategy for a small to medium sized manufacturing business organisation.

2   Systems Approach

The operations system of any manufacturing organisation is dependent on the interaction of a number of sub-systems together with the environment beyond the boundary of the system.   If the manufacturing system with its inherent sub-systems are to function efficiently then effective management at all levels is essential.   The basic system as shown in Fig.2 relates to any manufacturing organisation, irrespective of size.

In many larger companies managers find themselves directly involved solely in a single sub-system thus being deprived of the holistic management approach to the system.   Outside the security of the large organisation boundary many of these 'departmental' managers find difficulty in integrating into a smaller industrial structure where many additional and often foreign responsibilities are imposed.

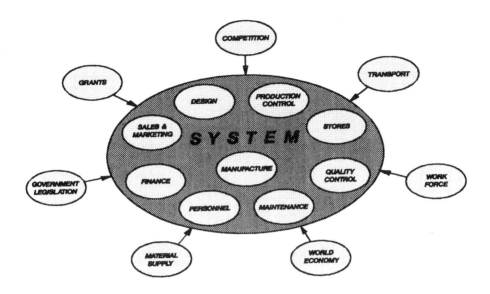

Fig.2 A Typical Manufacturing Organisation System

3 Management Learning Programme

Learning focuses around the preparation of a five year Business Plan.
This entails the design, implementation and operation of a plant
suitable for the manufacture of a marketable product or range of
products. The programme consists of four main phases; equipment,
facilities, personnel and finance. Duration of the programme is 24
weeks, on a part-time basis, and throughout an atmosphere conducive to
that of industry is projected.

Participants are arranged into small management working groups, usually
four in size. Ideally multi-disciplined groupings are preferred both in
terms of academic and industrial background, thus promoting experiential
learning together with peer learning. Each group maintains its own
identity with members simulating the role of specific phase managers.
Leadership of the group is rotated over the four phases. The groups are
not required to actually design a product but rather, through market
research, to identify an existing product or range of products currently
being manufactured. Critical design assessment and improvement is
encouraged and a full manufacturing specification for each component
comprising the product is required. The diverse range of products
selected to date has included multi-functional exercise machines,
kitchen utensils, golfing equipment and cleaning products. Import
substitutes often prove quite popular and indeed are encouraged as this

is a criterion of some grant agencies. Programme tutors act as group
facilitators with support being more directive biased than knowledge
orientated.

The iterative process adopted in the programme, particularly in the
early phases, is illustrated in Fig.3. Groups are required to address
each element of this process culminating in a detailed inventory of
equipment for both manufacture and ancillary services. In addition,
plant layouts are produced together with evidence of a reasoned approach
towards final plant location . A computer factory simulation package is
available to optimise work flow and maintain maximum machine
utilisation. Information relating to human resource requirements and
financial budgeting emanates from the process and is developed in the
later phases of the programme.

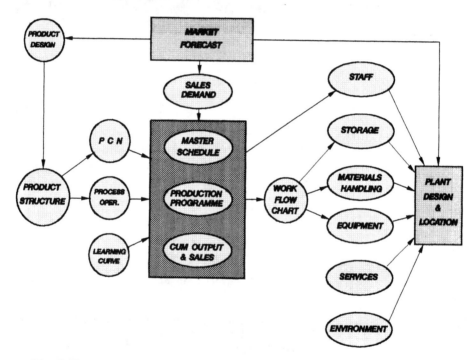

Fig.3 The Iterative Process to determine Manufacturing Requirements

3.1 The Work Plan

Throughout the learning programme sub-systems are examined in depth,
allowing participants to more fully recognise their interaction and
experience the implication this has on the entire manufacturing system.
Details of the business plan identifying phase elements is as follows:

Phase 1 Market research. Product selection. Product specification and drawings. Product structure. Process operations. Tooling tree. Production cycle network. Economic batch size. Selection of process/manufacturing equipment. Material handling equipment. Support services and office equipment.

Phase 2 Marketing plan. Master schedule. Production programme. Work flow chart/Operation sequence. Final equipment selection. Health and safety aspects. Storage facilities. Support services. Office accommodation. Effluent and waste disposal. Selection of plant location. Time scale chart. Plant layout. Light, heat and power requirements. Site plan.

Phase 3 Organisation structure. Identification of direct and indirect personnel. Job descriptions. Education and training policy. Induction and training programme. Recruitment and training timescale chart. Wages and salaries. Working hours. Holidays, sick leave and benefits. Policy regarding unions. Terms and conditions of contract of employment. Disciplinary procedure.

Phase 4 Sources of finance. Capital equipment costs. Rent,leases,hire charges and rates. Grants. Asset depreciation. Operating and material costs. Sales budgets. Cash flow projections. Cash flow reversal point. Breakeven point. Return on capital invested. Profit and loss trading accounts.

3.2 Method of Assessment

Each group is marked independently according to the work plan outlined above. The breakdown of marks is as shown below:

Phase	Content	Max. Marks
1	Documentation relating to Equipment	20
2	Documentation relating to Facilities	20
3	Documentation relating to Personnel	20
4	Documentation relating to Finance	20
5	Business Plan and Oral presentations	20
	Total Marks	100

Marks are allocated to each member of the group based on the individual's contribution as assessed by the current phase leader in consultation with the group members. Marks are calculated as follows:

```
Individual's    =   Group phase    x   Leader's assessment
phase mark          mark               on contribution
```

Phase leaders are required to give a fifteen minute presentation to all participants and tutors at the end of each phase. This is followed by a ten minute question and answer session. Throughout the assessment stage tutors role-play as representatives of a financial institution interested in funding such ventures. The oral presentation marking scheme considers the areas of technical content, structure of presentation, use of visual aids, delivery and adequacy of response to questions. The tutors in their final assessment put emphasis on the following:

* commercial viability of the product;
* thoroughness of the documentation;
* professionalism of each group and its members.

4   Conclusion

It is evident that the success of the manufacturing industry will be dependent on managers who adopt a holistic systems approach. Already some larger organisations have realised how critical the adoption of such an approach is to the future success of their business. If the success rate of newly formed Northern Ireland businesses is to improve, particularly in an increasingly competitive European Market, then a high calibre of "complete" manufacturing manager is vital.

The programme enables entrepreneurial qualities to be cultured ensuring that those who successfully complete the programme possess the knowledge and confidence to launch new products within their present employ and to establish their own manufacturing company in the future. Past participants are now actively practising this holistic approach.

References

Hitchins, D. and O'Farrell, P. (1985) Inter-regional comparisons of small firm performance.
West, A, (1988). A Business Plan, Pitman.
Grant, N.M. and McKeown, R.H. (1991) A Rationale for the Development of a Business Organisation using an Interactive Systems Approach, Proceedings of Irish Manufacturing Conference.

Producing the Kind of Engineer that Industry Needs

C.J. Moore, K.M. Holford

School of Engineering, University of Wales College of Cardiff

Abstract

University education is to undergo considerable changes. The effect of these changes on engineering education must be considered if the standard of engineering graduates is to be maintained. This paper identifies approaches to engineering education which will achieve this aim as well as helping to produce graduates who are better equipped for a career in industry.

The importance of attracting a wider range of students and promoting engineering as a professional career is emphasised. Ways in which student interest and performance can be improved are discussed and the importance of changing the current teaching philosophy to complement this is highlighted. Work carried out in Cardiff with these aims in mind is described.

Key Words: Engineering Awareness, Access, Industry, Independence, Modularisation.

1   Introduction

Government proposals for the future of University education indicate higher student numbers, necessitating a modular approach. Whilst the benefits in terms of efficiency are recognised, the effect of this 'production line' system on the standard of engineering graduates is questioned; is there a danger of producing inexperienced graduates who gain the qualifications they expect without developing the other skills they need? By structuring courses such that students can move between Institutions taking standard subjects, the respected Honours degree course will be reduced to something approaching "A- level" teaching, albeit with a specific theme.

An added danger is the increasing tendency to place responsibility for student performance on the educator. This inevitably leads to an over emphasis on examination success as opposed to an appreciation of the subject as well as resulting in an understandable apathy on the part of the student. The responsibility for performance should remain with the student who, through guidance, will also develop other responsibilities associated with a professional career.

Engineering is one of the few areas where industrial participation is increasing both at research and undergraduate level. Industrial collaboration is vital for the formation of engineers who, by repeated exposure not only to new technology but also to problems encountered in the field will enter industry with an increased awareness of industrial aspects.

Recent reports by working parties comprised of representatives from both academia and industry have proposed an undergraduate course, Engineering Council (1988) and post graduate course, Parnaby (1990), both of which emphasise the need for a well structured course upon which engineers can build their careers. Employers expect engineering courses to give students a true image of engineers in industry: as an authority on technology, a leader of others and a communicator.

This paper, discusses the implications of increasing student numbers, and indicates some factors which need to be considered if Universities are to produce the kind of engineer that industry needs;

* Initially introducing an awareness of the engineering function in Schools;
* Attracting a wider range of students from a broader background;
* Emphasising individual student responsibility for their performance;
* Promoting career interest as well as providing academic timulus;
* Increasing industrial involvement with the undergraduate syllabus;
* Early emphasis on the need for adaptability initiative and independence.

2   The Implications of Increasing Student Numbers

An increase in University student numbers looks certain. This increase will have a number of effects, including a change in the staff-student ratio, larger lecture groups, less tutorials and more distinctly a move towards a modular approach. The indication is that we will be expected to teach 'more for less', CVCP (1992), and that engineering students will benefit from less contact hours, Engineering Professors' Conference (1991).

Ways to overcome these effects have been suggested: greater use of post graduates for teaching, 'small group' teaching techniques and increased emphasis on computer aided learning. These suggestions in themselves bring problems, primarily in terms of resources. It is difficult to foresee effective computer aided learning without a massive increase in most current University computing resources and facilities.

These considerations introduce the argument for modularisation where students will be given freedom of choice and mobility, but at what cost? If modularisation is to be effective, it will mean a standardisation of the degree schemes, so that equivalent modules can be taken in different institutions and pieced together at the end of a three or four year period to produce a complete degree. The degree will therefore have to adhere to a strict syllabus in a similar fashion to the existing A level schemes.

The 'production line' style of teaching may be suited to some degree schemes, but it is difficult to foresee how engineering will benefit from this approach. It can be anticipated that the onus on the already over-emphasised examination process will be increased, as in this mass-teaching approach students will need to pass a module before moving to the next. This will result in Universities becoming more conscious of examination success rates as a means of promoting their establishment in an increasingly competitive environment.

Many academics regard the switch to modularised courses as inevitable, indeed the CVCP is already discussing the possible advantages of this method (CVCP 1991). It is the authors' opinion that this unnecessary haste to accept modularisation has precluded objective consideration of the implications involved. It is interesting to note that a report from the Engineering Professors' Conference (EPC 1991) on the future pattern of first degree courses fails to include modularisation in it's recommendations. It is apparent that a greater degree of coherence and consideration is required before this major step is taken.

Engineering is a career which encompasses many fields of knowledge and requires a large number of skills. Many industries are already concerned that engineering graduates are not of a high enough standard. There are a number of necessary considerations if the graduate engineer is to be made more suited to industry.

3   Initially Introducing an Awareness of the Engineering Function in Schools

The recruitment of engineers has been a concern of both industry and higher education for a number of years. Compared to many other countries, British engineering degrees attract neither the number nor quality of students required. This is frequently attributed to a lack of awareness of engineering within the school environment. In order to attract young people to engineering careers, schools must be provided with support in the form of both literature and role models.

Currently, school leavers do not consider engineering as a career option, or of the few that do, many see it as a second rate profession with no status or prospects. Finniston (1980) noted that Britain does not acknowledge the crucial importance of engineering in the economic stability of the country. He considered that the engineer's role in society was not adequately recognised and that engineers in the United Kingdom were less highly regarded than their counterparts in countries such as America and Japan. It is the authors' opinion that this is still the case twelve years on, with neither pupils nor parents perceiving the engineer's role in society. Somehow the reputation of engineering as a challenging, professional career has to be established.

The Engineering Education Scheme (1990) has tried to achieve this by bringing together schools and engineering industries on a project basis so that potential students can have a taste of 'real' engineering. This project is proving to be successful in promoting engineering as a potentially interesting career. However, despite this and other such initiatives (Engineering Council: Neighbourhood Engineers and Opening Windows on Engineering), lack of career prestige remains apparent and engineering is still not seen to be on a par with law, accountancy or medicine as a professional career. An Engineer's Professors Conference Bulletin (1990) identified areas of concern. Firstly, the number of applications to read engineering at University had fallen in recent years and continued to decline, despite an overall rise in University applications. Furthermore, engineering courses are seen by both school pupils and students to be uninteresting compared to other courses.

In answer to these problems, the University of Wales, Cardiff has recently been attempting to raise the profile of engineering in schools by providing specific engineering information and attending recruitment fairs and careers forums, thus providing the necessary literature and role models for the promotion of engineering careers. Inviting school pupils to attend Summer Schools has also been used to increase awareness. The figures for applications for 1992 are encouraging as detailed below. (Note; Different processing techniques were used between the two years, so the dates at which data were recorded differ).

National change overall	(15.12.91)	+ 9.85
UWCC change overall	(28.02 92)	+ 8.38
School of Engineering change	(28.02.92)	+23.01
National change, Civil Engineering	(15.12.91)	+15.03
UWCC change, Civil Engineering	(28.02.92)	+18.98
National change, General Engineering	(15.12.91)	− 2.93
UWCC change, Integrated Engineering	(28.02.92)	+20.00
National change, Mechanical Engineering	(15.12.91)	+13.05
UWCC change, Mechanical Engineering	(28.02.92)	+29.59

This indicates that Universities can influence student applications. There is af lack of awareness of engineering at school level and this is the responsibility of both higher education and industry.

It has been shown by the Engineering Council that introducing engineering in schools is beneficial. Introducing a stronger engineering influence into the course work could be equally advantageous. This could be achieved by introducing more 'engineering' concepts into the A level Physics, Mathematics and Chemistry syllabi or simply by emphasising the engineering implications of the existing course content. More ambitiously, an 'Engineering' A level could be introduced which would enable students to study engineering and its principles in a more academic way than the existing BTEC Courses.

4   Attracting a Wider Range of Students from a Broader Background

It has always been recognised that engineering needs to attract students from a broad range of backgrounds, as many engineers will not follow a typical A level route to University. For entry to UWCC, equivalent qualifications such as BTEC are considered, as are Irish Highers, Access courses, European and International Baccalaureate and many overseas qualifications. A Foundation year is already available for those with inappropriate qualifications. However, the benefits of an engineering degree still need to be emphasised, by increasing society's awareness of the role of the Professional Engineer and their required qualifications.

At UWCC, Physics A level has been dropped as an entry requirement for Engineering and the first year content has been extended to accommodate this change. This has proved successful as it has widened access to include students who, through poor advice or indecision, did not take Physics A level. It also ensures that a broad knowledge of relevant Physics is gained by every student despite their background.

The introduction of courses which are based on a broad engineering education which is relevant to industry as opposed to engineering science will also prove successful in attracting students from different backgrounds, Holford et al (1991) and Watton and Holford (1991).

The changes which engineering has recently undergone have widened access for students. However, it is difficult to foresee how Engineering courses could change further to allow even wider access without reducing the quality of the degree or by extending to a four year course.

5   Emphasising Individual Student Responsibility for their Performance

There is a currently increasing trend to place the responsibility for student performance with the educator. Although in some ways this can be beneficial, there are implications which cannot be overlooked.

University education is gradually reverting to teaching as opposed to lecturing. Students in engineering are not encouraged to read a subject, and instead are merely learning to pass an exam. This is inevitably effecting their overall understanding of engineering and students are becoming increasingly reliant on detailed lecture notes, hand outs and tutorials to obtain a degree.

With the increased pressure on lecturing staff to perform, the onus is on good examination results. Unless classes exhibit a suitable level of exam performance, the lecturer's ability is questioned. Consequently, lecturers are tempted to 'ensure' that their students pass by 'teaching' them what they need to know and providing hand outs to ensure that adequate notes are taken. The academic demands of the students are thus reduced, resulting in apathy as the course presents no challenge. In addition, on the rare occasion the student is presented with something new, they are unwilling to deal with it as they have become unfamiliar with encountering new and challenging situations.

The implications of this 'spoon feeding' approach are particularly worrying when educating potential engineers, who, by definition, need to be resourceful, adaptable and capable of understanding and absorbing new information. Traditionally, graduates are seen to be people who can think on their own, organise their own work, take the initiative and be prepared to investigate problems. By reverting to a 'taught' degree, where all that it is required is an examination pass which can be achieved by learning lecture notes, it is difficult to see how these additional qualities will be acquired.

This approach is detracting from the student's skill and initiative and only succeeds in diminishing any incentive to learn about engineering. By returning the emphasis for learning to the students, enthusiasm for the subject will be restored.   This is the only way to produce useful and competent engineers, capable of thinking on their own and making effective decisions.

6   Promoting Career Interest and Providing Academic Stimulus

One way of promoting career interest is to include more 'real life' examples in the syllabus. This does not have to detract from the academic content of the course: it merely means relating the content to the career, so that the students gain a better understanding of the theoretical concepts, instead of seeing them as academic exercises.

More involvement with long term research projects and increased use of industrial collaborators will encourage career interest. Many students may have specific interests which are not catered for by the existing collaborators . These students should be encouraged to form links with new industrial contacts.

In Cardiff, we have introduced a Students' Professional Engineering Record to encourage the students to take a responsible approach to their career, which is similar to the Professional Log book required of Chartered Engineers.

7   Increasing Industrial Involvement Within the Undergraduate Syllabus

The importance of industrial involvement with engineering education has long been recognised, particularly by Finniston (1980). This has resulted in a greater level of industrial involvement with academia by the formation of the Engineering Council in 1982. Corfield (1984) noted that the more progressive educators had asked industry to identify its requirements and have adopted a more flexible attitude to proposals. Crossland (1989) states that Universities need to rely on funding from industry and commerce to subsidise diminishing government grants and that furthermore collaboration with industry is necessary to ensure the courses are relevant to industrial needs. Indeed Cardiff, like many other engineering departments, has an industrial advisory board comprising of representatives from local industry. It is the authors' opinion that initiatives such as these are not enough. Engineering academics should be involved with industry on a continual basis, so that the benefits which can be gained from one another are apparent. There is generally a lack of communication between academia and industry at a local level and both parties would benefit from a better rapport.

8   Early Emphasis on the Need for Adaptability, Initiative and Independence

The range of disciplines which an engineer must grasp has grown dramatically with the increasing complexity of materials, products and micro computing. A graduate engineer is unlikely to begin a career in a specific job. They are more likely to be responsible for many different areas, some of which will be unfamiliar. No single degree scheme could hope to impart the breadth of experience needed in engineering today. It is therefore vital that we educate students to be responsible for their own learning, so that the degree educates engineers to be communicators, adaptable, independent and to have initiative. This will more adequately prepare graduates for their career, helping them to deal with the unfamiliar situations with which they will inevitably be faced.

9   Conclusions

The implications of increased students numbers and modularisation are worrying and if this new approach to University education is to be successful, careful consideration must be given to the dangers involved. By reverting to teaching techniques and a regimented course structure, we run the risk of demoralising our students, smothering their intellect and suffocating their creativity. By spoon-feeding undergraduates with the academic essentials without encouraging them to gain a full understanding of engineering, we are not encouraging them to think and work on their own. Consequently we are not adequately preparing them for their potential work environment. If engineers are taught to pass exams rather than to be engineers, the transition to a career in industry will be a painful and difficult one, during which the graduate will be constantly unsure and insecure. By adopting some of the approaches suggested in this paper, graduates who are better equipped for their chosen career could be produced.

This paper indicates that the future of engineering is not just in the hands of industry: it is also the responsibility of Universities. With effective co-operation, promotion and consideration, engineering could attain the respect it has long deserved.

References

Corfield, Sir K.(1984) - Getting the Engineers We Need. Proc. IMechE. Vol. 198, No 14. pp 243-248.
Crossland, B. (1989) - The Lifelong Education and Training of Mechanical Engineers. George Stephenson Lecture. Proc. IMechE., Vol 203 part B pp 140-144.
CVCP Paper N/91/139 (1991) on the possible advantages of modularity.
CVCP Report (1992) "How to do more with less".
Engineering Council (1984) Opening Windows on Engineering.
Engineering Council (1987) Neighbourhood Engineers - A Regional Scheme.
Engineering Council (1988).An Integrated Engineering Degree Programme.
Engineering Education Scheme (1990). Supported by The Sainsbury Trusts.
Engineering Professors Conference (1990) Bulletin. No 17. New Directions in Engineering Education.
Engineering Professors Conference (1991) - The Future Pattern of First Degree Courses in Engineering. Occasional Paper, No.3.
Finniston, Sir Montague. (1980): Engineering Our Future. Report of the Committee of Inquiry into the Engineering Profession. HMSO. London.
Holford, K.M., Jones, R.D. and Watton, J. (1991)- The Integrated Engineering Degree Programme. ICWES 9. Cambridge. 1991. ISBN 0-905927-63-X
Parnaby, J. (1990). Report to the S.E.R.C. The Engineering Doctorate.
Watton, J. and Holford, K.M. (1991) The IEDP - From Perception to Practice. Proc. Conf. "Innovative Teaching in Engineering". Ellis Horwood Ltd. Chichester pp 32-37 ISBN 0-13-457607-1.

Master of Engineering Degree Course for Engineering Education

A.H. Pe

School of Civil Engineering, Portsmouth Polytechnic

Abstract

The changes that have taken place in the Civil Engineering industry require a new breed of graduate engineer who is well versed in technical matters and is also a competent manager and financier. This paper sets out to explain how this particular course has been designed so that the student responds to the challenge and adapts to the needs of the industry. The paper relates to the experience gained in running such courses. It recommends ways in which this model may be adopted for promoting Engineering Education Worldwide in this particular discipline.

<u>Keywords</u>: Engineering, Degree, Master, Civil.

1 Introduction

Master of Engineering courses were first formulated after the publication of the Finniston Report in 1981. It highlighted the need for well trained and qualified engineers who are capable of meeting the challenges of the profession in the 1990s. Many of these courses were formulated and offered in several British universities and polytechnics. These courses had to be distinctive. They have been extended and enhanced and therefore are spread over a four year period including a period of training in industry. They are first degree courses and are not postgraduate Masters courses. They are intended to produce the future captains of industry, hence the need for major industrial involvement in both design, implementation and assessment of these courses.

It is also important to consider the type of students who will be undertaking these courses. They will be the smaller section of students who are well motivated, innovative, capable of solving engineering problems and have the potential to develop entrepreneurial and leadership skills. It is the purpose of academic staff to identify such students and have them participating on the course.

It is a challenging task for the lecture programme to fulfil these aims. But over the past years it has been proved that these courses can be run successfully and consequently they have become well established here in Britain.

It is now important to seek how these course models may be adopted for use in other parts of the world so that engineering education may be further enhanced.

2   The Course Structure

The course is structured such that students on both the Bachelor and
the Masters undertake the same course during the first and second
year. The first year is structured to provide the fundamental
principles of engineering and the second year to help apply theory to
practice. The students are then offered an opportunity to opt for the
MEng if they feel confident enough to enter for the selection process.
This process is explained later in the text since if selected to join
the course the student then undertakes two further years. The third
year consists of an intensive study programme based at college from
October to March followed by an industrial placement period from April
until September of that year.

After successfully completing this period the students return to
college for the final year of the course. This consists of a lecture
programme from October to mid-February and the undertaking of a design
project from then until early July when the academic year ends. It
may be clearly seen that, once the students have started in the third
year of the MEng course, they are kept fully occupied until the
completion of their course in early July of the following year.
During this time the students will have undertaken two sets of
examinations together with an industrial attachment period, plus
undertaking a Group Design Project. Assessment of these performances
and the allocation of marks are explained in later text.

3   The Course Content

As indicated in Appendix 1 the usual engineering subjects are all
included. Apart from these subjects, additional lectures are provided
by external lecturers from industry. During the course students are
also posed set open-ended problems from industry.

The students are encouraged to solve these problems in a flexible
and adaptable manner. In this respect the design project serves a vital
role to develop engineering judgement and communication skills. Also
during group design activities students are encouraged to develop both
commercial and leadership skills whilst appreciating the significance
of team work. Major emphasis is placed upon students to be aware of
impact of engineering projects upon the environment and to appreciate
the best, least expensive engineering solutions to proposed projects.

4   The Selection Process

This part of the course is obviously one of the most important aspects
of the course. The process must be such that the right type of
student to study the course needs to be chosen. The details of the
process are provided in later text.

Students are chosen who are not only suited to sustain academic
rigour but also able to develop during the course to the needs of
industry in the future.

The selection process is devised such that during this period the
students are able to display their own abilities in logic, engineering
judgement, practical application, oral presentation, group
participation and communication skills. An interview panel consisting

of academic staff and representatives from industry make a final
choice on the basis of performance, marks attained and academic
records. Offers are then made to the students who are at liberty to
either accept or reject the offer.

5   Industrial Input to the Course

This is of major significance to the course and their participation is
as follows:

(i)   Advice and guidance provided by Members of the Industrial
          Advisory Board.

(ii)   Provision of Professional Counselling Service to a group
          of students as "Industrial Tutors".

(iii)   Provision of design projects so that students are exposed
          to real problems.

(iv)   Provision of industrial training during the attachment
          period of and participation in assessment programmes.

(v)   Provision of the much valued awards and prizes to high
          achievers which are most welcome by students concerned.

As a consequence of this effort made by industry students feel
closely linked to the industrial environment. Also this has helped
students to think about their future in a particular discipline and
thus enable them to establish closer links with industrialists to
shape out their future careers.

6   Professional Experience

The students leave college for attachment in industry for approximately six months and attain valuable experience.

The main objective is for the students to apply knowledge gained at
college to an engineering project. During this period the students
will have to adapt rapidly to the new environment. Obviously
agreement will be made with the industrialist concerned, regarding the
development of engineering skills, innovative problem solving,
implementation of agreed proposals and a further awareness of both
financial and managerial skills. Monitoring of the students is
undertaken by lecturers during the placement period.

In order to assess the progress made, students are made to keep a
record of work undertaken and prepare a report for submission on their
return to college at the end of eleven weeks. There are two of these
reports to be submitted together with a "Candidate's Report" which is
of the students' choice. These reports, together with their oral
presentation, form the assessment for the professional experience
attachment period.

7   Group Design Project

This section of the work is undertaken during the final semester of
the final year of the course. The topics offered are those agreed
with industrial colleagues dealing with a real project. The design
brief normally consists of the project which may be undertaken by a
group of students. The work should be of a typical design of a unit
together with the preparation of suitable drawings, specifications,

bills of quantities, costings and proposed construction method.
The work has to be undertaken for a set deadline. During this
period students are expected to work on a group basis as well as with
individual specialisms. Students are encouraged to consult both
academic staff as well as specialists from industry. Once completed
the work submitted is assessed both on an individual performance
within a team and also the group performance. Here again industrial
colleagues assist with the assessment of these projects.

8   The Final Year Student Exchange Programme

Amongst the several international links with universities in other
parts of the world that Portsmouth has, the one with the Grand Ecole
D'Ingeneurs of St. Etienne, France is extremely active. At the outset
both Institutions were involved only with industrial placement
exchanges which were then extended to also undertaking "Design
Projects".

Presently the exchange programme is at a stage where final year
student exchanges have taken place. This means that the students will
have spent a total period of 14 months in a different country and
university. This has meant supervision by staff of visiting students
who are in the final year of the course. It has been a new experience
for both students and lecturers involved. At present this scheme is
at its early stages but indications are encouraging and therefore will
continue in the future. From the student point of view it is a major
achievement in undertaking a course in a different language with the
added bonus that the students end up with degrees from both
universities in two countries.

9   The Assessment of the Course

This is undertaken by examination performance, coursework attainment,
continuous assessment and marks obtained for Professional Experience
and Design Project marks. This is spread over a period of two years
and consequently the assessment is well spread throughout the course.
It can be said of the system adopted, that the students are well
tested in both academic performance and engineering application.

There is no classification for the award of this degree but a
distinction is awarded to those whose performance is considered to be
outstanding. The system has been well tested over the years and the
final results confirm the expected performance of the students
ability.

10   Conclusion

The course that has been designed specifically to meet the needs in
the civil engineering industry has been unique. The author has
identified all the major advantages of this course without finding
disadvantages in its implementation. These may be identified as
follows:

1. A course has been produced which is suitable to industry
   and is now recognised as the right type of training for future
   engineers.

2. The right type of students have been identified for undertaking this course and therefore can be extended slightly more than the majority of the Bachelor course students.
3. The duration of the course is just about right, bearing in mind future degree courses where continuing education will encompass the major part of the training to qualify as Chartered Engineers.
4. The course fulfils the criteria to meet the academic standards for the Degree Validation and also for those of the Professional Institutions and Engineering Council.
5. The exchange programme offered on the course is most relevant to current needs where students who expect mobility are able to take advantage of the scheme.
6. In terms of World Engineering Education this model offers an excellent opportunity to be adopted for development of International Exchange Programmes.
7. Graduates, who have joined industry, have been successful in seeking progress through the promotion process. They have been successful in serving the profession in a competent and able manner.

Acknowledgement

The author wishes to thank the Head of School of Civil Engineering, Professor B.E. Lee, The Director of Studies, Mr. P.B. Johnson and Staff of the Course Team for their support and encouragement for presenting this paper.

References

Finniston, Sir M. (1980) "Engineering Our Future", Report on the Committee of Engineering Profession, HMSO publication, pp 21-26.
Earls, I.C. (1988), "What is MEng?", Proceedings of a Conference on M.Eng courses, pp 15-18.
Pe, A.H. (1989), "Industrial Training for Undergraduate Degree Courses in Civil Engineering", World Conference Proceedings, pp 135-141.
Pe, A.H. (1991), "Professional Experience Relevant to Master of Engineering Courses in Civil Engineering", World Conference Proceedings, pp 256-260.
Ward, R., "Teaching Management to Engineering Students", World C Conference Proceedings, pp 64-69, Hamilton, Canada.
Duggan, T.V. (1989), "How Technology Will Change Engineering Education", Int. J. Appl. Eng. Ed.5, 687-690.
Duggan, T.V. (1989), "Future International Cooperation in Engineering Education", Int. J. Appl. Eng. Ed.5 - 687-690.
Duggan, T.V. (1990), "Trends and Attitudes to Change in Engineering Education", Proc. ASEE, Annual Conference, Toronto.
Duggan, T.V. (1991), "An Overview of Engineering Education in Europe", Australasian J. of Engrng Ed.2, 155-156.
Council for National Academic Handbook, 1991-92.
Definitive Document (1991), Master of Engineering Course in Civil Engineering, Portsmouth Polytechnic.

Master of Engineering Degree Course

Appendix No. 1

First and Second Year	Third Year		Fourth Year	
October to July	October to March	March to September	October to mid-February	February to June
Modules	Modules		Modules	
Geotechnical Engineering	Geotechnical Engineering	P	Geotechnical Engineering	D
Mathematics	Numerical and Computing Methods	R O F	Numerical and Computing Methods	E S I
Structural Engineering	Structural Engineering	E S S	Structural Engineering	G N
Water Engineering	Water Engineering	I O N A L	Water Engineering	
Civil Engineering Practice	Construction Management		Construction Management	P R
Communications	Materials Engineering	E X P	Operational Research	O J E
Fieldwork	Highway & Traffic Engineering	E R I	Management of Traffic	C T
	Environmental Engineering	E N C E	Environmental Engineering	
	Field Study		Field Study	

The Institute of Technology Management

J.G. Walker, R.S. Stevenson, N. Longworth, J.R.I. Norrie
Centre for Continuing Education, University of Southampton

Abstract
This paper describes the origins and development of the Institute of Technology Management, a partnership of HEIs and industry. It explains how it came into being, why it is perceived that industry and commerce have a need for the modular programme on offer and the reasons that individual short modules are available as well as a degree. The benefits that accrue from operating as a partnership are described as are some of the issues that have had to be addressed. The range of modules in the programme is covered briefly with an indication of what further modules may be required. The issue of marketing such a programme is addressed and the paper concludes with the vision of developing this into a pan-European Institute.
Keywords: Technology, Management, Partnership, Institute, Quality, Modular, Education, Training, ITM

1 Introduction

Technology Management links the disciplines of engineering, science and management in order to plan, develop and deploy **technological** capabilities so as to shape and accomplish the strategic and operational objectives of an organisation.

Key elements of Management of Technology in industrial practice are:

1.the assessment of technological options, including identification and evaluation;

2.research and development itself, including determination of project feasibility;

3.integration of the company's overall effort;

4.implementation of a product and/or process; and

5.obsolescence and replacement.

The practice of Technology Management might be defined as the design, implementation and administration of the activities, functions and relationships needed within organisations to achieve economic and social objectives through technological innovation. For this definition we are indebted to Dr M A Dorgham of the Open University. (International Journal of Technology Management, Vol 1, 1986)

Quite simply, technology management can be described as being "a business strategy in which advanced technologies are put into effect within an integrated framework for the whole enterprise".

2 The need for training in Technology Management

The rapid pace of change in commerce and industry and the need to respond quickly to innovation in order to compete effectively in world markets is creating significant challenges in both technology and management infrastructures. For industry the understanding of the underlying dynamic behind technological and scientific development is often crucial for survival; the understanding of new management practices enables companies to cope and compete effectively. Industry needs to be responsive to such pressures; universities must be even more aware and fast-moving in providing the sort of Continuing Education most needed during the 1990s.

The current perception of needs both in executive management in industry and in the more forward-thinking educational establishments is that innovation and management are not, and should not be, separate activities. There is a requirement for new thinking and new educational strategies and techniques which emphasise this interdependence and inter-relation. This must be between development and delivery, between content and method, between technology and management. Universities should be at the forefront of these strategies, and in some of their new practices - modular degrees, educational technology, relations with industry - they are. But the real challenge is in the essential understanding of these new concepts at the course development stage to provide education which is presented acceptably and is relevant to the needs of both education and industry in the 1990s.

3 The origins of the partnership

The whole project originated a few years ago with a survey of the training needs of local industry. This focused primarily on manufacturing industry and revealed that the range of training was probably outside the capability of any one academic institution. It would clearly be a sound approach to harness and capitalise upon the combined strengths of a number of collaborating institutions with an appropriate mix of skills, experience and facilities, such as laboratories. The partnership was therefore set up between the Universities of Southampton, Portsmouth and Bournemouth, Southampton Institute of Higher Education and the Open University.

It was also seen as being important to have the continued involvement, and support, of industrial partners. This would ensure that a constant monitoring of what was being offered could take place, to be certain that it continued to match the requirements of industry. A bonus deriving from the academic partnership is that it increases the number of industry links that are available to be used.

4 Industry requirements

Meetings with representatives of local industrial organisations and with specific larger companies have revealed a keen interest in this programme. Industrialists have reviewed the modules as currently defined and confirm that these modules are all relevant to what they see as the needs of industry for training in technology management.

The programme sets out to enable greater value to be gained from technical and managerial skills in industry. It should strengthen the technical and managerial competence of experienced professionals and managers in manufacturing and related industries. It should enhance the career flexibility and job effectiveness of those who participate, broadening their technical horizons, managerial perspectives and personal skills. As a result, they should be capable of accepting broader and more responsible rôles, both technical and managerial, within an atmosphere of continual change.

5   Advanced Manufacturing Technology to Technology Management

The origins of this project were specific to the manufacturing industry, as Advanced Manufacturing Technology (AMT). The principles addressed, though, are very applicable across a much broader spectrum of industry and commerce.

The first steps in the development of the project were on the basis of a Master's degree in AMT. Further discussions revealed that an important change should be made, broadening the programme to encompass what is generally known as Technology Management. The requirement for training is by no means limited to manufacturing and many people in all areas of industry and commerce would welcome the opportunity of receiving training in Technology Management - using the word Technology in its broadest sense.

6   Provision of learning outcomes or of qualifications?

The people in industry for whom this is relevant are normally those who are progressing in the company and hence are already carrying out vital roles. They will already have competence in some of the areas which are addressed by this programme. The requirements of industry are, therefore, best addressed by providing a series of modular courses which may, or may not, be taken by the same participants. The participants cannot usually be released for more than a week or so at a time, and it is difficult to release them more than once or twice in a year. Though there is no specific reason against, industry does not, in general, see much advantage in the acquisition of further qualifications for its employees. There is still, however, a great deal of interest in some quarters in the availability of qualifications. Therefore it has been decided that a Master's degree, and a diploma, should still be made available which may be an added incentive for some participants to extend their training to achieve these qualifications.

7   The partnership

Each of the academic partners has something unique and specific to offer, including expertise in AMT and management, laboratory facilities, technical specialisms and available distance and open learning materials. In order to ensure that the overall course has credibility and industrial recognition, it is essential to capture all these components.

The participation of industry in the development and delivery of courses and materials is also vital. It will be the responsibility of each participating academic institution to extend and develop relationships with industry so that we continue to be confident that the real needs as perceived by industry are being met.

Inevitably, having a partnership also brings some disadvantages. There are differing cultures, a range of different internal systems and approaches all of which have to be satisfied. Nowhere is this more apparent than in the area of accreditation where each institution jealously guards its own system and standards. It has been necessary to have several iterations of discussions over draft procedures - and these are still continuing.

8   Choosing the modules

The overall content has been derived from discussions between the academic partners and checking with people from industry. The academic partners have then jointly devised a logical way of dividing this into separate modules for which there is a rationale, aims and objectives, teaching and assessment methods as well as content.

The original concept was to create a programme which essentially divided into five strands, or themes, namely technology in context, improving business processes, industrial information technology, strategic management and future trends. Further analysis of the content has led us to dividing the field of technology management into some 20 or so modules, each one to be covered within a week as a residential course and with a similar amount of additional private study.

As the modules are offered individually it is necessary that each should be of a 'stand-alone' nature. This will inevitably create some overlap in certain areas but this is not believed to be a problem as the overlap will be quite small.

9   Structure of the programme

For those participants who wish to progress to the Master's degree there are several modules which are regarded as compulsory. These are:

a) Technology in context - the application of technology for long term business benefit

b) Continuous improvement - concepts and principles of total quality management, the business as a process and methods to continuously improve that process.

c) Managing business change - the factors generating a need for change, the effects of change and active promotion and implementation of change for the benefit of the organisation.

d) Management of information technology - techniques to analyse, plan and monitor its use within the organisation, and managing information technology within the context of the business.

e) Future technologies and techniques - a framework for examination and evaluation of emerging technologies, incorporating them into strategies and their influence on opportunities.

The programme includes other modules covering product design and development, materials and processes, manufacturing systems, management of projects, logistics, the application of computers, industrial systems, communications, responsibility of management, competitiveness, organisational models, personal and professional skills, managing the development of people, information technology trends, management of education and training technology and women in technology management.

10 The participants

The programme is planned to suit those in industry, of graduate status, who have several years' experience. It will be of great benefit both to those who have engineering experience and are moving to management and to those who have management expertise and need a better knowledge of technology.

Thus, it should be beneficial to those who already have experience in industry, with a technical or management background and are of degree status or level. It should increase their vision to broader horizons, fill gaps in their knowledge, give a higher level perspective of their organisation and give greater clarity of vision. The aim is to increase their effectiveness in terms of management and personal skills and greater objectivity, enabling them to shoulder more and broader responsibilities thereby increasing their value as members of the management team. This training should increase their ability to handle change and to face up to competition.

Though it is envisaged that many participants will be aged between 25 and 35 it is clear already that the programme will attract many who do not match this stereotype but who will find it beneficial for their own specific circumstances.

11 Further developments

The programme of modules has never been envisaged as being complete and able to remain static. As new requirements are identified there will be a need for additional modules to be created. Since the original list was generated there have been a few additional modules added, such as Management of Education and Training Technology, Women and Technology Management and Environmental Issues, Management Strategy and Competitiveness.

At the time of writing, a survey is being initiated that will examine other courses at the participating institutions to see if there are other subjects that should also be considered.

The approach we have adopted for marketing is to find out, by mailshots, which companies are interested in availing themselves of this training and then marketing directly to these companies at a personal level. We anticipate that it will remain difficult to build up the programme but we envisage that, by delivering good quality courses, this hurdle will prove to be only temporary.

12 The Institute

The organisation and administration of the Technology Management programme should provide a flexible interface with potential customers and should be capable of speedy responses. There are several important reasons why we believe it is necessary to set up a company to do this. The main reasons are:
- to provide an organisational framework for the five academic partners to work

together as a single entity
- to have flexibility and responsiveness to meet changing customer needs
- to be able to operate with charitable status
- to have convenient treatment for taxation, reclamation of VAT, etc
- to have limited liability
   In order to meet these objectives we have registered a company, The Institute of Technology Management Limited.

13   European programmes and partnerships

What this paper has covered so far has been limited purely to the UK, and generally to the geographic area that weather forecasters refer to as central southern England. The initiatives are by no means limited to this. Through various European Community funding programmes work has been going on to involve organisations in other EC member states who have been working on similar projects. This includes France, Italy, Portugal and Belgium and approaches are also being made to some of the Eastern European countries. Under the EC FORCE Programme a partnership has been established to create a unique 'twinning' relationship allowing training-limited companies to learn from the more advanced education and management practices of the training-rich. The partners already have strong links with small and medium sized enterprises (SMEs) through the Training and Enterprise Council, regional Chambers of Commerce and, in Portugal, Fundetec is an organisation with a specific mission to deal with the needs of SMEs.
   This, through international exchanges, is aimed at establishing a European Institute of Technology Management which will develop a common training programme - creating and delivering training modules to SMEs and others in several countries of Europe and will also train the trainers on the uses of education technology to develop new modules in Technology Management.
   We anticipate further developments in this direction with exchanges aimed both at establishing specific courses and at establishing new modules for the Institute.

14   Conclusion

Work on the Technology Management programme is giving the academic partners a valuable insight into the needs of industry and the way in which industry operates. It also provides industry with some training which is vital if industry is to retain, and indeed improve, its competitiveness.
   By forging new, or stronger, links with industry there is also a direct benefit to the academic partners in creating new ideas and opportunities for research and consultancy. The close relationships implied by establishing the partnership in this way will ensure that the academic partners are at the "leading edge" in industry's practice and thinking in these key areas. Setting up the Institute of Technology Management gives a marketing focus to the whole venture.

Models of Circuits with Electric Arc for Teaching and Practical Needs

Z. Dmochowski

Electrical Department, Technical University of Bialystok

Abstract
The paper presents experience gained by the educational and scientific staff of the Electrical Departament at the Technical University of Bialystok in utilizing models of circuits with electric arc both for the needs of education and industrial practice. Algorithms and computer programs were developed by a number of degree candidates within the framework of M.Sc. - dissertations, that permit models of high-power a.c. circuits with electric arc to be analyzed. The programs developed may be used both for analysis of nonsinusoidal waveshapes in the curricula of Theoretical Electrotechnics as well as in computation and laboratory - simulation classes in the subjects : Electroheat, Electrical and Electroheat Installations, etc.
Keywords: Model, Electric Circuit, Electric Arc, Education, Industrial Applications

1.Introduction

Circuits with electric arc play a significant role in engineering education as well as in design and industrial practice.

The Technical University of Bialystok has for many years cooperated with the metallurgical and machine industry in the field of measuring and diagnostic systems for electroheat installations such as steelmaking and foundry arc furnaces. As a result of that cooperation, a set of systems was developed that allows physical magnitudes and parameters of high - power a.c. electric arcs, such as current, voltage, active power and radiation coefficients to be measured, Dmochowski (1986, 1990, 1991).

The problems mentioned above have currently been introduced into the curricula in the subject: Electroheat Installations for students who specialize in Power Engineering. Algorithms and computer programs were developed by a number of degree candidates in the framework of M.Sc. - dissertations, that permitted models of high -

power a.c. circuits with electric arc to be analyzed.
    On assumption, they were developed as user's programs
thus intended to serve both the needs of education as
well as the needs of designers and operators of
steelmaking and foundry arc furnances.

2 The "MODELE" program

The "MODELE" program, that was developed, allows the
operation of steelmaking and foundry arc furnances to be
analyzed on the basis of their linear and nonlinear models
Kamiński (1989).

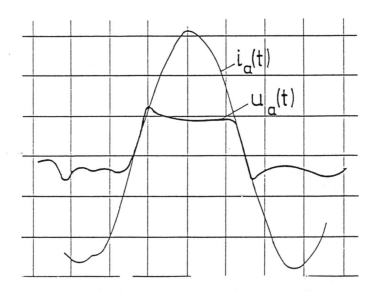

Fig.1. Oscillograms of instantaneous values of the
       $u_a$arc voltage and the $i_a$arc current recorded
       in the 40th minute of melting in an arc furnace
       for production of cast iron, with rated capacity
       $m=25*10^3$ kg and rated power S=12 MVA.

    In the case of the linear model the assumption is made
that the high – current circuit of an arc furnace consists
of a constant resistance and reactance, and that the both
voltages: the supply and voltage are sinusoidal.
    For the nonlinear model the waveshape of the arc voltage
is rectangular while the supply voltage is sinusoidal. This
case is close to the results of experimental investigations
(Fig.1).

The departure of arc current from sinusoidal depends on the value of the arc voltage and on the equivalent circuit reactance which is a function of the current's rms value.

Comparison between the models enables the students to study the effect of the model type on the variation of essential characteristics of arc furnaces.

The programs are written in the PASCAL language and adapted to computations made with the aid of IBM XT or AT class computers Kaminski (1989).

2.1. Linear mathematical model of an arc furnace

From the educational and applicational viewpoint the following characteristics calculated on the basis of this model are of importance·
- instantaneous values of the supply phase voltage u, the arc voltage u_a and the arc current i as a function of the ωt angle,
- 3-phase active powers of losses P_v, arcs $P_=$ and the total power P_1 as functions of the arc current rms value I,
- electric efficiency and the power factor φ as a function of the arc current I rms value,
- total 3-phase reactive power Q_1 and apparent power S_1 as a function of the arc current I rms value,
- arc radiation coefficient k_p as a function of the arc current I rms value,
- resultant resistance R_s and reactance X_s of the circuit as a function of the arc voltage U_a rms value.

Those characteristics are computed and printed out and at the same time it is possible to obtain print - outs that correspond to a given rms value of the arc voltage between 0 (exploitational short - circuit) and U_p (phase voltage) (Fig.2).

In addition results are being printed out that concern the important case in which the highest value of the arc active power P_{amax} occurs that corresponds to a determined rms value of the $U_{a\ max}$ arc voltage.

2.2. Nonlinear mathematical model of an arc furnace

A nonlinear mathematical model of an arc furnace was developed on the basis of experimental investigations on the assumption that the arc voltage has a rectangular waveshape and the arc current i is in phase that voltage.

On the assumption that the phase angle of arc current is zero, the arc voltage u_a can be described by the Fourier series Kaminski (1989), Sakulin (1983).

$$u_a = \frac{4}{\pi} U_a \sum_{n=0}^{\sim} \frac{\sin[(2n+1)\omega t]}{2n+1} \qquad (1)$$

with U_a - amplitude of the rectangular arc voltage.

With those assumptions the arc current i will be nonsinusoidal and the degree of nonsinusoidality increases with the value of the arc voltage. This can be visualised in

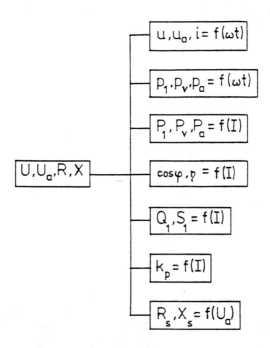

Fig.2. Diagram of the computer program for determining characteristics of steelmaking and foundry arc furnaces.

the characteristics being printed out (Fig.3) as well as by printouts of the current values of the first harmonic I_1 and of higher harmonics I_h.

The problem of arc current distortion is of special interest for the subject: "Theoretical Electrotechnics" while the trends of characteristics of arc furnaces, especially for the nonlinear model, are of interest for the subject: "Electroheat Installations" when selecting the operation range of a furnace with the effect of change in circuit resistance and reactance and in the supply voltage (supply voltage fluctation) taken into account.

3. The "SIMULT" program

The "SIMULT" program, that has been developed, allows the operation of steelmaking and foundry arc furnaces to be analyzed on the basis of the nonsymmetrical 3-phase nonlinear model Pieńkowski (1991).

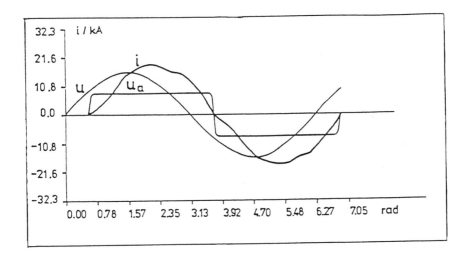

Fig.3. Trace of the u supply voltage, u_a arc voltage
and i arc current as a function of ωt for an arc
furnace with a rated capacity of $m=5*10^3$kg at an
arc voltage amplitude of $U_a = 100V$.

The equation of state was used in the algorithm and not only the parameters discussed in the "MODELE" program are being established but also a harmonic analysis is carried out, and the program is especially suitable for analysing the effect of voltage fluctuation in one, two or three phases. Using parameters of arc furnaces operated in Poland as well as abroad, the students easily obtain information on the properties of those installations and the characteristics determined in this way have also a practical value.

4. Conclusions

The following conclusions can be drawn from the experience of the Electrical Department at the Technical University in Bialystok:

(a)   Suitably selected dissertation topics allow algorithms and programs to be developed that permit circuits with electric arc to be analyzed.

(b)   The "MODELE" and "SIMULT" programs concern linear and nonlinear 3-phase symmetrical and asymmetrical models.

(c)   The nonlinear symmetric and asymmetrical models with square-wave shaped arc voltage are the most useful ones.

(d)   The programs find application first of all in such subjects as Theoretical Electrotechnics, Electroheat as well as Electric and Electroheat Installations.

References

Dmochowski, Z.(1991) Problems of measuring arc radiation factors in steelmaking arc furnaces, in Proceedings of Seminar on Heat transfer in electroheat, International Union for Electroheat, Tour Atlantique, Paris, 145 – 152.

Dmochowski, Z., Kierus, K. (1986) The problem in quantitative measurements in polish steel mills and foundries, in Proceedings of 2nd European Electric Steel Congress, Associazione Italiana, Piazza Velasca, Milano, P.3.3.1.– P.3.3.14.

Dmochowski,Z. (1990) Heavy-current measuring transducers, Polish Technical Review, 1–2, 187–188.

Kaminski, T. (1989) Comparison of mathematical models of circuits with electric arc using computer simulations, MSc. thesis, Technical University of Bialystok, Electrical Department, Bialystok (in Polish).

Sakulin, M. (1983) Elektrowärme, Habilitation, Technische Universität, Graz.

Pienkowski, B. (1991) Analysis of the effect of supply voltage on the variation of operation characteristics of steelmaking arc furnaces based on the "MODELE" computer program, MSc. thesis, Technical University of Bialystok, Electrical Department, (in Polish).